CHEAP EATS '88

Edited by David Mabey

Published by
Consumers' Association and
Hodder & Stoughton

Which? Books are commissioned and researched by
The Association for Consumer Research
and published by Consumers' Association,
2 Marylebone Road, London NW1 4DX and
Hodder & Stoughton,
47 Bedford Square, London WC1B 3DP

Typographic design by Tim Higgins
Maps by Eugene Fleury

British Library Cataloguing in Publication Data

Cheap eats '88.
    1. Great Britain. Inexpensive restaurants—Directories
    I. Mabey, David   II. Consumers' Association
    647'9541

    ISBN 0–340–41619–X

Typeset by Wyvern Typesetting Limited, Bristol
Printed and bound in Great Britain by
Hazell, Watson & Viney Limited
Member of BPCC plc
Aylesbury, Bucks

Contents

Introduction

Everyone knows that the cost of eating out can be ridiculously high. Most of us know what it is like to take a friend out to lunch and end up with a bill that is substantially larger than anticipated. Often the really memorable thing about the meal is not the quality of the food, but the price.

Cheap Eats tells a very different story. The 1600 restaurants, cafés and bars listed in the guide are in the front line in the battle for affordable food. Their enemies are not only the bastions of extravagant luxury, but also the cheap-skate and the mass-produced. The fact is that there are good, honest, enjoyable places serving decent, fresh food in virtually every town and city across the country. *Cheap Eats* points you in the right direction.

What is cheap?

Cheapness is relative, which means that the price limits of the book are flexible. Like its predecessor, *Budget Good Food Guide*, *Cheap Eats* focuses on places where it is possible to eat for around £5. But in practice, anywhere that offers the prospect of a decent meal for under £10 a head can be considered. Many places are much cheaper, selling three samosas for as little as 50p, say. In none of them is it necessary to break the £10 barrier. The value for money is exceptional.

Freshly cooked food, quality and value for money are the critical factors. Low prices on their own are insufficient to merit a restaurant being included in *Cheap Eats*. Inspectors have been tough and rigorous in their judgments, in an effort to raise standards even higher. They have gone where no 'restaurant guide' inspectors have gone before. They have visited back-street Indian cafés, black-pudding stalls and shellfish bars, checked out vegetarian bistros, wine bars, pubs, restaurants in theatres and art galleries, pizza places, pasta bars and much more. They have sampled dim-sum snacks in Cantonese restaurants right across the country, eaten steaks, burgers, Spanish tapas and Japanese yakitori.

Many of the addresses from *Budget Good Food Guide* have survived, but hundreds have been weeded out. Sometimes this is because they have closed down or changed out of recognition, sometimes because they have priced themselves out of the book with unjustifiable increases, sometimes because readers quite simply voted them out. The result is the most comprehensive picture of affordable eating out in Britain as yet published. Here are places that you can visit with a few pounds in your pocket. Unless you are treating your friends you won't need your cheque book or credit card.

The great divide

One of the most striking discoveries of *Cheap Eats* is the difference between eating out in the North and South. North of a line from Warwickshire to the Wash, there's an impressive concentration of cheap eating places in Birmingham, Bradford, Leeds, Liverpool and other towns. To the South – apart from London and the one or two exceptional cities such as Oxford and Brighton – addresses are spread much more thinly. It is surprising how few decent cheap eating places there are in a county such as Hertfordshire. Perhaps they have been killed off by Home Counties' affluence, because there's no shortage of expensive, overpriced restaurants in the area.

London may still have the biggest choice of cheap eating places in the land, but cities such as Manchester and Glasgow are closing the gap. Cheap restaurants in the North manage to thrive in all kinds of situations and circumstances – affluent, cosmopolitan, even derelict. Neighbourhood cafés still feed their locals in spite of the developers, and in spite of the temptation to move into dressed-up 'family food' with all its gaudy razzmatazz. Unlike corner shops, which have struggled against competition from the supermarket chains, corner cafés and restaurants can often beat off the challenge from their fast-food rivals.

The presence of thriving Chinese, Asian, Cypriot and other communities in many northern cities has opened up new possibilities for cheap eating. But even traditional English eating places are showing a dogged instinct for self-preservation: market cafés, pie stalls, bakeries and tea-rooms still produce classic regional specialities and people buy them. There is a great divide between this enthusiasm and full-blooded celebration of genuine fresh food and the sanitised, antiseptic atmosphere that hangs over many comparable eating places in the South.

Edwina Currie was wrong. The North is not unhealthy, not backward in its diet or eating habits. The evidence is in the pages of *Cheap Eats*. There may be a lot of saturated fat in the pies, fish and chips and black puddings, but it's also easier to find healthy vegetarian food in Leeds than in Luton. It is encouraging how many new vegetarian restaurants have sprung up in the Midlands and the North within the last year. (Colin Spencer writes in detail about the state of vegetarian food on page 13).

Kids' stuff

In 1987, my family was rudely evicted from a perfectly ordinary family restaurant in a Suffolk seaside town, simply because my daughter expects to be heard as well as seen. It was a reminder that child prejudice is rife in Britain. There is an antiquated notion that proper restaurants are no place for children.

Like die-hard pubs they are 'for adults only'. Most children's experience of eating out is confined to the predictable, monotonous rituals of the fast-food chains. Heaven knows what they will make of restaurants and cafés that are serving something different. The myth is reinforced by hundreds of perfectly creditable eating places throughout the land that assume there's one kind of food for grown-ups, and another for kids. The standard children's menu is a disgrace, and an insult to our children.

As adults and parents we can introduce our children to painting, music, dancing. But when it comes to eating out, the best we can do is offer them sausages and fish fingers. As a nation we don't seem to like taking our children to restaurants. No other country or culture has this attitude. The Indians, Italians, French, Japanese, Spanish, all of them understand that meals should be shared. It is second nature, part of everyday life. When the Chinese eat out, they eat together, often three generations around a big table. Many of their restaurants are specifically designed with plenty of open space between the tables, and wide aisles that allow room for push-chairs as well as dim-sum trolleys. Waiters can cope because they are used to children, and the food is tailor-made for all ages. I have seen Chinese mothers feeding their eighteen-month old babies on some of the best dim-sum snacks in the land.

The contrast between this and the average British family restaurant shows how far we have to go. It isn't a question of education, but of first-hand experience. We ought to take our children out for meals more often, show them some of the possibilities and, at the same time, convince the restaurant trade that here are the customers of the future.

Informal, fast-food restaurants are the obvious solution to every parent's problem – that the hours, prices and pace of many places are just not geared to children. But there are other solutions. *Cheap Eats* offers 1600 alternatives to burgers and French fries. The beauty of the addresses in this guide is that most of them really are suitable for family meals. The food isn't expensive, turnover is fast, dishes can be quickly prepared and speedily served. The atmosphere is informal, there's no stuffiness or standing on ceremony; no need for children to be as quiet as mice – although they shouldn't be allowed to run riot. More and more are also open right through the day. Apart from a small number of places that are out of bounds, most genuinely welcome – rather than tolerate – kids. There's no need to turn our children into little gourmets but exploring *Cheap Eats* is a start.

Supporting the cause

Cheap Eats depends on your support for its survival; it relies on feedback. Buying the book is one way of improving the state of cheap food in this country; using it will pay dividends, reporting on meals – good and bad – will help us to develop and improve the coverage for further editions. We also need to know about new, undiscovered places that deserve support and recognition. The report forms at the back of the book are there to be filled in.

The convenience trap

This is really a book about craftsmen who are prepared to produce fresh food without short cuts, but there is another, all too familiar side to the coin. Convenience items are the villains of the piece: cartons of UHT milk and cream; sachets of sauces and mustard put on to the plate like a plastic garnish; 'soup of the day' that is powder from a packet with a few bits of vegetables added; square pieces of processed cheese and waterlogged ham that are designed to fit between pieces of sliced bread; steak and kidney pies where the pastry lid is cooked separately and fitted on at the last minute. These are some of the current horrors that need to be challenged. If as customers we do not approve of these things, then now is the time to complain if we are to make an impact and begin to change the face of eating out in Britain. Your reports are needed.

DAVID MABEY
December 1987

How to use the guide

Regions
Counties are grouped together in regions for easy use. In each region, listings are alphabetical according to town or location. For a breakdown of the regions into counties see the contents page. Greater London, Scotland and Wales are sections in their own right. At the back of the book there is a list of all establishments in England according to town.

Prices
Specific prices quoted in the text are correct at the time of going to press. They are intended as general guidelines and may change in the course of a few weeks or months.

Licence
Establishments are licensed unless otherwise indicated in the entry. A number have wine or table licences only. Others may operate a 'bring your own' policy, sometimes with corkage.

Children
All establishments welcome, rather than tolerate, children accompanied by adults, unless otherwise stated. There may be restrictions on the times and places within the restaurant where families with children can eat. As there are legal restrictions on children under 14 in licensed premises where alcohol is served, it is always worth asking the landlord or proprietor if they have any objections. Many will happily accommodate children, but it is always courteous and diplomatic to ask first.

Wheelchairs
Establishments have been given a wheelchair symbol (&) if they tell us that there is full wheelchair access to the dining room or eating area. The words 'also WC' indicate that there is also full wheelchair access to the toilets.

Opening times
Pub opening times indicate when food is available, not necessarily full licensing hours.

The rating system

Every establishment in the book has been awarded a rating on a scale of 1 to 10. This is intended to give the book a viewpoint and a sense of perspective, and also to highlight the very best cheap eating places in the guide. All of them serve good food and offer value for money, but some set their sights higher than others. There is clearly a significant difference between a small take-away chippie and a high-class vegetarian bistro: the rating system is a way of differentiating between the two. In practice all entries rate from **5/10** to **9/10**.

5/10
This category is for establishments that may not be restaurants or cafés at all. They are the oddballs of the guide: black-pudding stalls, Indian sweet-centres, tiny shellfish bars, take-away snack bars, perhaps a few tables at the back of a shop or gallery.

6/10
This is for establishments that are useful in their area. They are not really worth a detour, but are definitely worth a visit if you are nearby. In this category are good-value pubs, standard curry houses, coffee-shops and so on.

7/10
Establishments in this category form the backbone of the book. The food they serve is above average – it may even be the best in the area. Once again they are a mixed bag: Cantonese restaurants serving good dim-sum and one-plate meals; enterprising bistros and vegetarian restaurants; reliable pizza and pasta places; wine bars with an imaginative choice of food.

8–9/10
These are the stars of *Cheap Eats*. The food served in these places is the best of its kind in the country. A rating of **8/10** is sometimes given to establishments where 'cheap eating' is a minor part of the operation, for instance country-house hotels with prestigious restaurants that also offer exceptional bar snacks or afternoon teas. A rating of **9/10** is reserved for establishments that typify *Cheap Eats* – often they are classic examples of a style or type of cooking, for example pasta bars or eel and pie shops. A rating of **9/10** in *Cheap Eats* does not necessarily correspond to a rating of **9/20** in *The Good Food Guide*.

A vegetarian top twenty

Colin Spencer, food writer and columnist for *The Guardian*, celebrates the rise of vegetarian cooking in restaurants and makes a personal selection of outstanding entries from *Cheap Eats*.

A few years ago I would never have guessed that vegetarian food would have hauled up her wholemeal skirts and with her lumpen legs jogged along towards stylish and gourmet food so soon. At this time, the restaurant scene for vegetarians was like a current pop star – mean, moody and sometimes a bit vicious, for we were considered to be second-class citizens, both ignorant and tasteless, who could be ignored and ripped off.

In the 1984 edition of *The Good Food Guide* I wrote about the disdain with which vegetarians were treated in such places as The Dorchester and Le Caprice. In those days, and it is only a few years ago, we were given either vegetable slops, an omelette or a salad with a pathetic mound of grated Cheddar. The scene had to change and as trendy cooking became leaner and more elegant so it lost the concept of vegetables being a garnish to the meat or the fish course. Vegetables began to take over and be the main substance of the meal. As this happened, we also saw a greater range of vegetables being grown or imported. There are many people who do not think of themselves as vegetarians but who have gradually come to exist on a diet which is mainly vegetables with the garnish being a little meat, game or fish. This is now not only the most elegant way of eating, it is also, as we know, the healthiest way.

Some of the upmarket restaurants now give time and thought to this cuisine, often giving as much space *pour les végétariens* as for *les poissons*. Cheaper restaurants are slower to follow, they still think in terms of stodge. God please preserve me from another vegetarian bake, preserve me too from bean lasagne (yes, I know it has complementary protein) and from macaroni or cauliflower cheese. And will there ever be an end to wholemeal quiche? Leaden pastry filled with a dry, bland custard studded with left-over vegetables must be one of the dullest if not most horrific experiences for the digestion. Wearily, I add also, that the easy solution to the request for vegetarian food will not do. There are still too many overcooked vegetables covered with a floury sauce seasoned with three-month-matured Cheddar, or wholewheat pasta swimming in a sauce made from tinned tomatoes which has never been near garlic, oregano or basil.

Pastry can be light and have flavour if made with half wholemeal and plain flour (though I applaud the chef at Food for Friends, in Brighton, who makes crumbly, light-textured pastries and breads from one hundred per cent wholemeal. Nor do pastry crusts have to be filled with sauces thickened by flour or cream – they can be fitted with purée of vegetables. If cheese is used it should be a small amount of the strongest flavour. It is more economical to use a sliver of matured Cheddar than a quarter of an ounce of imported. It is even more economical to use a little blue cheese. So many cooks still have lapses of memory on the time they steam or boil vegetables and nothing is sadder than limp leeks or that stench of overcooked brassicas. Some of the most nutritious dishes are mixtures of grains and pulses. There is a huge untapped range here, where you might have mixtures of millet and lentils, lightened with green beans and fruit, served on a bed of leaves. These are salads as complete meals. The ingredients could not be cheaper, the preparation is modest and yet no one that I know of is experimenting with these.

Yet I must now be the first to admit the scene has changed radically; it is improving; good vegetarian food is much more widely available. One of the most interesting trends reflected in *Cheap Eats* is how Chinese restaurants (not known for their vegetarian ingenuity over here, though the Buddhist tradition in China is strong) are beginning to have either a vegetarian menu or a special dish, as at the Mandarin Palace in Ilford, Essex, Panda in Leicester, or the Far East in Liverpool.

My top twenty from *Cheap Eats* are merely in alphabetical order and not all of them are vegetarian restaurants. I have chosen them for their use of the lighter ingredients, judicious yet generous use of herbs and spices, for their ingenuity and imagination, and therefore their exploring of new recipes. As one might expect, seven are in Greater London. Also, the Indian vegetarian tradition, because of its authenticity and appeal, is by far the strongest presence in the list. One would have to go far, for value for money and the most exquisitely delicious meal, to beat Munbhave, Ragam or Sabras.

Occasionally I have mentioned a place like Ryton Gardens, which cooks traditional vegetarian dishes with a light hand. But generally I have gone for places that serve dishes like walnut, mushroom and basil pâté (Gannets in Newark), timbale of parsnips (the enterprising Herbs, Coventry), or mushroom florentine (Clinchs, Chichester). The movement towards quality vegetarian food will, without doubt, continue, for the demand is constantly renewed and strengthened by younger people who, for environmental or moral reasons, choose to avoid animal flesh.

The restaurants

Bobby's (Vegetarian)
Leicester (East Midlands)

Christys (Vegetarian)
Greater London

Clinchs Salad House
Chichester (South East)

Delanys (Vegetarian)
Shrewsbury (West Midlands)

East West (Vegetarian)
Greater London

Food for Friends (Vegetarian)
Brighton (South East)

Gannets
Newark (East Midlands)

Gingers (Vegetarian)
Glossop (East Midlands)

Herbs, Trinity House Hotel
Coventry (West Midlands)

Hockneys' (Vegetarian)
Greater London

Kalpna (Vegetarian)
Edinburgh (Scotland)

Mandeer (Vegetarian)
Greater London

Melissa (Vegetarian)
Chelmsford (East Anglia)

Munbhave (Vegetarian)
Greater London

Orchard House (Vegetarian)
Keswick (North West)

Ragam
Greater London

Ryton Gardens
Coventry (West Midlands)

Sabras (Vegetarian)
Greater London

La Santé (Vegetarian)
Birmingham (West Midlands)

Wine Bar
Woodbridge (East Anglia)

The best of the year

David Mabey chooses seventeen places that typify the best of *Cheap Eats*. All of them rank as top of their league in what they set out to achieve.

AFTERNOON TEA
Sheila's Cottage Ambleside
(North West)
A brilliant cottage café serving superb local produce. Excellent teas and a marvellous array of cakes, breads and pastries.

ALL-DAY EATING PLACE
Greenstocks, Cotswold House Hotel
Chipping Campden (South West)
The new face of cheap eating: it is open twelve hours a day, the atmosphere is like a civilised family living-room and the food suits all tastes and needs.

BISTRO
Bakestone Caernarfon (Wales)
Genuine, unadorned bistro cooking with the emphasis on fresh seasonal ingredients. A refreshing antidote to rarified nouvelle cuisine.

BREAKFAST
Justin de Blank (Greater London)
Noted for its bread and croissants, prize-winning sausages and much more. Breakfast begins at 8.30 a.m.

DIM-SUM
New World (Greater London)
A theatrical show, with a succession of dim-sum trolleys wheeled round by waitresses.

EEL & PIE SHOP
F. Cooke (Greater London)
A unique London institution – one of a dying breed.

ETHNIC CAFÉ
Munchy Munchy Oxford (Central)
Serves the best and most imaginative South-East Asian food in the country.

FAMILY RESTAURANT
Chicago Rib Shack (Greater London)
Great food, great entertainment. One of the best places to take children in the capital during the day.

FAST FOOD
Wong Kei (Greater London)
Offers the best-value in Soho Chinatown. Cantonese fast food is served with daunting speed and efficiency

GALLERY/THEATRE CATERING
National Gallery (Greater London)
One of the few places in the capital where £5 really will buy three courses. It proves that top quality food can co-exist with institutional surroundings.

HEALTHY FOOD
Village Bakery Melmerby
(North West)
Natural food produced and served without zealous attitudes or dogma.

INDIAN CAFÉ
Kashmir Bradford (North East)
Sets the standard for Indian café food across the country. Unbeatable value.

LOCAL FOOD
Angel Inn Hetton (North East)
Dedicated to the cause of Real Food. Ingredients are local, dishes are cooked to order, and the bar menu proves that quality doesn't have to be fussy.

NEWCOMER
Miller Howe Kaff Windermere
(North West)
A high-class café for the 1980s, serving
food to the standard of a serious
restaurant, but at a fraction of the
price.

PIZZAS
Pizzeria Castello, (Greater London)
The best of the independent pizza
houses. Outstrips the chains for
quality and value.

PLOUGHMAN'S
Royal Oak Hotel Manchester
(North West)
Serves an unbeatable ploughman's
with excellent bread and huge chunks
of cheese.

PUB FOOD
Three Horseshoes Powerstock
(South)
Remarkable village pub with a
restaurant. Excellent local fish, West
Country cheeses and home-grown
vegetables. A gem of its kind.

The top ratings

GREATER LONDON

9/10
Andrew Edmunds
Le Bistroquet
Brilliant
Chicago Rib Shack
Chuen Cheng Ku
F. Cooke
Dining Room
Efes Kebab House
Ganpath
Grahame's Seafare
Great Nepalese
Hard Rock Café
Hockneys
Justin de Blank
Kettners
Mandeer
Melati
Munbhave
National Gallery
New World
Pizzeria Castello
Poons
Le Poulbot
Rani
Rebato's
Rouxl Britannia
Sabras
Soho Brasserie
Spago
Sree Krishna
Upper Street Fish Shop
Wong Kei

8/10
Ajimura
Beehive
Brewer Street Buttery
Café Pelican
Charco's Wine Bar
Cherry Orchard
Chicago Pizza Pie
  Factory
Cork & Bottle
Cosmos
Country Life
Dalat
East West
Ebury Wine Bar
Equatorial
Food for Thought
Frascati
Geales Fish Restaurant
Gentry
Hodja Nasreddin
Hoults
Ikkyu
Inebriated Newt
Jack's Place
Joe Allen
Laurent
Leek's Fish Bar
Lou Pescadou
Mr Tang
Neal's Yard Bakery &
  Tea Room
Pasta Underground
Paulo's
Pizzeria Condotti
Pollo
Punter's Pie
Ragam
Rodos
Solopasta
Star
Suruchi
Tung Kum
Victoria & Albert
  Museum
Wine Gallery
Yerakina
Zamoyski's

SOUTH WEST

9/10
Chipping Campden
  Greenstocks,
  Cotswold House Hotel
Northleach Fossebridge
  Inn
Torquay Mulberry Room
Torrington Rebecca's

8/10
Bath Moon & Sixpence
Bristol Vintner Wine Bar
Cheltenham Retreat
Cirencester Shepherds
  Wine Bar, Fleece Hotel
Corse Lawn Corse Lawn
  House Hotel
Frome Settle
Gloucester College Green
Mevagissey Mr Bistro

SOUTH

9/10
Powerstock Three
  Horseshoes
Salisbury Harper's

8/10
Avebury Stones
Lacock Red Lion
Marlborough Bentley's
  Wine Bar
Polly's Tea Rooms
Salisbury Just Brahms
Southsea Barnaby's
  Bistro
Upton Grey Hoddington
  Arms
West Bexington Manor
  Hotel

SOUTH EAST

9/10

Brighton Food for
  Friends
Tunbridge Wells
Downstairs at
  Thackeray's

8/10

Biddenden Three
  Chimneys
Brighton Chilka
Mock Turtle
Canterbury Cogan
  House
  George's Brasserie
Folkestone India
Limpsfield Limpsfield
  Brasserie
Tonbridge Office Wine
  Bar

CENTRAL

9/10

Oxford Browns
Munchy Munchy
Speen Atkins
Yattendon Royal Oak

8/10

Berkhamsted Cooks
  Delight
Eton Eton Wine Bar
Hungerford Galloping
  Crayfish
Inkpen Swan Inn
Oxford Oxford Bakery &
  Brewhouse
Pangbourne Copper Inn
Stanton Harcourt
  Harcourt Arms
Watton at Stone George
  & Dragon

WEST MIDLANDS

9/10

Birmingham Los Andes
Chung Ying
Brimfield Roebuck
Coventry Herbs
Weobley Jule's Cafe

8/10

Birmingham Adil
Days of the Raj
Forbidden City
Satay House
Clun Old Post Office
Dorrington Country
  Friends
Hereford Effys
Kenilworth Ana's Bistro
Ryton-on-Dunsmore
  Ryton Gardens
Shipston-on-Stour White
  Bear
Shrewsbury Delanys

EAST MIDLANDS

9/10

Plumtree Perkins Bar
  Bistro

8/10

Fotheringhay Falcon
Leicester Bobby's
Water Margin
Litton Red Lion
Nottingham Ocean City
Shogun
Ten
Stretton Ram Jam Inn
Tideswell Poppies

EAST ANGLIA

9/10

Chelmsford Melissa
Southwold Crown
Spilsby Buttercross
Wells-next-the-Sea
  Moorings
Woodbridge Wine Bar

8/10

Burnham Market Fishes
Cambridge Browns
Upstairs
Colchester Wings,
  Mercury Theatre
Diss Diss Coffee House/
  Thai Restaurant
Easton White Horse
Framlingham Market
  Place
Harwich Pier at Harwich

King's Lynn Riverside
  Rooms
Long Melford Black
  Lion Hotel
Norwich Brasserie l'Abri
Orford Butley Orford
  Oysterage
Stamford George

NORTH WEST

9/10

Ambleside Sheila's
  Cottage
Chester Abbey Green
Dent Stone Close
Kendal Moon
Liverpool Far East
Manchester Little Yang
  Sing
On the Eighth Day
Pearl City
Yang Sing
Melmerby Village Bakery
Wilmslow Yang Sing
  Bistro
Windermere Miller Howe
  Kaff

8/10

Ambleside Rothay Manor
Blackpool Bistro
  Number Sixteen
Danish Kitchen
Caldbeck Parkend
  Restaurant
Cockermouth Wythop
  Mill
Congleton Oddfellows
  Wine Bar
Liverpool Armadillo
La Grande Bouffe
Mayflower
Manchester Assam
  Gourmet
Basta Pasta
Hopewell City
Indian Cottage
Kosmos Taverna
Royal Oak Hotel
Sanam
Woo Sang
Preston Auctioneer
Ullswater Sharrow Bay

NORTH EAST

9/10

Barnard Castle Market
Place Teashop
Bradford Kashmir
Elland Berties Bistro
Hetton Angel Inn
Newcastle-upon-Tyne
Madeleine's
Ripon: Old Deanery
Whitby Magpie Café

8/10

Epworth Epworth Tap
Golcar Weavers Shed
Harrogate Betty's
Ilkley Olive Tree
Betty's
Leeds Carageen
Vegetarian Café
Jumbo Chinese
Sang Sang
Newcastle-upon-Tyne
Jade Garden
Northallerton Betty's
Scarborough Sarah
Brown's
Sheffield Nirmal's
Tandoori

Sowerby Bridge Ash Tree
Wath-in-Nidderdale
Sportsman's Arms
York Bees Knees
Betty's

SCOTLAND

9/10

Canonbie Riverside Inn
Cullipool Longhouse
Buttery
Edinburgh Handsel's
Wine Bar
Kalpna
Glasgow Rogano's
Ubiquitous Chip
Linlithgow Champany
Inn Chop and Ale House

8/10

Colbost Three Chimneys
Edinburgh Alp-Horn
Helios Fountain
Loon Fung
Waterfront Wine Bar
Glasgow Belfry
Cafe Gandolfi
Loon Fung
P.J.'s
Willow Tea Rooms

Inverness Brookes
Perth Timothy's
Tarbert West Loch Hotel
Ullapool Ceilidh Place
Wester Howgate Old
Howgate Inn

WALES

9/10

Caernarfon Bakestone
Cardiff Armless Dragon
Cilgerran Castle Kitchen
Cowbridge Basil's
Brasserie
Llandewi Skirrid Walnut
Tree Inn

8/10

Aberaeron Hive on the
Quay
Aberystwyth Gannets
Cardiff Riverside
Carmarthen Hoi San
Hay-on-Wye Lion's
Corner House
Llandybie Cobblers
Newport Cnapan
Swansea Schooner
Trefriw Chandler's

Greater London

Ajimura [8/10]

51–53 Shelton Street, WC2   map 14
TEL 01-240 0178

Open noon to 3, 6 to 11 (10.30 Sun)
Closed Sat L and Sun L; bank hols

The healthiness of this long-standing
westernised Japanese restaurant menu is a
major plus. Its authenticity can be more
kaftan than kimono, but the good-value
set lunches or snacks at the sushi bar are
commendable. Clear soups, sashimi from
£4, grilled salmon, marinated pork and
ornately carved fruits all figure. Avocado
sashimi is just that – raw carved avocado.
Saké puts the bill up.

Albion [7/10]

2 New Bridge Street, EC4   map 13
TEL 01-353 8852

Open for food noon to 3

The Barnetts have been at this pub for 34
years. The dining-room on the first floor is
without frills, but the steaks at £4.95 come
straight from Smithfield up the road and
are some of the best in the area. Chips are
thick cut. Sunday lunch is an institution,
but weekdays are less discovered.

Ambrosiana Crêperie [7/10]

194 Fulham Road, SW10   map 13
TEL 01-351 0700

Open noon to midnight &
Closed Christmas Day

On the café dragway of Fulham Road that
reaches a bottleneck around the ABC, the
Ambrosiana has held its prices and its
leisurely atmosphere while many others
have come and gone. There are 41 savoury
and 28 sweet crêpes, as well as steaks and
a snack menu through the day. Service
is swift.

NEW ENTRY | Andrew Edmunds [9/10]

46 Lexington Street, W1   map 14
TEL 01-437 5708

Open noon to 3, 5.30 to 11 & (also WC)
Closed bank hols

Small wine bar in the heart of Soho, filling
the ground floor and basement of a narrow
building. Tables are wooden, with paper
cloths. The menu is fashionable and well
handled – avocado and toasted goats'
cheese, asparagus soup, Roquefort salad.
Service is friendly. Reasonably priced
wine, too.

Antipasto & Pasta [7/10]

511 Battersea Park Road, SW11   map 12
TEL 01-223 9765

Open noon to 3, 7 to midnight (11.45 Sun) &
(also WC)
Closed Christmas Eve to Boxing Day; bank hols

More consistent than many of the pasta
bars that have sprung up. Portions are
generous and the flavouring distinct, as in
rigatoni with Gorgonzola. The bits and
pieces – the house wine, the espresso, the
ripe avocado in the Mozzarella salad –
make it more of an inexpensive trattoria
rather than a grazing ground. There is
another branch with the same times and
menu in Abbeville Road, SW4 (01-675
6260).

NEW ENTRY | Anwars [6/10]

64 Grafton Way, W1   map 13
TEL 01-387 6664

Open 10am to 10pm &
Closed Christmas Day

The top end of Whitfield Street is a bastion
of old London India. Anwars advertises
itself as a 'budget curry house' and is the
cheap daytime alternative to the
prestigious Lal Qila, just round the corner
in Tottenham Court Road. It functions as
a café, with Formica-topped tables and
queues by the array of curries and snacks
kept in a battery of metal pans and trays.
Prices are low and the range takes in meat
and chicken curries, tandooris, samosas
and an interesting choice of vegetarian
items. Unlicensed.

Applejacks [7/10]

255 Eversholt Street, NW1   map 13
TEL 01-387 0641

Open 10 to 3 &
Closed Sat, Sun; 2 weeks in summer; 1 week at Christmas; 1 week at Easter

Three-course set lunches in this café that makes a virtue of its ordinariness, are excellent value. Home-made soups, mushrooms with garlic mayonnaise, chicken à la king, salads, crumbles, and sponges all feature. At other times there are home-baked snacks. The menu changes daily. It is run as a work experience project by Camden Council for people with learning difficulties and has commendably stuck to its ideals in the food arena, too, concentrating on fresh produce. Unlicensed.

Archduke [7/10]

Concert Hall Approach   map 13
(off Belvedere Road), SE1
TEL 01-928 9370

Open 11 to 3, 5.30 to 11 &
Closed Sun; Sat L; bank hols

In recognition of the great British summer, the terrace has been converted into a conservatory. Attached to the restaurant under the railway arches is a hi-tech multi-level wine bar – crucial, given the lack of alternatives for South Bank art-goers. Sausages are an evening speciality: pork, venison, Bavarian smoked, merguez. The after-theatre supper menu can work out under £10 in the restaurant for some showy cooking, such as lamb in green ginger. Plenty of atmosphere, a contribution to culture, with jazz, and closely packed tables.

Baalbek [7/10]

18 Hogarth Place, SW5   map 12
TEL 01-373 7199

Open noon to 3, 6 to 11 &
Closed Sun; Sat L

Tucked away from the bustle of Earls Court is this microcosm of a Lebanese restaurant. The sixteen starters are mostly classics – hummus, stuffed vine leaves, aubergine purée with sesame oil – and precede half a dozen stews at £4 each, including couscous and grilled meats. Vegetarians could eat most of what is

offered. Good value, though extras, especially drinks, push the bill up: Arabic bread is 25p, chips £1.

Babu [6/10]

156 The Broadway, Southall   map 12
TEL 01-574 5281

Open 10am to 10.30pm &

An impressive display of sweets is on show behind the counter, all seemingly made on the premises. The dining area is split into a café in the front, which is well used as a meeting place, and a family room at the back. Lamb curries are spicy, quite hot from the sauce, and the meat tender. Rice is £1. Take-away samosas and paan.

Babur Brasserie [7/10]

119 Brockley Rise,   map 12
Forest Hill, SE23
TEL 01-291 2400/4881

Open noon to 2.30, 6 to midnight
Closed Christmas Day and Boxing Day

A cross between a new-wave Indian restaurant – beige table linen, Mogul panels, exotic cocktails – and an old high-street tandoori – red glass candle mantles, plastic plants, corner bar. The Babur e bhojan, taking in four meat dishes, rice and nan, is excellent value at £6.95, as is the Sunday lunch buffet. Non-meat dishes are increasingly prominent on the menu. Babur was the first Mogul emperor of India.

NEW ENTRY Bar Escoba [7/10]

102 Old Brompton Road, SW7   map 13
TEL 01-373 2403

Open 11 to 11 (10.30 Sun) & (also wc)

A Spanish-style wine bar with a restaurant at the back. Lots of posters of old movies, terracotta coloured tiles and sea-green walls painted in marbled effect lend an atmosphere lately enhanced by young Spaniards who will on occasion get up and do an impromptu flamenco. The long bar in the large front area serves tapas throughout the day: patatas bravas – big chunks of potato with lots of garlic in tomato sauce; paella croquettes – deep-fried croquettes filled with spiced rice and pieces of ham; chorizo – very spicy sliced chorizo served hot; prawns in garlic and olive oil served in a terracotta dish; and a good-sized portion of mushrooms with coriander and garlic in a wooden bowl. Jamon Serrano is an enormous plate with layers of smoked ham, olives and tomatoes. One not very Spanish tapa is the chicken satay (two skewers) with lemon and chilli, tasty but expensive for £2.50. They readily replenish the bread basket which is essential when you're having tapas. The owners are, surprisingly, Trusthouse Forte.

NEW ENTRY Barocco [6/10]

13 Moor Street, W1 map 14
TEL 01-437 2324

Open noon to 10.45 & (also wc)
Closed Sun

This very small café/espresso bar now also serves pasta. Choose from a selection all at £1.50 – spaghetti/tagliatelle/ravioli/rigatoni – and top it with a sauce for 50p or 70p – napoletana, al burro, pesto genovese, alla vongole, alla romana (mushroom and meat), parmigiano (tomato and meat). Omelettes are £2, salads £2, fillet steak £5.50. Prints of Venice and the leaning Tower of Pisa adorn the white walls and potted plants hang from the ceiling.

Beehive [8/10]

Beehive Place, SW9 map 12
TEL 01-274 1690

Open noon to 3, 7 to 10.30
Closed Sun D; Christmas

Exposed beams, wooden floors, bamboo blinds, oriental masks and plenty of greenery provide the setting for one of the more accomplished vegetarian restaurants south of the river, it uses organic produce where possible. The menu changes monthly, taking on themes from different countries, perhaps Indonesia or India. Cosmopolitan dishes abound: Vietnamese spring rolls; Mexican corn soup with pecan nuts; tomato pasta with pistachio sauce

cut with cognac; broccoli and almond strudel. The move into candlelit dinners has spread to waitress service at lunch.

Beewees [7/10]

95 Stroud Green Road, N4 map 12
TEL 01-263 4004

Open noon to 3, 6 to 11 (5 to 10 Sun)
Closed Sun L and Mon L; Jan

One of the better Caribbean restaurants: the menu covers all the standards like rice and peas, ackee and saltfish, stuffed rotis and a fine goat curry. The home-made rum punch enjoys a good local reputation, too.

NEW ENTRY B.G.'s [7/10]

542 Kingsland Road, E8 map 12
TEL 01-254 3718

Open noon to 3, 6 to 11 (12 Fri, 1 to midnight Sat) & (also wc)
Closed Sun

'Having tried the rest, now try the best' boasts the menu of this homespun, welcoming, if a bit disorganised West Indian restaurant. It's more gospel than rasta, prices are down around £3.50 for main course, and the choice runs to more than fifty dishes, though not everything is always available. Everything seems to come with rice. Beyond the standard rotis, curried goat, and black-eye pea soup are specials such as Rundown – spinach, saltfish and coconut – or cow-heel in sauce with home-made bread. Interesting drinks, too.

NEW ENTRY Birley's [7/10]

12–13 Royal Exchange, EC3 map 13
TEL 01-929 0931

Open 7am to 3pm
Closed Sat, Sun; bank hols

A line of white-aproned sandwich-makers stand behind two chill cabinets of cold cuts of meat, salads and bowls of mayonnaise and make up to order. The range is wide and there is a daily special, such as steak and mushroom (£3). The trimmings, for instance the boxes and the silver wrapping, are sensible, as is the counter of fresh fruit juices. The take-away lunch-box – orders taken on the phone and free delivery in the City – comprises half a smoked salmon sandwich, three-layered club sandwich, bean salad, dessert plus white wine or mineral water for £4.95. Not quite the Rolls-Royce of sandwich bars, but a reliable Daimler parked at the back of the Bank of England. There are branches at 2 Cannon Street, EC4 (TEL 01-626 8594), and 17 Cullum Street, EC3 (TEL 01-621 0763).

NEW ENTRY Bistro du Village [7/10]

72 Cleveland Street, W1
TEL 01-637 2154

Open 11.30 to 3, 6 to 11.30 &
Closed Sun; Sat L

This feels like a classic 1960s Soho eating place. The name, the bare floorboards and the red chairs suggest a bistro, but the style is more like a trattoria without the Chianti bottles, and there are echoes of an anachronistic Continental restaurant in the long menu and good humour of the place. The list of dishes is painted on the window and chalked on a big board: French onion soup, kidneys in red wine, spaghetti bolognese, veal with Marsala sauce, chicken cacciatore and much more. Also look for the specials, such as gigot of lamb with flageolet beans or fresh mussels. It's possible to have two courses plus a glass of quaffable house red and a frothy cappuccino for under £10.

Le Bistroquet [9/10]

273–275 Camden High Street,   map 13
NW1
TEL 01-267 4895

Open noon to midnight (11 Sun) &
Closed 3 days at Christmas

The brasserie has a separate wine bar menu and snacks, such as steak with onions and frites for under £5. The menu changes several dishes each month and is essentially regional French. It stands out from similar places in that it makes sensible use of luxuries – balsamic vinegar in the avocado vinaigrette – and the

market – monkfish sauté with mange tout, soya and madeira – and stays with what it is good at – mostly the classic bistro dishes like salad niçoise or bratwurst with potato salad. Eating in the bar area is about £5, the restaurant is more expensive, but not that much. Good country wines too.

Bleeding Heart [7/10]

Bleeding Heart Yard,   map 13
Greville Street, EC1
TEL 01-242 8238/2056

Open for food noon to 11 &
Closed Sat, Sun; bank hols

Hidden away in the heart of Hatton Garden, in the very far corner of the yard, is a basement wine bar feeding off a more expensive restaurant. The brasserie menu has a thick French accent. Plenty of charcuterie and other starters are about £2, steak haché et frites and other main dishes about £4. On hot days there are tables outside and the lunchtime fug subsides in the evening, when it becomes more romantic.

Bloom's [7/10]

90 Whitechapel High Street, E1   map 12
TEL 01-247 6001

Open 11.30 to 9.30 (3 Fri) &
Closed Sat; Fri D; Christmas Day; Jewish hols

Bloom's survives on its reputation. Virtually nowhere else in London still produces this style of Ashkenazi Jewish cooking. The original East End branch retains the atmosphere of between the wars. The kosher menu is at its best with its broths and salt beef. Gefilte fish, chopped liver, lockshen et al are more variable. When the waiters are in a good humour, everything picks up. There is another, newer branch (it opened in 1965) at 130 Golders Green Road, NW11 (TEL 01-455 1338). The hours and menu are similar, the dining-room smaller and the prices a shade higher.

Bombay Inn [7/10]

177 King Street, W6   map 12
TEL 01-748 1156

Open noon to 2.30, 6 to midnight ₺ (also wc)
Closed Christmas Day and Boxing Day

Probably the pick of the many less expensive tandoori houses on King Street. The décor is typical red plush and subdued lighting, the service is untypically affable. Most of the meat on the menu is lamb. The dhansaks, tandoori chicken dishes, onion bhajias and fresh vegetables are all good. Licensed.

Bombay Mix [7/10]

7–9 Woolwich New Road, SE18   map 3
TEL 01-854 0035/9245

Open 10.30 (noon Sun) to 10.30
Closed Tue D; Christmas Day and Boxing Day

Lunches are great value in this large, clean café/restaurant with well-spaced tables and bentwood chairs. On Sundays you can eat as much as you like for £6.50 (£5.50 for vegetarian menu), while during the rest of the week there is a choice of three curries, black lentil dhal and either pilau rice or two bhaturas, for around £3.

Bombay Samrat [7/10]

108 Cricklewood Broadway, NW2   map 12
TEL 01-452 0463

Open 10 to 8 ₺
Closed Tue

Southern Indian vegetarian cooking is absurdly cheap and this small, expanding restaurant is no exception. The average meal costs about £2.50. Snacks, take-aways and even outside catering are built round a menu of fifty home-cooked dishes. Good thalis, also masala dosai, iddly sambar and uttapam. Drink lassi or spiced tea.

Bon Ton Roulet [7/10]

127 Dulwich Road, SE24   map 12
TEL 01-733 8701

Open 7pm to 10.30pm
Closed Sun; 2 weeks Aug; 1 week at Christmas

Now expanded: more space, an upstairs, and a drinks licence applied for. Sally Sherratt's guiding principles of running a restaurant on café prices remain intact. On average a full meal will be around £10 for leeks vinaigrette, pork cassoulet, braised lambs' hearts or, more whacky, chicken with peanut butter. It is all fresh and the gutsy dishes can be impressive.

La Bouffe [7/10]

13 Battersea Rise, SW11   map 12
TEL 01-228 3384

Open 12.30 to 2.30, 7.30 to 11
Closed Sat L; Sun D

Battersea Rise is now full of restaurants. The Bouffe is deeply French and offers good-value meals, the cheapest of which is £6.95. The menu changes daily: avocado salad, gammon with parsley sauce, a trio of vegetables, coffee and good baguettes are typical. Lunch offers a small à la carte menu plus a one-course set meal, with a glass of wine and coffee for £5.50.

NEW ENTRY   Braganza [7/10]

56 Frith Street, W1   map 14
TEL 01-437 5412

Open 9am to 11.30pm (5.30pm to 11.30pm Sat)
Closed Sun; Sat L

The ground floor of this spectacular conversion is run as a cheap café/bar open for breakfast and through the day. Seeing the décor is worth the price of a cup of coffee, but there are also fashionable one-plate meals of warm salads with lots of leaves; marinated fish; goats' cheese in various guises and calf's liver with raspberry vinegar. The eclectic wine list favours the New World. More expensive, formal meals upstairs.

La Brasserie [7/10]

272 Brompton Road, SW3   map 13
TEL 01-584 1668

Open 8 (10 Sun) to noon for breakfast ₺
Closed Christmas Day and Boxing Day

The breakfast business meeting has failed to catch on in London because hardly anywhere, apart from hotels, opens before 9.30, but this all-day brasserie wakes up at 8, which is a start. It is very French but can manage le bacon et les oeufs as well as large cafetières of coffee, fresh bread, croissants and the papers. Main meals are comparatively expensive – about £17 a head – but it is possible to snack outside the peak times.

Brewer Street Buttery [8/10]

56 Brewer Street, W1 map 14
TEL 01-437 7695

Open 9 to 6
Closed Sat and Sun; bank hols

First-class café specialising in some middle European dishes like piroshki as well as the standard sandwiches and roast menu. The freshly squeezed oranges and the Gaggia coffee machine for espresso give it trimmings a long way ahead of the usual. The menu changes daily and includes a vegetarian choice. Service is maternal. Fine pastries. Quite a gem in its own way. A licence has been applied for.

Brilliant [9/10]

72–74 Western Road, Southall map 12
TEL 01-574 1928

Open noon to 3, 6 to 11.30 (midnight Fri and Sat) ᵫ (also WC)
Closed Mon; Sat L and Sun L

This is the best representative of neighbourhood Indian cooking in Southall, and compares well with many places in central London. The décor has benefited from a facelift, but the kitchen has resisted the temptation to follow the red-flock curry-house path. Butter chicken and jeera chicken are perennial favourites and the kitchen serves up a good version of keema peas. Some new vegetarian dishes have been added to the menu. Drink Kenyan or Kingfisher beer, otherwise stay with lassi.

NEW ENTRY Brizzi Snack Bar [6/10]

131 Drummond Street, NW1. map 13
TEL 01-380 0857

Open 7.30am to 3pm
Closed Sat, Sun; 4 days at Easter; 10 days at Christmas

One of the few western eating places among the Indian cafés and grocers in

Drummond Street. This spotless café serves the best cooked breakfasts and fry-ups within walking distance of Euston Station, and is a more interesting bet than the station's 'food court'. Dishes are cooked to order, and prices are low: egg, bacon, sausage and tomato is £1.70; liver, bacon and chips is £2, spaghetti carbonara is £1.90. The owners are planning to open a pasta/wine bar in the basement. Take-aways. Unlicensed.

NEW ENTRY Brunel [5/10]

134 Great Portland Street, W1 map 13
TEL 01-636 0674

Open 7.30am to 4pm
Closed Sat, Sun

Slick, clean and spacious New York-style sandwich bar – pick any combination from twenty fillings to take away or eat sitting at one of the stools. Dressings run through horseradish to cocktail to mustard, thus adding further possibilities. Telephone orders delivered within walking distance.

Bunga Raya [7/10]

785 London Road, Thornton Heath map 3
TEL 01-689 4612

Open 7pm to 10.30pm ᵫ (also WC)

All the key points of Malay cooking are offered in this attractive café: good satay, plenty of fish, especially prawn and crab dishes, potent curries in coconut milk, and rice or noodles.

Bunjies [6/10]

27 Litchfield Street, WC2 map 14
TEL 01-240 1796

Open noon to 11
Closed Sun L; Aug bank hol

The folk music is giving way increasingly to the food at this valuable vegetarian restaurant within striking distance of Leicester Square. From outside it looks seedier than it is. Pine tables and chairs, white walls and little annexes give a cosy feel, which may explain why it is taken over by foreign students in summer. The menu revolves on an axis of wholemeal quiches, pasties, crumbles, and salads. No licence but plenty of non-alcoholic drinks; you can also bring your own. Friendly service. Wednesday is cabaret night.

Burgh House Buttery [6/10]

New End Square, NW3   map 12
TEL 01-431 2516

Open 11 to 5.30
Closed Mon and Tue; 2 weeks at Christmas

On a fine day the garden of this Queen Anne house is a handsome place to eat. More usually the basement is used, where it is not unlike sitting at someone else's kitchen table. The food is cheap and home made. The short menu favours old-fashioned dishes, such as chicken Marengo with rice for £2.80 or coronation chicken with salads for £2.20. The cakes, tarts and trifles are persuasive attractions through the day. Wine is 70p a glass.

Busabong [6/10]

331 Fulham Road, SW10   map 12
TEL 01-352 4742

Open 12.30 to midnight (10.30 Sun)
Closed Christmas Day to 29 Dec

The seminal London Thai restaurant has expanded into a shop offering all manner of Thai activities. Free delivery of take-away dishes is available within the area. Eating in the restaurant itself can work out at £15 a head or more, though there are cheaper ways, if you choose carefully. The fast food counter is the bargain, offering fine hot dishes, two of which can be had with a plate of rice for £3.50, or else there is a copious noodle soup.

Café Delancey [7/10]

3 Delancey Street, NW1   map 13
TEL 01-387 1985

Open 9.30am to 11.30pm & (also wc)
Closed Sun; Christmas Day, Boxing Day and 1 Jan

Nowhere has marked the up-turn in Camden's sociability as acutely as here – a continental-style café, open all day, calling itself 'the place to meet', and also the place

for breakfast, with eight daily papers on offer. The mood is stylish and the menu shuffles along through the day, ranging from sausages or steak sandwiches to steak and kidney pie. Some seasonal dishes are coming to the fore and the wine list is being upgraded, both of which give it increasingly the air of a restaurant.

Café Pelican [8/10]

45 St Martin's Lane, WC2   map 14
TEL 01-379 0309/0295

Open 11 to midnight & (also wc)
Closed 22 to 31 Dec

The Pelican swallows vast numbers of customers. Although the more ambitious restaurant dishes are not necessarily successful, the plainer bistro standards – steak and frites or a plate of charcuterie – are. The health-conscious items on the menu, like the pasta with tofu, can show unusual flair. Good cheeses and some good wines beyond the house bottles also make it a valuable stopping point, elegantly decorated as an imitation of a French brasserie, with enough tables to make booking unnecessary.

Calabash [7/10]

33 King Street, WC2   map 14
TEL 01-836 1976

Open noon to 3, 6 to 10.30
Closed Sun

The restaurant in the basement of the Africa Centre is one of the most accessible introductions to the range of African cooking. The menu has dishes from Egypt, Uganda, Nigeria and Zaïre among others. From the West Coast comes chicken and groundnut stew, from Malawi a dish of beef with potatoes and peppers, and from Algeria there's grilled lamb with rice. Main dishes are around £4, but the price doesn't include vegetables. House wine is £1 a glass.

NEW ENTRY Canton [7/10]

11 Newport Place, WC2   map 14
TEL 01-437 6220

Open 24 hours

This Cantonese café between the Polar Bear and the Kings Head has the longest opening hours in Chinatown. Its Night Café licence runs till 5.30 in the morning, but in practice it never closes. A recent facelift has created more tables and a bit more space than before. The long menu aims to please everyone. For good value and authentic Cantonese cooking stay with the one-plate rice and noodle dishes, the hot-pots, soups and savoury porridges. Shiny lacquered duck with rice is a bestseller. Otherwise there's a list of set meals, sweet-and-sour, and chop sueys for western devils who might baulk at the sight of the bright orange intestines and offal in the window.

Carioca [7/10]

239 High Street, Bromley map 3
TEL 01-460 7130

Open noon to 2, 6 to 11 (11.45 Fri and Sat) &

More personalised than the average curry house. The handwritten menu holds a few surprises – ratatouille among them – but otherwise deals in carefully composed versions of chicken tikka masala, rogan josh and good-value thalis.

La Carpa D'Oro [7/10]

40 The Broadway, Mill Hill, NW7 map 12
TEL 01-906 3494/959 3924

Open 11.30 to 3, 5.30 to 11 & (also WC)
Closed Sun, Mon

A fish and chip sign hangs outside. As well as take-aways there is a full restaurant menu; last summer more seats were added. Grilled sardines or grilled mushrooms, followed by hake fried in matzo meal, salmon meunière, or halibut with boiled potatoes or chips, or salad, are the style. A griddle provides an alternative to deep frying. Desserts include home-made almond meringue. Espresso coffee.

Le Casino [7/10]

77 Lower Sloane Street, SW1 map 13
TEL 01-730 3313/1732

Open 11am to 1am
Closed Christmas Day and Boxing Day

One of Peter Ilic's group of cut-price bistros. This branch began by opening twenty-four hours a day, but times are now in line with the other branches. For details see entry for Lantern.

NEW ENTRY | Centrale [6/10]

16 Moor Street, WC2 map 14
TEL 01-437 5513

Open 11 to 11
Closed Sun; bank hols

Two doors down from the Barocco, it is the smallest of the four pasta places in the area (Pollo, Barocco and Presto). There is no licence and only five black vinyl booths with Formica tables in an area the size of someone's kitchen. Needless to say it gets extremely hot as the tiny kitchen is just behind the bar counter. The usual selection of pasta dishes is extended by omelettes, chicken salads and so on. Tagliatelle alfredo is especially good. Lettuce, cucumber and tomato salad comes with oil and vinegar to dress yourself.

Chaglayan Kebab House [7/10]

86 Brent Street, NW4 map 12
TEL 01-202 8575

Open noon to 3, 6 to midnight &
Closed Sun

Inexpensive little Turkish café with two rows of tables, a dark, candle-lit atmosphere and a short, inexpensive menu. Kebabs are the main business, served with rice, potatoes and salad. The kleftiko is also excellent. Occasional belly-dancing.

Charco's Wine Bar [8/10]

1 Bray Place, SW3 map 13
TEL 01-584 0765

Open 11 to 3, 5.30 to 11
Closed Sun; bank hols

Go early. The cold buffet at lunch-time is quickly decimated at this elegant, split-level wine bar off the King's Road. Unlike much of the competition, it has space enough to swallow a crowd. The choice is of superior wedding-reception-style fare – smoked poultry, good pies, salmon, salads, plenty of mayonnaise. At night the menu becomes more fashionable with a set three-course meal around £10, but one course and a drink costs less. Better than average value for the area.

Chequers [7/10]

18 Chalk Farm Road, NW1   map 13
TEL 01-485 6544

Open 10am to midnight & (also WC)
Closed Christmas

The chess players' retreat has a strictly vegetarian menu. Three of the twenty salads on offer are £2.95; alternatively try the whole buffet for £5.95. In winter there are spicy soups; the proprietors also pride themselves on their cheesecake. Very busy on Saturdays and Sundays because of Camden Lock market.

Cherry Orchard [8/10]

241–245 Globe Road,   map 12
Bethnal Green, EC2
TEL 01-980 6678

Open noon to 10.30 &
Closed Sun, Mon; 1 week Aug; 1 week at Easter; 1 week at Christmas

Evenings at the Buddhist women's co-operative are now more formal, with waitress service and a wider selection of dishes, but the prices are still pegged tightly; it can be hard to spend £5. The cooking stays within the realms of salads and crumbles, with a few less usual dishes, like leek and root au fromage. The garden seats twenty.

Chicago Pizza Pie Factory [8/10]

17 Hanover Square, W1   map 13
TEL 01-629 2669

Open 11.45 to 11.30 (noon to 10.30 Sun)
Closed Christmas Day

Theme supremo Bob Payton's empire was built on these deep-pan, indulgently USA-style pizzas. As with his other places, it is the razzamatazz of the cheer-leader décor that lifts the evening out of the ordinary: videos, music and college-girl waitresses. If Britain is the 52nd state then this is the frontier town and the affable Mr P. the colonising colonel.

Chicago Rib Shack [9/10]

1 Raphael Street, SW7   map 13
TEL 01-581 5595

Open 11.45 (noon Sun) to 11.30 (10.30 Sun)
Closed Christmas Eve D to Boxing Day; 31 Dec D and 1 Jan

The Shack – Bob Payton's premier venue – says more about Americana than about food. A gastronomic Disneyland, it has side shows of ribs, cocktails, barbecues, potato skins, pecan pie. The onion pie and the ribs themselves are best ordered by lengths. It's all very messy and the waitresses issue bibs along with the reflex 'enjoy-your-meal'. Expect a long wait at the crowded bar at peak hours. Among the best places in the capital to take children. If the queues are too long, head round on to Knightsbridge to Windy City, the latest addition to Mr Payton's empire. It's a shade more grown up and a shade more expensive – allow about £15 a head, especially if you drink beer.

Chinatown [7/10]

795 Commercial Road, E14   map 12
TEL 01-987 2330

Open noon to 3, 6 to 11 &
Closed Christmas Eve to Boxing Day

Perhaps now the pick of the East End Chinese. The rather westernised menu nevertheless provides precise cooking. Billingsgate is just down the road, so fresh fish is a feature of all the restaurants round here. Crisp roast duck, rice and soups have all been of the standard of Soho Chinatown. A vegetarian menu has been added and improvements made to the bar and toilets. Bookings only.

NEW ENTRY | Cho Won [7/10]

27 Romilly Street, W1   map 14
TEL 01-437 2262

Open noon to 3, 6 to 11 & (also WC)

The downstairs of this Korean restaurant is like a café, with minimal décor and views of the kitchen; upstairs is almost Japanese, with low tables and cushions to sit on. Extremely good-value lunches leave change from a fiver. Have, say, kalbi jeon sik – marinated beef rib, barbecued and served with rice, pickled cucumber and bean sprouts. The price includes a glass of wine. An extra 90p brings a dish of powerful kim-chee. Barley tea is free. The full menu is more expensive.

NEW ENTRY | Christys [7/10]

122–126 Wardour Street, W1   map 14
TEL 01-434 4468

Open 8 to 11.30 (12.30 to 11 Sun) & (also WC)

The yuppy face of vegetarianism. Clean almost to the point of coffee-bar antiseptic, it makes a pretentious but overdue and laudable attempt to develop vegetarian restaurant cooking into something more refined than pulses and wholemeal. The thrust of the menu, though, is towards healthiness rather than innovation. A good place for non-vegetarians, who may be reassured to find quiches, baked potatoes, lasagne, and crêpes. The daily menu holds interest in terms of mushroom and Chinese cabbage soup or aubergine terrine with basil and tomato sauce. Has quickly established a good reputation in vegetarian circles and may yet become a green version of Langan's Brasserie.

This restaurant was closed as we went to press.

La Cloche [7/10]

304 Kilburn High Road, NW6   map 12
TEL 01-328 0302

Open noon to 3, 7 to midnight &
Closed Christmas Day and Boxing Day

The second of Peter Ilic's group of cut-price bistros. For details see entry for Lantern.

Como Lario [7/10]

22 Holbein Place, SW1   map 13
TEL 01-730 2954

Open 12.30 to 2.30, 6.30 to 11.30 &
Closed Sun; bank hols

Of the same vintage as its namesake Perry, Como is a place of contrasts – set somewhere between café and trattoria, often with a queue to get in. The value of the pasta and main dishes – around £5 – is unusually good and attracts an elegant, restaurant-going crowd. Very useful after the theatre at the Royal Court and heroically inexpensive for SW1.

NEW ENTRY | Compton Green [7/10]

14 Old Compton Street, W1   map 14
TEL 01-434 3544

Open 11.30 to 10.45 &

Vegetarianism is striving to emerge from its brown-sandalled chrysalis and without being quite the embodiment of the new tomorrow, this is another laudable Soho effort to put on the clothes of a restaurant. The dining-room of what was a fish and chip shop doubles as an art gallery, with the addition of live music most nights, but all the cooking is done on the premises. It aims to be slick and trendy, is open through the day, and has not abandoned its healthy vegetarian principles one jot – vegan cappuccino is made with soya milk. Typical dishes are: Mexican enchiladas with guacamole and tortilla chips;

31

moussaka; tofu kebabs with peanut sauce.
Wines are organic, teas herbal.

Conservatory [6/10]

218 Trinity Road, SW17   map 12
TEL 01-767 5810

Open noon to 3, 7 to midnight &

The vaulted, glass-roofed building filled
with vegetation makes this one of the
more attractive pizzerias and accounts for
much of its popularity. Seafood and
vegetarian dishes expand the menu, but
pizza and pasta are the main lines and,
without being cheap, nonetheless keep the
bill in check.

F. Cooke [9/10]

41 Kingsland High Street, E8   map 12
TEL 01-254 2878

Open 10am to 10pm (6pm Tue and Wed,
8pm Mon and Thur) & (also WC)
Closed Sun; bank hols

Only a handful of London's original eel
and pie shops survive, but Cooke's keeps
the tradition alive in splendid style. It is a
unique East End institution, with
meticulously preserved turn-of-the-
century décor, and a reputation for quality.
Fred and Chris Cooke are proud of their
trade and don't take short-cuts. They deal
in eels, getting supplies from Billingsgate
and direct from fishermen; they always
use real potato for their mash and fresh
parsley for the liquor. Pies are baked at the
back of the shop each day. Unlicensed.

Cooke's Eel and Pie Shop [6/10]

84 The Cut, SE1   map 13
TEL 01-928 5931

Open 10.30 to 3 (3.30 Fri and Sat) &
Closed Christmas; bank hols; 2 weeks July

One of the few remaining Cockney-style
eateries. The main business these days is
in meat pies but eels with parsley liquor
are the connoisseur's traditional choice.
Here they are as good as any in London.
Popular and comfortingly old fashioned.
Take your dirty dishes up to the counter as
you leave.

Cork & Bottle [8/10]

44–46 Cranbourn Street, WC2   map 14
TEL 01-734 7807

Open 11 to 3 (noon to 2.30 Sun), 5.30 to 11
Closed Christmas Day, Boxing Day and 1 Jan

There is always a scramble for tables in
this understandably popular basement
wine bar close to Leicester Square.
Discomfort is compensated for by the
cosmopolitan choice of food and the
wisely chosen wine list. To eat there
might be anything from smoked chicken
with avocado to spicy beef and pepper pie.
To drink, the choice is from good plonk to
classy vintages from interesting vineyards.
A bit too discovered for its own good, but
otherwise a gem.

Cosmo [7/10]

4–6 Northways Parade,   map 12
Finchley Road, NW3
TEL 01-722 2627

Open noon to 11.30 &

Honest, sustaining, middle of the road,
middle European dishes keep this thirty-
year-old landmark of Swiss Cottage eating
alive. The pastries, served with coffee and
whipped cream, are its heart – the
Sachertorte and the Apfelstrudel in
particular – but there are hot dishes, such
as goulash or sweet-sour braised beef in
raisin sauce with red cabbage and
dumplings, that are worth pursuing.

Cosmos [8/10]

Landor Road, SW9   map 12
TEL 01-274 3853

Open 7pm to 1am & (also WC)
Closed Mon; Christmas Day and Boxing Day

The meze is enormous in this tiny, family-
run taverna. For £5.50 a succession of
taramosalata, hummus, tsatsiki, fried fish,
three sorts of sausage and so on arrive with
hot pitta. As always in Greek cookery, the
lengthily braised dishes tend to
overshadow other main dishes – stifado,
afelia and kleftiko are all exemplary.
Service is amicable and the dining-room
gets busier as the evening wears on.

NEW ENTRY Costas [7/10]

18 Hillgate Street, W8   map 12
TEL 01-727 4310

Open noon to 2.30, 5.30 to 10.30
Closed 10 days at Christmas; 3 weeks July to mid-Aug

The Papadopoulus family have run this small fish restaurant for the last five years, using fish straight from the coast each day. The range of haddock, plaice, cod, rock salmon, mackerel and lemon sole is priced between £2 and £4. The rest of the menu strays into unusual territory, featuring Greek specialities like taramosalata, octopus, fish soup, and baklava. There is retsina to drink.

Country Life [8/10]

123 Regent Street, W1   map 13
(entrance in Heddon Street)
TEL 01-434 2922

Open 11.30 to 2.30
Closed Sat and Sun

The value of the vegetarian buffet in this basement off Regent Street is under-written by a worldwide crusade. This is a healthfood restaurant in the widest sense – you can have your blood pressure taken if you want, or join a give-up-smoking class. The basement sells take-aways and sandwiches as well as an imaginative spread of salads, dressings and hot dishes. It is all uncomfortably persuasive. Unlicensed. Children welcome.

Cranks [7/10]

8 Marshall Street, W1   map 13
TEL 01-437 9431

Open 8 (10 Sat) to 10.30 ⅋
Closed Sun; bank hols

17–18 Great Newport Street,   map 14
WC2
TEL 01-836 5226

Open 8 to 8.30
Closed Sun; bank hols

11 The Market, Covent Garden,   map 14
WC2
TEL 01-379 6508

Open 10 to 8 (7 Sun)
Closed Sun; bank hols

9–11 Tottenham Street, W1   map 13
TEL 01-631 3912

Open 8 (9 Sat) to 8
Closed Sun

NEW ENTRY Unit 13, 10 Adelaide Street, WC2   map 14
TEL 01-379 5919

Open 10.30 to 10.30
Closed Sun; bank hols

If you could have just one restaurant on an otherwise deserted desert isle, then the sensible choice would be Cranks. The menus are middle-of-the-road vegetarian, bringing to mind the parent company's old slogan, 'Guinness is good for you'. The cause is worthwhile and every branch is exceptionally clean. If some of the soups are a bit thin it may be because they are vegan. Savouries, salads, crumbles and breads are all good.

Crowders, Greenwich Theatre [6/10]

13 Nevada Street, SE10   map 12
TEL 01-858 1318

Open noon to 2.30, 6 to 11 ⅋ (also wc)
Closed Sun; Christmas; bank hols

There is a good atmosphere, when it is not squeezed out in the crush pre- and post-shows, that bears out the theatre wine bar's name. The large room is filled with wooden furniture and lace lampshades. The drinks bar is on one side, the food on the other, arranged as a help-yourself choice of cold joints – rare roast beef, whole turkey – quiches, salads, and cold fish. Sweets are confined to cakes, but are above average. Book for performance times.

Crowns [7/10]

3–4 Crown Passage, Pall Mall,   map 13
SW1
TEL 01-839 3960

Open 9.30 to 8 ⅋
Closed Sat, Sun

'All our food is made in our own kitchen. We use only fresh produce. This has to be the right way as we are busy five days a week.' Above the more expensive restaurant is the all-day wine bar. Tables are at a premium at peak hours. Portions are generous. The chill cabinet holds health-conscious salads and restaurant staples, like pâté or smoked salmon. There are also hot dishes, such as pasta or cod florentine, at £4.65.

Curri-Express [6/10]

17 Swallow Street, W1   map 13
TEL 01-434 3959

Open 10 to 6
Closed Sun; bank hols; Christmas Day

A tiny café serving some of the cheapest Indian food in the West End. The short menu has specials of the day, and the full lunch is great value for around £3. Meat curries are pungently spiced, Basmati rice is well cooked, and there are decent vegetable dishes, such as spicy potatoes with red beans. Food comes on throwaway plates for convenience and stools are arranged around a high shelf (no tables or chairs). The place also does a fast trade in take-away samosas. Unlicensed, but the range of soft drinks extends beyond Coke.

Curry Paradise [6/10]

49 South End Road, NW3   map 12
TEL 01-794 6314

Open noon to 3, 5.30 to 11.30 (midnight Sat and Sun) &
Closed Christmas Day

A small paradise indeed, with carved wooden partitions, ethnic paintings, and little rooflets with pillars. The comprehensive menu sets out to cater for most whims, but the cookery is singularly lacking in grease and packs plenty of flavour. Capsicum bhaji are unusual, as are the prawns with okra. Service is sedate, doubtless to enable you to linger, but it should be easy enough to eat for less than £5.

Dalat [8/10]

11 Willesden Lane, NW6   map 12
TEL 01-624 8521

Open 6pm to 11pm &

This small Vietnamese restaurant is amazingly popular. The décor is a Spartan assembly of veneered wood, but the 45-dish menu, with a choice of three set menus, is accessible and inexpensive. Notable are deep-fried prawns, spring rolls with lettuce to dip into a fish sauce, chicken with lemon grass and chilli, and pork balls with rice paper, cucumber sticks, mint leaves, coriander leaves, pickled garlic and shredded lettuce. Dip the rice paper in water, make a parcel of the pork and all the other bits and dip into the sauce. Service is cheerful and helpful.

Daphne [7/10]

83 Bayham Street, NW1   map 13
TEL 01-267 7322

Open noon to 3, 6 to midnight &
Closed Sun

Smartly appointed in a terraced house in Camden Town. The food here is a cut above the average taverna, and meze is still exceptional value at £5.75. Otherwise the menu blends the familiar – avgolemono, stifado, afelia – with the unexpected – stuffed squid, casserole of lamb with spinach and beans, swordfish kebabs. Greek coffee comes with Turkish delight.

Daquise [7/10]

20 Thurloe Street, SW7   map 13
TEL 01-589 6117

Open noon to 11.30 &
Closed Christmas Day and Boxing Day

In the heart of museumland, this Polish restaurant is worth remembering, though under new management the Polishness of its menu has been diluted. A set lunch of minestrone and meatballs is £3.40, but look for the surviving eastern dishes on the main menu, such as stuffed cabbage or bigos, which set it apart from the usual run of the mill, as does the choice of seven vodkas and Polish Tatra lager.

Design Centre Restaurant [6/10]

28 Haymarket, SW1   map 14
TEL 01-839 8000

Open 10 (noon Sat, 1 Sun) to 5.15 (7.30 Wed)

Black and white café-cum-restaurant in the Design Centre. Food is on display on well-lit shelves. Staff are friendly and helpful and there is often a long queue. Sandwiches, salads, cakes and pastries fill the menu – very useful in the area.

Diana's Diner [7/10]

39 Endell Street, WC2   map 14
TEL 01-240 0272

Open 8.30 to 7 (9 to 2 Sat) &
Closed Sun; Sat D; 1 week at Christmas

One of the few places left in Covent Garden not wholly given over to tourism. Diana Berns has made this a local institution. On a fine day there are tables outside. Inside it is filled with pine and colourful posters. The menu lists all the usual café dishes with egg, with sausage, with chips etcetera, but also has daily specials, such as cottage pie or chicken Kiev. The chips are excellent and the salads, like everything else, generous. If it gets too crowded, take-aways are offered.

Dining Room [9/10]

1 Cathedral Street, SE1   map 13
TEL 01-407 0337

Open noon to 3, 7 to 10
Closed Sat, Sun and Mon

The Dining Room is exactly that – a room for eating, with half a dozen large tables that are shared. It is like a dungeon, with bare walls and occasional rays of light streaming in from the world above. The cooking is committed without being zealous in the cause of vegetarianism. Produce is organic and the menu roams adventurously for the likes of cream of almond soup; seaweed and chestnut fritters with dill mayonnaise; okra and

chickpea stew, and buckwheat noodles with broccoli and pine kernels. Unpasteurised cheeses, such as Irish Milleens, are served with oatcakes. To drink there are herb teas, fruit juices and elderflower wine.

Dino's Grill [7/10]

76 Commercial Street, E1   map 12
TEL 01-247 6097

Open 5 to 5.30 (6 to 2.30 Sun) &
Closed Sat; 2 weeks Aug

On the north side of Commercial Street, 75 yards east of Christ Church, Spitalfields and just across the road from the market, this family-run café has been on the site for 28 years. Son Dino now serves, while father cooks and mother does take-aways. It is quality traditional English café food: home-made steak and mushroom pie, thick chips, liver and bacon, peaches and ice-cream, fruit pie and custard. Fried breakfasts.

Di's Larder [6/10]

62 Lavender Hill, SW11   map 12
TEL 01-223 4618

Open 10 to 6 &
Closed Sun; bank hols; 2 weeks Aug

This shop-cum-daytime vegetarian café has its own bakery, providing fresh wholemeal and wholegrain breads. Diana Kilpatrick is also responsible for the organic wines. There are only a few tables, making it a crush of a meeting place; children are very welcome. The short menu deals with much of the produce available in the shop – fresh pasta, salads, savoury snacks, cheesecake.

Diwana Bhel Poori [7/10]

114 Drummond Street, NW1   map 13
TEL 01-388 4867

Open noon to 10
Closed Mon; Christmas Day

121 Drummond Street, NW1   map 13
TEL 01-387 5556

Open noon to midnight
Closed Christmas Day

50 Westbourne Grove, W2   map 12
TEL 01-221 0721

Open noon to 3, 6 to 11 (noon to 11 Sat, Sun) &
Closed Mon; Christmas Day

The best-known bhel-poori houses in
London (there's also a branch in Paris). The
two cafés in Drummund Street helped set
the style during the 1970s. The range of
South Indian snacks and curries takes in
all the classics, from puris, chats and dahi
vada to more substantial dosais. Thalis are
excellent value: £3.90 pays for dhal, rice,
two vegetables, a savoury snack,
poppadums, raita, shrikhand, mango
pickle, plus breads. Unlicensed, but there's
salt or sweet lassi, fruit juice or mango
milk shake – or you can bring your own
wine.

Dizzy's Diner [6/10]

256–258 High Street, Beckenham   map 3
TEL 01-650 6010

Open noon to 2.15, 6 to 11.30 (7 to 10.30 Sun)
Closed Christmas Day, Boxing Day and 1 Jan

The glitzy neon outside is matched by
whirling fans and posters of 1950s movie
stars, but the effect is still more of a
revamped pub than downtown LA. The
menu is that custom-built model followed
by the Hard Rock Café and Bob Payton's
chain – potato skins, burgers, nine ways,
steaks, vegetarian pancakes, banana split,
and apple pie. At happy hour between 6pm
and 8pm the rainbow cocktails are all
£1.25, which makes the place even better
value. Service is slick – so, for that matter,
is the clientele.

Dover Street Restaurant & Wine Bar [6/10]

8–9 Dover Street, W1   map 13
TEL 01-629 9813/491 7509

Open 12.30 to 3, 6.30 to 3
Closed Sun; Sat L; bank hols L

This Mayfair basement, host to many a
live band, stays open late and serves drinks
until 3am. There is a standard menu of
steaks, baked potatoes, and salads, which
can make it invaluable in the area.

NEW ENTRY | Downs [6/10]

Arch 166, Bohemia Place, E8   map 12
TEL 01-986 4325

Open 11 to 11 (10.30 Sun) & (also wc)
Closed Christmas Day and Boxing Day

Trains on the North London Link line
rumble over the arches above this cheery
wine bar that offers a £5.50 business lunch
and attracts crowds in an area starved of
good restaurant food. There are seats
inside the arch and a few more at the back
in a pleasant conservatory. The special
lunch may offer deep-fried mushrooms
and steak, while the main menu has
chicken in white wine sauce, spinach,
mushroom and aubergine pancake, and
scallop and prawn brochette. Short wine
list.

Dulwich Tandoori [7/10]

54 Lordship Lane, SE22   map 12
TEL 01-693 3012

Open noon to 2.30, 6 to midnight &
Closed Christmas Day and Boxing Day

A strong local following reaffirms our view
that this is an above-average Indian
restaurant. The décor has lately had a
facelift. The menu stays on familiar
ground but the freshness of the spicing and
the care in the cooking are evident in the
chicken tikka and the tandoori dishes.

Ealing Tandoori [7/10]

9–10 High Street, The Green, W5   map 12
TEL 01-567 7606

Open noon to 3, 6 to midnight

Large, well-appointed and reputable Indian
restaurant. Service is friendly, portions are
generous and prices reasonable. Full range
of curries, plus some specialities,
including butter chicken and tandoori
king prawns.

Earth Exchange [7/10]

213 Archway Road, N6   map 12
TEL 01-340 6407

Open noon to 3, 6 to 10.30
Closed Tue, Wed, Thur; Mon L, Fri L and Sat L

Well-regarded workers' co-operative. The emphasis is towards the healthy and the nutritious. Thick, full-bodied soups, for instance potato and split pea; interesting casseroles, for example Casablanca; unusual salads, such as date and cucumber. Cakes are heavy duty but excellent. Wines are organic or there is a spicy apple juice.

East West [8/10]

188 Old Street, EC1 map 13
TEL 01-608 0300

Open 11 to 10 (3 Sat and Sun)
Closed bank hols; 10 days at Christmas

Much revered in vegetarian circles for its impeccable macrobiotic credentials. The centre has a bookshop and grocery as well as a new take-away counter. The self-service restaurant works to a simple formula – two plate sizes are on offer, one at £2.95, the other at £3.95. Both are sufficient for a full meal and both change daily. The organic policy stretches to the wines. No meat, no animal fats, no sugar, no dairy produce, with a balance between grains, vegetables and protein.

Ebury Wine Bar [8/10]

139 Ebury Street, SW1 map 13
TEL 01-730 5447

Open noon to 2.45 (2.30 Sun), 6 to 10.30
Closed Christmas Day and Boxing Day

The high quality food and wines at this long-standing wine bar beside Victoria coach station can push the bill over £10, but there is no need to spend this much. The menu is based on grills – steaks from £5.50 for rump to £7.50 for fillet – a cold salad table, plus enterprising cooking such as tuna and pepper tart, and garoupa fish in filo pastry with a red wine sauce. All the food is prepared on the premises. Minimum food charge is £5. Twenty wines by the glass. Club-like atmosphere.

Efes Kebab House [9/10]

80 Great Titchfield Street, W1 map 13
TEL 01-636 1953

Open noon to 11.30
Closed Sun; Christmas Day and 1 Jan

Turkish cooking has been overshadowed by Greek (Cypriot, really) in this country but deserves equal, some say more, attention. This is where to start. The range of the meze in the bustling cavernous restaurant kept by the brothers Kazim and Ibrahim is extensive. There are no fewer than nineteen variations of kebab. Take-aways and quick lunches are the cheapest options, but £10 should cover an evening meal with wine. Well used by Turks.

Elgin Lokanta [6/10]

239 Elgin Avenue, W9 map 12
TEL 01-328 6400

Open noon to midnight &

A thriving take-away trade sustains this smart little Turkish restaurant. The simpler meze and kebabs are the main virtues, but it is open until midnight and on Sundays, too, which makes it invaluable in the area.

El Greco [6/10]

73 Windmill Road, Enfield map 12
TEL 01-363 0685

Open 5pm to midnight (noon to 3, 5.30 to 10.30 Sun) & (also wc)
Closed bank hols

Two brothers run this boisterous taverna. Two things stand out: the good-value meze, and the fact it is open late in an area that otherwise closes early.

Equatorial [8/10]

37 Old Compton Street, W1 map 14
TEL 01-437 6112/6093

Open noon to 2.45, 6 to 11.15 (11.30 Sat and Sun) &
Closed Christmas Eve to Boxing Day

A bevy of waitresses in full-length sarongs move smoothly through three floors of this inexpensive Singaporean restaurant. Fixtures are consistently good noodle dishes, such as meehon goreng or hokken mee, big bowls of laksa soup, and satay with a dark peanut sauce. Chicken comes with soy, onion and chillies, or creamy yellow coconut sauce. Excellent-value lunches for under £5. Drink Tiger beer.

NEW ENTRY Erawan [7/10]

161 Mitcham Road, SW17   map 12
TEL 01-672 3972

Open noon to 2.30, 6 to 11.30 (7 to 10.30 Sun) &

The small dining-room with its silky wallpaper, Thai posters and mobiles houses some potent Thai cooking. Fish soup is a bargain and comes in a big metal container sitting on a gas burner and filled with lots of mussels, prawns, pieces of white fish and squid; chicken soup comes with lemon grass. They also have one-plate noodle dishes, which at around £3 are a good-value lunch.

NEW ENTRY Ethiopia 2002 [7/10]

341A Harrow Road, W9   map 12
TEL 01-286 5129

Open noon to 2.30, 7 to 10.45 &
Closed Christmas

Ethiopian cooking is some of the hottest currently to be found in London, being two or three degrees fiercer than most Indian dishes and on a different scale to Szechuan or Thai. Meals revolve round a central course served on a sheet of enjira flour bread, like a thick pancake, set with little piles of different stews. It is eaten with the fingers. Coconut sorbets go some way to ease the heat afterwards. The coffee – Ethiopia was a major producer before the present troubles – is excellent.

L'Express [7/10]

16 Sloane Street, SW1   map 13
TEL 01-235 9869

Open 9.30 to 6 (6.30 Wed)
Closed Sun; bank hols

Along the avenue that now also houses Yves St Laurent and Valentino, this bijou basement offers snacks that cut a dash in matching separates: quails' egg and asparagus salad; carpaccio; goat's cheese salad; white chocolate mousse. Cheap it is not, but equally there is no need to be over

lavish. Afternoon teas and breakfasts are well within the range of this book and few people end up spending more than £10.

Falafel House [7/10]

95 Haverstock Hill, NW3   map 12
TEL 01-722 6187

Open 6pm to 11.30pm
Closed Christmas Eve to Boxing Day; Good Fri

The twin virtues of friendly service and some honest, greaseless cooking illuminate this otherwise dimly lit Middle Eastern restaurant. Copious soups, from avgolemono to bean, good falafel (spiced rissoles made from white, dried beans deep fried in oil) and latkes compete with hummus and tarámosalata before perhaps a couscous. Open on Sunday nights.

NEW ENTRY The Firkins [6/10]

Falcon and Firkin

274 Victoria Park Road, E9   map 12
TEL 01-985 0693

Open 11 to 3, 5.30 to 11 (noon to 2, 7 to 10.30 Sun) & (also wc)
Closed Christmas Day, Boxing Day and 1 Jan

Ferret and Firkin

114 Lots Road, SW10   map 12
TEL 01-352 6645

Open 11 to 3, 5.30 to 11 (noon to 2, 7 to 10.30 Sun) &
Closed Christmas Day D, Boxing Day

Flounder and Firkin

54 Holloway Road, N7   map 12
TEL 01-609 9574

Open 11 to 3, 5.30 to 11 (noon to 2, 7 to 10.30 Sun) &
Closed Christmas Day and Boxing Day

Fox and Firkin

316 Lewisham High Street, SE13   map 12
TEL 01-690 8925

Open 11 to 3, 5.30 to 11 (noon to 2, 7 to 10.30 Sun) & (also wc)
Closed Christmas Day; Boxing Day L and 1 Jan L

Frog and Firkin

41 Tavistock Crescent, W11   map 12
TEL 01-727 9250

Open 11 to 3, 5.30 to 11 (noon to 2, 7 to 10.30 Sun)

Goose and Firkin

47 Borough Road, SE1   map 13
TEL 01-403 3590

Open 11 to 3, 5.30 to 11 (noon to 2, 7 to 10.30 Sun) & (also WC)
Closed Christmas Day, Boxing Day and 1 Jan

Pheasant and Firkin

166 Goswell Road, EC1   map 13
TEL 01-253 7429

Open 11 to 3, 5.30 to 11 (7 to 11 Sat; noon to 2, 7 to 10.30 Sun) & (also WC)
Closed Christmas Day, Boxing Day and 1 Jan

Phoenix and Firkin

Windsor Walk, SE5   map 12
TEL 01-701 8282

Open 11 to 3, 5.30 (6 Sat) to 11 (noon to 2, 7 to 10.30 Sun)
Closed Christmas Day and Boxing Day

David Bruce's eight affiliated Firkin pubs are like CAMRA come to life – bare boards, bawdy jokes, home-brew beer, falconic memorabilia at the Falcon, and bar staff in Firkin T-shirts. There is also good pub grub at reasonable prices, for London. Choose a filling – meat, cheese, prawns, pâté, salad – for the large baps or try the quiches, ploughman's, Cumberland sausages or daily specials, such as chicken and bacon flan with salad, beef tatties and peas, or cheese and onion pie. No dish is over £2. More restricted choice of food in the evening.

NEW ENTRY Fallen Angel [7/10]

65 Graham Road, N1   map 13
TEL 01-253 3996

Open 12.30 to 9 & (also WC)

Close to Angel tube station, this vegetarian restaurant used to be a pub and

still uses the central bar as a service area. Flowers are on all the tables and there is a fish tank in the corner. Soups, including leek and potato, are recommended and for the main course there are vegetable pancakes, moussaka, spring roll with pear and ginger sauce, and dhal with rice and hazelnuts. Date crumble or fresh fruit salad to finish off. Fully licensed or try some of the herbal teas: peppermint, fennel or rosehip.

Faulkner's [7/10]

424–426 Kingsland Road, E8   map 12
TEL 01-254 6152

Open noon to 2, 5.15 to 10 (noon to 10 Sat) &
Closed Sun and Mon; Christmas to New Year

Formerly a branch of London's finest fish and chip shop, the Seashell, now under the ownership of an international casino/leisure group, bought for a cool £4 million. Mr Faulkner, the Svengali who developed and created Seashell, is still in charge. The name has changed, but the basic principles of using fresh fish each day remains solid.

Flamingo [7/10]

7 South Norwood Hill, SE25   map 3
TEL 01-653 3759

Open 6pm to 10pm (10.30 Sat) & (also WC)
Closed Sun D

The menu in this family-run taverna is split between Greek and English. One side comes with rice, the other with chips. On special occasions, dishes come with both. The place is popular, so booking is worthwhile; the atmosphere can get quite frantic. No licence and corkage at £1 help keep the bill well down, even for three courses.

Fleet Tandoori [7/10]

104 Fleet Road, NW3   map 12
TEL 01-485 6402

Open noon to 2.30, 6 to 11.30 (noon to 11.30 Sun) & (also WC)

A consistent neighbourhood curry house with a strong local following. Vegetarian dishes are good – especially creamy muttar paneer and channa masalladar. The vegetarian thali for under £8 brings onion bhajia, puri, poppadum, vegetable curry, sag aloo, dhal, pilau rice, nan, coffee and sweet. Drink lassi or lager.

Food for Health [7/10]

15 Blackfriars Lane, EC4   map 13
TEL 01-236 7001

Open 8 to 3 &
Closed Sat and Sun; bank hols

One of the biggest and oldest of London's vegetarian restaurants. Despite being hidden under the Blackfriars railway arches it is well discovered and fills up early at lunch-time. The cafeteria dispenses middle-of-the-road stir-fries, huge omelettes, casseroles, pastas, and salads. Usually there is at least one hot sweet of the old-fashioned school of pies and crumbles. There is a shop section, too. When the history of modern vegetarianism is chronicled, Nolan Highton will be seen as a key figure who won over many meat-eaters.

Food for Thought [8/10]

31 Neal Street, WC2   map 14
TEL 01-836 0239

Open noon to 8
Closed Sat and Sun; 2 weeks at Christmas

So small, it is best considered as a take-away with a few seats. Siriporn Duncan, who established its reputation over eight years, has left and been replaced by a team on rotation. The style is more structured but much the same: inventive soups, a choice of three main dishes – perhaps a bake, a stir-fry and something sauced, such as mushroom and cauliflower in lemon parsley – then crumbles and bakes to finish. Fridays has seen nationalist themes: French, Italian, Greek, Indian. Excellent value.

NEW ENTRY | Footstool [6/10]

St John's, Smith Square, SW1   map 13
TEL 01-222 2779

Open 11.30 to 3.30 (from 6pm on when there is a concert)
Closed Sat and Sun

The crypt of the baroque St John's Church, Smith Square (now a concert venue) has been converted into a large restaurant. There are two sections: one is waitress service, for which allow about £13 a head; the other is cheaper and self-service, offering a hot dish plus the likes of game pie, quiche, roast beef, or ham. Salads are good and change daily. The cheeseboard is fresh, as are the cakes and desserts. Fully stocked wine bar with excellent house white.

Fortnum & Mason [7/10]

181 Piccadilly, W1   map 13
TEL 01-734 8040

Open 9.30 to 11.30 &
Closed Sun; bank hols

The Fountain, on the ground floor by the famous grocery shelves, stays open late for after-theatre custom. The post-shop hours entrance is at the side of the building. Breakfasts are also good value at £4.25 (plus service) for full English, or there is a cold buffet of ham, beef, tongue or chicken. The menu is audaciously, aristocratically ambitious, offering everything from consommé with cheese straws, to prune and walnut salad. Elegant teas, of course, and over thirty variations on the ice-cream soda/milk shake theme. A restrained grill menu operates in the evening. Snacks are also available in the mezzanine patio bar, and more expensive lunches in the fourth-floor restaurant. Licensed.

Fox and Anchor [7/10]

115 Charterhouse Street, EC1   map 13
TEL 01-253 4838

Open for food 6 to 3 &
Closed Sat and Sun; Christmas; last week Aug

The Anchor enjoys a rather bigger reputation than it has a right to these days. But the main points, for which it is rightly known – good steaks, enormous mixed grills, steak and kidney pie, all of which can be consumed with a pint of excellent Burton ale – are intact. It has become an eating pub rather than a drinking one, which is perhaps why the brewery finds it necessary to offer a dull wine list, brand-name soups, prawn cocktails and cliché salads. The menu would have been better left alone. Breakfasts are an institution now – starting at 6.30am for the market workers at Smithfield over the road.

Frascati [8/10]

33 Heath Street, NW3   map 12
TEL 01-431 3274

Open 12.30 to 2.30, 6.30 to 11.30
Closed Mon

This small, somewhat cramped trattoria close to the tube station outshines many of the new-wave pasta bars for value and quality. Minestrone is home made, salads are dressed with good quality oils, and the pasta and sauces are varied and freshly made. A blackboard menu has daily specials between £4 and £5. Service is accomplished, as are the house wines. All round an excellent restaurant in miniature, including the prices.

Gaby's Continental Bar [6/10]

30 Charing Cross Road, WC2   map 14
TEL 01-836 4233

Open 8am to midnight (noon to 10 Sun)
Closed bank hols

Not smart, but clean and cheap, this mainly Middle Eastern café offers a wide range, from moussaka to kebabs to sandwiches as well as vegetarian dishes. Portions are generous. Easy to eat for less than £5.

NEW ENTRY | Ganpath [9/10]

372 Grays Inn Road, WC1   map 13
TEL 01-278 1938

Open noon to 3, 6 to 10.15 (10.45 Fri and Sat) &
Closed Sun; bank hols

The best of a cluster of Indian restaurants around King's Cross Station. The sign says 'South Indian brasserie' – in fact the kitchen dishes out a mixture of no-frills curry-house staples, including a pungent, earthy sag gosht, plus South Indian vegetarian specialities, such as bhajias, iddly, samosas, fresh masala dosai with

coconut relish and thick sambar for dipping. There are interesting vegetables, too. The mood is casual and beguilingly eccentric – the tube trains shake the dining-room as they rumble underground. Stay with the vegetarian dishes and it's possible to eat for under £5. Drink lassi or lager.

Geales Fish Restaurant [8/10]

2 Farmer Street, W8   map 12
TEL 01-727 7969

Open noon to 3, 6 to 11.30 (11 Sat) &
Closed Sun, Mon; 2 weeks at Christmas; last 3 weeks August

The Geale family has run this cottagey fish and chip restaurant since 1919. Fish comes fresh each day from Grimsby and is fried in beef dripping; chips are cooked in vegetable oil. Cooking is done to order and the menu depends on the market – which means anything from haddock to shark. Main courses are around £5 and chips start at 60p, so it's possible to eat and drink well for less than £10 – unless you order a bottle of the house Champagne.

General Trading Company [7/10]

144 Sloane Street, SW1   map 13
TEL 01-730 6400

Open 9 to 5.15 (1.30 Sat)
Closed Sun; bank hols; Christmas Eve to 1 Jan

This being Sloane Square, the extensive breakfast menu does not start until 9am. But late risers get the papers, free-range eggs, Ayrshire bacon, and fine sausages, served beneath the eclectic choice of a useful presents shop. The cooking, though, is a cut above most in-house store dining-rooms. The blackboard menu stays with the same items as Justin de Blank's other restaurants: salads, casseroles, good baking. It is small and gets crowded at lunch-time.

NEW ENTRY | Gentry [8/10]

253 High Street, W3   map 12
TEL 01-992 7502

Open noon to 5 (3 Sun), 6 to 11 &
Closed Christmas Day

The owners are Polish and the cooking in this beamed restaurant is continental, with a strong Polish accent. Go for the authentic specialities, such as ten-inch potato pancakes stuffed with mushrooms, meat dumplings with sauerkraut salad, and hot salt beef with horseradish, latkes and sour cucumber salad. Goulash soup comes in a wrought-iron cauldron hung over a small flame, with a ladle for serving. During the week there are café-style lunches, with a traditional English roast for the whole family on Sundays. Polish lager is £1.50 a bottle.

| NEW ENTRY | **Ginnan** [7/10] |

5 Cathedral Place, EC4   map 13
TEL 01-236 4120/5150

Open noon to 2.30, 6 to 10
Closed Sun; Sat D; Christmas

The Ginnan is one of the best-kept secrets in the city. At night it is a relatively expensive Japanese restaurant – about £15 a head – but lunch is comfortably affordable. Set meals are arranged according to the choice of main course – rice, soup and pickles, around perhaps tempura or simmered pork. The turn-round is fast – about twenty minutes a table. Drink green tea.

| NEW ENTRY | **Goan** [6/10] |

16 York Way, N1   map 13
TEL 01-837 7517

Open noon to 1am &

Just a few cluttered tables and a photo of the Aga Khan make up the functional décor. It is a no-frills café that serves unusual Goan specialities, including an authentic pork vindaloo. There are interesting and cheap fish dishes too: mackerel stuffed with spices is £1.30. Other prices are very low: rice 50p, Goan vegetable bhaji £1. The most expensive dish on the menu is whole stuffed pomfret at £3.

Goddard's Eel and Pie House [6/10]

45 Greenwich Church Street,   map 12
SE10

Open 11 to 3 (10.30 to 4.30 Sat) &
Closed Mon

Still going strong after three generations, this pie and eel house is nearly just as big an attraction as the Cutty Sark down the road. Pies and pasties are baked each day on the premises and are served with mash. Fruit and cream for sweet. Take-aways also available.

Gouldies [7/10]

46 Broadwick Street, W1   map 13
TEL 01-437 5210

Open 7.30 to 4.30 (4 Fri) &
Closed Sat, Sun; bank hols; 2 weeks at Christmas

A great selection of vegetarian snacks is available at this small, well-run wholefood snack bar and take-away. Filled jacket potatoes, vegetarian moussaka, pasties, pizzas, carrot quiche, samosas, stuffed peppers, spinach boreks and stuffed vine leaves are just some of the dishes on offer. Breakfasts are served from 7.30am; alternatively, call in for a wholemeal apple crunch in the afternoon.

Govinda's [7/10]

9 Soho Street, W1   map 13
TEL 01-437 3662

Open 11.30 to 8 (noon to 4 Sun)
Closed Sun D; Christmas Day and Boxing Day

The Krishna followers' self-service restaurant is ten years old and still offers some of the cheapest food in the West End. The restaurant is on two levels; the ground floor is an L-shaped room and there are tables in the basement too. The menu is basic and pragmatic, almost every dish having either potato or rice tucked into it. Thick, warming pea soup with courgettes, spicy samosas, brown rice with carrots in ghee, and bean sprouts and carrots with a brown rice salad and tahini dressing are regular themes. Unusual items include couscous and veggie burgers. Herb teas.

Grahame's Seafare [9/10]

38 Poland Street, W1 map 13
TEL 01-437 3788/0975

Open noon to 2.45, 5.30 to 8.45 (7.45 Fri) &
Closed Sun; Mon D

A surprising number of good-value eating houses live off the human traffic of Oxford and Regent Streets. This Jewish dining-room is one of the longest established and its fish – fried in matzo flour – is some of the best in London. The smoked salmon is also excellent. A loyal clientele return for other Jewish dishes like tumblers of cold borshch and gefilte fish. Service is reassuringly old-fashioned.

Granary [6/10]

39 Albemarle Street, W1 map 13
TEL 01-493 2978

Open 11.30 to 8 (2.30 Sat)
Closed Sun

The large canvas awning shouts into the street while inside is all pine. Some fairly pushy selling of dishes can take place at the counter in an effort to get people to buy a main dish, salad, and a sweet. The size of the portions is such that there is no real need for three dishes. The repertoire is a sensible mix of casseroles and buffet dishes like chilli con carne, risotto, avocado and spinach bake with prawns. 'Healthy country food' without being vegetarian is the watchword. The spacious, airy dining-room is another attraction.

W. R. Grant [6/10]

499 Staines Road, Bedfont, Feltham map 3
TEL 01-890 3845

Open 11 to 2, 4 to 10.30 (8 Mon)
Closed Sun

The Grant family have been in business here since 1936. They sell prime cuts of wet fish at half supermarket prices, as well as exemplary fish and chips cooked in

groundnut oil. No frozen fish is used and the quality shows in the Peterhead cod and the blonde wings of skate. Good value: fish and chips is £1.60. Smartly dressed staff in straw boaters and striped aprons cope well with the queues. Take-away only. Unlicensed.

Great Nepalese [9/10]

48 Eversholt Street, NW1 map 13
TEL 01-388 6737

Open noon to 2.45, 6 to 11.45
Closed Christmas Day and Boxing Day

Even in the cynic's view of London Indian restaurants – that they are universally mediocre and can only be differentiated by their décor – the Great Nepalese stands out for its value and the genuineness of its cooking. It stands within earshot of Euston station and thrives as a neighbourhood eating place. The atmosphere is happy-go-lucky, and the cooking has something of the pungency of the best Indian cafés in Bradford. The kitchen doesn't forget its Nepalese roots, which means light spicing, lots of fresh herbs and proper attention to pulses, vegetables and unusual side dishes, such as brilliant green coriander pickle or kerauko achar (a cold dish of potatoes with sesame seeds). Nepalese classics, such as masco bara, bhutuwa chicken and aloo bodi tama are excellent; the boiled Basmatic rice is as good as any in London. Drink lager and finish with a shot of devastating Nepalese rum.

Greenhouse [6/10]

16 Chenies Street, WC1 map 14
TEL 01-637 8038

Open 10 (1 Sat) to 10 (6 Mon)
Closed Sun; bank hols; 2 weeks Christmas

Dark basement vegetarian restaurant housed under the Drill Hall, an alternative theatre and women's centre. The cooking is healthy and usually a cut above the average – spiced pumpkin soup, aubergine pâté, courgette and hazelnut loaf with tomato and basil sauce. The menu changes daily and offers a pair of starters, main dishes, four salads and a wide selection of desserts. Somerset Pie is spring vegetables and leeks under a potato topping. The queues and cramped premises militate against it at peak hours especially, but take-aways are encouraged. High chairs are provided for children.

L.S. Grunts Chicago Pizza Co [7/10]

12 Maiden Lane, WC2　　　　　map 14
TEL 01-379 7722

Open noon to 11.30 (9 Sun)
Closed Christmas Eve D to Boxing Day

Footstep motifs on the walls lead across the brick courtyard to the glitzy neon-signed warehouse. The raised platform along the longest wall shows a thirty-foot 3-D mural of the Chicago skyline. There can be long waits for a table but the service is fast and American. Pizzas come in big pans for a minimum of two. The choice is short and true Chicago – Some Like It Hot is with chillies; Memories are Made of This, with mushrooms. The sausages are excellent. To start there is garlic bread, and to finish ice-creams, or the excellent chocolate cheesecake. American beers and good cocktails. A good place for children (even babies, as there are nappy-changing facilities in the ladies).

Habitat Café [6/10]

156 Tottenham Court Road, W1　　map 13
TEL 01-631 3880

Open 10 (9.30 Sat) to 5 (6 Thur and Sat)
& (also WC)
Closed Sun; Christmas Day, Boxing Day

208 King's Road, SW3　　　　　map 13
TEL 01-351 1211

Open 10 (9.30 Sat) to 5 (6 Wed)
Closed Sun; Christmas Day, Boxing Day
and 1 Jan

Both stores have airy, self-service food counters. Coffee and cakes feature through the day, with a range of fresh salads – tuna, potato, Waldorf, green, prawn – and quiches at lunch-time. Predictably, it is more modern, well-thought-out and better value than most other big department store catering.

Hard Rock Café [9/10]

150 Old Park Lane, W1　　　　　map 13
TEL 01-629 0382

Open noon to 1am &
Closed 24 Dec to Boxing Day

The spirit of the late 1960s lives on in this otherwise elite and historic corner of Mayfair. Here are still the best hamburgers in Britain. Imitation chains flatter what is the genuine article – yes, that is David Bailey's Olympus on the wall. The collection of rock 'n' roll cult memorabilia is as authentic as the steak in the burgers or the smell of hickory on the ribs. The soda fountain is pure Bobby Vee. Expect to wait half an hour in the ever-present queue. Happy hour from 5.30 to 6.30 is marginally quieter.

NEW ENTRY Hare Krishna Curry House [6/10]

1 Hanway Street, W1　　　　　map 13
TEL 01-636 5262

Open noon to 10.30 & (also WC)
Closed Sun

Not connected with the Hare Krishna movement as such, but Indian music plays and the atmosphere is authentically oriental. A long list of starters features pancakes served with chutneys, or savoury split black-pea doughnuts with yoghurt and a mild chutney sauce, aubergine and bean curry, or brown rice with nuts and raisins. Delicious roti and good choice of desserts.

NEW ENTRY Harrisson's [5/10]

2 Lower John Street, W1　　　　map 14
TEL 01-437 4733

Open 7.30 to 4.30 &
Closed Sat, Sun

'Quality sandwiches, tailor-made to your requirements', is the boast of this no-table Soho sandwich bar. And roughly speaking that's what you get, plus a handsome choice of relishes to spread across the thick fresh wholemeal bread. Club sandwich is turkey, ham and Emmental; avocado is an optional extra. Salads are crisp; chocolate cake just so. A hot soup of the day is also available and there is free delivery on orders over £7.50.

NEW ENTRY Harry Morgan's [7/10]

31 St John's Wood High Street, NW8   map 13

TEL 01-722 1869

Open noon to 3, 6 to 10 ₺ (also WC)
Closed Mon; Fri D; 10 days at Easter; 2 weeks Sept

Good Jewish home cooking is a rarity for eating out, but this traditional Yiddish restaurant can provide inexpensive meals of lean salt beef, fried liver, calf's foot jelly, latkes and spicy burgers. The bill can creep up if you go to three courses, but the sweets are often the least effective part of the meals.

NEW ENTRY Hearth Café, Earthworks [5/10]

132 King Street, W6   map 12

TEL 01-846 9357

Open 11.30 to 6 (10.30 Thur, Fri and Sat)
Closed Sun; Christmas to New Year; bank hols

From outside it is hard to believe there is room for a café in this cluttered food store. When you finally make it past all the thousands of things healthy people need to stay healthy there is a surprisingly large kitchen/counter that leads in turn into a very large room shared with a book shop and crockery and furnishing section. Main-course flans come surrounded by inventive salads such as noodle and olive, or curried bread, raisin and nut. Other offerings include fennel tortilla, and apple and apricot kernel sundaes. The blackboard menu gives instructions on how to get tea – pay 35p for a cup of hot water and select your own leaves from a choice of tea, such as mint and camomile. Long queues at peak times.

Henry J. Bean's [7/10]

195–197 King's Road, SW3   map 13

TEL 01-352 9255

Open 11.30 (noon Sun) to 11 (10 Sun) ₺ (also WC)
Closed Christmas

54 Abingdon Road, W8   map 12

TEL 01-937 3339

Open 11.30 to 11 ₺
Closed Christmas

The best value of Bob Payton's restaurants – or at least the cheapest, because it is self-service. Order at the bar, wait for the number to come up on the TV screen, and pick up the burgers, chilli dogs, potato skins in a basket from the food counter. The atmosphere is US high school, with bobby-sox décor and music. The King's Road branch has a garden at the back. The choice of real ales and American beer is excellent, albeit pricey.

Hockneys [9/10]

98 High Street, Croydon   map 3

TEL 01-688 2899

Open noon to 10.30
Closed Sun and Mon; 2 weeks at Christmas; 1 week Easter; 2 weeks late Aug

Hockneys is also Croydon's Buddhist Centre (with courses on Buddhist cookery as well as yoga) and the Independent Arts Centre. The restaurant is on the first floor above the wholefood grocery shop and take-away counter. By vegetarian standards, it is wondrously spacious and light – a sort of Sonny's of Barnes meets Joe Allen or Orso. The walls are lined with interesting Matisses and the bare tables set with wine glasses, though there is no licence – corkage £1.35. The menu, given the Buddhist influence, shows some subcontinental leanings in the form of lassi to drink or sweet dahl soup, but also some vigorous colour combinations. Peacock pie is a mix of black-eye beans, coriander, cheese, coconut and tomato sauce, and a Roman candle is a 'cocktail' of rum syrup, red grape juice and orange juice. The freshness of the cooking lends an unusual vitality that lifts it well above the average.

Hodja Nasreddin [8/10]

53 Newington Green Road, N1   map 12

TEL 01-226 7757

Open noon to 2am ₺
Closed Christmas Day

Low prices and long opening hours are the attractions at this fine, family-run restaurant in the heart of London's Turkish community. The menu has familiar kebabs, minced doner, and dolmas, as well as some more esoteric items such as iskembe corbasi (tripe soup with garlic and vinegar), or sucuk (salami in hot spicy sauce). The special mixed grill served with taramosalata, yoghurt and garlic, rice and salad is exceptional value at £4.75.

Hollywood Bowl [6/10]

5 Market Parade, East Street,   map 3
Bromley
TEL 01-460 2346

Open noon to 2.45, 6 to 11.15 (11.45 Fri and Sat, 11 Sun) &
Closed Sun L; bank hol Mons

Born in Bromley, rather than the USA, but the formula is plain: loud rock and roll, enormous burgers with different toppings, potato skins with sour cream and chives, plus, lately (a very English introduction, given the Californian setting), vegetarian dishes. Well oriented to children, with high chairs and free lollipops, best of all for adults is the offer of any flavour of ice-cream with any liqueur.

Hoults [8/10]

20 Bellevue Road, SW17   map 12
TEL 01-767 1858

Open noon to 3, 5.30 (6 Sat) to midnight (7 to 11.30 Sun) &
Closed 1 week at Christmas

The drawback at this excellent wine bar-cum-restaurant is its popularity. The short menu is enterprising and good value for one or two courses: smoked chicken and avocado salad, half a pint of prawns with garlic mayonnaise, steak and kidney pie, or half a roast duck with gooseberry sauce. Some of the ingredients stand out from the normal – langoustines from Loch Fyne or Dutch calves' liver. There is always a vegetarian dish of the day. Wines are similarly well chosen. The atmosphere is convivial and spills on to the terrace overlooking the Common on summer

evenings. Expect to pay anything up to £16, depending on how much of a restaurant you take it to be.

Hungry's [6/10]

37A Crawford Street, W1   map 13
TEL 01-258 0376

Open 8 to 5 (9 to 3 Sat) &
Closed Sun; 2 weeks at Christmas

The old tea-house décor of blue flowery benches and blue tablecloths remains, but in effect this is an American-style sandwich bar with a small restaurant attached. The food photos on the walls have a sense of humour – an egg coming out of a squeezed lemon. The choice of sandwiches runs to 88 permutations and mathematically there must be more: salt beef, pastrami, chopped liver, avocado and bacon – the range is unusually imaginative. There are also salads in huge glass bowls, baked potatoes filled with chilli con carne for £2.65, blueberry or apple pie. Excellent lunchtime venue.

NEW ENTRY Ikkyu [8/10]

67 Tottenham Court Road, W1   map 13
TEL 01-636 9280

Open 12.30 to 2.30, 6 to 10.30
Closed Sat; Sun L

One of the least expensive and most relaxed Japanese eating places in the West End. The entrance, near Goodge Street tube station, doesn't look like a restaurant at all, but the basement dining-room buzzes like a good café. Cheap set meals from the handwritten menu feature fish with miso soup, rice and pickles. There's also a good range of sushi and yakitori, as well as peasant-style dishes such as stewed potato with meat or fried tofu with ginger sauce. Whisky comes by the bottle; green tea is free.

Imperial Tandoori [6/10]

48 Kennington Road, SE1   map 13
TEL 01-928 4153

Open noon to 2.30, 6 to 12 & (also wc)
Closed Christmas Day

A wide, empty aisle down the middle of the restaurant, with tables against the walls, gives the impression of an aeroplane – albeit a rather festooned one. The menu is the standard South London permutation of tandooris, birianis, and dhansaks. The cooking, though, has an edge over rivals, from the pilau through to the aloo gobi.

India Club [7/10]

143 The Strand, WC2   map 13
TEL 01-836 0650

Open noon to 2.30, 6 to 10 (8.15 Sun and bank hols)
Closed Christmas Day

Look for the little sign saying 'Indian Restaurant' at the entrance to the Strand Continental Hotel. Climb a couple of flights of stairs, then through the door into the yellow-walled canteen. Huge plastic trays of food are whisked from the kitchen by beguilingly eccentric waiters. The food is rough and ready but it's amazingly cheap and a great ethnic bargain. Highlights are fiery chilli bhajias, vegetarian dosas and pagoda chicken with coconut chutney. Breads are first-rate, though the rice can be soggy. A man sits in a wooden booth by the kitchen door, like a ticket collector. He takes money. Don't wait for a bill, just go up and pay. Unlicensed, but everyone brings bottles of wine or cans of lager.

Indian Ocean [7/10]

359 Holloway Road, N7   map 12
TEL 01-607 0801

Open noon to 3, 6 to midnight (1 Fri; noon to 1 Sat; noon to midnight Sun) &

Smarter and more upmarket than its neighbour, the Holloway Tandoori, this Indian restaurant offers good-value Bengali food for between £7 and £10. The menu has fresh fish cooked Bengali style, as well as tandoori trout and prawn curries; there are also masala dishes of brains, plus the usual tikkas, rogan josh and birianis. Vegetables are often the best part of the meal. The dish of seeds and betel nuts at the end is like 'a pot-pourri for the mouth'.

NEW ENTRY Indian YMCA [6/10]

41 Fitzroy Square, W1   map 13
TEL 01-387 0411

Open 12.30 to 1.45, 7 to 8

An extremely cheap, well-discovered venue for no-frills Indian food. The bare but spotlessly clean canteen serves all-comers, although the clientele is mostly Indian. Lunch centres on a couple of vegetable dishes, a couple of curries and dhal, but there's more choice in the evening. Take-aways at lunch-time. Unlicensed.

Inebriated Newt [8/10]

172 Northcote Road, SW11   map 12
TEL 01-223 1637

Open noon to 3, 7.30 to 11.30 (11 Sun to Thur) &
Closed weekday L; 5 days at Christmas

A sprawling mix of dining-rooms on different levels finally leads up to a conservatory at the back. This is an excellent-value venue for anything from a hamburger to a three-course meal. The menu has some extrovert descriptions – Fergieburger (with smoky barbecue sauce); Hot Lips (chilli con carne); Banana-drama. A good place to take children.

Jack's Place [8/10]

12 York Road, SW11   map 12
TEL 01-228 8519/1442

Open noon to 3, 6.30 to 11
Closed Mon; Sat L; Sun D

This is Le Gavroche of cheap eating. The average meal with drinks is about £12 but this extraordinary restaurant serves such enormous portions that the place demands inclusion. Dover sole is the size of a small briefcase. The dishes of the day usually have the edge over a menu that is cluttered with those-you-have-loved favourites: melon boats; whole avocado vinaigrette; duck à l'orange. The generosity is larger than life, as is the décor, inches thick in bric-a-brac, business cards and signed portraits of world leaders, including President Reagan.

Jai Krishna [7/10]

161 Stroud Green Road, N4   map 12
TEL 01-272 1680

Open noon to 5.30 (10.30 Fri and Sat)
Closed Sun

Mrs Chowdhury has steered clear of
standard Indian restaurant décor and
planted her unlicensed, vegetarian menu
in what to all intents looks like a café or
bistro. Order at the counter, café style. The
short menu gets an extra dimension from
the use of more exotic vegetables such as
okra, guvar or the marrow-like dudi dal, as
curries. Thalis are excellent value at under
£4. Service is prompt.

Japan Centre [6/10]

66–68 Brewer Street, W1   map 13
TEL 01-439 8035

Open 11.30 to 7
Closed Christmas

The cheapest and fastest Japanese cooking
in London is found at this food bar in the
basement of the commercial centre. A
short repertoire deals in home-style
cooking – noodles and soups act as
substance to more exotic flavours, such as
yam root, pickles or a side dish of tempura;
a picture menu helps. Ask for the green
tea; alternatively, there are soft drinks.

Jason's [7/10]

50 Battersea Park Road, SW11   map 12
TEL 01-622 6998

Open 6.30pm to 11.45pm &
Closed Sun; 2 weeks Aug

A good-value, long-established taverna
decked out with the mandatory dripping
candles and evocative posters, and a big
room downstairs for parties. It is always
busy and booking is vital. The meze is the
easy way through the menu, but look for
squid in tomato sauce, or braised dishes –
afelia and kleftiko. The yoghurt with
honey is a good finish. Salads are
refreshing and a welcome antidote to the
high levels of protein.

Joe Allen [8/10]

13 Exeter Street, WC2   map 14
TEL 01-836 0651

Open noon to 1 (midnight Sun)

Some of the glitter has been stolen by its
younger sister Orso, round the corner, but
this basement is nevertheless a cheaper
and good alternative. The feeling is more
New York than Italy, compounded by
some abrupt service and the chatter of
business across the tables. Meals can be
expensive, but don't have to be, if you stay
with the very good hamburgers (not listed
on the blackboard, but always available)
and huge bowls of spinach salad filled with
bacon and avocado, served with a choice of
dressings. The fast American food is
usually better than the attempt at
fashionability. Plenty of wines and the
confidence not to play any music at all.

Julie's [7/10]

135 Portland Road, W11   map 12
TEL 01-229 8331

Open 12.30 to 2.30 (2.45 Sun), 7.30 to 11.15
(10.15 Sun)
Closed 24 to 27 Dec; four days from Good Fri;
Aug bank hol Mon

Small bar on a quiet residential street
where you can have starters and puddings
from the menu of the attached restaurant
downstairs. Aubergine mousse, sauté crabmeat with mustard sauce or spinach, and
Feta cheese and crispy bacon salad have all
been praised. Drink sparkling white wine
or splash out and have a champagne
cocktail.

Just Around the Corner [7/10]

446 Finchley Road, NW3   map 12
TEL 01-431 3300

Open 7pm to midnight, plus noon to 3 Sun
Closed Christmas Day and Boxing Day

One of Peter Ilic's group of forward-
looking bistros. This one is unique
because it has no prices – you simply pay
what you think the meal is worth. For
other details, see entry for Lantern.

Justin de Blank [9/10]

54 Duke Street, W1　　　　　　　map 13
TEL 01-629 3174

Open 8.30 (9 Sat) to 3.45, 4.15 to 9
Closed Sun; Sat D; bank hols

The quality of the ingredients and the cooking in this brick and cane self-service would not be out of place in an expensive restaurant. With a break of half an hour mid-afternoon it is open for a realistically timed breakfast at 8.30, through to 9 at night. First-class bread and croissants from de Blank's own bakery, his prize-winning sausages, and superb cheesecakes feature alongside casseroles, tarts, even stir-fries. The sagacity of approach and the genuine balance of the menus make it more of a good health eaterie than many that carry the name. The flavour is cosmopolitan but at heart it is modern British cooking with a liking for vivid spicing, as in orange and cumin with chicken. It's also good for value, as in turkey and sausage pie.

Just William Wine Bar [6/10]

6 Battersea Rise, SW11　　　　　map 12
TEL 01-228 9980

Open noon to 3, 5.30 (6.30 Sat) to 11
Closed Sun L; 6 days at Christmas

At the back of the swisher Pollyanna's restaurant is this mini-wine bar with a few tables stuck in alcoves (useful if you are in a group), which stops drinkers bunching at the bar. The blackboard menu opens with pâtés and taramosalata at £1.75 before steaks and burgers and even some sauced dishes, for about £4.50. Intelligent wine list to match.

Kettners [9/10]

29 Romilly Street, W1　　　　　　map 14
TEL 01-734 6112

Open noon to midnight &
Closed Christmas

London's most elegant pizza house and the star of the Pizza Express chain (see entry). The historic Soho building has a champagne bar and a piano lounge as well

as a grand fast-food dining-room. The pizzas are up to the mark – Italian, freshly baked and generously topped with genuine fresh ingredients. There's a choice of sixteen, from King Edward (four cheeses on a potato base) to Veneziana with capers, olives, pine kernels, sultanas, Mozzarella and tomatoes. Otherwise the menu has burgers, BLT, steaks and chilli.

Kitchen Yakitori [7/10]

12 Lancashire Court,　　　　　　map 13
New Bond Street, W1
TEL 01-629 9984/409 1303

Open noon to 3, 6 to 10
Closed Sun; Sat D

Offers one of the best introductions to Japanese cooking and also one of the cheapest. This tiny cupboard of a restaurant has a busy, cramped basement with a pine bar, as well as a ground-floor room for overspill. The menu revolves around £5 for changing main courses sandwiched by pickles, soup, rice and orange segments. Specials might be grilled salmon, tofu steak and chilled noodles or eel in various guises. Set meals – a succession of dishes cooked by different methods – show the potential of the cuisine. Green tea comes in elegant pots. Turnover is fast and you are not expected to linger.

Knoodles [7/10]

30 Connaught Street, W2　　　　　map 13
TEL 01-262 9623

Open noon to 3, 6.30 to 10.45 & (also WC)
Closed bank hols; Christmas Day, Boxing Day and 1 Jan

This split-level pasta bar aspires to being a restaurant. Beyond the central theme of daily made pasta in different shapes, plus sauces, the menu takes on chilled soup, gravlax, chicken breast stuffed with Chinese vegetables and so on. Expect hard chairs and paper cloths, but general good humour from the staff. The choice narrows by the sweet course to perhaps just crumble or chocolate mousse, but coffee comes with Amaretto biscuits.

Kowloon [6/10]

21–22 Gerrard Street, W1   map 14
TEL 01-437 1694

Open noon to 11.30 &
Closed Christmas Eve and Christmas Day

First and foremost an excellent Chinese
bakery, with one of the best and freshest
selections in Soho. All kinds of buns and
pastries sweet and savoury are piled high
in the window: char-siu buns, moon cakes,
lotus-paste balls, pasties filled with green
beans or spicy curry, and lots more
besides. There are tables in the dining-
room behind the bakery counter, and a
more formal restaurant to the right. Best
bets for a cheap meal are the one-plate
noodle dishes; the brisket version has
plenty of very tender, fragrant meat spiced
with aniseed and a good rich meaty gravy.
Specials are worth exploring, too. Orange
segments often arrive during the meal.

Lahore Restaurant [6/10]

218 Commercial Road, E1   map 12
TEL 01-791 0112

Open noon to 11 & (also WC)

Seven-days-a-week Pakistani café
specialising in cheap meals. For less than
£2.50 it is possible to eat chicken tikka,
shami kebab, chana with cinnamon, and
dhal or spinach curry. Portions are
generous. No licence.

La La Pizza [6/10]

138 London Road,   map 12
Kingston-upon-Thames
TEL 01-546 4888

Open 5.30 to midnight & (also WC)
Closed Christmas Day

Pizzas are named after colourful Italians –
Vivaldi is topped with pepperoni,
mushrooms and anchovies, while Verdi
comes with artichoke hearts, salami and
boiled egg. A Kingston on the other hand is
smoked bacon, Mozzarella, tomato and
herbs. For non-pizza lovers there is lasagne
or cannelloni; smaller pizzas will be made
for children. 'Garlic or capers will be added
at no extra cost on request.'

Lantern [7/10]

23 Malvern Road, NW6   map 12
TEL 01-624 1796

Open noon to 3, 7 to midnight (11 Sun) &
Closed Christmas Day and Boxing Day

The original branch of Peter Ilic's six-
strong stable of cut-price bistros. Menus
are virtually the same at all branches,
prices of all main dishes are fixed at £4.25
and there are some whacky combinations
of ingredients. Profiteroles come filled
with crab to start, or cold with chocolate
to finish; smoked chicken might be stuffed
with mushrooms and wrapped in filo
pastry. The atmosphere is dark, crowded
and orchestrated by classical music. It is a
formula, but it works well, and as a group
these places fill a gap at the lower end of
the restaurant market.

Laurent [8/10]

428 Finchley Road, NW2   map 12
TEL 01-794 3603

Open noon to 2, 6 to 11
Closed Sun D; last 2 weeks Aug

Couscous – the North African dish of dry,
savoury semolina topped with vegetable
and/or lamb casseroles, and served with
hot harissa sauce – is becoming one of
those dishes that, like crêpes and fondues,
turn into reasons to open restaurants. This
well-established, candlelit ground floor in
the mainly residential part of the top of
Finchley Road is one of the best. So
successful has it been that Laurent
Farnigia has given up putting anything else
on his menu. There are three versions:
vegetarian, complet or royal, which
includes a mixed grill. Either side there is
brique à l'oeuf (a crisp, deep-fried pancake
filled with egg) and ices or crêpes Suzette.
The full works, including Moroccan or
Algerian wine, will top £10. Take-aways.

Leek's Fish Bar [8/10]

23 Lavender Hill, SW11   map 12
TEL 01-228 9460

Open 5.30pm to 11pm & (also WC)
Closed Sun

Rita Leek's menu has moved on a goodly stage from most chip shops, though it centres on cod, haddock and plaice, all deep fried. The variety of fish extends to trout, sea bass and halibut and any can be steamed for preference. Either side are prawn cocktails, avocado vinaigrette, mushy peas, pickled cucumbers, chocolate mousse, bread-and-butter pudding. Other 'created' dishes, like fish cakes and soup, demonstrate that this is a kitchen that knows what it is doing. The dining-room is workmanlike with checked PVC cloths and prints on the wall.

Leonardo [6/10]

1 Grand Parade, Upper   map 12
Richmond Road West, SW14
TEL 01-876 3543

Open noon to 3, 6.30 to 11
Closed Sun; bank hols; 2 weeks Aug

It's worth booking at this cool, tiled wine bar because it is very popular. The short menu includes chicken wings in garlic, minestrone soup, pasta dishes, and good sirloin steak. Service is cheerful and friendly and there's live guitar music at the weekends. All Italian wine list.

NEW ENTRY | Ley-On's [7/10]

56 Wardour Street, W1   map 14
TEL 01-437 6465

Open 11.30 to 11.15 &
Closed Christmas Day and Boxing Day

In the early 1930s this was a Lyons tea-shop. Before the Second World War it was taken over and turned into a chop-suey house, making it one of the oldest surviving Chinese restaurants in Soho. It is only a hundred yards from the heart of Chinatown and the pandemonium of the Wong Kei (see entry), yet it could belong to another culture. The tea-room legacy shows in the marble-tiled walls, the gold-framed mirrors and the massive pillars painted green. There are plants every-where and music plays softly. It may not be the first choice for dim-sum or one-plate meals, but it serves good versions of both. Look for the glutinous rice steamed in lotus leaves or braised ducks' feet

wrapped in a bean curd skin. A dish of fried noodles with seafood, plus a bowl of exemplary hot-and-sour soup would make a decent lunch.

Lido [7/10]

41 Gerrard Street, W1   map 14
TEL 01-437 4431

Open 4pm to 4.30am

At 4am this spruced up Cantonese café has few rivals in the West End. It buzzes with activity, the main noise being the regular thud of the cleaver on the chopping board. Much of the cooking is done in the window, and the display of edibles is one of the most comprehensive and baffling in the neighbourhood. The main business here is in one-plate rice dishes – crispy pork, soya chicken, duck – which come with a big bowl of murky stock full of carcase. There are noodle dishes, too. Portions are big, prices low.

Linda's [7/10]

4 Fernhead Road, W9   map 12
TEL 01-969 9387

Open noon to 2, 6 to 10.15
Closed Sun; Sat L

Linda's caused a small ripple across the gastronomic pond of London when it opened in 1982 as the city's solitary Vietnamese restaurant. To date the cuisine has not made the expected impact, but that may yet come, as it is full of potential. Undeterred by their notoriety, Robin and Linda Blaney have kept this a low-key operation, almost a café moving into a small bistro. The set meals start at £4.95 at lunch-time and £6.95 at night, and are a good place to start as portions from the *carte* are small and put the bill up quickly.

Little Caesar's Pizza [6/10]

56 Tooting High Street, SW17   map 12
TEL 01-767 8585

Open 11 to midnight (11 Mon and Tue)
& (also WC)
Closed Christmas Day

America's third largest pizza chain –
founded in Detroit 26 years ago – is
particularly good value – two take-away
pizzas cost the same as one. There are also
sandwiches, salads, and frozen yoghurt
desserts. Décor is functional.

NEW ENTRY Lorelei [6/10]

21 Bateman Street, W1　　　　　map 14
TEL 01-734 0954

Open noon to 11
Closed Sun; bank hols

Don't be put off by the bags of flour piled
up against the walls and stored in the old
fireplace in this small Italian pizzeria-
cum-café, or by the enormous poster of a
topless mermaid. The pizzas are terrific.
Choose from a dozen or have a cheese
salad with simple oil and vinegar dressing.

NEW ENTRY Lou Pescadou [8/10]

241 Old Brompton Road, SW5　　　map 13
TEL 01-370 1057

Open 12 to 3, 7 to midnight &

The cut-price outlet of London's successful chain of French fish restaurants. It
is not especially cheap, but then the
suppliers are the same as for the other
restaurants. Excellent fish dishes are
backed up by pasta, pizzas and dishes of
the day. There is no booking and if it is full
you have to have a drink at the bar, which
adds to the bill. Normandy cider suits the
French seaside mood well.

Maharani [6/10]

117 Clapham High Street, SW4　　　map 12
TEL 01-622 2530

Open noon to 3, 6 to midnight & (also WC)

After twenty years, still the most popular
of the curry houses on Clapham High
Street. When the long, narrow room, with
rows of tables on either side, fills up, the
back room is used (useful for party
bookings). Dhansaks, kormas and the
usual tandoori dishes are recommended.
Service is sometimes rushed.

NEW ENTRY Maison Bertaux [7/10]

28 Greek Street, W1　　　　　map 14
TEL 01-437 6007

Open 9 to 6
Closed Sun and Mon; 4 weeks July to Aug

Small, French, family-run pâtisserie with a
few tables at the back where it is possible
to eat excellent croissants, cakes and
quiches rather than taking them away.
There are teas and coffees to drink. The
shop dates from 1871 and has been in the
Vignaud family since the early 1920s.
Children welcome.

NEW ENTRY Maison Sagne [7/10]

105 Marylebone High Street, W1　　map 13
TEL 01-935 6240

Open 9 to 5 (12.30 Sat)
Closed Sun; Easter Monday, Good Friday

A local institution since it opened in 1921
and still one of the most characterful of
London's tea-rooms. The eating area is
part of the shop and serves coffees and
croissants, plus light lunches of salads,
omelettes and good vol-au-vent. It is on
the baking of cakes and brioches that its
reputation rests. Customers queueing to
buy get muddled up with everyone else.
Very old Vienna – the perfect venue for
afternoon tea.

Mandeer [9/10]

21 Hanway Place, W1　　　　　map 13
TEL 01-323 0660

Open noon to 3, 6 to 10
Closed Sun; bank hols

Still one of the least developed Indian
vegetarian restaurants in London. Best
bets for cheap eaters are the self-service
lunches in the light, airy Ravi Shankar
Hall, where first-rate samosas, bhajias,
vegetable curries and rice are served from a
range of steel containers on the counter. In
the dark basement dining-room the mood
of uncompromising Indian vegetarian food
is more obvious. There's no fish, no dairy
produce, lots of tofu, unpolished brown
rice, even some dishes cooked without

spices, garlic or onions. It preaches food as philosophy. Thalis are a good way of exploring the possibilities of the cooking; Wednesday's special, for £6.50, has kichadi (rice and mung dhal), kadhi (spiced yoghurt), stuffed vegetables, three puris, raita, chutney, poppadum and gulab jamun.

Man Fu Kung [7/10]

29–30 Leicester Square, WC2 map 14
TEL 01-839 4146

Open 9am to 1am & (also WC)

One of Chinatown's big three dim-sum houses. The huge ground floor has a bar running down most of one side and the trolleys wheel their way past pillars, down the alleys of tables, carrying piles of snacks in steaming baskets stacked one on top of the other. The choice is extensive, taking in all manner of dumplings, wrapped in pasta-like dough, bread-style dough, or just plain bean curd skin. There are roast meats, too, and a full Cantonese menu in the evening. The atmosphere is very much of the old school and its popularity with Chinese is borne out by the fading splendour of its décor.

Manna [7/10]

4 Erskine Road, NW3 map 12
TEL 01-722 8028

Open 6.30pm to midnight &
Closed Christmas Day and 1 Jan

Venerable for being one of the oldest of north London's vegetarian restaurants, but frustratingly disorganised – largely stemming from the one, L-shaped diningroom where people share tables, and which no one ever seems to have thought to rearrange. The menu could have been designed for your last meal before the nuclear winter, offering portions of often very substantial cooking. Salads are excellent, but an unusual amount of cream and sugar adds weight to the bakes. Soups, for instance mulligatawny, are hearty. The real choice seems to come at the end of the meal, with crunches, mousses and rosehip teas.

Marine Ices [7/10]

8 Haverstock Hill, NW3 map 12
TEL 01-485 8898

Open 10 to 10.30 (11 to 6 Sun)
Closed Christmas Day and Boxing Day

The legendary ice-cream parlour, designed in 1947 to look like the bridge of a ship, still dispenses some of the finest ice-cream in London (and distributes to four hundred other outlets, reputedly). The parlour has expanded beyond its range of sundaes, coupes, bombes, and cassatas to become a small trattoria serving good pastas and pizzas plus a dish of the day, but a few tables are reserved exclusively for ice-cream consumption. The story is that Gaetano Mansi was sent to England at the age of twelve to learn the ice-cream business with some distant relatives in Bermondsey. He opened his first business in 1908 in Drummond Street, near Euston, then a second in Euston Road and came to Haverstock Hill in 1930. Book for the restaurant.

Maxie's Wine Bar [6/10]

7 Boston Parade, W7 map 12
TEL 01-567 9708

Open 11.30 to 3 (noon to 2 Sun), 5.30 to 11 &
Closed Christmas Day, Boxing Day and Easter Sun

Formerly Maxim, but otherwise unchanged. London's first Chinese wine bar features live music, the best of Chinese finger food – sesame toasts, spare ribs, spring rolls, even sesame baps filled with roast duck or pork – plus some casseroles and sizzling dishes and a range of wines. Not as polished or as big as its younger sister in Knightsbridge, but valuable in an area very short on places to eat out.

Melati [9/10]

21 Great Windmill Street, W1 map 14
TEL 01-437 2745

Open noon to 11.30 (12.30 Fri and Sat) &
Closed Christmas Day

The sex industry still hangs on grimly in this corner of Soho, which makes the

Melati's flash of South-East Asian colour the more welcome. The small, bustling dining-room looks like a coffee bar but serves a full range of Malaysian and Indonesian dishes. The rice and noodle one-plate dishes provide excellent filling meals almost by themselves. The laksa soup is superlative, while Sam's Trifle is amazing – a tri-layered purée of fruits, green from sweet avocado, orange from mango, yellow from pineapple, served with a straw and a garnish of pineapple. The ice-creams can be equally unusual.

NEW ENTRY Mercury [7/10]

140 Upper Street, N1   map 13
TEL 01-354 4088

Open noon to 3, 7 to midnight
Closed Christmas Day and Boxing Day

The most recent of Peter Ilic's group of cut-price bistros. This branch has the added feature of a so-called 'nutritionally balanced menu' as well as the same range as the others. For details see entry for Lantern.

Methuselah's [7/10]

29 Victoria Street, SW1   map 13
TEL 01-222 3550

Open 9am to 11pm &
Closed Sat and Sun

Serves the most respectable glass of wine within striding distance of the Houses of Parliament; the food in the wine bar section runs a close second. There are standards that feature in all of Don Hewitson's wine bars (see Shampers and Cork & Bottle) – smoked trout mousse or Lincolnshire sausage hot-pot à la Beaujolais – but there is always a safe spread of salads, pies and gateaux. Prices in the brasserie part are more inflated.

Metro Wine Bar [7/10]

28 Basil Street, SW3   map 13
TEL 01-589 6286

Open noon to 2.30, 5.30 to 10.15
Closed Sun; Sat D; bank hols; Christmas

There are two good reasons for visiting this elegant basement wine bar. First, it shares its kitchen with the prestigious Capital Hotel; second it has a Cruover machine for dispensing fine wines by the glass. The food shows its class with salad of seafood and young vegetables, the pea soup, the fish pâté, and the well-kept cheeses served with a basket of bread. Otherwise the menu includes grilled sardines with mustard sauce, leek flan, and venison sausage with red wine. First courses from the menu are now available between 2.30 and 6.30pm.

Millwards [7/10]

97 Stoke Newington   map 12
Church Street, N16
TEL 01-254 1025

Open noon to midnight &
Closed 1 week at Christmas

More of a restaurant than most vegetarian venues. The menu bills itself as 'Continental vegetarian' and bears this out with 'brochette de legumes and rice' or 'terrine of vegetables en croûte'. The dining-room, a former tyre salesroom, is spacious and airy, but usually crowded. For all the style, it is the wholesomeness of the cooking that stands out. Lunches are very cheap, dinners with wine come close to £10.

Moti Mahal [6/10]

94 The Broadway, Southall   map 12
TEL 01-571 2620

Open 11 to 10

The range of beautifully laid out sweets sets this modern, westernised café apart from others in the neighbourhood. It is a well-used meeting place and the TV runs non-stop videos of Indian films. Also on the picture menu are tikkas, kebabs and tandooris, to eat in or take out.

Mrs Beeton's [7/10]

58 Hill Rise, Richmond   map 12
TEL 01-940 9561

Open 10 to 5, 6.30 to 10 &
Closed Sun D and Mon D; Christmas

The most famous of all co-operatives – a different cook every day, each an amateur but all producing inexpensive and often surprising meals in the soup, pâtés, roasts, casseroles and gateaux idiom. Dinner has now been annexed by one of the co-op's longest standing contributors, Carole Shuter, who after 13 years has developed a taste for restaurateuring and offers a choice of five main courses. Expect to pay under £5 during the day, and under £10 at night.

Mrs Bridge's Kitchen [6/10]

49 Chislehurst Road, Chislehurst   map 3
TEL 01-467 2150

Open 8 (9 Sat) to 2
Closed Sun; bank hols; 2 weeks in summer, 1 week at Christmas

The menu of this café underneath the arches by the station announces that the minimum charge at lunch is 85p and that it is a condition of the licence that alcohol will not be served with any meal costing less than £1.25. The all-day breakfast is a fraction more expensive at £1.65, but otherwise the gist is good honest café fare at honest prices. Out of ordinary are Pan Haggarty (potato, cheese and onion pie) at £1.15; casserole of chicken for £2; and home-made treacle tart at 65p a slice. Most people spend about £2.

Mr Tang [8/10]

61–63 Shaftesbury Avenue, W1   map 14
TEL 01-734 4488/5001

Open noon to midnight
Closed Christmas Day

Mr Tang's tall red sign is one of Shaftesbury Avenue's most distinctive landmarks. The restaurant caters for a cosmopolitan market, pulling in passing tourists and businessmen as well as Chinese families and staff from the Chinese Embassy. The kitchen caters for all-comers and the long menu wanders into Peking and Szechuan, but shows its mettle with Cantonese dishes and the page of interesting specialities, such as stuffed aubergine with prawns and black-bean sauce, and beef and Chinese mushroom

hot-pot with crunchy lily flowers. Rice is some of the best in London, because portions are steamed individually in clay pots for each table. Best bets for a cheap meal are dim-sum, served through the day.

NEW ENTRY | Muffin Man [5/10]

12 Wrights Lane, W8   map 12
TEL 01-937 6652

Open 8.15 to 5.45 (5 Sat) &
Closed Sun; bank hols

Quiet tea-shop off the Kensington High Street, providing a refuge for shoppers. Muffins appear through the day. Cakes and gateaux are home made; scones for tea come with clotted cream. Prunes for breakfast.

Mulfords Wine Bar [7/10]

127 Shepherds Bush Road, W6   map 12
TEL 01-603 2229

Open noon to 3, 5.30 (6 Sat, 7 Sun) to 11 (10.30 Sun)
Closed Sat L and Sun L; bank hols; 24 Dec to 1 Jan

This wine bar benefits from being part of a wine shipping business. Many of its own bottles appear on the list, including house champagne at £13.50. The cooking is uncharacteristically enterprising for a wine bar. The menu shoves along with the markets, mixing steaks and baked potatoes with bistro-style dishes like blanquette de veau or walnut, bacon and watercress flan. The atmosphere is relaxed and cheerful.

Munbhave [9/10]

305 London Road, Croydon   map 3
TEL 01-689 6331

Open 6pm to 11pm (midnight Sat) &
Closed Mon (exc bank hols); 3 weeks Aug

Even though Southern Indian vegetarian food is no longer the rarity it was when Kesh Tank opened, there are many who hold that this remains the best in South London and even rivals the North-West London firmament of Sabras and Rani. Highlights include crisp samosas, bhel pooris filled with chickpeas and potatoes, freshly made puris and raita. Thalis are a bargain, but the whole menu is excellent value for money.

Museum of London [7/10]

150 London Wall, EC2   map 13
TEL 01-726 4446

Open 10 (noon Sun) to 5
Closed Mon

A cut above the usual museum canteen fare. All the food is prepared on the premises and served from a long counter in a blue room filled with standing lamps and blonde-wood furniture. The choice of salads, quiches, baked potatoes and soups is supplemented by fine English cheeses and a choice of teas. Sandwiches include beef and horseradish, bacon and cheese, celery and mayonnaise, chicken, mayonnaise and almonds. The same firm, Milburns, also runs the Victoria & Albert museum canteen.

Mustoe Bistro [7/10]

73 Regent's Park Road, NW1   map 13
TEL 01-586 0901

Open 6.30pm to 11.15pm (1 to 3, 6.30 to 10.45 Sun) & (also WC)
Closed Christmas and Easter

Primrose Hill locals must be unusually supportive customers – restaurants here outlive most of their rivals elsewhere. Mustoe pre-dates all of them, using a simple formula of plain fresh food served with drinkable vin ordinaire. The short menu is mainly English and French: lamb Shrewsbury; beef casserole; kidneys in Worcester sauce; vegetarian risotto. Vegetables and wholegrain bread come with generous amounts of butter. The décor is pine booths; service is genial. Sunday lunch is unusually cheap.

NEW ENTRY Nanten Yakitori Bar [7/10]

6 Blandford Street, W1   map 13
TEL 01-935 6319

Open 12.30 to 2.30, 6.30 to 10
Closed Sun; Sat L; 1 to 3 Jan; bank hols

This Japanese café continues to provide authentic Japanese food with likeable service. The action centres on the snake-like bar, where customers perch on stools and watch the cooks at work at the grill and the steaming pans. Yakitori (grilled items) are the main business, and the range includes skewered chicken breast, wing tips, gizzard, and asparagus rolled with pork. There are good-value set lunches, otherwise stay with the one-dish meals, such as noodle soups or tempura on rice to keep the bill in single figures. The separate list of specialities is worth exploring. Drink tea or saké.

National Gallery [9/10]

Trafalgar Square, WC2   map 14
TEL 01-930 5210

Open 10 (2 Sun) to 5 (7 Wed in July, Aug, Sept)
Closed Christmas Eve, Christmas Day and 1 Jan

One of the very few places in central London where it is possible to eat three courses and have a glass of something for about £5. For example, a chilled cucumber soup, grilled trout, flapjack and a glass of wine come to £5.10. The quality is unusually good; the place may yet take the laurels from Justin de Blank's other, much longer established restaurant at Duke Street. Although it gets busy, the cavernous, institutional basement rambles under the gallery, affording great swathes of open space between tables.

NEW ENTRY Nautilus [7/10]

27–29 Fortune Green Road, NW6   map 12
TEL 01-435 2532

Open 11.30 to 2, 5 to 10.30
Closed Sun

Anything and everything to do with the sea covers the walls of this chip shop-cum-fish restaurant – plastic life size lobsters and crabs; fish nets; green plates with blue dolphins painted on them, and some large glass fish. In between all this are three short rows of dark red booth seats and black tables. Cornish rock salmon, fresh rainbow trout and special Dover salmon all feature alongside more usual lines, and fish sizes are big. Frying is in matzo meal.

Neal's Yard Bakery & Tea Room [8/10]

6 Neal's Yard, WC2   map 14
TEL 01-836 5199

Open 10.30 to 8 (5 Wed, 4.30 Sat)
Closed Sun; bank hols; 1 week Christmas to New Year

Neal's Yard is the rightful inheritor of Covent Garden's previous incarnation as a fruit and vegetable market. The shops are excellent, as is the bakery and tea-room, though the premises are Mother Hubbard style. Prices brook no argument – very few main courses top £2.50 – and the dishes benefit from being freshly prepared. Breads are first class, soups generous, fruits worthy. Cakes are made without sugar.

Newens & Sons [7/10]

288 Kew Road, Kew   map 12
TEL 01-940 2752

Open 10 to 5.30 (9.30 to 1 Mon) & (also wc)
Closed Sun; bank hols

For nearly two centuries the Newens family has been baking. Maids of Honour are reputed to have been invented here. But over and above, this is a pleasant tea-room. Pastries, cakes, even home-made chocolates are served on blue and white china by benign waitresses. Wonderfully English.

New World [9/10]

Gerrard Place, W1   map 14
TEL 01-734 0677/0396

Open 11 to midnight
Closed Christmas Day

Dim-sum is probably the cheapest and best meal available to families. The Chinese expect to serve children and cope with them admirably. The neat little bamboo steaming baskets provide equal fascination for adults. Here are some of the best in London: plates of cold roast duck, chicken and suckling pig; little dumplings filled with minced pork or shrimps; spare ribs, both the long, sticky, roast version and also the tiny steamed knuckles in black-bean sauce. All of these are walked round the large, cavernous dining-rooms in steel trolleys. Dim-sum is served only until 6pm, after which a menu, which is more expensive, comes into operation.

North Sea [7/10]

7–8 Leigh Street, WC1   map 13
TEL 01-387 5892

Open noon to 2.30, 5.30 to 10.30 &
Closed Sun

Good fish and chip shops are a thing of the past. The North Sea swims against the tide. Fish is delivered daily, then deep fried in egg and matzo meal or else grilled. The gimmicky novelties, like the prawn cocktails and the seafood platter, show the same imagination and respect for quality.

Nosherie [6/10]

12–13 Greville Street, EC1   map 13
TEL 01-242 1591

Open 8 to 5 &
Closed Sat and Sun; bank hols; 10 days at Christmas

The deeply Jewish roots of Hatton Garden's gem trade are evident in this small café-cum-take-away bar. The salt beef sandwiches kept the reputation going when such things were not as common as they are today. But the waitresses also serve filling soups, latkes, blintzes and chopped liver. It's well named and the longer it goes without changing, the more character it seems to acquire.

Oasis [7/10]

113 Lower Clapton Road, E5   map 12
TEL 01-985 2675

Open noon to 2.30, 5 to 11 (noon to 2, 7 to 11 Sat and Sun)
Closed Christmas Day, Boxing Day and 1 Jan; bank hols

A wine bar turning into a restaurant. The menu stretches from steaks and vegetarian food, such as wine and nut pâté, to classic French calf's liver with red wine sauce. Portions are generous. The atmosphere is upwardly mobile.

October Gallery [7/10]

24 Old Gloucester Street, WC1   map 13
TEL 01-242 7367

Open 12.30 to 2.30
Closed Sun and Mon; 22 Dec to 7 Jan

A splendid lunch-time only café secreted away in a gallery. The far end of the long white room is partitioned off and has half a dozen tables, each seating about eight. The blackboard menu is, like the exhibits, cosmopolitan and free in spirit, taking in hummus on the one hand and Pavlova on the other. Portions are generous and unrefined. Leek and potato soup is unblended; the stews potently sauced. Best to go early as it gets busy. No licence, no corkage.

NEW ENTRY | Odette's [7/10]

130 Regent's Park Road, NW1   map 13
TEL 01-586 5486

Open 12.30 to 2.30, 7.30 to 11
Closed Sun; Sat L; bank hols; last 2 weeks Aug

The wine bar, with cavernous alcoves, benefits from sharing the kitchen with the popular and accomplished restaurant. The menu is imaginative and certainly the food seems just a cheaper version of the restaurant: chopped French beans with prawns in a light creamy dressing; deep-fried Camembert with gooseberry preserve; jacket potato with sour cream and lots of smoked salmon. The desserts are wonderful – lime mousse cake with crème anglaise and chocolate truffle cake, a cross between a cake and mousse. The huge wine list is almost entirely French. House wine is Pays de l'Aude at £5.

Olive Tree [6/10]

11 Wardour Street, W1   map 14
TEL 01-734 0808

Open 11 to 11.30 (10 Sun and bank hols)

Valued as an inexpensive, non-Chinese venue close to the West End cinemas. The menu has a Middle Eastern slant, featuring kebabs, but also couscous, stuffed aubergines, hummus and so on.

Vegetarians, who tend to do conspicuously badly in the nearby Chinese restaurants, fare well. The prints on the walls are for sale.

Orange Brewery [6/10]

37–39 Pimlico Road, SW1   map 13
TEL 01-730 5378

Open 11 to 3, 5.30 to 11 (noon to 2, 7 to 10.30 Sun) &
Closed Christmas Day D

The brewery is in the basement of this panelled free house. The ales are SW1, SW2, Pimlico Porter (darker for winter) and Pimlico Light (lighter for lunch). A short menu is not quite as heroically revolutionary but plays the part with a range of sensible pub-style bakes – all about £5.50. Typical are steak and kidney pie; goulash; chilli con carne. The ploughman's comes with four different kinds of salad leaves, no less.

NEW ENTRY | Or-Li [7/10]

293 Finchley Road, NW3   map 12
TEL 01-794 7924

Open noon to 2am (4pm Fri; from sunset to 4am Sat/Sun) &

Probably the only kosher Moroccan restaurant in London. It has a family feel to it and a devoted following. The cooking is as good as you are likely to find without spending a lot more. Aubergines come in various guises in tahina or tomato sauce. Falafel dinner brings hummus, falafel balls, cucumber salad, red pepper and tomato dip plus tahina. Vegetable couscous is light; and eaten with pickled chillies and home-made pitta bread is delicious. Kosher wines.

Ormes [7/10]

67–69 Abbeville Road, SW4   map 12
TEL 01-673 2568

Open noon to 5, 6.30 to 12
Closed 5 days at Christmas

The wine bar and restaurant join up at the back. The décor is of the quaint old-tat school and the service makes up in charm anything else that is missing. The menu is up to date, offering modern British dishes such as pumpkin, carrot and ginger soup and plenty of warm salads alongside the Cordon Bleu variations on which it has survived for a number of years.

Oval Tandoori [6/10]

64A Brixton Road, SW9   map 12
TEL 01-582 1415

Open noon to 2.30, 6 to midnight ⅋ (also WC)
Closed Christmas Day

The cooking in this seemingly archetypal old-style tandoori house is, by common consent, above average. The familiar range of the dishes is expanded with a few less familiar items, such as lamb with cauliflower, and chicken liver massala. The fish tikkas, and also much of the meat cookery, are especially worthwhile. Service copes admirably with the large through-put. Full meals might cost as much as £10 but it is not necessary to spend that much.

Pacifico [7/10]

5 Langley Street, WC2   map 14
TEL 01-379 7728

Open 11.30 to 11.45 (noon to 10.45 Sun)
Closed Christmas Eve to Boxing Day; 1 Jan

The international face of Mexican food, with branches in Paris and Amsterdam. The décor is saloon, but for all its rough and tumble image, there is space between the tables, the music is often calming after the bustle outside, and there is a cheap way through a menu of chilli and cocktails. Tacos and tortillas dominate, filled or topped depending on how hot you like your food.

| NEW ENTRY | **Pasta Underground** [8/10] |

214 Camden High Street, NW1   map 13
TEL 01-482 0010

Open noon to 3, 6 to 11.30
Closed Christmas Eve to 1 Jan

Another addition to the Camden High Street restaurant menagerie is this pastel, airy basement. Of the more unusual sauces for good pasta dishes there is cream cheese and chive with tagliatelle, and ravioli is stuffed with blue cheese and walnuts. The menu also takes in chicken brochette marinaded in lemon and ginger, or veal with tuna. Bread is fresh and liberally sprinkled with sesame seeds. Crème caramel or blueberry mousse to finish off. Related to the Camden Brasserie, one door down, which is good value too, but likely to be nearer £13 a head, rather than the £5 to £7 here.

Pattaya [7/10]

9 Claremont Road, Surbiton   map 3
TEL 01-399 2710

Open noon to 2.30, 6 to 11 (11.30 Fri and Sat) ⅋ (also WC)

Like other Thai restaurants, the Pattaya has become upwardly mobile; the same goes for its prices. A full meal might be as much as £15 but, as with Cantonese restaurants, there is a cheap way through the menu – stick to Eastern principles. The soups are copious and varied and at the back of the menu there are excellent-value one-plate rice and noodle dishes. Take-aways, too. Sundays are for booked parties only, the minimum number of people being four.

Paulo's [8/10]

30 Greyhound Road, W6   map 12
TEL 01-385 9264

Open 7 to 11 ⅋
Closed Sun; bank hols

What would have been the sitting-room of this terraced house is filled with posters of Brazil and maps of Rio de Janeiro. A large cloth parrot and hammocks swing from the ceiling in this fun and inexpensive Brazilian restaurant. For £6.95 help yourself to as much as you like; spicy chicken pieces, pork soufflé, black-bean stew and rice are just a few of the interesting dishes on offer, plus a wide range of salads. Gazpacho, palm heart salad and Brazilian-style crab to start. Pudim de chocolat and pavé to finish. Licensed but you can also bring your own.

Pavilion [7/10]

Finsbury Circus Gardens, EC2   map 13
TEL 01-628 8224

Open 11.30 to 3, 5 to 8
Closed Sat and Sun; bank hols

Built like a gardener's hut in the circular
sweep of the gardens, where bowls are still
played. Upstairs is the wine bar, serving a
range of fresh salads and thick slices of rare
roasts. Exotica include quail eggs and
excellent wines, notably those from the
Alsace and smaller vineyards. The
pistachio and pine room gets crowded with
city dealers who know a good champagne.

Penang Satay House [6/10]

9 Turnpike Lane, N8   map 12
TEL 01-340 8707

Open 6pm to 11pm (midnight Fri and Sat)
Closed Sun; bank hols

Set meals start at £9 at this attractive
Malay restaurant filled with bright
parasols, but it is possible to eat for less,
sticking with the soups, the noodle and
rice dishes. Specialities include satay,
Asian prawns, spare ribs, and orange
chicken. The Malayan dishes are
noticeably better than the attempts at
western compromises.

Peppe's Pizza [6/10]

761–763 High Road,   map 12
Leytonstone, E11
TEL 01-539 7451

Open noon to 3, 6.30 to 11.30 (midnight Fri;
noon to midnight Sat; noon to 11 Sun)
Closed Christmas Day, Boxing Day, 31 Dec
and 1 Jan

The small pizzas in this bustling, friendly
eaterie are big enough for two. Mixed
salads are equally generous. Together they
make this one of the best value places to
eat in E11. Children are welcome, and it is
usefully open on Sundays.

Peter Buchan & Son [6/10]

115 Station Road, Hampton   map 12
TEL 01-979 3706

Open 8.30 to 1.30, 5.30 to 10, plus 2.15 to 5 Tue,
Thur and Fri
Closed Sun and Mon

Under new ownership, but this fish and
chip shop still holds to the fine principles
laid down by Mr Buchan himself, using
fresh fish from the wet shop. The frying is
done in dripping. Chips are fresh potatoes.

Peters [5/10]

59 Pimlico Road, SW1   map 13
TEL 01-730 5991

Open 7am to 10pm (4pm Sun)
Closed Christmas Day and Boxing Day

Peters is a throwback to the days when
this was not such an upmarket part of
town. It is sustained by a constant
through-put of cab drivers, who appreciate
the size of the portions and the
camaraderie. The menu is middle-of-the-
road café fare – all day breakfasts, chicken
with pasta, omelettes, all with chips. Open
early, which makes it good for breakfast.

Le Petit Prince [6/10]

5 Holmes Road, NW5   map 12
TEL 01-267 0752

Open 12.30 to 2.30, 7 to 11.30 (11.45 Fri and Sat)
Closed Sat L, Sun L and Mon L; Christmas Day
and Boxing Day; bank hols

The atmosphere is almost too close to its
French North African roots for comfort,
being small, loud, and very much a café
with a high turnover and a shortage of
décor. The couscous is the central
recommendation but the sidelines, such as
kebabs or braised dishes, also have good
reports from a hard core of regulars.

NEW ENTRY Pho [7/10]

2 Lisle Street, W1   map 14
TEL 01-437 8265

Open noon (11 Sun) to 10 &

Pho (pronounced 'far') is the Vietnamese
word for a soup with beef in it. This
excellent café in the heart of Chinatown
still has the look of a take-away with half a
dozen tables and a sign outside, saying

Saint Michel Snack Bar. The short menu is half snacks, half main dishes. Soups are a feature and come with great bunches of fresh coriander and wedges of lemon; spring rolls are stuffed to bursting and served with pickled turnips and a potent dip. Otherwise there are satays, curries, and good rice and noodle dishes with a healthy vegetarian bias. Set lunches are under £4. Drink tea. Unlicensed.

NEW ENTRY Phoenix [6/10]

39 Gerrard Street, W1   map 14
TEL 01-437 1956

Open 10 to 8
Closed Christmas Day

The most genuine Cantonese take-away in town. The extraordinary window display makes it clear that this is no place for chicken chop-suey. Whole sides of suckling pig hang from hooks; alongside are whole barbecued ribs and strips of barbecued pork; and there are shiny lacquered ducks and soya-cooked chickens. Beneath, on trays, are duck wings, liver, coils of intestines and other anatomical curiosities. The style is simple: a man cleaves the meats on a chopping block and other helpers match them with rice, noodles and vegetables which are kept warm in a battery of canteen-style basins. Cheap and fast. All the roasting is done daily on the premises.

Pigeon [7/10]

606 Fulham Road, SW6   map 12
TEL 01-736 4618

Open noon to 3, 7 to 1
Closed Christmas Day and Boxing Day

One of Peter Ilic's group of cut-price bistros. For details see entry for Lantern.

Pissarro's [7/10]

1–5 Kew Green, Richmond   map 12
TEL 01-940 3987

Open 11.30 to 3, 5.30 to 11 (noon to 2, 7 to 10.30 Sun)
Closed Easter Sunday; Christmas Eve to Boxing Day

Part of the more expensive Jaspers, but with its own kitchen. The menu ranges from earthy bangers and mash to outré fruits de mer au riz, but prices stay within the cheap eater's range. Robust dishes are usually the best; wines also have the accent on value. The split-level dining-room acquires atmosphere from the stone fireplace. For once, the name is a genuine association: the painter lived and worked here.

Pizza Express [7/10]

23 Bond Street, Ealing, W5   map 12
TEL 01-567 7690
252 Chiswick High Road, W4   map 12
TEL 01-747 0193
2 College Road, Harrow   map 12
TEL 01-427 9195
30 Coptic Street, Bloomsbury,   map 13
WC1
TEL 01-636 3232
10 Dean Street, Soho, W1   map 14
TEL 01-437 9595
35 Earls Court Road,   map 12
Kensington, W8
TEL 01-937 0761
227 Finchley Road, Swiss Cottage,   map 12
NW3
TEL 01-794 5100
363 Fulham Road, Chelsea, SW10   map 12
TEL 01-352 5300
895 Fulham Road, Fulham SW6   map 13
TEL 01-731 3117
15 Gloucester Road, SW7   map 13
TEL 01-584 9078
94 Golders Green Road,   map 12
Golders Green, NW11
TEL 01-455 9556
64 Heath Street, NW3   map 12
TEL 01-435 6722
14 High Parade, High Road,   map 12
Streatham, SW16
TEL 01-677 3646
456 High Road, Wembley   map 12
TEL 01-902 4918
189 High Street, Beckenham   map 3
TEL 01-650 0593
41 High Street,   map 12
Kingston-upon-Thames
TEL 01-546 1447
84 High Street, Wimbledon, SW19   map 12
TEL 01-946 6027

20 Hill Street, Richmond   map 12
TEL 01-940 8951

Kettner's, 29 Romilly Street, W1   map 14
TEL 01-437 6437

11 Knightsbridge, SW1   map 13
TEL 01-235 5550

230 Lavender Hill, SW11   map 12
TEL 01-223 5677

137 Notting Hill Gate, W11   map 12
TEL 01-229 6000

26 Porchester Road, W2   map 12
TEL 01-229 7784

64 Tranquil Vale, Blackheath, SE3   map 12
TEL 01-318 2595

144 Upper Richmond Road,   map 12
Putney, SW15
TEL 01-789 1948

305 Upper Richmond Road West,   map 12
East Sheen, SW14
TEL 01-878 6833

335 Upper Street, Islington, N1   map 13
TEL 01-226 9542

154 Victoria Street, SW1   map 13
TEL 01-828 1477

29 Wardour Street, W1   map 14
TEL 01-437 7215

15 Widmore Road, Bromley   map 3
TEL 01-464 2708

Open noon to midnight
Closed Christmas Day and Boxing Day

If the pizza is Britain's number one fast food then the Express chain of branches, mostly in London, is the pick of the chains. Bases are thin, freshly baked, and the toppings, even the Mozzarella, are of a grade above the usual. Surroundings are clean and functional without being anywhere to linger longer than for half a carafe of wine. All are good with children. Bromley has a garden and jazz on Sundays; Gloucester Road has a disco in the basement.

NEW ENTRY   **Pizza Roma** [7/10]

31 Northcote Road, SW11   map 12
TEL 01-223 6878

Open noon (1 Sun) to 3, 6 to midnight (11 Sun)
& (also WC)
Closed Mon; Wed L and Thur L; Christmas Day and Boxing Day

Small, dark Italian restaurant at the Clapham Junction end of Northcote Road.

The décor is simple: dusty pink PVC tablecloths, wooden chairs, and posters of Italy on the walls – the Spanish Steps, Venice and so on. The menu includes about fifteen pizzas, ten pasta dishes, calzone and a few specials on the board – pollo sorpresa, mussels, and maybe a veal dish. Putanesca is topped with chillies, pepperoni, olives, anchovies and Mozzarella. Desserts, especially the tiramisu, are well above the average. Short Italian wine list with a gutsy house red.

NEW ENTRY   **Pizzeria Bel-Sit** [6/10]

439 High Road, Woodford Green,   map 12
E18
TEL 01-504 1164

Open noon to 2.30, 6 to 11 & (also gents WC)
Closed Sun; Mon L; bank hols; July

Authentic, Italian-style pizzas are served in this pizzeria with Paulo Rossi décor and a motley collection of prints and three-dimensional scenes hung at angles in the dining-room. The range tops thirty, mostly about £3. Other dishes can put the bill up. The place is run by Italians who love kids.

Pizzeria Castello [9/10]

20 Walworth Road, SE1   map 13
TEL 01-703 2556

Open noon (5 Sat) to 11 & (also WC)
Closed Sun; Christmas; bank hols

Probably the most booked-ahead pizza hut in London, and rightly so, because the atmosphere bubbles. This Italian-run pizzeria on the Newington Butts roundabout has a restaurant on the ground floor and a wine bar downstairs. Glamorous it is not, with only a few photographs of American footballers to enliven the dull yellow walls, and yet for all this café-like feeling, the pizzas, cooked in big ovens by the entrance, are excellent. Four Seasons is piled high with mushrooms, pepperoni, Mozzarella, ham and so on. Extra toppings can be added, and olives, chillies and capers are available on request. Well-dressed salads, garlic bread and bombes complete the equation. The house wine is better than average, as is the espresso.

Pizzeria Condotti [8/10]

Mill Street, W1   map 13
TEL 01-499 1308

Open 11.30 to midnight &
Closed Sun; bank hols; Christmas Day and
Boxing Day

The suave frontage and efficient service
give this pizzeria an exclusivity that its
prices undermine. Pizzas cost between
£3.90 and £4.50. They are soft-based, crisp-
edged, and spicily topped. The rest of the
menu is a cut above the average, with
interesting salads, and cheesecake and
apple pie to finish.

Pollo [8/10]

20 Old Compton Street, W1   map 14
TEL 01-734 5917

Open noon to 11.30
Closed Sun; Christmas Day

The only thing wrong with the Pollo is its
popularity, with which, at peak times, it
can barely cope. This unassuming little
Italian café, looking like a 1950s coffee bar,
offers superb value. The pasta is freshly
made and as good as anywhere in London.
The menu reads like a dictionary of pasta
shapes, with an atlas of Italy for the
sauces. Other dishes are more of the
meat-and-two-veg. school, without the
cachet of the pasta, but equally generous.
Water, wine, espresso are all decent
imports.

Poons [9/10]

4 Leicester Street, WC2   map 14
TEL 01-437 1528

Open noon to 11.30 & (also ladies wc)
Closed Sun; Christmas

Soho Chinatown is now a major tourist
attraction and Poons is one of the
landmarks. This branch is less of a café
than the Lisle Street original, but the
cooking can be first-rate. Wind-dried foods
are the Poon family's speciality: the
window is hung with flattened ducks
looking like edible frisbees, two kinds of
sausage, hard, black belly-bacon and all

kinds of offal. Choose one-plate rice or
noodle dishes for a quick cheap meal,
otherwise try the uncompromising
Cantonese specialities, such as braised eel
with belly-pork and garlic.

Poons [7/10]

27 Lisle Street, WC2   map 14
TEL 01-437 4549

Open noon to 11.30
Closed Mon; Christmas

The original branch of Poons is a little café
in a crooked house. It is still a favourite
with many who remember the early days
of Soho Chinatown. The classic wind-
dried meats are unmissable, and for cheap
meals there are one-plate rice and noodle
dishes, in the old Cantonese style. A plate
of wind-dried meats plus a bowl of noodle
soup would make a good lunch. Other
specialities, such as oil-soaked squid, and
stewed bean curd with crispy pork and
shrimp paste, are also reasonably priced.
Service is fast and matter-of-fact.
Downstairs is very cramped, so be
prepared to share a table – as well as your
pot of tea. Unlicensed.

Le Poulbot [9/10]

45 Cheapside, EC2   map 13
TEL 01-236 4379

Open noon to 3
Closed Sat and Sun; Christmas Day

Go early. The upstairs – a very badly kept
city secret – is small, cramped, and bistro-
ish, but very good French food is served by
Roux brothers' trainees. The menu moves
with the markets, and takes in good,
peasant-style casseroles as well as some
modern sauced dishes. Bread, cheeses,
coffee and so on are of a similar standard to
the executive side of this operation,
downstairs, but at a quarter of the price.

NEW ENTRY | Presto [7/10]

4 Old Compton Street, WC2   map 14
TEL 01-437 4006

Open noon to 11.30 &
Closed Sun

Some say this is now the best of the four excellent-value Italian pasta bars-cum-cafés in this corner of Soho. Very much like an American diner, with red Formica tables and black vinyl booths, but the Italian touches are the Ruffino bottles and the garlic hanging from the ceiling. The menu includes all the old favourites: tortellini is the real thing and the sugo is a delicious meaty sauce with lots of garlic. They have a wine licence, unlike the Centrale and Barocco, and good Italian mineral water in Madonne de Mercede. Service prefers regulars.

Le Provence [7/10]

Kew Station Approach, Richmond map 12
TEL 01-940 6777

Open noon to 2 (Sat L only), 6 to 9.15 &
Closed Sun and Mon; L Tue to Fri; Aug to Sept; Christmas

The Frenchness of the name is not totally brought out on a short menu of roast chicken; liver and bacon. There are about five specialities, which come with pommes boulangère; other dishes come with chips. The sense of value is reinforced by the lack of a licence, which means regulars – of which there seem to be many, so book, especially at the end of the week – bring their own. The red check cloths and dripping candles add a Gallic accent.

Punjab House [6/10]

37 Balham High Road, SW12 map 12
TEL 01-673 1105

Open 11am to 2am &
Closed Christmas Day; bank hols

This small, Formica café specialises in bargains. A spectacular breakfast on Sundays costs about £4; lunchboxes, vegetarian or not, for £2 or £2.50, include two curries, rice, chapati. The opening hours have been extended to 2am, which is useful in an area that otherwise closes at 11pm.

Punter's Pie [8/10]

183 Lavender Hill, SW11 map 12
TEL 01-228 2660

Open noon to 3, 6 to 11.30
Closed 24 to 30 December

The pies are all £3.95: parson's is shepherd's pie; punter's pie, steak-and-kidney; Pacific, smoked fish in egg sauce. The split-level dining-room and wine bar is attractive in peach, with posters. Alternatives include pizza, pasta, soufflé, and even Punjab parcels – lamb wrapped in filo pastry and topped with yoghurt. Desserts are all £1.95: chocolate mousse pie, banoffi pie; and the proprietors make their own sorbets. Around thirty wines; house wine £4.95. Grolsch and Beck beers. Happy hour is from 6pm to 8pm when all cocktails are half price and there's thirty per cent off wine. Seating outside in the summer.

Ragam [8/10]

57 Cleveland Street, W1 map 13
TEL 01-636 9098

Open noon to 3, 6 to midnight & (also wc)
Closed bank hols, Christmas Day and Boxing Day

A modest South Indian restaurant specialising in dishes from the Kerala coast. Kaallan is a curry made with mango, yoghurt, coconut and spices; avial is vegetables flavoured with coconut and curry leaves. As well as vegetarian dishes, such as iddly, masala dosai and vada, there's a full range of meat, poultry and seafood curries. To drink, there's sweet, salt or fruit-flavoured lassi; or wine and lager.

Raj Bhel Poori [7/10]

19 Camden High Street, NW1 map 13
TEL 01-388 6663

Open noon to 11.30 & (also wc)

No meat and no licence combine to keep bills in check at this Southern Indian café. The menu has the now-familiar selection of samosas, dosas, bhel pooris, bhajias and iddlys, and there's no objection to making up a full meal from the list of starters and snacks. In the evening there are specials, such as channa batura, cashew-nut pilau, and vegetable biriani. Thalis are good value. No corkage is charged if you take your own wine; otherwise drink the salt or sweet lassi.

Rajput [7/10]

144 Goldhawk Road, W12   map 12
TEL 01-740 9036

Open noon to 3, 6 to 11.45 &

There is a full range of curries and tandoori dishes at this reliable, neighbourhood Indian restaurant. Vegetarian thali at £5.95 brings vegetable curry, dhal, palak aloo, chapati, pilau rice, raita, poppadum, dessert and coffee (the meat version is £8.25). Other specialities include murgh makhani, tandoori chicken cooked with tomatoes and cream, and gosht badam passanda – lamb cooked with yoghurt, cream and butter.

Rani [9/10]

3–5 Long Lane, N3   map 12
TEL 01-349 4386/2636

Open noon to 2, 6 to 10.30
Closed Mon; Tue L; Christmas Day

The converted tea-shop has a sitar and drums perched up in one corner, reminder of its new role as one of the premier Indian vegetarian restaurants in the capital. The mood is still informal, prices are low, but service is first-rate and the food is subtle. Highlights from the menu are the samosas, aloo dhai poori, masala dosa, and stuffed parathas. Curries are unexpectedly good: stuffed aubergine and potato on Tuesday; tindora (baby cucumbers) on Friday; valour and papdi bean on Sunday. Mini lunch-time thalis are £2.95, and there are twenty per cent discounts on early and late evening meals.

Ravenscourt Park Teahouse [6/10]

Off Paddenswick Road,   map 12
Ravenscourt Park, W6
TEL 01-748 9513

Open 8 to 5.30 &
Closed Christmas Day

On a sunny day there can hardly be a finer venue in West London for afternoon tea.

The old pavilion has been lovingly restored, a picnic area has been fenced off and filled with white garden furniture, and there are views over wide expanses of the park. The range of twenty herbal teas almost outshines the menu, which stays comfortably within the confines of pies, quiches and samosas. No longer strictly vegetarian; hot dishes and a new salad bar are the key points.

Ravi Shankar (Bhel Poori House) [7/10]

133–135 Drummond Street, NW1   map 13
TEL 01-388 6458

Open noon to 11 &

One of the big three Indian vegetarian restaurants in Drummond Street (see feature). The pine tables and chairs, feeling of light and space, and becalmed atmosphere suggest a serious-minded wholefood café. In fact, the food is good-value Gujerati, with plenty of bargains in the thalis. Around £3.50 pays for a tray of curries, breads, rice, pickles and sweets. Also, look for the daily specials such as aloo palak (a dish of spinach and potatoes), served with chapati for around £2.50. Drink lassi, freshly squeezed juices, or wine.

NEW ENTRY Raw Deal [6/10]

65 York Street, W1   map 13
TEL 01-262 4841

Open 10 to 10 (11 Sat)
Closed Sun; 24 Dec to 2 Jan; bank hols

Set in a row of expensive specialist shops in a mainly residential street is this dark-tabled self-service vegetarian restaurant. There is always a soup of the day. Pancakes filled with courgettes and bean sprouts are covered with nuts. Desserts may be high on sugar, but include fruit salad with water-melon, bananas and pineapple, or wholemeal trifle.

Rebato's [9/10]

169 South Lambeth Road, SW8   map 12
TEL 01-735 6388

Open noon to 2.30, 7 to 11.15 &
Closed Sat L; Sun; bank hols; Christmas Eve

The front half of this ballroom of a Spanish restaurant deals exclusively in tapas – trays of sardines, octopus, spicy sausage, baby eels, anchovies, and excellent tripe. Especially good are the tortilla, chicken livers, and freshly cooked, battered calamares. Bacalao is served in a little Le Creuset-type dish in rich tomato sauce; very silky indeed. A full range of Torres are sold at good prices. Very authentic. Very, very busy.

Redfords [7/10]

126 Golders Green Road, NW11   map 12
TEL 01-958 2229
313 Hale Lane, Edgware   map 12
TEL 01-958 2229

Open noon to 2.30 (3 Sun), 5 to 10.30
Closed Christmas Day and Boxing Day

This pair of up-market fish-shop-cum-restaurants fry in nut oil, and use an egg and matzo-meal batter. The Edgware branch looks newer than it is, with chrome chairs, bright green colour scheme, mirrors and pink neon lights. Tartare sauce and ketchup are in small white bowls on the tables. Plaice and lemon sole are offered on or off the bone; salmon, poached or smoked; gefilte fish, fried or boiled. Chopped herring, smetana and pickled cucumbers give the menu a still stronger Jewish flavour.

Reeds, Austin Reed [6/10]

103 Regent Street, W1   map 13
TEL 01-734 6789

Open 9.30 to 5 (6 Thur) &
Closed Sun; most bank hols; Christmas Day

On the first floor, by the riding department, this restaurant veers on the edge of expensive. Tables are well spaced and covered with white and peach coloured linen; the chairs are Windsor. Waitresses are smartly dressed in pink and white pinstripe shirts and grey skirts. Through the day there are open sandwiches, jacket potatoes, salads and so on, but the lunch menu includes

moussaka, steak-and-kidney pie and Reeds's pâté, for between £4 and £7. A minimum charge of £4.50 operates at lunch-time. Afternoon tea, at £4.75, brings sandwiches, fruit cake, scones with clotted cream and a selection of gateaux; the place is an oasis away from the buzz of Regent Street. Even cheaper are tea and scones for £1.75.

Refectory [7/10]

6 Church Walk, Richmond   map 12
TEL 01-940 6264

Open 10 to 2, 7.30 to 8.45 & (1 step)
Closed Mon; Sun D, Tue D and Wed D; Christmas; Easter

Three evenings a week this fixture of Richmond eating out operates as a more expensive restaurant, but its main business is in the morning, for coffee and lunches. The Kingsleys' daughter Harriet and her husband Martin have taken over and redecorated throughout last autumn. Vegetarian themes show ever more strongly in flans and bakes. The potted meats or fish, with salad, make inexpensive meals. Other dishes show a liking for old British cooking, such as the pies and treacle tart to finish. The wine list has an interesting selection of English and Australian wines.

Rendezvous Snack Bar, Swiss Centre [7/10]

Leicester Square, W1   map 14
TEL 01-734 1291

Open noon to midnight
Closed Christmas Eve and Christmas Day

Inside the imposing trade centre which broods over a corner of Leicester Square, are four eating places. The Rendezvous is the snack bar, which is rarely as cheap as you might expect it to be. Choose carefully. There are copious soups, half a dozen permutations of coverings for rösti potatoes, and specialities, such as pork with mushrooms, asparagus and grilled bacon all on toast, for £4.90. Service is predictably efficient, if impersonal. A good place to take children, albeit a bit pricey.

Reuben's [6/10]

20A Baker Street, W1   map 13
TEL 01-935 5945

Open 11.15 to 10 &
Closed Sat; Fri D; Jewish hols

The oldest building in Baker Street houses this well-established, unlicensed kosher restaurant and food bar. The cooking is Ashkenazi: safe, dependable and filling. Half a dozen people work behind the food counter, serving huge portions of salt beef, gefilte fish, latkes and so on. High Formica counters around the room with stools provide space to eat, plus tables outside.

Richmond Harvest [6/10]

5 Dome Buildings,   map 12
The Quadrant, Richmond
TEL 01-940 1138

Open 11.30 to 11 (10.30 Sun)
Closed Christmas Day to 2 Jan

Vegetarian bistro with enterprising salads, as well as main courses such as aubergine crumble, or courgette and cashew casserole. Being open all day makes it doubly useful.

Rodos [8/10]

59 St Giles High Street, WC2   map 13
TEL 01-836 3177

Open noon to 2.30, 5.30 to 11.30 &
Closed Sat L, Sun; bank hols

The meze at this off-the-track West End Greek restaurant is one of the biggest in London. Fifteen different dishes, from hummus and grilled haloumi to quail in butter with wine and lemon, and red mullet, all come in vast quantities. The atmosphere is relaxed, the service personal, and the normal taverna clichés are not overworked.

Ron & Cyn's [6/10]

26 Sutton Court Road, off Long   map 3
Lane, Hillingdon
TEL Uxbridge (0895) 32981

Open 11.30 to 1.30, 5 to 9 &
Closed Sun and Mon

This is a first-class take-away fish and chip shop: family run, and using top grade fish. Among the best of its kind in West London.

Rouxl Britannia [9/10]

4 Sydney Street, SW3   map 13
TEL 01-352 3433

Open 7.30am to 11pm (noon to 11 Sat, 10 to 11 Sun)
Closed bank hols

Triton Court, 16 Finsbury Square,   map 13
EC2
TEL 01-256 6997

Open 7.30am to 9pm & (also WC)
Closed Sat, Sun

These two French-style cafés, both of which have more expensive restaurants attached, offer the best value in London of their kind. They open early for breakfasts and stay open – until 11pm at Chelsea. The menus range from omelettes, to gravlax, to confit of duck. Daily specials can be as complex as a mousse of scallops with a mushroom sauce for £2.50, a product of sous-vide cooking. Pastries, pâtés and soups are all of an exceptional quality, as are the house wines. The city branch is spectacularly sited inside the Triton Court.

Roxy [6/10]

114 The Green, Southall   map 12
TEL 01-574 3476

Open 9am to 10.30pm (11 Fri and Sat)

A truism of Southall's many places to eat out is that, unless the café or shop is a sweetmeat specialist, the savoury dishes are invariably better. This is the case here, one of the oldest cafés, properly called Sagoo & Takhar, but known universally as Roxy, the name over the door. It is as much a place to meet, as somewhere to eat. Of the two bleak dining-rooms, the café rather than the family room is most usually full. Curries are as good as you would expect in this area.

NEW ENTRY Roxy Café Cantina [6/10]

297 Upper Street, N1 map 13
TEL 01-226 5746

Open noon to 3, 5.30 to 12 (noon to midnight Sat, noon to 11.30 Sun) & (also WC)
Closed Christmas Day and Boxing Day

A large pink fluorescent sign in the window announces this high-ceilinged Mexican restaurant. The Mexican touches to the décor are a few sombreros and some clay jugs, and the menu includes chicken enchiladas in a tomato and chilli sauce. Large salads take in finely chopped tomatoes, cucumbers, red cabbage and carrot in a vinaigrette dressing. Other elements are more plain Americana: burgers, potato skins; but there are Mexican beers, for instance Dos Equis and Tecafe.

Sabras [9/10]

263 Willesden High Road, NW10 map 12
TEL 01-459 0340

Open 12.30 to 3, 6.30 to 10 (12.30 to 10 Sat and Sun) &
Closed Mon

The best Indian vegetarian food in London is served behind this redecorated shop-front. It scores with a wide-ranging menu, genuinely authentic flavours, and a subtlety lacking in most other comparable restaurants. It is also extremely good value. Classic farsan snacks, cold puris, Gujerati specialities, and brilliant vegetable dishes, such as channa aloo, stuffed ravaiya and undhiu (a winter speciality of aubergines, sweet potatoes, bananas, and garlic), are excellent. Good value thalis, buffet-style lunches. Unlicensed, but bring your own.

NEW ENTRY Sagarmatha [7/10]

339 Euston Road, NW1 map 13
TEL 01-387 6531

Open noon to 3, 6 to midnight &
Closed Christmas Day and Boxing Day

A box-like dining-room opposite Thames TV, drawing in passing trade from the Euston Road. The wood-carvings, prints and photos of the Himalayas are reminders that this is a Nepalese restaurant, although the menu indiscriminately mixes various Indian dishes. Look for specialities such as momo (steamed dumplings), choala (cold lamb with ginger and garlic), and chauchau (noodles with chicken, prawn and vegetables). Other Nepalese staples, such as bhutuwa chicken, and aloo bodi tama, are capably handled. Nepalese thali is £6.85, and there are buffet lunches. Related to the Gurkhas Tandoori, 23 Warren Street, W1, which has a less interesting menu.

Samsun [7/10]

34 Stoke Newington Road, N16 map 12
TEL 01-249 0400

Open 11 to 9 &

This popular café in the heart of London's Turkish community (see feature map), serves some of the most genuine Black Sea cooking in the area. The omelettes and chips are distractions from a blackboard menu that specialises in slow-cooked stews, such as meat with cauliflower, or rissoles and potato. Fresh bread is on the table. Kebabs and mixed grill are well reported too, and sweets delve into the exotic for crystallised pumpkin.

Sawasdee [7/10]

26–28 Whitfield Street, W1 map 12
TEL 01-631 0289

Open noon to 3, 6 to 11.30
Closed Sat L and Sun L; bank hols; Christmas

Useful basement Thai restaurant, in a predominantly Greek and expense account area. A full run on the *carte* will go over £15, but, as with all Thai menus, it is relatively easy to eat inexpensively on the soups, noodle dishes, and rice dishes. Popular items, often quite hot from chilli, like satay, curries, excellent fish, are of a standard. Take-aways.

NEW ENTRY Seafresh Fish Restaurant [7/10]

80–81 Wilton Road, SW1 map 13
TEL 01-828 0747

Open noon to 3, 5 to 10.45 (noon to 10.45 Sat)
Closed Sun; 10 days from Christmas Day;
bank hols

The reputation of the Leonidou family's
fish-and-chip restaurant has grown
steadily over 23 years. It is now held,
properly, to be one of the best in London.
All the fish is fresh. Dover sole and king
prawns, fried or grilled, add exotic variety.
The décor is simple, and the take-away
section thrives. Victoria station is 400
yards away.

Seashell [7/10]

49–51 Lisson Grove, NW1   map 12
TEL 01-723 8703

Open noon to 2, 5.15 to 10.30
Closed Sun and Mon; Christmas to New Year

London's most famous chippie is now
under the ownership of casino group
Pleasurama, and its creator, John Faulkner,
has gone to his East End branch (see
Faulkners). Promises to keep the same
staff and use the same suppliers for matzo-
or batter-fried or grilled fish seem solid. It
would be a shame to see this modern
institution change.

NEW ENTRY Seoul [7/10]

89A Aldgate High Street, EC3   map 13
TEL 01-480 5570

Open noon to 3, 6 to 9.30
Closed Sat, Sun; bank hols

Inexpensive Korean restaurant near the
Aldgate pump, much used by the Korean
community. The long menu features
many classic dishes, such as bulgogi bap
(marinated strips of beef cooked at the
table and served with rice) and man doo
guk (steamed meat dumplings in broth).
Other one-dish meals, such as dongass
(deep-fried pork and vegetables with soup
and rice) or onmyun (soft noodles in hot
beef soup) can keep the bill around £5.

Shampers Wine Bar [7/10]

4 Kingly Street, W1   map 13
TEL 01-437 1692

Open 11 to 3, 5.30 to 11 &
Closed Sun; Sat D; bank hols; Christmas Day
to 27 Dec

The third in Don Hewitson's trio of West
End wine bars (see Cork & Bottle, and
Methuselah's), has imaginative cold dishes
and some intelligently chosen wines,
particularly house champagne. The
basement has been given over to grills and
a brasserie (£10.50 for two-course lunch
with coffee), but it is cheaper to eat,
although more crowded, upstairs.

NEW ENTRY Shan [6/10]

200 Shaftesbury Avenue, WC2   map 14
TEL 01-240 3348

Open noon to 10 & (also WC)
Closed Sun

This cramped, plastic-seated café marked
by a Coca-Cola sign serves some of the
cheapest Indian vegetarian food in the
West End. Thalis are under £5; there are
also set lunches and dinners for as little as
£3.50. As well as the classic snacks,
curries and birianis, the menu is strong on
pulses and interesting vegetables, such as
cassava. Unlicensed.

NEW ENTRY Simpson's of Cornhill [6/10]

Cornhill, EC3   map 13

Open 11.30 to 3
Closed Sat, Sun

Lunch in this long-established City
institution can be fast and as boisterous as a
prep-school dinner. Food is traditional and
good value: a huge portion of steak and
kidney pie can be accompanied by
favourites such as bubble and squeak or
braised onion. Sweets are spotted dick or
rhubarb pie with custard, all served briskly
by the unflappable waitresses. Queues
stretch down the wooden stairs but
turnover is quick. A good selection of wines
with Alexis Chanson Blanc at £6.95.

Soho Brasserie [9/10]

23–25 Old Compton Street, W1   map 14
TEL 01-439 9301

Open 10 to 11.30 &
Closed Sun; Christmas Day, Boxing Day and 1 Jan; bank hols

The Brasserie, owned by Ind Coope, is a model of the thematic restaurant. The menu stays within its limits and offers a good choice, in terms of contrasts, of essentially modern bistro dishes, like warm salads or fish soup. Service is prompt, and there is no cost-cutting on important things like bread or coffee. The real value is at the front, where a bar menu is served from the same kitchen as the restaurant. One-plate salads, or saucis-sons, and a glass of wine, are bargains.

Solopasta [8/10]

26 Liverpool Road, N1　　　　　map 13
TEL 01-359 7648

Open noon to 3, 6 to 10.30
Closed Sun and Mon; bank hols; Aug

A café rather than a pasta bar, serving some of the best in North London. There's a choice of half a dozen fresh pastas, made every night above the restaurant. These can be paired up with various sauces, laid out in bowls in the centre. Favourites are wholemeal tagliatelle with pesto genovese, and spaghetti carbonara. The garlic and herb bread is first-rate, the zabaglione much loved, and the house red quaffable. Take-aways.

Southgate Technical College [7/10]

High Street, Southgate, N14　　　map 12
TEL 01-886 9570

Open 12.15 Mon to Fri, plus 7 to 9.45 Tue and Thur
Closed College vacations

Catering colleges often offer excellent-value lunches cooked by the students. The main difficulty is getting a table, which invariably has to be booked well ahead. Lunch (between 12.15 and 2pm only) costs £3.95, and offers a trio of dishes at each course. The style is antiquated and classical, but none the worse for that. A February meal was haché de porc en gelée vinaigrette; raie au beurre noir; profit-eroles au chocolat. Dinner, at 7pm on

Tuesdays and Thursdays, runs to an extra course, but is in the vein of cod en croûte. 'Students have instructions not to accept gratuities' – a good move against the out-dated practice of tipping.

Spaghetti Western [7/10]

25 High Street, Wimbledon, SW19　map 12
TEL 01-946 7779

Open 11 to 11

Boisterous, family-run pasta bar, which seems to have avoided the malaises of many others – high prices, watery sauces, rubbery pasta – and stuck to its standards. Conventional dishes, like spaghetti carbonara, are well done, and the atmos-phere retains its buzz.

Spago [9/10]

6 Glendower Place, SW7　　　　map 13
TEL 01-225 2407

Open noon to 3, 5.30 to midnight &

Personally run pasta/pizza café, with a loyal following among young expatriate Italians, and a menu that stays successfully within the limits of what it can achieve in a small space. There are a dozen thin, sparsely but spicily topped pizzas (also garlic and rosemary pizza, which passes for garlic bread), and ten pastas which are more varied than usual: seafood in a paper bag; wild mushroom. New additions include more casseroles and, occasionally, mussels. For cold evenings, the soups and Italian sausage dishes are copious.

Sree Krishna [9/10]

194 Tooting High Street, SW17　　map 12
TEL 01-672 4250

Open noon to 3, 6 to 11 (11.45 Fri and Sat) & (also wc)
Closed Christmas Day, Boxing Day

The Sree Krishna has been a landmark for eating out south of the river for many years – inexpensive, over-popular, but offering delicately spiced southern Indian vegetarian cooking to rival all bar the very best. Standard meat and fish curry dishes are lifted by sensitive touches in the kitchen. Look especially for the dosas, fried plantain, avial, and green banana bhaji. As with the cooking, the dining-room is just big enough, simple but comfortable. Drink lassi or ginger beer. Long queues at peak times.

Star [8/10]

22 Great Chapel Street, W1   map 13
TEL 01-437 8778

Open 7 to 5 &
Closed Sat and Sun; Christmas Day and Boxing Day; bank hols

Well named. From seven in the morning, the usual breakfast fry-up is supplemented with rump steak and egg (£4.50), or smoked haddock and two poached eggs (£2.50). Bookings are taken for champagne breakfasts. Lunch has a new Italian dimension of pastas and sauces, perhaps veal with lemon and basil, fruit and cheese, all for £5.50. Also on a good day there may be poached salmon (£4.25) among the roast and vegetables, before the first-class British puddings, like crumbles and trifles.

NEW ENTRY Star Bhel-Poori House [7/10]

17 New Road, E1   map 12
TEL 01-247 0855

Open noon to 3, 6 to 11 & (also wc)

The best bhel-poori house in the East End. Prices are low, quality is high. Good choices from the menu are dahi balle (black-pea fritters with yoghurt and sweet-and-sour sauce, topped with hot spices), dahi balle chat (chickpeas, puris, yoghurt and sauce) and also papri chat with potatoes. Gujerati set meals are better than the standard thali. Also look for the daily specials, such as channa with chapatis for £2.50. Good lassi to drink.

Station Grill [6/10]

Braganza Street, SE17   map 13
TEL 01-735 4769

Open noon to 3, 5 to 10
Closed Sun; Sat L; Christmas; bank hols

Extremely cheap, family-run restaurant with many dishes, like omelettes, around £2, and not much over £4. Everything is maroon, except for the rainbow-coloured seersucker tablecloths. The grille on the window outside is off-putting, but the atmosphere inside is genuine. The menu is a bit of a United Nations, taking in curries, wiener schnitzel and kebabs, but there's not much arguing with rump steak at £3.65.

NEW ENTRY Suruchi [8/10]

18 Theberton Street, N1   map 12
TEL 01-359 8033

Open noon to 3, 6 to 11

One of the smartest new bhel poori houses in London, with airy green décor, bamboo blinds and subdued classical music. It looks more like a French restaurant than an Indian vegetarian café. As well as excellent bhel pooris, the menu has masala dosai, dahi vada, khati (vegetable kebabs), pani poori (crisp wheat balls with a sauce of tamarind and dates), and iddli sambar (steamed rice sponge cakes dipped in spicy sambar). Excellent rasmalai to finish. Good value thalis. Unlicensed, but bring your own (there's a branch of Oddbins fifty yards away). Related to Baba Bhel Poori House (see entry).

Taste of India [7/10]

343 Brighton Road,   map 3
South Croydon
TEL 01-686 8606

Open noon to 2.30 (3 Sat and Sun), 6 to 11.30 (midnight Sat) & (also wc)
Closed Christmas Day and Boxing Day

Abdul Khalique's restaurant continues to be popular with locals. As well as the usual selection of curries, dhansak and tandoori dishes it still has a set menu at £15 for two, which brings king prawns, tandoori lamb chops, karahi gosht, chicken dhansak, vegetable curry and rice, and to finish off kulfi and coffee.

Tea Rooms des Artistes [6/10]

697 Wandsworth Road, SW8   map 12
TEL 01-622 6349

Open 11 to 11
Closed Sun and Mon

The area around Wandsworth Road is now one of the most affluent in south-west London but, regardless, this vegetarian restaurant remains ramshackle. Tables and chairs are rickety, candlewax spills on the tables, the toilets are not among the finest, but it is a characterful place to go for a bottle of wine and some vegetarian staples from a limited menu: one hot dish, a salad, puddings. Portions are priced according to the size of the plate. The music is loud and howls back a decade.

Texas Lone Star [7/10]

154 Gloucester Road, SW7   map 13
TEL 01-370 5625

Open noon to 11.30
Closed Christmas Day

117 Queensway, W2   map 12
TEL 01-727 2980

Open noon to 3, 6.30 to 12.30
Closed Sun; Christmas Day, Boxing Day and 1 Jan

One of the pioneer theme fast-food diners of the late 1970s, and one of the few not owned by Bob Payton. The format is simple: a thick slice of Wild West décor – a statue of a Red Indian greets at the door and country music plays loud – and a menu to match, with chilli hot beans, ribs and burgers. The Queensway branch is smaller, slower and quieter but otherwise identical. A good place for children.

Three Lanterns [7/10]

5 Panton Street, SW1   map 14
TEL 01-839 5031

Open 11.45 to 11 (8.30 Sun and bank hols) &
Closed Christmas Day

A great survivor from the days when cheap food in the West End was synonymous with grills, plates of spaghetti and meat and two veg. Apart from the Cantonese cafés in Chinatown, this busy place serves some of the best-value food within walking distance of Leicester Square. The atmosphere is still that of an old-fashioned continental café, with canteen-style tables; ebullient Italian waiters, and a classic menu of roast beef and Yorkshire pudding, mixed grill, massive freshly made omelettes, goulash with rice and chips, apple pie and custard. Prices are low, the atmosphere irresistible.

Trappers [6/10]

148 Upper Richmond Road, SW15   map 12
TEL 01-788 6324

Open 6pm to 11.30pm (noon to 11.30 Sat and Sun) &
Closed Christmas Day to 28 Dec

London's only Canadian log cabin restaurant might surprise a few trappers with its menu of rogan josh, quiche, and spaghetti bolognese alongside the more home-steading spare ribs, giant T-bone steaks and enormous burgers, topped with everything from garlic mayonnaise to barbecue sauce. The frontier atmosphere goes down well with children, as do sludge pie, banana splits and knockerbocker glory. Daily specials feature on the blackboard. There are six vegetarian dishes. Take-aways, plus a local delivery service.

NEW ENTRY | Triangle [7/10]

23 Richmond Way, W14   map 12
TEL 01-602 5724

Open 11.30 to 3, 5 to 10.30
Closed Christmas Day and Boxing Day

Takes its name from the triangle at the back, overlooked by the more expensive restaurant. The bar snacks, though, are considerably cheaper. Marrows are stuffed with cheese, carrots, mushrooms, courgettes and red pepper; chef's salad is bacon, croûtons, lettuce, radiccio, endive and tomatoes; hot little parcels are stuffed with Boursin cheese; and there are pasta dishes and omelettes. Good wine selection, as the proprietors have an interest in Hurt & Daniel Wines in Surbiton.

Tung Kum [8/10]

205–207 High Street, Croydon   map 3
TEL 01-688 0748

Open noon to 2.30, 5 to 11.30 ᕔ (also WC)
Closed bank hols

Superb cheap lunches are among the highlights in this reliable Cantonese restaurant, now revamped. Less than £3 buys a set lunch. Otherwise, there are good roast meats, and one-plate rice and noodle dishes for an inexpensive feast. The full menu has some unusual specialities, such as cuttlefish in black-bean sauce, and roast chicken in salt.

209 [6/10]

209 Kensington High Street, W8   map 12
TEL 01-937 2260

Open noon to 3, 6 to 10.30

One of the first Thai restaurants in London. There is none of the décor of the newer generation, but some of the inexpensive one-plate meals remain. There is no holding back on the chilli, which fires through the curries and fish dishes. The nam prik sauce has been as powerful as anywhere this side of Bangkok.

Unicorn Café Bar [5/10]

Arts Theatre Basement,   map 14
Great Newport Street, WC2
TEL 01-240 3787

Open 11 to 11 (6 Sun)
Closed most bank hols

The vegetarian canteen attached to the children's theatre provides good-value meals. The salad bar is their pride, but other dishes, like the quiches, falafel and pitta bread are equally worthwhile. Sweets tend to be less zealous. The range of herb teas is supplemented by wines.

Upper Street Fish Shop [9/10]

324 Upper Street, N1   map 13
TEL 01-359 1401

Open 11.30 to 2, 5.30 to 10 ᕔ
Closed Mon L; Sun; 2 weeks at Christmas; bank hols

The queue and the bright red awning pick out north London's premier fish-and-chip shop from Islington's main dragway. The

feel is of a campus café. The walls are papered with posters advertising forthcoming events. Alan Conway stays in front of the friers and his wife Olga serves and chats. Fried fish is the main business, but the range extends to rarer fish, like skate and sea bass, or there is a poached fish of the day. The nursery puddings are among the finest of their kind. Unlicensed.

Valentino's [7/10]

147 Green Lanes, N13   map 12
TEL 01-889 1847

Open noon to 2.30, 6.30 to 11.30
Closed Sun; Mon L; Aug

Named after the film idol, but more of a character actor itself: a trattoria owned and run by the same family for nine years, offering a menu of operatic dimensions, with 35 starters, 30 pasta dishes, 15 steaks. The pasta offers the best value. Variations include Romana with walnuts, garlic and chilli, and fettuccine Cesare with prawns, onions, cream and wine.

NEW ENTRY Vasis [7/10]

80 Cleveland Street, W1   map 13
TEL 01-580 7312

Open noon to 3, 5.30 to midnight
Closed Sat L; Sun in winter; Christmas Day and Boxing Day

A better than average little taverna in the Cleveland Street/Charlotte Street drag of the London Aegean. It is small and compact, with Grecian pictures on the walls and a wine rack that hovers over diners. On the expensive side, but useful in the area, being notable for excellent tsatsiki and taramosalata. Main courses tend to be good variations of classic braised dishes. The real value is in the meze, at £7 for a dozen courses – minimum two people.

Venus Kebab House [7/10]

2 Charlotte Street, W1   map 13
TEL 01-636 4324

Open noon to 3.15, 5.30 to 11.30 ᕔ
Closed Sun; Christmas; bank hols

For more than twenty years the Lemonaris brothers have been serving no-nonsense Greek-Cypriot food in their busy taverna. Their menu is in the old style, a these-you-have-loved mixture of chips, kebabs and braised dishes such as kleftiko and afelia. The special mixed grill is a bargain at £3.90 for kebabs, spicy sausages, smoked pork loin, plus rice and salad. Full meze is about £8 a head. When it's fine, sit at one of the pavement tables with a plate of food and a bottle of retsina.

Veritable Crêperie [7/10]

329 King's Road, SW3   map 13
TEL 01-352 3891

Open noon to midnight
Closed Christmas Day and Boxing Day

London's first and longest-running crêperie. Galettes, made with buckwheat flour, come in twenty recommended variations or with optional extras, right up to caviar and smoked salmon at £3. Crêpes are confined to sweet. The range of ciders matches well.

Victoria & Albert Museum [8/10]

Henry Cole Wing,   map 13
Cromwell Road, SW7
TEL 01-589 6371

Open 10 to 5 (2.30 to 5.30 Sun) & (also WC)
Closed Fri; bank hols

As with viewing the other treasures of the museum, the queue takes a slow pace round the cafeteria, allowing plenty of time to admire the finer points of red and white kidney bean salad; the curve of the cucumber mousse; the slow death of the steak-and-kidney pie on the hot plate. But no, this is not just one of the most handsome dining-rooms of any institutional building – huge arched ceilings, lavishly spaced tables in modern pine to brighten the historic basement – but also serves exemplary canteen food. A choice of teas, mineral waters, beers, English wines; a small selection of good salads; a few hot dishes; plus very good sweets. A seafood bar should be open now. All round, the standard is very high.

La Vida [6/10]

164 Cherry Orchard Road, Croydon   map 3
TEL 01-681 3402

Open 6pm to 10.30pm (11 Fri and Sat) &
Closed Sun and Mon; bank hols

More of a restaurant than many vegetarian venues. The menu changes daily, usually offering five starters, main dishes and as many salads. The ingredients are strictly free range and wholefood, but there are more than one or two nods to more conventional menus, as in borshch, melon with yoghurt and cinnamon, or spaghetti bolognese. Loseley ice-cream to finish.

Villa Estense [7/10]

642 King's Road, SW6   map 12
TEL 01-731 4247

Open 12.30 to 2.30, 7 to 11.30 & (also WC)
Closed Sun; bank hols

On Saturdays and Sundays this most westerly of the big Chelsea trattorias offers special children/family lunches, which can make for a big occasion. The menu doesn't break much new ground, but pasta and pizzas are handled with skill and care; pizzas are especially good. Choose carefully, and the bill need not get out of hand. Better value than its more famous rivals.

Volker Europa [6/10]

18 Orange Street, WC2   map 14
TEL 01-930 8849

Open 11 to 3, 5.30 to 11
Closed Sat and Sun; bank hols; Christmas; Easter

A cramped basement of a wine-cum-sandwich bar. Food and wine are ordered at the bar and brought to the table by pleasant waitresses. No fuss about money until the end, unlike some other wine bars. Huge baked potatoes stuffed with ratatouille or bolognese; decent cheeses, and bacon and salad club sandwiches are at the cheaper end of a menu that otherwise interests itself in the Black Forest, with especially good Germanic sausages. Eight champagnes give the wine list a feeling of class.

Way In Restaurant, Harrods [7/10]

Brompton Road, SW1 map 13
TEL 01-730 1234

Open 10 to 5.30 (6.30 Wed) & (also wc)
Closed Sun; Good Friday and Easter Mon;
Christmas Day and Boxing Day

There are a dozen catering outlets in the store, from juice bar in the food hall, to proper restaurant. The Way In is perhaps the most accessible. The 'express' lift beams you up to the fourth floor where, partitioned off from the men's clothes department, is this café, decorated in high-tech black and white, offering healthy snacks at surprisingly low prices. Main dishes are rarely much above £5. The menu offers Chinese salad with spicy soy sauce; choice of soups; club sandwiches; exotic salads; summer puddings; and there is a selection of cocktails and milk shakes.

Whitechapel Café, Whitechapel Gallery [6/10]

80 Whitechapel High Street, E1 map 12
TEL 01-377 6182

Open 11 to 4.30 (6.30 Wed) & (also wc)
Closed bank hols

A simple, unadorned part of the gallery is given over to an essentially, but not exclusively, vegetarian café, open through the day for coffee and bakery, as well as for hot and cold dishes at lunch-time. The style is baked potatoes, hummus, hot stuffed filo pastries, chocolate cake, and treacle tart, all cheerful home cooking, well presented. If you are not visiting the art gallery there is an entrance through a small archway, just beyond the main entrance. It is signposted, but a far larger sign, 'Ahmed Fashions', marks the spot.

White Swan [6/10]

Riverside, Twickenham map 12
TEL 01-892 2166

Open for food noon to 3, 6 to 11

The blackboard menu at this lovely riverside pub is revealed, quite dramatically, about one o'clock, adding good hot pub dishes like soups, roast beef, or bubble and squeak to the repertoire of sandwiches available the rest of the day and in the evening. Well discovered, largely because of its fine location.

Wilkins [6/10]

61 Marsham Street, SW1 map 13
TEL 01-222 4038

Open 8 to 5 &
Closed Sat and Sun; bank hols

A few doors down from the Department of Environment is this small vegetarian restaurant with mandatory pine tables and chairs, wooden floor and white walls. Burners keep the soups hot; casseroles are filled with high-fibre beans; and the good quiches have, of course, wholemeal bases. The short menu comes into its own with the sweets, which are as numerous as all other courses put together. No smoking. Take-aways are available, but the shop three doors down sells baps too.

Windmill [7/10]

486 Fulham Road, SW6 map 13
TEL 01-385 1570

Open noon (7 Sun) to 11 &
Closed bank hols; 1 week at Christmas

The zealous 1960s image that characterised the Windmill has been traded in during expansion, and the restaurant is considerably smarter than before. The cooking is some of the healthiest in London, and more and more use is made of organics, even for wines, now a licence has been granted. Soups, salads, good bakes are a cut above average. Prices are commendably pegged around £5.

Windmill Fish Bar [6/10]

211 Kennington Lane, SE11 map 13
TEL 01-582 5754

Open 11.30 to 2.30, 5 to midnight
Closed Sun

The local gentrification means that this fish bar, with its inelegant exterior, is surrounded by three antique shops. But this is the bargain of the lot, a genuine old-fashioned chippie. Cod, skate and plaice

are fried on and off the bone for around
£1.50. Chips are real potatoes, fried twice.

Wine Gallery [8/10]

232 Brompton Road, SW3   map 13
TEL 01-584 3493
49 Hollywood Road, SW10   map 12
TEL 01-352 7572
294 Westbourne Grove, W11   map 12
TEL 01-229 1877

Open noon to 3 (2.30 Sun), 7 to midnight (11
Sun) &
Closed Christmas Day and Boxing Day

This trio of elegant wine bars, spawned by
the more expensive Brinkley's restaurant,
run an imaginative modern British menu
that shames many a more expensive
venue. The choice can run up to three
dozen dishes, from old-fashioned kedgeree
to picturesque timbale of scallops with
lobster sauce. Very little is over £4. The
atmosphere in each is English pastels,
stripped pine and watercolours. The wine
lists are equally intelligently assembled,
with an eye for value at around £6, even if
the wines are rather cheaper at their off-
licence by the Hollywood Road branch.

Wong Kei [9/10]

41–43 Wardour Street, W1   map 14
TEL 01-437 3071/6833

Open noon to 11.30 & (also WC)
Closed Christmas Day

It is cash only in this spacious Cantonese
eating house. The average customer
spends only £4, because this is one of the
best examples of Chinese cheap eating.
Through four floors, lifts deliver a range of
125 dishes. The soups, like bean curd, or
pork and pickled vegetable (70p), and the
rice dishes, with crispy pork or roast duck
and chicken (£1.80), are the truly
inexpensive items. Look also for the
noodle and congee dishes. The quality of
the meat can be judged in the window. The
cooking rivals most in Chinatown.

Woodlands [7/10]

37 Panton Street, W1   map 14
TEL 01-839 7258

77 Marylebone Lane, W1   map 13
TEL 01-486 3862
402a Wembley High Road,   map 12
Wembley
TEL 01-902 9869

Open noon to 3, 6 to 11 &
Closed Christmas Day and Boxing Day

The point about Woodlands is the décor.
These three restaurants have a style that is
not the usual backdrop for South Indian
vegetarian food in London. The
Marylebone Lane branch is cool and
modish; Panton Street looks classical in
pink; Wembley is different again. With a
12.5 per cent service charge, the bill can
easily slip into double figures, although
the cheap 'express thali' provides a quick
lunch for £6. The cook works best with
classic dosas, iddlys and uthappan, rather
than curries and rice.

Yerakina [8/10]

10 Kentish Town Road, NW1   map 12
TEL 01-485 5743

Open noon to 3, 6 to midnight & (also WC)
Closed Sun

'Eat when hungry, sleep when tired', says
the legend on the menu. This has quickly
established itself as one of the best-value
Greek/Cypriot places. The meze, at £8 a
head, is extraordinary value for thirty
dishes, but it is possible to pick fewer
dishes and eat less expensively. Afelia and
moussaka are generous, individual starters
of taramosalata or hummus, piquant.

NEW ENTRY Zamoyski's [8/10]

85 Fleet Road, NW3   map 12
TEL 01-794 4792

Open noon to 3 (2 Sun), 5.30 to 11 (10.30 Sun) &
Closed Christmas Day, Boxing Day and 1 Jan

Middle European wine bar-cum-
restaurant, with some excellent, varied
traditional Polish dishes: salt beef,
borshch, stuffed cabbage, bigos. The soups
are particularly good and varied, from wild
mushroom to nettle, to cucumber.
Vegetarians and kosher diets are catered
for. Jazz on Wednesdays, gypsy music on
Fridays.

London's Chinatown

London's Chinatown – an area of Soho taking in Gerrard Street, Lisle Street and part of Wardour Street – offers some of the best-value food in the capital. It has also developed into a full-blown tourist attraction with street festivals, colourful decorations and even oriental-style telephone boxes.

For more than twenty years this neighbourhood has been dominated by old-style Cantonese cooking, although the more fashionable Pekingese and Szechuan styles are beginning to make an impact. For cheap eating there are dim-sum snacks, excellent one-plate rice and noodle dishes, and in many of the cafés it's possible to have two or even three courses for under £10.

Chinatown is almost exclusively Chinese, but there are one or two exceptions. Pho (see main entry), virtually on the corner of Lisle Street and Wardour Street, is an excellent Vietnamese café serving good soups, snacks and noodles. There's also a small take-away next door, offering a few Vietnamese dishes alongside more recognisable Chinese ones.

1 Jade Garden
15 Wardour Street.
Smart, spacious Cantonese restaurant serving dim-sum. Well-favoured by local Chinese.

2 Chuen Cheng Ku
17 Wardour Street.
Enormous Cantonese emporium serving some of the best dim-sum in Chinatown, as well as some of the cheapest lobster in London (£7 to £8). (See entry.)

3 Kai Kee
19 Wardour Street.
Small café noted for its one-plate rice and noodle dishes. Roast meats hang in the window.

4 Super Cake Shop
21 Wardour Street.
Brilliant range of oriental buns and confectionery. Look for the buns with savoury fillings.

5 Yungs
23 Wardour Street.
Excellent Cantonese restaurant strong on fish. Open later than most of its rivals.

6 Welcome Supermarket
32 Wardour Street.
Less dynamic than some other supermarkets in the neighbourhood, but a useful source of tinned and dried goods.

7 Wong Kei
41 Wardour Street.
Some of the cheapest and fastest Cantonese food in Chinatown. Go for the soups, noodles and rice dishes. (See entry.)

8 Mr Tang
61–63 Shaftesbury Avenue.
Favoured by tourists and members of the Chinese Embassy. Go for the dim-sum, which are ordered from the menu. Other meals can be more expensive. (See entry.)

9 Mayflower
68 Shaftesbury Avenue.
Directly opposite Mr Tang (see above). Serves a wide-ranging menu of authentic Cantonese dishes. Local Chinese seem to receive better treatment than passing Westerners.

10 Chinatown
30 Wardour Street.
Smarter and more elegant than most other restaurants in the neighbourhood. The name suggests a high profile, but it doesn't yet pose a threat to Yung's across the road. Good-value one-plate meals.

11 London Chinatown
27 Wardour Street.
Not related to its next-door neighbour (see No. 10), but connected with the famous Maxim's chain. Fish is good, portions are generous and there's a good range of

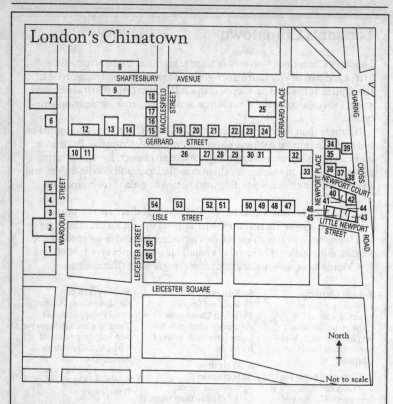

London's Chinatown

Not to scale

dim-sum and one-plate
meals. It doesn't quite
live up to its glittering
heritage.

12 Kowloon
21 Gerrard Street.
The left-hand side is
dominated by the bakery
selling excellent buns and
cakes to eat in or take
away; the right is a cheap
restaurant. (See entry.)

13 Tai Ko Lok
18 Gerrard Street.
Straightforward
Cantonese restaurant
with a good display of
meats in the window.
One-plate meals and
soups are up to the mark.

14 Lee Ho Fook
15 Gerrard Street.
Interesting because it pre-
dates many of its
neighbours. Go for the
roast pork and duck;
there's also a display of
cakes in the windows. Big
portions, low prices.

15 Dumpling Inn
15A Gerrard Street.
Small, westernised
restaurant featuring
Pekingese food. Peking-
style, crescent-shaped
dumplings are the
speciality.

16 Sun Luck
2 Macclesfield Street.
Small restaurant on the

fringes of Chinatown.
Useful because it stays
open late.

17 Lee Ho Fook
4 Macclesfield Street.
Related to No. 14. An
impressive array of roast
meats hangs in the
window. A sign says
that soup is free as long
as it lasts.

18 Furama
5 Macclesfield Street.
The restaurant is on the
edge of Chinatown, the
style is westernised and it
seems to cater for stray
custom.

19 Far East
13 Gerrard Street.
An excellent bun shop.

20 Super
11 Gerrard Street.
Another good bun shop.

21 Fook Lam Moon
10 Gerrard Street.
A long-standing, reliable
Cantonese restaurant.

22 Mandarin
8 Gerrard Street.
One of the few rest-
aurants in Chinatown
specialising in Pekingese
food, with the intention
of attracting western
customers unused to the
potency of Cantonese
cooking.

23 Dragon Gate
7 Gerrard Street.
Chinatown's original
Szechuan restaurant has
lost some of its style and
individuality since the
old team moved to the
Si Chuen in Old
Compton Street.

24 Lok Ho Fook
4 Gerrard Street.
A cool, calm dining-room
serving an interesting
range of savoury and
sweet dim-sum, as well as
plenty of one-plate rice
and noodle dishes.

25 New World
1 Gerrard Place.
One of the biggest
restaurants in the area,
with one of the longest
menus in Chinatown.
This vast 700-seater
emporium serves the best
dim-sum in the
neighbourhood. (See
entry.)

26 Loon Fung
37 Gerrard Street.
Another emporium-sized
restaurant with a long,
complex menu. Much
favoured by local
Chinese.

27 Phoenix
39 Gerrard Street.
Genuine Cantonese take-
away, with all kinds of
meats in the window and
a battery of canteen-style
basins of noodles, rice and
vegetables. (See entry.)

28 Luxuriance Peking
40 Gerrard Street.
As its name suggests this
is a smart, flashy Pek-
ingese restaurant that
looks out of place sand-
wiched between a Can-
tonese take-away and a
Cantonese late-night café.

29 Lido
41 Gerrard Street.
Excellent Cantonese café
open until the small
hours. Basic, cheap and
very popular. Much of the
cooking is done in the
window, and it's worth
watching. (See entry.)

30 Loon Fung Supermarket
31 Gerrard Street.
A superb selection of
oriental foodstuffs from
teas to dried fish to fresh
fruit and vegetables.

31 New Loon Fung
31 Gerrard Street.
Situated above the
supermarket, this
elegantly decorated
restaurant has a menu
that spans Cantonese,
Pekingese and Szechuan
cooking, and there are
three pages of seafood
specialities.

32 Friendly Inn
47 Gerrard Street.
The name and the décor
are westernised, but this
is a useful, well-
established Cantonese
with a short, inexpensive
menu. Less frantic than
some of its neighbours.

33 Canton
11 Newport Place.
Re-camped café with the
longest opening hours in
Chinatown. It never
closes. Good for soups,
hot-pots and one-plate
meals. (See entry.)

34 Golden Gate
16 Newport Place.
Related to the excellent
provisions shop in Lisle
Street (see No. 54), with a
similar range.

35 Chinatown Fish & Meat Market
14 Newport Place.
Second only to Richards
in Brewer Street for its
excellent range of fresh
fish. Look for live
lobsters, eels, carp and
exotica.

36 Sunki Mini Market
Newport Court.
Part of the flashy new
Chinatown complex.
Excellent for fresh fruit
and vegetables.

37 Hop Hing Hong
33 Newport Court.
Tiny Chinese
supermarket.

38 The Garden
37 Newport Court.
Part westernised snack
bar, part Chinese bun
shop. A curious cultural
hotch-potch.

39 Man Poh
59 Charing Cross Road.

Claims to sell some of the cheapest Chinese food in the UK. Attracts all kinds of tourists, but few Chinese, who prefer to pay a few pennies more just round the corner.

40 Sunki Mini Market
Newport Court.
A branch of No. 36 across the Court.

41 Sun Luen Café
24A Newport Court.
Small café serving good cakes and buns, bowls of bean curd and cups of tea.

42 Happy Garden
47 Charing Cross Road.
Close to Leicester Square tube station, this is the signpost to Chinatown for passing tourists. Good displays of roast meats in the window.

43 Hong Ning
15 Little Newport Street.
Small pharmacy specialising in Chinese medicinal herbs.

44 Sun Luen Snack Bar
14 Little Newport Street.
Tiny café with a Coca-Cola sign, related to No. 41. Useful for tea and buns Chinese-style.

45 Shing Wo
12 Little Newport Street.
A small supermarket.

46 Good Food
10 Little Newport Street.
One of the smart new additions to Chinatown, set in three cramped

rooms. Chinese come for the hand-made noodles and old-style Cantonese one-plate meals; Westerners seem to prefer the more fashionable Pekingese specialities.

47 Poons
27 Lisle Street.
The original café is the cheapest of the Poons mini-empire: it offers the famous wind-dried specialities and other dishes for a much smaller outlay than the Covent Garden branch. (See entry.)

48 Man Lee Hong
26 Lisle Street.
Like the Man Poh (see No. 39), this makes great claims about its cheapness. Very popular, despite the local competition.

49 Chan Mai May
25 Lisle Street.
Slightly smarter and more expensive than its next-door neighbour. Standard range.

50 Po Sau Tang
24 Lisle Street.
Herbalist and pharmacy.

51 Mr Kong
22 Lisle Street.
Seeks to emulate the style and flashiness of Fung Shing (see No. 53), but lacks the consistency. The menu is long and intriguing, and full meals are likely to be well into double figures.

52 See Woo
18 Lisle Street.
Arguably the best Chinese supermarket in the neighbourhood, with a vast display of staples and rarities.

53 Fung Shing
15 Lisle Street.
Rated as the best and most consistent Cantonese restaurant in Chinatown. The décor is green and elegant; the bill is likely to be around £15 a head with drinks.

54 Golden Gate
Lisle Street.
Smaller than the See Woo (No. 52) but just as enterprising. It packs a brilliant display of edibles into a small space. Look for the bean curd and live shellfish.

55 Joy King Lau
3 Leicester Street.
Despite the expensive westernised look, it is possible to eat cheaply here by staying with the one-plate meals. Dim-sum are ordered from the main menu and appear ready-plated.

56 Poons
4 Leicester Street.
More upmarket than the Lisle Street original (see No. 47), but less pretentious than the Covent Garden branch. Very popular and on the tourist trail. Excellent wind-dried meats and authentic Cantonese specialities. (See entry.)

London – Drummond Street

Drummond Street is slightly shabby and prone to bouts of development, but for more than thirty years it has been one of the most concentrated centres of Indian food in London. In the space of two hundred yards there is virtually every type of outlet, from video shops, Islamic book centres and halal butchers to modish new vegetarian restaurants and paan shops.

Many of the local businesses are entrenched: Universal Halal opened in 1959; the Ambala Sweet Centre started trading in 1965. Even more historic was the Shah Restaurant at 124 Drummond Street, which opened in 1951 and was one of the very first Indian restaurants in the capital. Its death in 1987 marked the end of an era. Ironically its place has been taken by Chutneys – a stylish, monochromatic Indian vegetarian restaurant that is very much in tune with the mood of the 1980s.

1 Anglo-Asian Food Supermarket
115–117 Drummond Street.
As the name suggests, this supermarket stocks a wide range of European and Indian produce. Good range of pickles, spices and pulses, plus a small selection of fruit and vegetables. Producers and suppliers of vegetarian curd cheese from the Asian Paneer Company.

2 Viniron Traders
119 Drummond Street. Known affectionately as the Patak shop, as it stocks the full range of Patak's pickles, spices and condiments. Also sells Bombay mix and other snacks, chapati flour, karahi dishes and Indian cooking utensils plus a brilliant selection of specially packed spices. Outside there's a fine choice of fresh fenugreek, coriander, tinda, valor and other exotic fruit and vegetables.

3 Diwana Bhel Poori
121 Drummond Street. Small, spartan café which did much to popularise Indian vegetarian food in the 1970s. (See entry.)

4 Raavi Kebab Tandoori Restaurant
125 Drummond Street. Basic café with a few pine tables and a big charcoal grill. Not much used by Westerners.

5 Savera Bakery
129 Drummond Street. Produces all kinds of breads, snacks, jeera biscuits and the like. A sign says that only vegetable fats are used in the baking. There is a branch at 155 Cannon Street Road, EC1.

6 Ravi Shankar (Bhel Poori House)
133–135 Drummond Street.
Popular rival to the Diwana Bhel Poori Houses. The Indian vegetarian food is authentic, the atmosphere is calm. (See entry.)

7 Ali & Son
134 Drummond Street. Grocers with a superb selection of exotic fruits, vegetables, herbs and nuts – from fresh dates to cassava to taro. Also stocks halal meat and fish.

8 Chutneys
124 Drummond Street. Fashionable new Indian vegetarian restaurant on the site of the legendary Shah. The décor is cool and monochromatic, the style is elegant and the food good value. At lunchtime there's a twelve-dish buffet for £3.50. Early reports suggest that this could be the new front-runner for Indian vegetarian food in the neighbourhood.

9 Universal Halal
122 Drummond Street. Advertises 'Fresh Meat, Tropical Fish'. The meat is impressively displayed. There's also a useful selection of fruit and vegetables. Established in 1959.

10 Diwana Bhel Poori
114 Drummond Street. A branch of the well-known Indian vegetarian cafés (see No. 3 and entry).

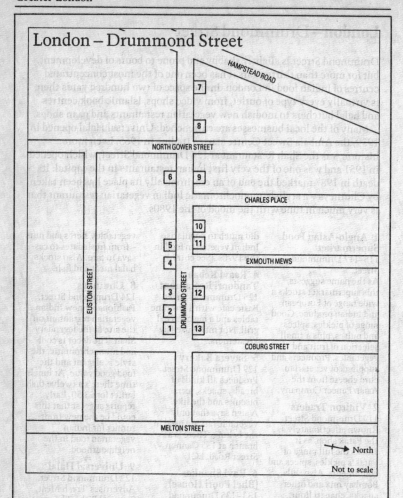

London – Drummond Street

HAMPSTEAD ROAD

7

8

NORTH GOWER STREET

6   9

CHARLES PLACE

10

5   11

4

EXMOUTH MEWS

EUSTON STREET

DRUMMOND STREET

3   12

2

1   13

COBURG STREET

MELTON STREET

→ North

Not to scale

11 Ambala Sweet Centre

110 Drummond Street. Starting trading in 1965 and now has branches in most towns and cities with sizeable Asian communities. This shop is the flagship, serving an impressive array of sweetmeats, as well as savoury snacks such as samosas and pakoras.

12 Gupta Confectioners

100 Drummond Street. Good snack and sweet take-away. Look for the pea rolls, pakoras, kachori and samosas, as well as the standard range of barfi.

13 Nature's Delight

96 Drummond Street. Describes itself as a 'Fresh Fruit Juice & Paan Centre'. Serves all kinds of fresh fruit drinks made from green coconut, water melon, sugar cane, lime, mango and much more. Also little parcels of spices, pulses and pastes, wrapped in paan leaves. At weekends there are often vegetarian hot dishes, too. Take away or stand at the little counter.

London – Southall

Southall has two main centres, divided by the Western Region line and Southall railway station. Turn left out of the station and you come to The Green and 'old Southall'. Turn right and you head towards South Road and The Broadway – the bustling focus of daily life in the neighbourhood. The area is full of grocers and supermarkets, travel agents advertising flights to India, saree shops, Asian video shops and lots of cafés, which are as much local meeting places as eating places. One or two of the restaurants – notably the Brilliant and the Maharajah – have moved deliberately upmarket, but this is a token gesture. Most of the cafés cater almost exclusively for the local Asian community and make no compromises to western tastes or western ideas of what a local Indian eating place should be. But they are friendly places, despite the culture gap, and the food they offer is very good value.

1 Butt Tandoori & Sweet Centre
10 High Street.
The range of sweetmeats has been increased, otherwise this small Formica and neon café/take-away serves a limited menu of curries and tandooris.

2 Chaat House
12 The Broadway.
Small, brick-walled café better known for its sweetmeats than savoury snacks – which goes against the local trend.

3 Harshidh Sweetmart
36A The Broadway.
One of the smallest, but one of the best specialist sweetmarts in the neighbourhood.

4 Best Fruit Fare
77 The Broadway.

5 Fruit of Paradise
79 The Broadway.

6 Southall Fruiterers
83 The Broadway.
Three fruit and vegetable shops almost in a row. Produce is displayed on

trestle tables spilling out on to the pavement. Excellent seasonal range.

7 Ambala Sweet Centre
89 The Broadway.
Modern-looking sweetmeat shop with an attractive display.

8 Tandoori Express at Jalebi Junction
93 The Broadway.
The trendy modern frontage in fluorescent pink leads to a promising café. Outside catering facilities available.

9 Royal Bombay Halwa
92 The Broadway.
Supplies the best Indian sweetmeats in the area. Excellent barfi, halvas, rasmalai and so on are made on the premises and attractively displayed. Tangy fruit-flavoured kulfi can be bought in cones.

10 Moti Mahal
94 The Broadway.
One of the faster-food cafés; Southall's version of MacDonalds and

Broomfields rolled into one. (See entry.)

11 Sweet
106 The Broadway.
Back-to-basics vegetarian café.

12 Gifto Cash & Carry
117–119 The Broadway.
Large general grocer/supermarket with big packs of spices, pulses and other dry goods.

13 Punjabee
118 The Broadway.
Tandoori, sweetmeat and chaat centre.

14 Sira Cash & Carry
128 The Broadway.
Largest specialist grocer's in the area, with a superb range of rice, pulses and spices, as well as fresh fruit and vegetables.

15 Dokal & Sons
133–135 The Broadway.
Similar to the Sira (No 14) and just across the road.

16 Sweet & Tandoori Centre
155 The Broadway.
Excellent modern café with a good range of

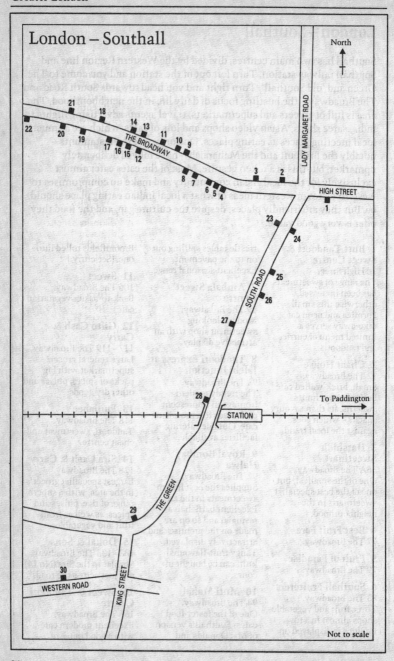

London – Southall

North

LADY MARGARET ROAD

THE BROADWAY

21
18
14
13
11
22
20
19
17 16 15 12
10 9
8 7 6 5 4
3 2

HIGH STREET

23
24
25
26
27
28

SOUTH ROAD

To Paddington

STATION

THE GREEN

29

30

WESTERN ROAD

KING STREET

Not to scale

sweetmeats and savouries. A large curry is £1.75.

17 Asian Tandoori Centre
157 The Broadway.
A new café on the site of Sagoo & Takhar (sister restaurant of the Roxy). Sagoo will be missed, but new owners offer a similar range of sweetmeats, curries and tandooris.

18 Babu
156 The Broadway.
Popular café and take-away. (See entry.)

19 Tandoor Kebab Centre
163 The Broadway.
Standard café with the standard range of sweet and savoury snacks.

20 Maharajah
171–175 The Broadway.
The staff boast that Mrs Gandhi ate here. It is one of the few restaurants in Southall that has moved deliberately upmarket. Prices are higher than at most of its neighbours and there is some compromising to western tastes, but dishes such as

butter chicken and jeera chicken are excellent. The nearest rival to the Brilliant (see No. 30).

21 Centre Point
166 The Broadway.
The best place to buy enormous pots, pans and hardware for authentic Indian home cooking.

22 Shahee Tandoori
241 The Broadway.
A mini-version of the Maharajah (see No. 20), with smart décor and pink tablecloths. Stands on its own.

23 Kwality
16 South Road.
Another good basic café serving sweet and savoury snacks.

24 Shaharisha
17 South Road.
Calls itself a restaurant, but is really a small café serving vegetarian snacks and sweetmeats to eat in or take-away.

25 Madhu's Brilliant
39 South Road.
Smartly decorated restaurant, not to be confused with the Brilliant (see No. 30).

26 Sira
43 South Road.
Branch of the big cash and carry grocers (see No. 14).

27 Bharat
80 South Road.
The nearest tandoori and sweet centre to the station. Useful and reliable.

28 Shahi Nan Kebab
South Road.
An extraordinary little hut built out on brackets over the side of the massive railway bridge. It is one of the tiniest fast food kiosks in the country with just room for a cold drinks cabinet and marinated meats on skewers – which are char-grilled at the back.

29 Roxy
114 The Green.
Otherwise known as Sagoo & Takhar, this is Southall's most famous café. (See entry.)

30 Brilliant
72–74 Western Road.
The best of Southall's restaurants. Upmarket, but still good value. (See entry.)

85

London – Stoke Newington

The area of N1 and N16, around Stoke Newington, Dalston Green and Newington Green, is the centre of London's Turkish community. Like Southall it has developed into a genuine neighbourhood that has not only cafés and restaurants, but solicitors, games parlours, video rentals, photographers and coffee-shops. Most of the grocers specialise in Turkish produce and even non-Turkish take-aways sell doner kebabs. The influence also appears in Chas and Dave's staunchly English pub in Green Lanes, which is known for its Turkish belly-dancers as well as its Cockney sing-songs.

Most of the local eating places are cheap and informal. For a proper evening out in upmarket surroundings, there are central London restaurants, such as Efes Kebab House.

1 Hodja Nasreddin
53 Newington Green Road.
Tiny, atmospheric, family-run restaurant open till the small hours. (See entry.)

2 Kofteci Vedat Kebab House 69 Newington Green Road.
Small café with a very limited menu comprising about five meze and four different kofte and shish kebabs.

3 Kayseri Ltd
47 Newington Green.
An excellent delicatessen specialising in sucuk (spicy sausage), pasturma (cured beef) and lokum (Turkish delight), all made on the premises. There are freshly made dips, such as hummus and taramosalata, sweet and savoury pastries, Turkish cheeses and tinned products. Also look for lahmacun – a spicy, thin-based mincemeat pizza eaten rolled up. Open long hours, seven days a week.

4 Mamara Kiraathanes
19 Green Lanes.
Small café serving good Turkish casseroles and kebabs.

5 Kuzey Kebab House
29–31 Green Lanes.
Spacious licensed restaurant with a long, wide-ranging menu. Excellent spicy sausages and kebabs. Also chips if you want them, and Turkish vegetarian specialities.

6 01 Adana Kebab
Green Lanes.
Very popular café with about half a dozen tables. Packed every lunch-time, which is a good sign.

7 Meric Kebab House
74 Green Lanes.
A Formica-dominated kebab house with a good range of spicy meats and kebabs.

8 Katives Lokanta
76 Green Lanes.
Small café with pinewood décor. An upmarket version of its next-door neighbour, the Meric.

9 Manor Farm Bakery
108 Green Lanes.
Superb bakery with a full range of Turkish breads, sweetened breads, salt biscuits, sesame rings and gateaux.

10 Mola Taverna
72 Stamford Hill.
Very comfortable restaurant and take-away with an attractive menu of meze and kebabs. Licensed and increasingly popular with local Turks looking for a quiet evening out.

11 Best Turkish Kebab 125 Stoke Newington Road.
High street Turkish take-away.

12 Yesil Ada Stores
115A Stoke Newington Road.
Good general food store with some interesting East Mediterranean produce, such as fresh olives in season, plus everything for genuine Turkish home cooking.

13 Birol's Grill & Kebab Bar 69 Stoke Newington Road.
Large corner restaurant and take-away specialising in Turkish grilled meats.

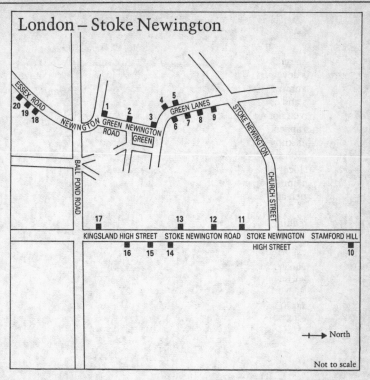

London – Stoke Newington

14 New Crazy Horse Steak & Kebab House
50 Stoke Newington Road.
Despite the anglicised name, this restaurant and take-away offers a good range of Middle Eastern specialities, meze, chicken and lamb kebabs, and Turkish pastries on a small menu.

15 Samsun
34 Stoke Newington Road.
Rated as the best Turkish café in Stoke Newington. (See entry.)

16 Ali Baba Kebab House 144 Kingsland High Street.
Licensed restaurant and take-away.

17 Turkish Food Market 109 Kingsland High Street.
A small food market, but good and well-stocked.

18 Guzelgun
332 Essex Road.
A café with multi-coloured lighting and plenty of red plastic. The atmosphere is lively, the menu has interesting meze and there is live music Monday to Thursday.

19 Lezzet Lokanta
330 Essex Road.
The best Turkish restaurant on the block.

The enormous menu spans classic Turkish, Middle Eastern, Central Asian and – surprisingly – Italian. The meze list is impressive, chicken and lamb doners are first-rate and there are a few pizzas for good measure. The house speciality is 'manti' – a Central Asian version of ravioli, brought to Anatolia by the Turkish hordes a thousand years ago.

20 Sultanahmet
326 Essex Road.
Very basic, slightly shabby kebab house that is rather overshadowed by its more illustrious neighbours.

South West

Avon

Cornwall

Devon

Gloucestershire

Somerset

ARLINGTON Devon   map 1

Arlington Court [6/10]

TEL Shirwell (027 182) 296

Open 11 to 6 & (also wc)
Closed Sat; Nov to Easter

Good-value, all-day restaurant in a
National Trust property. For lunch there
are home-made soups, salad rolls, and
casseroles, plus generous ploughman's
with big hunks of mature Cheddar.
Afternoon tea is scones and home-baked
cakes with lashings of clotted cream and
cherry jam. Pots of tea or local cider to
drink.

ASHCOTT Somerset   map 1

Ashcott Inn [6/10]

50 Bath Road
TEL Ashcott (0458) 210282

Open for food 11.30 to 2.30, 6 to 10 (noon to 1.30,
7 to 9.30 Sun) &

New owners continue to put the emphasis
on food in this roadside pub not far from
the M5. The delicatessen cold table is a
major attraction, otherwise the menu
ranges from home-made pâté and
ploughman's to ratatouille, ham and eggs,
and moussaka. There are also char-grilled
steaks and plenty of sweets. Darts, shove-
ha'penny and a skittle alley in the bar;
swings and a slide in the garden. Beers
from Flowers, Butcombe and Eldridge
Pope.

AUST Avon   map 2

Boar's Head [6/10]

Main Road
TEL Pilning (045 45) 2278

Open for food noon to 2, 7.30 to 9.45 & (also wc)
Closed Sun

This out-of-the-way pub is close to the M4
in a village that sits virtually under the
Severn Bridge. The Broomes don't serve
chips. Instead they offer bowls of home-
made soup, potato, cheese and onion hot-
pot, and steak in French bread, as well as
sandwiches, ploughman's, and omelettes.
The cold buffet is a big attraction with its

assortment of pies, cheeses, roast joints,
and seafood backed up by a huge range of
salads. More expensive formal meals.
Courage beers.

AWRE Gloucestershire   map 4

Red Hart Inn [6/10]

TEL Dean (0594) 510220

Open for food noon to 2, 7 to 10 & (also wc)
Closed Mon L (exc bank hols)

As a sign of the times, this village pub now
has a complete vegetarian menu, with
dishes such as chilli-bean pâté, red cabbage
ragout, and lentils provençale. At the other
extreme there are good-value three-course
meals with an eight-ounce rump steak as
the centrepiece. Other bar snacks range
from ploughman's to home-made pies and
curries. Sunday roasts are £5.45 for three
courses. More expensive restaurant menu.
Beers include local brews.

BARNSTAPLE Devon   map 1

Heavens Above [7/10]

4 Bear Street
TEL Barnstaple (0271) 77960

Open 10 to 3
Closed Sun; bank hols; Christmas and New Year

Every town should have a little vegetarian
restaurant like this. The style couldn't be
simpler: a short menu of dishes prepared
from fresh ingredients, served in a setting
of paintings and fresh flowers. Pizzas,
quiches, rice loaf, or cashewnut rissole,
can be eaten with interesting salads, and a
one-dish lunch will leave change from £2.
Sweets range from bread pudding and fruit
flapjacks to real ice-creams and halva.
Cider comes from Hancocks of South
Molton; the coffee is from Nicaragua –
otherwise try the home-made lemonade or
banana lassi. Take-aways.

Lynwood House [7/10]

Bishops Tawton Road
TEL Barnstaple (0271) 43695

Open noon to 2, 7 to 10 &

This is a family business. Mrs Roberts and
one son do the cooking; Mr Roberts and

son number two run the bar and restaurant. Cheap, bistro-style meals are served downstairs from a menu dominated by fish: fresh Taw salmon mayonnaise, lobster salad, mousse of lemon sole, and sauté of prawns, as well as fish soup. There's also a daily pasta dish, plus burgers, omelettes, and steak sandwiches. More expensive restaurant meals. 'Executive' take-aways available.

BATH Avon   map 2

Huckleberry's [6/10]

34 Broad Street
TEL Bath (0225) 64876

Open 9 to 9.15
Closed Sun; Christmas Day

A wholefood coffee-house serving good-value vegetarian dishes throughout the day. Breakfasts are things on toast or muesli; lunches and high teas take in healthy soups, quiches, savoury bakes, and crumbles, as well as curries and casseroles. A full plate of salad is £2.75. During the evening there are more formal meals upstairs with an international flavour. Wine by the glass.

Moon and Sixpence [8/10]

6A Broad Street
TEL Bath (0225) 60962

Open noon to 2.30 (2 Sun), 5.30 to 10.30 (11 Fri and Sat) &
Closed Christmas Day, Boxing Day and 1 Jan

Go at lunch-time for cheap eating. The converted post office is a casual, crowded bistro during the day, with an excellent buffet of cold meats, terrines, and salads. A three-course lunch in the upstairs restaurant can be had for £10, when the menu features dishes such as a warm salad of chicken livers with Marsala sauce, and fillet of monkfish with green peppercorn sauce. Sunday brunch is kedgeree and Bucks Fizz. Coffee is good and so are the wines.

Pasta Galore [7/10]

31 Barton Street
TEL Bath (0225) 63861

Open noon to 2.30, 6 to 10.30 (11 Thur to Sat) &
Closed Sun

The best place for fresh pasta in Bath. The tagliatelle, linguine, pappardelle and spirale are made daily at the shop around the corner in Broad Street, and served with authentic sauces – pesto genovese, marinara, bolognese, amatriciana. To start there's bresaola, Mozzarella with fresh tomatoes, or crostini. To finish there are Italian cakes, ice-creams and sorbets. Tables outside in good weather. Interesting Italian wines.

Pump Room [7/10]

Stall Street
TEL Bath (0225) 444477/444488

Open 10 to 5 & (also WC)
Closed Christmas Day and Boxing Day

Most restaurateurs would give their right arm for a dining-room impressively laid out under the great dome of the historic Pump Room, with tables overlooking the Roman baths. The Four Seasons restaurant has closed and now all meals are served under the one roof. Through the day there are cakes and pastries, including Bath buns and Sally Lunns, afternoon teas include scones and clotted cream or gentleman's relish, and chocolate cake, and there is a full range of lunch-time food, taking in soups, salads, cold cuts, and hot dishes. English cheese is served with Bath biscuits. Wine by the glass as well as home-made orange and lemon squash.

Sally Lunn's [6/10]

4 North Parade Passage
TEL Bath (0225) 61634

Open 10 (noon Sun) to 6

Sally Lunn came to this bakehouse in 1680 and started making her famous confections for the local townspeople. Today, they come topped with smoked salmon pâté, chilli or vegan vegetable curry. There are also salad versions with goats' cheese or turkey breast, and sweet ones with jam, clotted cream or cinnamon butter. Blended tea, fresh ground coffee and wine by the glass. The house is also a museum.

NEW ENTRY | Tarts [7/10]

8 Pierrepoint Place
TEL Bath (0225) 330280/330201

Open noon to 2.30, 7 to 10.30
Closed Sun; Christmas Day, Boxing Day
and 1 Jan

This unpretentious cellar restaurant is in a listed Georgian building, once the home of Lady Hamilton. Lord Nelson lived across the road, and there's an underground passage connecting the two houses. Lunch is flexible and it's possible to have as much or as little as you like. Go for the specials, such as stir-fried chicken and Chinese vegetables, lamb cutlets with mint hollandaise, or poached brill in brandy and crab sauce. Savoury pancakes are popular, too. Alcoholic home-made ice-creams to finish. Full evening meals are more expensive. House wines by the glass.

BISHOPS LYDEARD
Somerset   map 1

NEW ENTRY | Kingfishers Catch [6/10]

Taunton Road
TEL Bishops Lydeard (0823) 432394

Open noon to 2, 7 to 10 &
Closed Mon; Christmas Day and Boxing Day

Iain and Caroline Faux have taken over this cottage restaurant (formerly Rose Cottage) at the foot of the Quantock Hills and have given it much more of the lively convivial atmosphere of a country pub. Three-course Sunday lunch is excellent value at £4.95 for chicken and leek soup, then a roast with all the trimmings, followed by good apple pie and first-rate coffee. During the week there are snacks such as home-made lasagne, gammon and rump steak with fried onions. Wines by the carafe.

BLEDINGTON
Gloucestershire   map 4

NEW ENTRY | Kings Head [7/10]

The Green
TEL Kingham (060871) 365

Open for food noon to 2; 7 to 10.15 &
Closed Sun D; Christmas Day

The pub is a converted cider-house on the green of a pretty Cotswold village. Inside, the beams and inglenooks have been preserved. For cheap eating there's an imaginative menu of ambitious pub-grub and it pays to go for the daily specials. Deep-fried aubergines with garlic mayonnaise or peanut roast with mushroom sauce are for vegetarians, otherwise there might be steak and wine pie, seafood cassoulet, or grilled sardines. Hot roast beef sandwiches are a good choice for a quick snack. Full meals in the dining-room cost over £10 a head. Wadworths and Hook Norton beers, rough cider and excellent house wines.

BOLHAM Devon   map 1

Knightshayes Court [7/10]

TEL Tiverton (0884) 254665

Open 11 to 5.30 & (also wc)
Closed Fri (exc Good Friday); 1 Nov to Easter
or 1 Apr

Devon has spawned an extraordinary network of local food industries, producers and suppliers. It is appropriate that restaurants in National Trust properties in the county should be supporting them. Knightshayes Court gets its cheese from Quicke's of Newton St Cyres, pâtés from Budleigh Salterton, real ice-cream from Salcombe Dairy and smoked trout from Silverton. The menu has good home-made soup, such as carrot and orange, salads, and home-made meringues with clotted cream. Devon cream teas come with home-baked scones and cakes. Hills cider or English wine from Highfield Vineyards, near Tiverton.

BRANSCOMBE Devon   map 1

Masons Arms [7/10]

TEL Branscombe (029 780) 300

Open for food noon to 1.45 (12.30 to 1 Sun), 7 to
9.30 & (also wc)

The beach is half a mile down the lane from this ivy-covered medieval inn. Inside is rather grandly old-fashioned, with a huge central hearth and wooden settles in the bar. Snacks are simple and traditional – home-made steak and kidney pie, omelettes with garden herbs, fresh local fish, plus ploughman's and salads. There are also steaks, kebabs, and apple strudel to finish. More expensive restaurant. Beers from Hall and Woodhouse, as well as Bass on draught.

BRISTOL Avon   map 2

Bell's Diner [7/10]

1 York Road, Montpelier
TEL Bristol (0272) 40357

Open 7pm to 11pm
Closed Sun and Mon

Once a grocer's shop, this is now a good neighbourhood bistro with a short, interesting menu. Dinners are priced on the main course, and a full meal can be had for around £8. Start with sweet pepper soup or spiced aubergine and sesame salad, before ragout of pork with apricots, baked halibut, or leek and Stilton croustade. Sweets range from chocolate brandy mousse to iced blackcurrant meringue cake. To drink there's wine, as well as Smiles Exhibition beer, first brewed by the previous owner, John Payne, in a back cupboard behind the bistro.

Berkeley Brasserie [7/10]

Berkeley Centre, 15–19 Queen's Road
TEL Bristol (0272) 294679

Open 9am to midnight
Closed Sun

New owners, the Bells, are putting more emphasis on the light, all-day brasserie menu, and this is what the place does best. Full English breakfasts are served from 9am, otherwise have anything from coffee and croissants to a bowl of onion or fish soup with a glass of wine. There are also omelettes, fashionable salads, steak with frites, and croque monsieur. Finish with imported French ice-creams, sorbets or home-made pastries. More expensive full meals at lunch and dinner.

Café de Daphne [6/10]

12 York Road, Montpelier
TEL Bristol (0272) 426799

Open 8 to 7 (2.30 Sat and Sun) &

A bustling, cosmopolitan café in a quiet backwater of Bristol among the ethnic shops and delicatessens. Stay for ten minutes or linger for an hour or more over breakfast, lunch or tea. The menu ranges far and wide for English fry-ups, pinto bean soup, pasta, hot bitter chocolate pudding, Jewish bagels with smoked salmon or home-made curd cheese, and Middle Eastern salads. Students flock in for Jamaican Sunday brunch, which includes fried banana, Jamaican beans, fried egg, and Jamaican bread. Good bakery next door. Wine by the glass, beer or juice.

NEW ENTRY Cherries Vegetarian Bistro [6/10]

122 St Michael's Hill
TEL Bristol (0272) 293675

Open noon to 2, 7 to 11.30 & (also wc)
Closed Christmas; last week July and first week Aug

Usefully placed within easy reach of the University and the hospitals. The menus for lunch and dinner are chalked up on blackboards. Lunch centres on simple dishes, such as courgette and potato soup with herb bread, quiches, jacket potatoes, and ploughman's. Evening meals are more ambitious, but it's still possible to have three courses for under £8: look for the stuffed marrow, or pancakes filled with vegetables. Excellent sweets include baked banana in orange and honey sauce, or trifle with a fresh fruit base. Wines, beers, coffees and teas to drink.

51 Park Street [7/10]

51 Park Street
TEL Bristol (0272) 28016

Open 10 (11 Sun) to 11
Closed Christmas Day and Boxing Day

This stylish brasserie has a new owner and has undergone some refurbishment, but otherwise very little has changed. Light snacks and full meals are served through the day: carrot soup, Toulouse sausages, chicken and tarragon pie, fresh pasta, and vegetarian specialities. To finish there's bread-and-butter pudding or chocolate and orange mousse. Cocktails as well as wines to drink.

Ganges [7/10]

368 Gloucester Road, Horfield
TEL Bristol (0272) 45234/428505

Open noon to 2.15, 6 to 11.30 &
Closed Christmas Day and Boxing Day

The décor is a vivid collage of red, green and gold and sets the tone for an authentic menu of North Indian dishes. The tandoori thali has a good selection, plus nan and rice. There are also familiar curries, from mild lamb pasanda to fiery chicken jhal noorpuri ('cooked with rarely found herbs'). Vegetable dishes are fresh and the vegetarian thali is good value at £5.25. Other set meals begin at £7.95 a head. Drink Kingfisher beer or try Indian Veena wine.

Guild, Bristol Guild of Applied Art [6/10]

68 Park Street
TEL Bristol (0272) 291874

Open 9.30 to 5 (4.30 Sat)
Closed Sun; bank hols

On the first floor of a department store. Light lunches feature home-made soup, quiches, salads, and specials such as tarragon chicken. Interesting home-made ice-creams to finish. During the day there are cakes and pastries with coffee or tea. Otherwise try Somerset cider or elderflower wine.

NEW ENTRY Half Baked Café [6/10]

7–9 Lawford Street, St Philips
TEL Bristol (0272) 552968

Open noon to 4.30
Closed Sat and Sun

Part of the Community Service Volunteer Project, this restaurant is a training ground for people of all capabilities who have an interest in catering. The décor is without frills, and so is the cooking. Vegetarian and meat dishes rub shoulders, although the style is wholefood. Courgette and cheese quiche, beef casserole with pulses, nut roast with fresh tomato sauce, and sticky date pudding have all been first-rate. Take-

aways and bookings for working breakfasts and suppers available. Unlicensed.

NEW ENTRY Henry J. Bean's [7/10]

St Augustine Parade
TEL Bristol (0272) 298391

Open 11.30 to 10 (10.30 Fri and Sat)

The most recently opened branch of this mini-chain of American bars, in which the style and menus are the same. For details see London and Aberdeen.

Malacca [6/10]

87 Whiteladies Road
TEL Bristol (0272) 738930

Open noon to 2, 7 to 11
Closed Sat L; Sun

A useful bet for creditable South-East Asian cooking in the heart of Bristol. The menu has Chinese and Indian touches, but the recommended dishes are the satays with thick peanut sauce, chicken with coconut and lemon grass, the pungent soups and the vegetable pancakes. Curries are good, too.

Mandarin [7/10]

81 Whiteladies Road, Clifton
TEL Bristol (0272) 735095

Open noon to midnight &
Closed Christmas

Bristol's best-known Chinese restaurant still offers authentic Cantonese food and good value for money, although the décor has been spruced up recently. Cheapest options are the one-plate meals listed under rice and noodles: a plate of rice piled up with pork, beef and seafood is substantial enough for lunch. Otherwise there are recommendations for the king prawns in batter, sweet-and-sour pork balls, and pineapple fritters. Set menus start at around £6 a head.

Pizza Express [7/10]

31 Berkeley Square
TEL Bristol (0272) 260300

Open 11.30 to midnight &. (also wc)
Closed Christmas Day, Boxing Day and 1 Jan

A branch of the highly rated pizza chain based in London (see entry).

Racks Wine Bar, Hotel Clifton [7/10]

St Pauls Road, Clifton
TEL Bristol (0272) 743943

Open noon to 3, 5.30 (7 Sun) to 11 (11.30 Fri and Sat)
Closed Christmas Day

Beef butties are an unexpected best-seller in this 1930s-style wine bar with huge potted palms and a live pianist. Everything is home made, from soups, such as mushroom and walnut, or watercress, to the dressings and mayonnaise with the salads. Otherwise the menu is international: lasagne, Kashmir beef, sweet-and-sour pork. Omelettes are cooked with a variety of fillings. Wine by the glass, as well as beers and cocktails. More expensive meals in the restaurant next door. No children.

NEW ENTRY	**Rajdoot** [7/10]

83 Park Street
TEL Bristol (0272) 268033/291242

Open noon to 2.15, 6.30 to 11.30 &.
Closed Sun L; L bank hols; Christmas Day and Boxing Day

One of a small chain of atmospheric Indian restaurants with branches in Birmingham, Manchester and Dublin. The style is flamboyant, with incense, turbaned waiters and huge prints in the dining-room. The cooking is North Indian and Punjabi, and best bets for cheap eaters are the set lunches at £5.50: tandoori chicken and nan, then a curry, dhal and rice, plus sweet and coffee. The full menu is more expensive.

Taj Mahal [6/10]

37A Cotham Hill, Cotham
TEL Bristol (0272) 745265/745278

Open noon to 2.30, 6 to midnight
Closed Christmas Day

Bristol's oldest Indian restaurant is still going strong, after twenty-eight years in business. Prices are reasonable for a standard range of North Indian curries and tandooris from rogan josh to lamb tikka. Thalis are from £6.50; the vegetarian version has three vegetable dishes, plus onion bahjias, dhal, rice and nan.

Vintner Wine Bar [8/10]

Crusader House, St Stephen's Street
TEL Bristol (0272) 291222

Open 10 to 2.30, 5.30 to 8.30
Closed Sat, Sun

The pick of the Bristol wine bars is an opulent network of cellars with a hidden garden overhung by St Stephen's church. On the blackboard menu there might be salmon pie, beef in red wine, or pork with apples and cider served with vegetables. There are also cheeses, salads, and cold joints (the beef is spot-on rare). Breakfasts of boiled eggs and 'soldiers', fry-ups, or croissants are served from 10am to 2.30pm. A dozen wines by the glass.

BROAD CLYST Devon   map 1

Killerton House [7/10]

TEL Exeter (0392) 881345

Open 11 to 6 &. (also wc)
Closed Nov to Mar

Killerton House is famous for its beautiful hillside garden and the Paulise de Bush costume collection. Like Knightshayes Court, Bolham (see entry), the tea-room-cum-restaurant makes use of some of the best local Devon produce from old and new enterprises: cheese from Quicke's of Newton St Cyres, ice-cream from Yarde Farm, Hele, and other dairy produce from Hawkridge Farmhouse, Coldridge. Bread and cakes are baked on the premises, and the menu ranges from ploughman's, casseroles and salads to Devon junket, treacle tart, and yoghurt with fresh fruit and Killerton honey. Cream teas are popular. Cider is from Hills, wine comes from the Killerton estate.

CHELTENHAM
Gloucestershire   map 4

Forrest's Wine House [7/10]

Imperial Lane
TEL Cheltenham (0242) 38001

Open 11 to 2.30, 6.30 to 11 &
Closed Sun; some bank hols

A long-established wine bar that has outlived many of its rivals. On the walls there are German prints as well as a blackboard menu listing soups, vegetarian dishes such as stuffed aubergines, and several daily specials ranging from frankfurters with potato salad to turkey fricassee, French lamb casserole, and plum kissel with cinnamon toast. Acceptable house wine.

Mayflower [6/10]

32 Clarence Street
TEL Cheltenham (0242) 522426

Open noon to 2, 6 to 11.30 &
Closed Christmas Day to 27 Dec

The best choice for good-value Chinese food in the Cheltenham area, although cheap eaters should stay with the set meals or go in a crowd. The menu of around 140 dishes has fashionable crispy seaweed, deep-fried crab claws, and chicken in a bird's nest, alongside spare ribs, prawn chop suey, and Cantonese roast duck. Toffee apples or toffee bananas to finish.

Retreat [8/10]

10–11 Suffolk Parade
TEL Cheltenham (0242) 35436

Open noon to 2.15, 6 to 9
Closed Sun; bank hols

Still one of the best places to eat cheaply in Cheltenham, despite the crowds, the noise and the smoke. Getting lunch can be a crush, but it's peaceful out on the patio. New cook Sophie Bracelin in putting more emphasis on cooking to order and her menu changes daily. The style is hot cucumber soup, chicken and avocado salad on Basmati rice, trout stuffed with bean

sprouts and spring onions, and kidney-bean burgers. Sweets are a high point: Eve's pudding (a light sponge with an apple filling) has been excellent. Drinkable house wine.

CHERITON BISHOP Devon   map 1

Old Thatch Inn [7/10]

TEL Cheriton Bishop (064 724) 204

Open for food noon to 1.45 (1.30 Sun), 6 (7 Sun, 6.30 winter) to 9.30 (9 Sun) &
Closed Christmas Day

A sixteenth-century thatched pub on the eastern border of the Dartmoor National Park. The bar menu has some adventurous touches and makes interesting reading: lamb savoury is topped with cheese and a breadcrumb crust, pork chops are cooked in wine, then garnished with caramelised apple rings, lamb's tongues are braised and served with a sherry-based sauce. Otherwise there are beef olives, slip soles stuffed with prawns and mushrooms, salmis of duck, and Boston corned beef hash. The mixed grill is a massive plateful of gammon, sausage, kidney, lamb cutlet, egg, tomato, mushrooms, potatoes and local hog's pudding. To finish, look for spiced bread pudding laced with Guinness, Creole baked bananas, and the honey and walnut tart. Ushers and Founders ale on draught, as well as local cider. No children.

CHIPPING CAMPDEN
Gloucestershire   map 4

| NEW ENTRY | **Greenstocks, Cotswold House Hotel** [9/10] |

The Square
TEL Evesham (0386) 840330

Open 9.30 to 9.30
Closed Christmas Day and Boxing Day

The hotel is a renovated Georgian building on the village square. New owners have set up Greenstocks as an all-day eating place and it has the civilised atmosphere of a family living-room. The range of food suits all needs. Lunches are the highlight, with the menu of grills and quiches boosted by daily specials such as a duo of pâtés (one smooth, one coarse), unusual soups, such as celery and sweetcorn with walnut, plus main courses ranging from grilled Brixham scallops wrapped in bacon with hollandaise, to chicken, kidney and French bean salad with basil vinaigrette. English breakfast includes black pudding, teas come with scones, shortbread or Cotswold rarebit, and suppers are the likes of Barnsley chop and sticky toffee pudding. Teas, cocktails and wine by the glass.

CHUDLEIGH Devon　　　　　　map 1

The Wheel [6/10]

Town Mills, Clifford Street
TEL Chudleigh (0626) 853255

Open 10 to 9
Closed Boxing Day

The ancient mill houses a co-operative craft complex, with the restaurant on the ground floor. Food is served throughout the day and the menu changes to make the best use of local and seasonal produce. Main dishes are hearty: chicken cobbler topped with a cheese scone, steak and kidney pie with three vegetables, fisherman's pie. There's also a country and Western casserole of pork, smoked sausage, baked beans and butter beans topped with potato. Start with home-made soup and hot bread, and finish with apple pie and clotted cream or chocolate roulade. House wine is around £5 a bottle.

CIRENCESTER
Gloucestershire　　　　　　map 4

Number One [6/10]

Brewery Court, Cricklade Street
TEL Cirencester (0285) 69290

Open 10 to 5 ♿ (also WC)
Closed Sun; Christmas Day, Boxing Day and 1 Jan

An attractive daytime coffee-shop with big picture windows looking out onto the courtyard. The range of food takes in well-prepared salads, baked potatoes, quiche, and more substantial dishes such as vegetable casserole or Hungarian goulash with brown rice.

Shepherds Wine Bar, Fleece Hotel [8/10]

Market Place
TEL Cirencester (0285) 68507/8/9

Open 10.30 to 2.30, 7 to 11 ♿ (also WC)
Closed Christmas Eve and Christmas Day

Sweetcorn and spinach soup, lambs' liver with raspberry vinegar sauce, and beef casserole with Guinness and orange are typical of the enterprising food served in this panelled wine bar attached to the Fleece Hotel. The menu is also bolstered by local smoked meats, interesting English cheeses, and stalwarts such as steak and kidney pie. The quality of the cooking is matched by a superb wine list.

COLYTON Devon　　　　　　map 1

 ## White Cottage Hotel [6/10]

TEL Colyton (0297) 52401

Open 12.15 to 2, 7.15 to 9 (residents only Sun D)
Closed 3 weeks Christmas to Jan

A small, family-run hotel in a fifteenth-century thatched farmhouse between the town and the River Coly. The Wellers offer a simple choice of lunch-time bar food: home-made cauliflower and Stilton soup with a brown cob, fresh crab sandwiches, and Cheddar ploughman's with three big hunks of cheese have all been good. Otherwise there are salads, omelettes, and grills. More expensive dinners. Tea and coffee as well as wine and beer.

CONGRESBURY Avon　　　　　　map 1

White Hart & Inwood [6/10]

Wrington Road
TEL Yatton (0934) 833303

Open for food noon to 2, 6.30 to 10
Closed Christmas D and Boxing Day

This is two places in one: the White Hart is the pub, the Inwood is the detached bar/buttery with its own licence. The food shows some enterprising touches – lamb in tomato and mint sauce with caramel potatoes, tuna and Brie salad, liver and walnut pâté. Jacket potatoes and ploughman's for the less adventurous. No children.

CORSE LAWN
Gloucestershire   map 4

Corse Lawn House Hotel [8/10]

TEL Tirley (045 278) 479

Open noon to 2, 7 to 10 ᴧ (also wc)

Baba and Dennis Hine's handsome Queen Anne house is best known for its prestigious restaurant, but excellent light meals are served in the bar. Home-made sausages, mushroom omelette, and barbecued spare ribs share the bill with dishes from the restaurant menu, such as hot shrimps croustade, feuilleté of calves' sweetbreads, and vegetable terrine with beurre blanc. The emphasis on fish extends to marinated grey mullet, grilled scallops with noodles, and an impressive shellfish platter. Sweets are the likes of summer pudding and caramel ice-cream. Impressive wines. A new drawing-room relieves some of the congestion in the bar at peak times.

COWLEY Gloucestershire   map 4

NEW ENTRY	Green Dragon [7/10]

Cockleford
TEL Coberley (024 287) 271

Open for food noon to 2 (1.30 Sun), 6 (7 Sun) to 10 ᴧ (also wc)

Imaginative, weekly changing menus bring the crowds to this tastefully renovated pub. Typically there might be bacon, walnut and endive salad, courgette and mushroom lasagne, salmon steak with avocado and dill dressing, and marinated stir-fried lamb with vegetables. A plateful of home-cooked ham with bread, mustard and a bowl of salad makes a good cheap lunch. There are also char-grilled steaks and interesting sweets, such as brandied cream cheese with fresh raspberries. Beers from Butcombes, Hook Norton and Wadworths. Children's room.

DARTINGTON Devon   map 1

Cranks [7/10]

Dartington Cider Press Centre, Shinners Bridge
TEL Totnes (0803) 862388

Open 10 to 5 ᴧ (also wc)
Closed Sun in winter

Part of the Dartington Cider Press Centre, an admirable showcase for some of the best produce to come out of Devon: hard and soft cheeses, wine, cider, mustards, honey. In the airy, pine-furnished restaurant there are excellent soups, such as tomato and lentil, huge varied salads (often with brown rice), pizzas, quiches, and sweet things ranging from apple and mincemeat turnover to banana crème brûlée. Cream teas are served every day in summer and there's plenty of room outside on the patio when the weather is fine. It can get very crowded at lunch-time and there's a minimum charge of £2 between noon and 2. Take-away picnic boxes.

DARTMOUTH Devon   map 1

NEW ENTRY	Cherub [6/10]

13 Higher Street
TEL Dartmouth (080 43) 2571

Open for food noon to 2, 7 to 9.45
Closed Sun

This impressive timber-frame building is the oldest in Dartmouth, and one of the few pubs with a Grade I preservation listing. The Milne family moved here from the Ashcott Inn, Ashcott, Somerset (see entry), and have maintained the standards set by their predecessors. Lunchtime bar food centres on local seafood, including oysters with hunks of brown bread, and crab with avocado. Also good are the freshly cut beef sandwiches, French onion soup, and chicken and cheese lasagne. More expensive dinners in the restaurant. Flowers and Blackawton Bitter on draught.

DODDISCOMBSLEIGH
Devon   map 1

Nobody Inn [7/10]

TEL Christow (0647) 52394

Open for food 11.30 to 2 (1.30 Sun), 7 to 10
Closed Christmas Day

The beamed ceilings and big inglenook
fireplaces testify to the history of this
sixteenth-century pub noted for its
prodigious wine list, well-kept beers and
fine food. In the bar there is Nobody pâté
laced with port and Nobody soup made
from chicken stock, herbs and fruit.
Otherwise the menu ranges from stuffed
pitta bread and lasagne to daily specials
such as goulash or venison casserole. The
spiced bread pudding is good, too. Full
meals in the restaurant (where children are
welcome) can take the bill into double
figures. Beers from Bass, Hall and
Woodhouse, and Hancocks. Devon
cheeses and clotted cream can be bought
to take away.

DOWN THOMAS Devon   map 1

Langdon Court Hotel [6/10]

TEL Langdon Court (0752) 862358

Open 11 to 2.30, 6.30 to 11.30 (noon to 2, 7 to
10.30 Sun) ර (also wc)
Closed Boxing Day and 27 Dec

An impressive Elizabethan mansion, once
the home of the merchant venturer Josias
Calmandy. In the bar there are simple
snacks such as soused herring, Greek Feta
cheese salad, steak sandwiches, and curry.
The more expensive restaurant has a good-
value vegetarian menu with dishes ranging
from pasta ragout to baked aubergines
stuffed with chickpeas. Two children's
rooms.

DUNSTER Somerset   map 1

NEW ENTRY Olde Tea Shoppe [6/10]

3 High Street
TEL Dunster (0643) 821304

Open 9 to 6 ර (also wc)
Closed Christmas Day; 3 Jan to 14 Mar;
weekdays 14 Mar to 4 Apr; 1 Nov to 18 Dec

The décor is exactly what you might
expect from an old-fashioned tea-shop in a
tourist village: dark wood, brass, cottagey
ornaments and displays of cakes and
puddings near the entrance. Lardy cake
and bowls of fresh raspberries come with
clotted cream, and the kitchen also
produces good bread pudding, meringues
and treacle tart. Lunch-time savouries
include herby pork sausages with jacket
potato, cheese platters, quiches, and
vegetable casserole. Good coffee, wine by
the glass.

EXETER Devon   map 1

Bottlescreu Bill's, White Hart Hotel [6/10]

South Street
TEL Exeter (0392) 37511

Open noon to 2, 7 to 10 ර (also wc)
Closed Sun; bank hols

The setting is a cave-like basement with
rough stone walls underneath the White
Hart Hotel. Food is a short menu of soup,
pâtés, salads, and cheeses, plus specialities
such as beefsteak and oyster pie, and
fisherman's pie. Two large fried eggs plus
four rashers of bacon and a cottage loaf
makes a mammoth late breakfast.
Inexpensive wines. No children.

Coolings [7/10]

Gandy Street
TEL Exeter (0392) 34183/4

Open 11 to 2.15, 5.30 to 10.45 ර
Closed Sun

Cold dishes dominate the choice of food in
this popular wine bar with a dimly lit
basement for sitting amid the arches.
There's spiced ham and egg, a crunchy
bean platter, tuna cheesecake, and smoked
chicken, all served with salads. The small
selection of hot food takes in lentil soup,
cottage pie with red cabbage, and
aubergine provençale. Interesting sweets
range from summer pudding to Belgian
fudge cake. Good choice of wines by the
glass; also look for the wines of the week.

NEW ENTRY | Herbies [6/10]

15 North Street
TEL Exeter (0392) 58473

Open 11 to 2.30, 7 to 10.30
Closed Sun; Mon D; bank hols

Bright and cheerful vegetarian restaurant
near the cathedral. The walls are hung
with paintings by local artists and there's
live music on Sunday afternoons. The
menu is simple and wholesome, with good
soups, such as Swiss chard or carrot and
orange, accompanied by garlic bread.
Other recommended dishes have included
pizza, mushroom pie with salad, samosas,
and banana split. Drink apple juice or
Wadworths Old Timer.

FALMOUTH Cornwall   map 1

De Wynn's Coffee House [6/10]

55 Church Street
TEL Falmouth (0326) 319259

Open 10 (10.30 Sun) to 5
Closed Sun Jan to mid-Mar; Christmas Day,
Boxing Day and 1 Jan

A Victorian-style coffee-house on the
waterfront, with original gas-lights and
bulging bow-windows. Home-made cakes
and pastries include some intriguing
recipes, such as rich Fiji fruit slice, coffee
cake with maple and apricot filling, and
Georgia pie made from cherries and nuts.
Cream teas come with home-made scones
and local cream. Light lunches are salads,
jacket potatoes, and hot dishes such as
chicken korma. Drink fruit juice or wine
by the glass.

FOSS CROSS
Gloucestershire   map 4

Hare & Hounds [6/10]

Nr Chedworth
TEL Fossebridge (028 572) 288

Open for food 11.30 to 2.15, 6.30 to 10.15 (12.15
to 2.15, 7.15 to 10 Sun) & (also wc)
Closed Christmas Day

An isolated Cotswold stone pub on the
Fosse Way not far from Chedworth. The
Turners say that everything except the

French bread is prepared on the premises.
Elizabethan chicken with apples, cider and
spices is a favourite, otherwise the menu
has soup, such as carrot and mint, fish pie,
steak and kidney cooked in ale with
dumplings, and omelettes. Also look for
specials such as pasta with mushroom,
tomato and calabrese sauce. Good walnut
and fudge cake to finish. Beers from
Wadworths, Hook Norton and Marstons
among others.

FROME Somerset   map 2

NEW ENTRY | Settle [8/10]

Cheap Street
TEL Frome (0373) 65975

Open 9 to 5.30 (2 Thur); 2.30 to 6.30 Sun &
Closed Sun Oct to end Apr

A traditional tea-room with settles
everywhere, mob-capped waitresses and
bare wooden floors. Margaret Vaughan has
been cooking here for twelve years or
more, serving traditional regional and
local dishes, some with a wholefood bias.
Pastry is wholemeal, rice is brown. Dishes
range from kedgeree and steak and kidney
pie to priddy oggies (cheese and pork
pasties), gammon with damson sauce,
omelettes, and filled jacket potatoes. One
oddity is cods' cheeks and tongues with
deep-fried potato skins and hot gooseberry
sauce. Frome Bobbins are figs, apricots and
sultanas steeped in cider and baked in
pastry whirls. All kinds of breads and
cakes come from the adjoining bakehouse.

GLASTONBURY Somerset   map 2

Rainbow's End Café [7/10]

17A High Street
TEL Glastonbury (0458) 33896

Open 10 to 4.30
Closed Sun and Wed

Chris Wilkinson's vegetarian café is still
excellent value for money, although the
menu is modest. The choice of quiches
(such as broccoli or sweetcorn and
mushroom), pizza, and salads is backed up
by daily specials ranging from Greek
cheese pie or mushroom and cashew-nut
raised pie to vegetable curry and lasagne.

Sweets are fruit crumble or chestnut and orange roulade; the fresh fruit salad is made without sugar. A new sun-lounge has been built on to the back of the café. Wine by the glass.

GLOUCESTER
Gloucestershire   map 4

College Green [8/10]

9 College Street
TEL Gloucester (0452) 20739

Open 12.15 to 2, 6.30 to 9.30
Closed Sun; Mon and Tue D; bank hols

This reliable bistro offers some of the best value in Gloucester, particularly at lunchtime when main courses are under £5. There are omelettes at one end of the price range, steaks at the other. In between, the menu might feature grilled mackerel with sage sauce, sauté chicken with lemon and tarragon or noisettes of lamb with Shrewsbury sauce. Start with asparagus tart or stuffed egg with beetroot salad, and finish with strawberry Pavlova. Evening meals will take the bill into double figures. House wines by the glass.

Comfy Pew [6/10]

11 College Street
TEL Gloucester (0452) 415648

Open 9 to 5.30 &
Closed Sun; bank hols

A useful day-time restaurant in a block of sixteenth-century timbered buildings close to the cathedral. Snacks and light dishes, such as macaroni cheese, curried prawns on toast, or turkey and mushroom pancakes, are always available along with home-made cakes and pastries. Good-value lunches feature dishes such as Gloucester sausage with Tewkesbury mustard, or Greenland halibut in wine and cream sauce. Soup and a main course will leave change from £4. Wine by the glass.

Golden Dragon [6/10]

95A–97 Northgate Street
TEL Gloucester (0452) 26525

Open noon to 2, 6 to midnight (2am Sat)
Closed Sun L

The great advantage of this city-centre Chinese restaurant is its late opening times. Choose carefully from the long menu to keep the bill below double figures. There are one-plate rice and noodle dishes, although these are expensive by Soho Chinatown standards. Otherwise the choice ranges from chicken and sweetcorn soup and sweet-and-sour king prawns to scallops with ginger and spring onions or duck with plum sauce. Set dinners from £9.55 a head. Children over six are welcome.

Moran's [7/10]

23 Worcester Street
TEL Gloucester (0452) 422024

Open 11.30 to 2, 6.30 to 10.45
Closed Sun; Mon L; Christmas Day; bank hols

Brian Moran's eye for design shows in the stylishly furnished rooms of this cocktail bar-cum-eating house. The menu is jazzy and you need to choose carefully to keep the bill in single figures. There are burgers, pasta dishes, steaks, pies, such as lamb and apricot, and specials ranging from turkey and cashew-nut curry with brown rice to fillet of pork with mushroom and tarragon sauce. Excellent garlic bread, crunchy salads, and locally made Italian ice-creams. Cocktails and wine by the glass.

GREAT RISSINGTON
Gloucestershire   map 4

Lamb Inn [6/10]

TEL Cotswold (0451) 20388

Open for food noon to 2 (1.30 Sun), 7 to 9.30
& (also WC)
Closed Christmas Day

There are views of high Gloucestershire and the Windrush valley from the garden of this extensively modernised seventeenth-century inn. Bar food and restaurant menus overlap, but the best value is for dishes such as home-made smoked mackerel pâté. English-style chicken and peach curry, breast of chicken stuffed with cream cheese and mushrooms, and home-made steak and kidney pie. Fruit pies or Loseley ice-creams to finish. Beers from Boddingtons, Wadworths, Hancocks and others.

HELFORD Cornwall   map 1

Shipwright's Arms [6/10]

TEL Manaccan (032 623) 235

Open for food noon to 2, 7 to 9 & (also wc)
Closed Sun D and Mon D in winter

A beautiful thatched pub with a unique location facing the Helford River. Summer lunches centre on local seafood and salads, as well as ploughman's and pasties. In the evenings there are barbecues out on the terrace overlooking the water, as well as more expensive, restaurant-style dishes indoors. Winter brings curries and casseroles. Devenish beers, reasonably priced wines.

HIDCOTE BARTRIM
Gloucestershire   map 4

Hidcote Manor Garden [6/10]

TEL Mickleton (038 677) 703

Open 11 to 5 & (also wc)
Closed Nov to end Mar

The tea-room is in one of the outbuildings of this National Trust manor, with mullioned windows looking out onto the gardens. The menu is standard tea-room fare and everything is home made, from soups, savoury flans and fruit pies, to hot dishes such as Mexican beef. A vegetarian speciality is always available. Big salads, English cheeses, English wine and English apple juice.

HORSINGTON Somerset   map 2

Half Moon [6/10]

TEL Templecombe (0963) 70140

Open for food noon to 2, 7 to 10 & (also wc)

This seventeenth-century pub has gained a reputation for the quality of its bar food. Look for the board of specials, which features dishes from home and abroad: mixed grill, kidney and mushroom cobbler, and farmhouse pie rub shoulders with chicken cacciatore, Spanish pork chops, and beef provençale. Start with

soup or cauliflower and potato medley, and finish with trifle or summer pudding. Curries on Thursday night. More expensive restaurant menu. There's a large garden for families in summer, and two log fires in winter.

KINGSTEIGNTON Devon   map 1

Old Rydon Inn [7/10]

Rydon Lane
TEL Newton Abbot (0626) 54626

Open 11 to 2.30 (noon to 2 Sun), 6 to 11 (7 to 10.30 Sun)
Closed Christmas Day

This fifteenth-century farmhouse is on two levels, with a converted cider-apple loft upstairs and a covered patio overlooking the walled garden. The daily changing list of bar meals is adventurous and international, taking in anything from guacamole with tortilla chips or home-made pizza to Indonesian nasigoreng, beef and vegetable chow mein, German pork schnitzel, and tandoori chicken. There's a strong showing of fresh Devon fish, plus game dishes such as hare and venison pie in season. Sweets come with clotted cream. Bass, Wadworths, and Old Rydon Ale on draught. Children welcome upstairs until 8pm.

LECHLADE Gloucestershire   map 4

Trout Inn [6/10]

St John's Bridge
TEL Faringdon (0367) 52313

Open for food noon to 2 (1.45 Sun), 7 to 10 (9.30 Sun) & (also wc)
Closed Christmas Day and Boxing Day

The pub is close to St John's Bridge and its riverside garden is a popular spot for an al fresco lunch. Go for the home-made dishes such as pizzas, burgers, cod florentine and chilli. Deep-fried courgettes with a garlic dip make a good snack. Sweets range from syllabub to passion-fruit cheesecake. Courage beers.

LIFTON Devon   map 1

Arundell Arms [7/10]

TEL Lifton (0566) 84666

Open for food 12.30 to 2.30
Closed 5 days at Christmas

Best known as a comfortable base for
fishing and shooting, this country inn
offers good sustenance for sportsmen and
tourists. Snacks are served in the cocktail
bar, with the emphasis on the cold table,
backed up by home-made soup,
ploughman's, pâté, and sandwiches with
local smoked salmon or South Devon rib
of beef. Daily specials are bar food
stalwarts with some fancy touches: ragout
of beef with fresh noodles, goujons of three
fishes with sorrel mayonnaise. Sweets
come with clotted cream. Sunday lunch is
a hearty roast. More expensive restaurant
meals. House Rioja is £6.50 a bottle.

LITTLE WASHBOURNE
Gloucestershire   map 4

Hobnails Inn [6/10]

TEL Alderton (024 262) 237/458

Open for food noon to 2, 6.45 to 10.30 ♿ (also
wc)
Closed Christmas Day and Boxing Day

Built in 1474, this country pub has one of
the biggest selections of filled Scottish
baps in the land. The range is anything
from liver and onions or gammon and
mushrooms to less daunting fried egg or
toasted cheese. Start with soup and finish
with home-made gateaux or flans. More
expensive restaurant meals. Whitbread
and Flowers beers on draught. Family
room.

LOOE Cornwall   map 1

Flower Pot [7/10]

Lower Market Street, East Looe
TEL Looe (050 36) 2314

Open noon to 2, 7 to 10
Closed 2 weeks in winter

New owners Graham and Sheila Murray
have given this quayside restaurant a fresh
lease of life. The emphasis is on fish and
there are good-value light lunch dishes for
£2.95. Menus vary with the seasons: in
summer there might be pan-fried
marinated red mullet, beef olives, or
talamouche ryba (puff pastry filled with

prawns and mushrooms in a cream and
wine sauce), all served with vegetables and
a basket of French bread. Start with
asparagus soup or fresh sardines, and finish
with apple pie or lemon and raspberry
parfait. Evening meals are more expensive.
Wines by the glass.

LOWER SWELL
Gloucestershire   map 4

Old Farmhouse Hotel [6/10]

TEL Cotswold (0451) 30232

Open for food noon to 2, 8 to 11 ♿
Closed Sun L and Mon L; 21 Dec to 27 Jan

Originally a sixteenth-century manor
farmhouse, this is now an agreeable
Cotswold hotel with a pleasant walled
garden for summer eating. Best bargains
are on the light lunch and bar food menu,
which includes ploughman's, omelettes,
Welsh rarebit, plus soup, and a dish of the
day such as steak and kidney pie. Egg and
prawns with garlic mayonnaise comes
with an imaginative salad, and to finish
there might be three-fruit crumble with
clotted cream. More expensive restaurant
menus.

LYDFORD Devon   map 1

Castle Inn [6/10]

TEL Lydford (082 282) 242

Open for food 11.30 to 2.30, 6 to 10 ♿ (also wc)

A small Tudor inn standing in the shadow
of an imposing medieval tower. Inside, the
bar is famous for its vast collection of
brightly decorated plates. Decent bar food
includes fresh steaks, chicken pie, curries,
and ploughman's, plus seasonal seafood.
Sweets, such as syllabub and treacle tart
are well reported. A children's adventure
playground has recently been completed.
Beers from St Austell and Ushers.

LYMPSTONE Devon   map 1

Globe Inn [6/10]

TEL Exmouth (0395) 263166

Open for food noon to 1.45 (1.30 Sun), 7 to 10 ♿
Closed Christmas Day, Boxing Day and 27 Dec

Excellent fresh seafood is the highlight in this popular pub by the Exe estuary. In summer there are salads and sandwiches of crab, lobster, and salmon; in winter there's soup and a choice of hot dishes. Puddings are rich, cholesterol-laden confections of clotted cream, ice-cream, fudge and nuts. Flowers I P A and Bass on draught, wine by the glass. No children.

River House [7/10]

The Strand
TEL Exmouth (0395) 265147

Open noon to 1.30 &
Closed Mon; Christmas Day to 27 Dec; 1 and 2 Jan

As its name suggests, this restaurant is right on the banks of the River Exe, with marvellous views across the water to Powderham Castle. Seafood and vegetarian dishes dominate the light lunch menu (£2.25 for a single dish). Paupiette of smoked trout with cucumber mousse, seafood gratin, and salmon and ginger in puff pastry share the bill with spinach and mushroom omelette, hot tagliatelle salad, and devilled stuffed mushrooms. The price includes a basket of locally baked bread. Additional starters and sweets can take the bill towards double figures. More expensive dinners. Children over five are welcome.

MANACCAN Cornwall   map 1

New Inn [7/10]

TEL Manaccan (032 623) 323

Open for food 11 to 2 (1.30 Sun), 6.30 (7 Sun) to 9.30 & (also wc)
Closed Tue D in winter; Christmas Day D

Local boats bring in the fish for this seventeenth-century thatched pub. Depending on the catch, the menu might feature monkfish provençale, big bowls of mussels with hunks of brown bread, skate with black butter or John Dory. Alongside this there's home-made soup, sausage and mash, and treacle tart. The garden is good fun for the children. Beers from Devenish.

MARHAMCHURCH
Cornwall   map 1

Bullers Arms [6/10]

TEL Widemouth Bay (028 885) 277

Open for food noon to 2, 7 to 10 (9.30 in winter)
Closed Christmas Day

This friendly pub shares the limelight with the local church as the hub of the village. It attracts the tourists, who call in for straightforward bar meals of omelettes, home-cured ham salad, steak and kidney pie, and grilled trout. Good real ales from the St Austell brewery. Children are welcome in the games room.

MAWGAN Cornwall   map 1

Yard Bistro [7/10]

Trelowarren
TEL Mawgan (032 622) 227

Open noon to 2pm for L & (also wc)
Closed Sun D; Mon in winter; 16 Dec to 1 Mar

The bistro is a converted coach house in the stableyard of the Vyvyan family estate. Light lunches are the best bets for cheap eaters: massive ploughman's with good cheese, fish from Helston, salads, and decent steaks. Home-made rolls and sorbets have been added to the more expensive evening menu. House wine is £5.25 a litre.

MEVAGISSEY Cornwall   map 1

Mr Bistro [8/10]

East Quay
TEL Mevagissey (0726) 842432/1

Open noon to 2 &
Closed Nov to Jan

The setting for this partisan Cornish bistro is a converted pilchard store by the quay. Chris and Romer Robins support their local fishermen by buying fresh from the boats, and cater for tourists without resorting to packet soups or frozen chips. The result is a genuine, no-frills eating place, where freshness also means good value. Simple lunches centre on the catch of the day – anything from plaice and haddock to squid, monkfish and shark – fried with chips or salad. A pauper's lunch of soup and garlic bread is £1.40. There are also salads of seafood or pâté, plus specials such as minute steak or cheese and potato pie. More ambitious evening menu. House wine by the glass, coffee by the mug.

MONKSILVER Somerset   map 1

Notley Arms   [7/10]

TEL Williton (0984) 56217

Open for food noon to 2 (1.30 Sun), 7 to 9.30 (9 Sun) & (also WC)
Closed Christmas Day

This charming village inn serves some of the best pub food in the area. The blackboard menu changes each day and might feature home-made pasta, stir-fried chicken with noodles, aubergine and potato pie, or smoked cod and spinach pancakes. Shepherd's Purse is pitta bread stuffed with garlicky lamb and salad. To finish there's treacle tart or lemon meringue pie with clotted cream. Ushers and Founders ale on draught. Children's room and a lovely cottage garden.

MORETONHAMPSTEAD
Devon   map 1

White Hart Hotel   [6/10]

TEL Moretonhampstead (0647) 40406

Open for food noon to 2, 6 to 8 &

A spacious and comfortable inn usefully placed on the edge of Dartmoor. The bar menu concentrates on old favourites, such as home-made pasties, grilled pork sausages, hot and cold roast joints, and steak and kidney pie. Dishes are served with country-fried or boiled potatoes rather than chips. Treacle tart comes with clotted cream, and cheese is from Quicke's of Newton St Cyres. Afternoon teas are served in the lounge from 3pm. More expensive restaurant menu. Bass and Flowers IPA on draught.

MULLION Cornwall   map 1

| NEW ENTRY | Old Inn   [6/10] |

TEL Mullion (0326) 240240

Open for food noon to 2 (1.30 Sun), 7 to 9.30
Closed Christmas Day D

The original part of this pub is a sixteenth-century thatched cottage. Inside it is decorated with relics from the eighteenth-century Dutch ship, *Hollandia*, which sank off the Cornish coast on her maiden voyage. Interest in the bar centres on the range of excellent home-made pizzas with half a dozen different toppings. The snack menu also has home-made soup, pasties, salads, and home-made fish pie. Grills in the evening from Thursday to Saturday. More expensive restaurant meals. Devenish beers. No children.

NEWTON POPPLEFORD
Devon   map 1

Buttered Scone   [6/10]

TEL Colaton Raleigh (0395) 68100

Open 10.30 to 5.30 &
Closed Wed; 20 Dec to 1 Mar

Useful, tea-shoppy restaurant well known for its excellent cooked breakfasts and cream teas. The former is a big fry-up, plus toast, marmalade, tea or coffee for £2.50. The latter has excellent home-baked scones, cakes, and freshly-made sandwiches for around £1.60. Until 2.30 there's also a good café menu of fish and chips, sausage and mash, quiche, and salads plus a vegetarian dish, such as macaroni cheese or Chinese stir-fried vegetables with rice. On Sundays, food is restricted to a lunch-time roast (noon to 2) and afternoon tea (3 to 5.30pm). Book for more expensive evening meals.

NORTH CURRY Somerset   map 1

Rising Sun   [6/10]

Lower Knapp
TEL North Curry (0823) 490436

Open for food noon to 2 (1.30 Sun), 7 to 9.45 (9.30 Sun)
Closed Mon L (exc bank hols); Christmas Day

A sixteenth-century beamed inn, now a Grade II listed building. The food is home-cooked cauliflower cheese with bacon, banana and ham bake, cottage pie or fisherman's pie – all served with plenty of chips. There are also vegetarian dishes, such as nut loaf, vegetable curry, or stuffed aubergines. Mini-menu for children.

NORTHLEACH
Gloucestershire   map 4

 NEW ENTRY ## Fossebridge Inn [9/10]

TEL Fossebridge (028 572) 721

Open for food 12.30 to 2, 7.30 to 9.30

Hugh and Suzanne Roberts of the White Bear, Shipston-on-Stour (see entry, West Midlands), have recently taken over this higgledy-piggledy inn on the banks of the River Coln. It has quickly emerged as one of the best pub/restaurants in the region, and food in the ancient Bridge Bar shows the class of the kitchen. The bar menu has a few pub staples, such as taramosalata and chilli con carne, but the best bet is to order one of the adventurous main dishes, drink a glass of wine and help yourself freely to the bread basket. Stuffed sea bass in flaky pastry, grey mullet with fennel sauce, and chicken breast in red wine sauce have all been cooked and presented with the flair of a serious restaurant. Vegetables are crisp, salads are elegant and there are home-made sorbets and English farmhouse cheeses to finish. More expensive restaurant meals. Four house wines by the glass, or Marstons Pedigree on handpump.

OLDBURY-ON-SEVERN
Avon   map 2

Anchor [7/10]

TEL Thornbury (0454) 413331

Open for food 11.30 to 2.30, 6.30 to 9.30
& (also wc)
Closed Christmas Day

The quality of the food in this old stone village pub means that there are big crowds at weekends. Michael Dowdeswell rings the changes and even regulars can find new things on the menu. Local salmon is a permanent fixture during the season, otherwise there might be rabbit pie, seafood chowder with rice, spiced lamb pilaff, chicken casserole, and pork Stroganoff. Oldbury tart or mango

cheesecake to finish. Children's menu. Well-kept Boddingtons, Marstons and Butcombes beers.

PADSTOW Cornwall   map 1

London Inn [6/10]

Llanadwell Street
TEL Padstow (0841) 532554

Open for food noon to 2, 6.45 to 9.30
Closed Christmas week

Seafood crocks are the speciality in this family pub: the standard version has crab, prawns and queen scallops topped with potatoes and cheese. Otherwise there are hot and cold seafood dips, fish and chips, roasts, and steaks. The cold buffet is good value at £2.50. St Austell beers. Children are welcome until 8pm.

PENZANCE Cornwall   map 1

Mounts Bay Vineyard [7/10]

Tolver Water, Long Rock
TEL Penzance (0736) 60774

Open 10 to 6
Closed Nov to Easter

Cornwall is better known for cider than wine, but Peter Rogers has established this vineyard as one of a new breed. Tours are encouraged and visitors can eat in the conservatory-style café. Vegetables and fruit come from the garden, and the short daytime menu features home-made soups, all kinds of quiches, pizzas, pasties, and salads, plus treacle tart and banana cheesecake. Cream teas are also available. As well as the wine, there's local cider, home-made lemonade and elderflower cordial to drink.

PLYMOUTH Devon   map 1

Ganges [6/10]

146 Vauxhall Street
TEL Plymouth (0752) 667810

Open 5.30 to 11.45 & (also wc)

A very creditable Indian restaurant. The atmosphere is relaxed and food is cooked to order. From the tandoori oven there is good shami kebab and chicken tikka, while curries have included pungent, hot prawn patia. There's also a vegetarian thali for around £6.

Plymouth College of Further Education [7/10]

Kings Road, Devonport
TEL Plymouth (0752) 264739

Open noon to 12.30, 7 to 7.45 ᵹ (also WC)
Closed Sat; Sun; college hols

This is one of the most forward-looking catering colleges in Britain, and has recently established a full diploma course in vegetarian cookery. The value-for-money in the catering restaurant is extraordinary: it is possible to have a four-course dinner plus coffee for £5.50. A typically adventurous vegetarian meal might begin with tsatsiki or tagliatelle with mushrooms before beans with hot peppers or rice and chestnut soup. Main courses, such as aubergine al forno or roast butterbeans with cauliflower, are served with mixed or potato and garlic salad. To finish there might be pears in red wine or fruit with yoghurt and honey. Menus vary with the syllabus, and can embrace anything from high-class modern French cooking to old-style haute cuisine.

 Broadway Restaurant, Theatre Royal [6/10]

Royal Parade
TEL Plymouth (0752) 665432

Open noon to 2.30; 5.30 to 10.30 ᵹ (also WC)
Closed Sun; Christmas Eve and Christmas Day

One of the most varied selections of food for theatregoers outside London. On the ground floor is a bar serving pizzas and Mexican dishes, as well as an all-day coffee-bar for snacks and cakes. On the second floor is an all-day buttery with salads, sandwiches and teas plus additional hot dishes at lunch-time. Between the two is the Broadway Restaurant. Full meals will break the £10 barrier – though not by much – and the menu centres on home-made game pie, steaks, and dishes such as pork normande.

For those watching the show, pudding and coffee are served in the interval. An afternoon menu of toasted teacakes, croissants and BLTs is also available from 2.30 to 5.30. Basic wines by the glass.

PORTISHEAD Avon   map 2

Peppermill [7/10]

3 The Precinct
TEL Bristol (0272) 847407

Open 9.30 to 2.30, 6 to 10 ᵹ (also WC)
Closed Sun; D Mon to Thur

Set menus are the best value in this restaurant between the M5 and Bristol. For less than £10 there are three courses: mushroom fries with Stilton dressing before breast of duck in plum brandy sauce or fillet of sole with wine, courgettes and tomatoes. Sweets include a good chocolate roulade. Three-course business lunches (around £4) offer fish and chips, omelettes, or savoury mince pancakes as staples. Wine by the glass.

ST COLUMB MAJOR Cornwall   map 1

NEW ENTRY **Not Just Pizza** [5/10]

2A West Street
TEL St Columb (0637) 880859

Open 11 to 11.30 (5 to 11 Sun in summer)
Closed Christmas Day, Boxing Day and 1 Jan; Sun L in summer; Sun D and L all week in winter

Small pizza take-away with three pine tables, run by an American and Cornish couple. The menu is short, centring on pizzas in three sizes with all kinds of mix and match toppings, plus excellent calzone, lasagne and burgers. Dial-a-pizza for delivery to your door. Unlicensed, but bring your own wine.

ST DOMINICK Cornwall   map 1

Barn Restaurant, Cotehele House [6/10]

TEL St Dominick (0579) 50652

Open 11 to 5.30 1 Apr to 31 Oct (limited opening Nov and Dec) ᵹ (also WC)
Closed Fri; Jan to Mar

The National Trust has a good reputation for the food served in many of its fascinating properties. This unaltered medieval house has its own forge, saddler's, carpenter's, cider press, water mill and quay once used by the Tamar sailing barges. The Barn Restaurant always has a daily vegetarian hot dish such as spinach and cheese pie or pepper and date croustade, along with meaty hot-pots, good soups, and sweets ranging from blackcurrant fool to almond sponge pudding with honey sauce. Sunday roasts are £4.75. Drink wine or cider.

ST IVES Cornwall   map 1

Woodcote Hotel [7/10]

The Saltings, Lelant
TEL Hayle (0736) 753147

Open 6 to 10.30
Closed Nov to Feb

Woodcote Hotel was established in the 1920s to cater exclusively for vegetarians. John and Pamela Barrett's fixed-price dinner menus (£5.50 a head) offer starters such as potato and oregano soup, followed by, say, savoury crêpes with casseroled potatoes and local vegetables, then strawberry cheesecake or bilberry and coconut slice. Organically-grown produce is used where possible. Unlicensed, but you can bring your own wine. The other attraction of the hotel is its unique setting overlooking the tidal estuary of the Hayle.

ST MICHAEL'S MOUNT
Cornwall   map 1

Sail Loft [6/10]

TEL Penzance (0736) 710748

Open 10.30 to 5.30 & (also WC)
Closed Nov to Mar

The National Trust restaurant is in a converted carpenter's shop and boat store on one of Cornwall's most distinctive attractions. It is separate from the island castle, and there's no admission charge. Light lunches include vegetable soup, pork and hazelnut pâté, and a Smuggler's Lunch (smoked mackerel with horseradish sauce, salad, and a nip of Smuggler's Ale), as well

as vegetarian dishes such as bulgur wheat and vegetable savoury. There are also excellent traditional teas with Cornish splits and clotted cream or crab with bread and butter. Wines by the glass; Cornish cider.

SHEPTON MALLET
Somerset   map 2

Blostin's [7/10]

29 Waterloo Road
TEL Shepton Mallet (0749) 3648

Open noon to 2pm &
Closed L Sat to Mon

Nick Reed puts the emphasis on fresh local produce in his brown-walled, brown-clothed bistro. Fruit and vegetables are from nearby farms and smallholdings, fish is from St Ives. Set lunches (Tuesday to Friday by arrangement) are good value at £6.95 for three courses. Fish soup or warm salad of chicken and smokey bacon might be followed by sweetbreads with tomatoes and basil, smoked pork loin stuffed with prunes, or monkfish with crab sauce. Sweets include home-made sorbets (sometimes flavoured with locally produced Babycham). More expensive evening meals. House wine is £4.95.

Kings Arms Inn [6/10]

Leg Square
TEL Shepton Mallet (0749) 3781

Open for food noon to 2 (1.30 Sun), 7 to 9.30
Closed Sun D; Christmas

Known locally as The Dusthole, because of its association with quarry workers, this has been a pub for more than three hundred years, and until recently was owned by the Showering family (of Babycham fame). It is now under the flag of Hall's Brewery, and the food is good value. Best bets are the daily specials, such as liver and bacon crumble, pork chop in cider, or lamb curry. Roast rib of beef is served on Sundays in winter. Otherwise the menu is grills and things with chips. Real ales include Halls Harvest Bitter, Wadworths 6X, and Gibbs Mew Bishop's Tipple. Skittles and games room.

SOUTH MOLTON Devon   map 1

Stumbles [7/10]

131–134 East Street
TEL South Molton (076 95) 4145

Open 12.30 to 2.30
Closed Sun; Boxing Day and 1 Jan

The attractions at this town-centre wine bar are the Mediterranean-style patio at the back and the eclectic international food. Eat cheaply at lunch-time from a menu that includes pizzas, baked eggs with cream, king prawns with aïoli, and a wide selection of fresh home-made pasta (from a newly installed commercial pasta-making machine). Sausages are from the excellent Heal Farm, Kings Nympton, and sweets take the form of apricot and hazel-nut meringue or fresh mango cheesecake. The wine list is as wide-ranging as the food.

STOW-ON-THE-WOLD
Gloucestershire   map 4

Prince of India [6/10]

5 Park Street
TEL Stow-on-the-Wold (0451) 31198

Open noon to 3, 6 to 11.30 & (also WC)
Closed Christmas Day and Boxing Day

A creditable neighbourhood curry house serving decent North Indian food in a setting of starched table linen and tiger prints. Tandooris and tikkas are good, and the chicken dhansak and prawn biriani have been recommended. Excellent rice and breads. Drink lager.

STROUD Gloucestershire   map 4

Mother Nature [6/10]

TEL Stroud (045 36) 78202

Open 9 to 4.30
Closed Sun; bank hols

A reliable vegetarian café at the back of a wholefood shop in the town centre. Home-made cakes, samosas, and bhajias are useful snacks, while at lunch-time there are more substantial dishes such as lentil and orange casserole, wholemeal pasta with spinach and cheese, or Chinese hot-pot with honey and ginger. Interesting salads and a big selection of cheeses. Take-aways. Unlicensed.

TAUNTON Somerset   map 1

Porters Wine Bar [7/10]

49 East Reach
TEL Taunton (0823) 56688

Open 12 to 2.30, 7 to 11 & (also WC)
Closed Sun

Joanna Porter's revamped wine bar has a well-chosen wine list and an interesting menu of cosmopolitan food. At lunch-time there are popular steak sandwiches and pitta bread with fillings such as chicken and peach or bacon and egg. More substantial offerings might include thick lentil and bacon soup, smoked haddock pâté, chicken korma, and beef bourguignonne. Sweets are home made and ice-cream is from Chard. A pianist plays in the evening.

TEDBURN ST MARY Devon   map 1

Log Cabin [6/10]

Pathfinder Village
TEL Tedburn St Mary (064 76) 394

Open 10 to 5, 7.15 to 9.30
Closed Sun D; Tue in winter

Home-cooked food in the unusual setting of a log cabin restaurant attached to a landscaped site of permanent 'mobile homes'. Ingredients are fresh and local; jams, chutneys, cakes, and scones are made on the premises. Lunch is a simple choice of home-made soup (such as tomato or mixed vegetable), omelettes, cottage pie, and ham salad. Dinners are more expensive, but a set meal can be had for £8, with dishes such as liver and bacon in lemon and wine sauce, or plaice fillet stuffed with prawns. Wine by the glass.

TEWKESBURY
Gloucestershire   map 4

Crown [6/10]

Worcester Road, Shuthonger
TEL Tewkesbury (0684) 293714

Open for food 11 to 2.30, 6 to 11 (noon to 2, 7 to 10.30 Sun) &

The pub is on the open road north of Tewkesbury. From the outside it is unremarkable, but inside the décor is deliberately nautical (a sign on the kitchen door reads, 'engine room crew only'). The menu has plenty of variety, from deep-fried fillets of chicken to local salmon with prawn sauce, as well as garlic mushrooms, chilli, and cauliflower cheese. A new feature is char-grilled steak and mushrooms in a home-made bap. Well-kept Marstons Pedigree on handpump. Children welcome at lunch-time.

| NEW ENTRY | **Telfords** [7/10] |

61 High Street
TEL Tewkesbury (0684) 292225

Open noon to 2, 7 to 11
Closed Sun; Boxing Day; 1 Jan; 2 weeks Feb; 1 week Nov

Outside it looks rather sober and four-square; inside it feels like a pretty, genteel bistro. Best bets for cheap eating are weekday lunches, when there's a good choice of single-dish meals. Typically there might be Camembert or Stilton pancakes, smoked chicken and celery salad, steaks, and dishes such as baked trout with shrimp butter or breast of chicken with tarragon cream sauce. Excellent freshly baked wholemeal rolls to start, dark chocolate mousse to finish. Full menus are more expensive. House wines by the glass.

TREBARWITH Cornwall   map 1

House on the Strand [7/10]

Trebarwith Strand
TEL Camelford (0840) 770326

Open 10 to 10 &
Closed Nov to Mar

An admirable bistro run on the principle of 'anything, anytime'. For twelve hours a day there's an enterprising choice of food with a strong vegetarian undercurrent. Lentil and sesame fritters, hazelnut and rosemary pâté, bean and bulgur casserole, and mushroom soubise with brown rice,

share the bill with pork and apple Stroganoff, and steak with Madeira sauce. The curries would not be out of place in a good Indian restaurant. Wednesday evenings' Pauper's Supper offers three courses for £5.95. Drinks include everything from half pint mugs of coffee and hot chocolate to alcoholic 'adult' milk shakes and local cider. The attached restaurant – with the same name – is more expensive.

Old Millfloor [6/10]

Trebarwith Strand
TEL Camelford (0840) 770234

Open 7.30 to 9 (also noon to 5.30 Sat and Sun)
Closed Sun D; Christmas Eve to Boxing Day; Feb

There are plenty of bargains on the menu at this small hotel. Set dinners (£8.50) are the likes of broad bean soup, turkey escalope cooked with mushrooms, orange and white wine, then peach and cream flan. From noon to 5.30 on Saturday and Sunday there are snacks of quiche and salad, ploughman's, farmhouse pie and even porterhouse steak. Cornish cream teas are also available. Unlicensed.

TORCROSS Devon   map 1

| NEW ENTRY | **Start Bay Inn** [6/10] |

TEL Kingsbridge (0548) 580553

Open for food 11 to 2.30, 6 to 10 (noon to 1.30, 7 to 10 Sun)
Closed Christmas Day D

The landlord has his own boat and beautifully fresh fish is the highlight in this fourteenth-century thatched pub. Seafood pie is a complete meal in a pot, prawns are served by the pint, and crab sandwiches are packed with meat. Huge servings of fish and chips include haddock, plaice, skate, or lemon sole. Steaks and burgers for meat eaters. Sweets include ice-creams from Salcombe Dairy. There's a family room and a patio overlooking the beach. Flowers beer, Hills cider.

TORQUAY Devon   map 1

 Mulberry Room [9/10]

1 Scarborough Road
TEL Torquay (0803) 213639

Open 10 to 5 &
Closed Mon

A creditable all-day restaurant in a resort
overrun with fast food chains. Lesley
Cooper runs the place almost single-
handed and succeeds by putting her faith
in cheap, real food with no fancy touches.
Lunches show the style: soups made from
proper stock, seasonal salads, ham baked
with honey, quiche made with fresh cream
on a buttery pastry base. Chicken is a
farmyard bird and there are gutsy hot
specials, such as beef and carrot suet
pudding, plus a small vegetarian
contingent in the shape of peanut rissole
with tomato and chilli pickle. Home-made
cakes and tarts are displayed on a
sideboard by the entrance. Sunday lunch is
a superb meaty roast. Don't miss the pure,
additive-free ice-cream sundaes. House
wine is £3 per half-litre.

TORRINGTON Devon   map 1

Rebecca's [9/10]

8 Potacre Street
TEL Torrington (0805) 22113

Open 9am to 10pm &
Closed Sun; Christmas Eve to Boxing Day

The centre of Torrington's social life: the
Lillys organise outings to the theatre,
provide packed teas or late suppers and
even supply the refreshments for the local
cinema. They stay open all day, serving
everything from breakfasts and lunches to
afternoon teas and dinners. It is always
packed, but no one minds the clutter or
the feeling of amicable chaos in the
cramped dining-room. Eating here is fun.
Some of the dishes have odd names:
Locket's Savoury is toast spread with
watercress butter topped with fresh pear
and melted Stilton, Crempog Las is a
Welsh mushroom pancake. Roast duck is
served with blackberries and orange, lamb
cutlets are wrapped in pastry with crab.
Vegetarians are offered bean-pot with pitta

bread, vegetable curry, homity pie or stir-
fried vegetables with sesame seeds.
Sweets, such as coffee roulade or
traditional Brown Betty, are served with a
huge bowl of whipped cream left on the
table. House wine is £5.85 per litre.

TOTNES Devon   map 1

NEW ENTRY **Café KL** [7/10]

Babbage Road
TEL Totnes (0803) 866402

Open 9 to 3, 7.30 on
Closed Sun; Mon D; Sat L

Roger Hawkins has turned this 1960s
office building into a South-East Asian
restaurant with an open kitchen. His
loyalties show in the organically produced
meat from a Dartmoor farm, and in the
fact that there are no products from South
Africa. The range of dishes spans Malaya,
Java, Singapore and Thailand with plenty
of choice for vegetarians. Interesting wines
from Australia, New Zealand and China,
as well as Tiger beer.

Lyssers [7/10]

6 Fore Street
TEL Totnes (0803) 864677

Open 11.30 to 2 & (also wc)
Closed Mon L; Christmas Day and 1 Jan

Rick Lysser lands some of the seafood
served in his relaxed fish restaurant
decorated with boat hooks and shepherds'
crooks. Good-value lunches might include
home-made soup, fish pie, poached lemon
sole or monkfish thermidor – all served
with excellent al dente vegetables. There's
steak and kidney pie for meat eaters and
the kitchen is willing to cook any
vegetarian dish on request. Crème brulée
and pineapple and brandy cheesecake have
been good sweets. More expensive dinners.

Willow [6/10]

87 High Street
TEL Totnes (0803) 862605

Open 9 (10 Oct to June) to 5, 6.30 to 10 &
Closed Sun; Mon D, plus Tue D and Thur D Oct
to June

A relaxed community vegetarian restaurant run as a three-way partnership. Paintings by local artists share the wall space with modern tapestries, the furniture is pine and there are fresh flowers everywhere. The food nails its colours to the mast with free-range, rennet-free, unrefined and organically produced ingredients used for dishes such as rich minestrone, mushroom pâté, vegan spanakopita, and fig, fennel and banana slice. There's an Indian menu on Wednesday night, and live music on Fridays. The family room has children's books, children's chairs and baby-changing facilities. Take-aways.

TREEN Cornwall   map 1

Logan Rock Inn [6/10]

TEL St Buryan (073 672) 495

Open for food noon to 2.30, 5.30 (7 Sun and in winter) to 9 &

Peter and Anita George's pub is close to a secluded beach and the famous eighty-ton rocking-stone that gives the place its name. Look for the home-made specials such as beef and vegetable pie or wholewheat lasagne. Steaks are popular in the evening. Beers from St Austell. Children's room.

TRURO Cornwall   map 1

Attic Feast [6/10]

Old Bridge Street
TEL Truro (0872) 40008

Open 10 to 5 &
Closed Sun; 2 weeks in Feb

Healthy trends show up on the menu in this upstairs vegetarian restaurant. Quiches are made with free-range eggs and wholemeal flour, low-fat cheeses appear in sandwiches or as fillings for jacket potatoes, and some of the cakes are sugar free. To start there might be vegetable pâté or savoury pancakes; to finish there's yoghurt muesli with fresh fruit. Drink tea, fruit juice, wine or 'hon-y-cup' – a concoction of honey, cocoa and carob.

Bustopher Jones [7/10]

62 Lemon Street
TEL Truro (0872) 79029

Open noon to 2.30, 6 to 11 (7 to 10.30 Sun) &
Closed Sun L; Christmas Day to 27 Dec; 1 and 2 Jan

Enterprising bistro food in a setting of wood panelling and stained glass from a Nonconformist chapel. Order at the bar and the food is brought to your table. For a light meal or snack there's fish soup, jacket potatoes, asparagus mousse with French bread, or quiche with salad. Kebabs, lasagne, and burgers are supplemented by specials such as Moroccan meatballs with noodles, American chicken pie, or courgette and crab gratin. Finish with sherry syllabub or BJ's special – coffee ice-cream with Amaretto, chocolate, cream and nuts. Good-value wines.

WELLS Somerset   map 2

Penn Bar and Eating House, Crown Hotel [6/10]

Market Place
TEL Wells (0749) 73457

Open 10 to 9 & (also WC)

The building dates from 1450, and is now a classic beamed inn with a good choice of bar food. On the cold side there are salads with home-made pâté, Somerset chicken, or roast topside of beef, plus ploughman's with mature Cheddar or Double Gloucester. Hot dishes are the likes of savoury flan, steak and kidney pie, plus soup, and jacket potatoes. Morning coffee and afternoon cream teas are also available.

WESTON-SUPER-MARE
Avon   map 1

Quantocks [6/10]

57 Regent Street
TEL Weston-super-Mare (0934) 415283

Open noon to 2.15, 7 to 10 &
Closed Christmas Day

Local seafood is the speciality in this popular, Edwardian-style bar. Salmon, Cornish crab, Teignmouth mussels and Brixham plaice have all found their way on to the menu. Alternatives are the likes of stuffed peppers and goulash. Another attraction of the place is the live jazz and country music (every day except Monday). Good coffee, wine by the glass.

WITHYPOOL Somerset   map 1

| NEW ENTRY | **Royal Oak Inn** [6/10] |

TEL Exford (064 383) 506/7

Open for food noon to 2, 6.30 to 9.30

A prosperous seventeenth-century village pub with loyalties to the local hunting and shooting scene. The bars are filled with antlers, mementoes and sporting prints. The food has a robust country flavour: home-cooked ham and eggs, locally baked Somerset pasties, excellent farmhouse sausages in four flavours – pork and garlic, pork and herb, venison and bacon, or spicy tomato. Most dishes come with first-rate chips. Otherwise there is decent home-made soup, Danish open sandwiches, ploughman's, including Somerset Brie, and pints of prawns. More expensive evening meals in the restaurant. Ushers and Founders ale on handpump. Children over ten are welcome.

WOODCHESTER
Gloucestershire   map 4

| NEW ENTRY | **Ram Inn** [6/10] |

TEL Amberley (045 387) 3329

Open noon to 2.30, 6.30 to 10
Closed Christmas Day

Cotswold stone pub in a rather gentrified hillside village with spectacular views across the valley. Inside are bare floorboards, bare walls and bare wooden tables. The food is a mixture of simple home-cooked dishes supplemented by more adventurous ideas. Interesting-sounding specialities are likely to be the best: fish chowder with smoky bacon, salmon pancakes, poacher's pot (actually a game casserole) and curried minced beef puffs have all been good. There is house wine by the glass, but the main attraction for drinkers is the excellent choice of real ales: Hook Norton, Archers, Boddingtons, Holdens and Old Spot Ale from the Uley Brewery in nearby Dursley.

WOOLVERTON Somerset   map 2

Red Lion [6/10]

TEL Frome (0373) 830350

Open for food 11 to 2.30, 6 to 11 &
Closed Christmas Day, 31 Dec and 1 Jan

This started life in the seventeenth century as a farm building, but has been extensively altered over the years. Food centres on stuffed jacket potatoes, with fillings ranging from curried prawns to bacon, fried onions and Stilton. Even more extensive is the long list of salad bowls, packed with all kinds of ingredients: Florida is sweetcorn, tuna, orange, pineapple and banana with Caribbean dressing; Aardvark is smoked sausage, avocado and garlic croûtons. There are also main salads, such as crab Louis or chicken korma, plus French bread rolls, and ploughman's. Wadworths beers.

South

Dorset

Hampshire

Isle of Wight

Wiltshire

ANDOVER Hampshire   map 2

Hare & Hounds [6/10]

Charlton Down, Wildhern
TEL Hatherden (026 475) 235

Open for food noon to 2, 7 to 10 & (also WC; 2 steps to ladies)
Closed Tue D and Sun D; Christmas Day and Boxing Day

An isolated country pub with a single bar and a dining-room at the back. The setting may be English, but much of the food has a Greek flavour. As well as taramosalata and char-grilled kebabs there are interesting dishes, such as kavouras (crab with aubergine in tomato and onion sauce), swordfish steaks, and spicy chicken livers in pitta bread. More expensive evening meals, although there is a set menu at £8.

ANSTY Dorset   map 2

Fox [6/10]

TEL Milton Abbas (0258) 880328

Open for food 11 to 2.30, 6.30 to 11 &
Closed Christmas Day; bank hols

The old Ansty brewery has, for many years, been a popular family pub. It is a business-like set-up, with games room for the children, a barbecue-grill and a baked-potato bar. It is best known, though, for its extensive cold buffet with more than a dozen cold meats and up to thirty different salads. There are plans to add a hot carvery. Beers from Hall and Woodhouse, Hook Norton and Wadworths.

ASKERSWELL Dorset   map 2

Spyway Inn [6/10]

TEL Powerstock (030 885) 250

Open for food noon to 2, 6.45 to 9.15 &

Some of the best-value pub food in the area is served at this comfortable country pub overlooking Askerswell Down. Variations on ploughman's come with good-quality ham or locally made sausages. The menu also runs to rabbit or turkey pie, steaks, and omelettes. Finish with fruit crumble or 80p-worth of home-made chocolate and

butterscotch nut sundae. Ushers beer on draught. Family room.

AVEBURY Wiltshire   map 2

Stones [8/10]

High Street
TEL Avebury (067 23) 514

Open 10 to 6 &
Closed late Oct to Easter

Dr Hilary Howard has proved that it is possible to thrive in a tourist hot-spot without selling chips or coke. Instead, the emphasis is firmly on fresh local ingredients, free-range eggs, organic flours, unpasteurised British farmhouse cheeses and home-grown herbs. The style is vegetarian, and the menu takes its cue from the nearby standing stones. Stonesoups might include spiced courgette or parsnip and orange. Main course 'megaliths' are the likes of mushroom pancake with sour-cream sauce, pizzas, or Mexican chilli bake with avocado. There are also massive, freshly made Stonewiches and a good mason's lunch of home-baked bread, cheese, Stones chutney, salads and apple. To go with the food there are herb teas and farm-pressed apple juice, plus Hugh Rock's elderflower wine and Wadworths 6X from the wood.

BASINGSTOKE Hampshire   map 2

Mardi Gras [6/10]

22 Westminster House, Potters Walk
TEL Basingstoke (0256) 26018

Open noon to 2, 6.30 to 10.30 (11 Fri and Sat) &
Closed Sun and Mon; bank hols

Smart, glass-fronted pizzeria modelled on one in New Orleans and run by the wives of two local GPs. Pizzas are made with genuine Mozzarella topping and come in two sizes (10 inch or 14-inch monsters, big enough for four people). Accompanying salads are fresh, and the menu also has baked stuffed mushrooms, steaks, and burgers. Try the home-baked pitta-style garlic bread. Imported beers, wine by the glass. Minimum charge £2.50 at lunchtime, £4 in the evenings.

NEW ENTRY | **Porter's** [7/10]

The Old Farmhouse, Harrow Way
TEL Basingstoke (0256) 476167

Open wine bar noon to 2.30 (2 Sun); restaurant
noon to 2, 7 to 10
Closed Christmas Day and Boxing Day; Wine
bar Mon; restaurant Sat L, Sun and Mon

Wine bar and restaurant in an old
farmhouse attached to the Viables Craft
Centre on the outskirts of Basingstoke.
Cheapest options are lunchtime snacks
served in the ground-floor wine bar, such
as quiches, imaginative salads, Mediterranean dips with pitta bread, and hot
dishes along the lines of chicken curry,
spicy beef and bean 'feast', and lasagne,
with Hungarian apple pie or coffee gateau
to finish. The cellar restaurant revolves
round more expensive char-grills –
anything from mixed satay kebab with
peanut sauce to duck with plum sauce.
More than thirty wines, including eleven
by the glass.

BECKHAMPTON Wiltshire   map 2

Wagon & Horses [6/10]

TEL Avebury (067 23) 262

Open for food 11.30 to 2 (noon to 1.15 Sun), 6.30
to 10 ও (also ladies wc)
Closed Mon D; Christmas Day

This popular sixteenth-century inn is less
ancient than nearby Silbury Hill or the
Avebury standing stones, but there's
plenty of history in its thatch and massive
stone walls. The dish of the day is a 'pig in
a poke', otherwise the menu is strong on
salads, double-decker sandwiches, and
grills. Pan-fried mackerel has been
excellent, and there's treacle sponge or
strawberry cheesecake to finish.
Wadworths beers on handpump.

BOURNEMOUTH Dorset   map 2

Le Buffet [6/10]

Old Christchurch Road
TEL Bournemouth (0202) 26031

Open 9 to 5 (3 Sat) ও
Closed Sun; Christmas Day and Boxing Day

Wholemeal bread is baked locally but
everything else is homemade in this tiny
vegetarian café with oil paintings on the
walls and a salad table displayed in the
window. Lunch-time dishes might include
koulibiac, lasagne, and stir-fried vegetables.
Freshly baked cakes are served with
morning coffee. Wine by the glass or bottle.

NEW ENTRY | **Coriander** [6/10]

14 Richmond Hill
TEL Bournemouth (0202) 22202

Open noon to 2.30, 6 to 11
Closed Sun L; Christmas Day and Boxing Day

Mexican dishes with a vegetarian slant are
the mainstay of the menu in this popular
town-centre restaurant. Tacos, chilli and
barbecued ribs share the limelight with
fresh coriander soup, guacamole and
cheese and spinach enchiladas. Mexican
beers to drink.

Crust [7/10]

Hampshire House, Bourne Avenue,
The Square
TEL Bournemouth (0202) 21430

Open noon to 2.30 ও

Good-value set lunches are served in this
reliable bistro with pinkish walls and
draped curtains. Three courses can be had
for £5.95 and there's a dish of the day for
£3.95. The style is home-made soups, such
as mushroom, then roasts, steaks, salads,
or fresh fish such as halibut or monkfish.
Finish with lemon and treacle tart or fruit
pie. More expensive evening meals.
Interesting, reasonably priced wines.

Henry's [6/10]

6 Lansdowne Road
TEL Bournemouth (0202) 297887

Open 11.30 to 2, 6 to 10.30 ও (also wc)
Closed Sun; Mon D; bank hols

Since the chefs bought this restaurant, the
menu has become more vegetarian, with a
number of vegan specialities. At lunch-
time there are cheap, speedy meals for
£1.75, including salads, jacket potatoes,

and savoury rice. The full menu is still excellent value for beanburgers, risotto and red-bean goulash. Many sweets contain no sugar. Wines from £3.50 a bottle. Book for Friday and Saturday nights.

BROAD CHALKE Wiltshire   map 2

Cottage House [5/10]

TEL Salisbury (0722) 780266

Open 8.45 to 12.45, 1.45 to 5.30 (2.30 to 5.30 Sun, and Sat May to Sept) &
Closed Mon (exc bank hols); Sun L; Sat pm Oct to Apr; 10 days at Christmas

During the 1850s the local vicar and Sydney Herbert formed the first Sydney Herbert Co-operative in this shop. It still functions as village store-cum-post-office, and Enid White has opened up the oldest part of the house as a tea-room. Cream teas are the attraction, with Wiltshire lardy cakes and clotted cream when available. Tea is usually from Miles—a small family concern in Porlock, Somerset. Unlicensed.

BURSLEDON Hampshire   map 2

Jolly Sailor [6/10]

Lands End Road
TEL Bursledon (042 121) 3787

Open for food noon to 2, 7 to 10
Closed Christmas Day

It's a steep walk down from the winding cliff-path to this riverside pub with its own jetty. New owners are running the place along the same lines as the previous ones, and there's praise for the excellent roast joints and locally made sweets. There's also a good selection of salads, plus real ales from Wadworths and Gales, among others. No children.

BURTON Wiltshire   map 2

Plume of Feathers [7/10]

TEL Badminton (045 421) 251

Open for food 11 to 2.30, 6 to 10.30 (11 Fri and Sat; noon to 2, 7 to 10.30 Sun) &

The setting is a classic four-hundred-year-old Cotswold stone pub with oak beams and timbers, but the food is mainly from the Far East. There are all kinds of curries with rice, poppadums and sambals. At Sunday lunch-time there's a full rijsttaffel—an Indonesian buffet with up to thirty little dishes. Otherwise the menu roams about for steak and kidney pie, mushrooms in port and cream, chicken Stroganoff, and Mexican chilli beef. Sweets range from Pavlova to Sachertorte. Ushers beers and some interesting Australian wines.

CALNE Wiltshire   map 2

Bowood House [6/10]

TEL Calne (0249) 812330/812102

Open 11 to 6 & (also WC)
Closed 17 Oct to 31 Mar

Bowood House, an outstanding example of eighteenth-century architecture, is privately owned by the Earl of Shelburne. It offers excellent facilities, including a good-value restaurant. The main attraction is the cold buffet (£4.95 a head), which has game pie made from pheasants from the estate, roast turkey, coronation chicken, Wiltshire gammon, and savoury cheesecakes to go with huge bowls of salad. There are hot dishes, such as beef Stroganoff, and a cheap menu for children. Afternoon teas. Wines by the glass.

CHARLTON Wiltshire   map 2

Horse and Groom [6/10]

TEL Malmesbury (0666) 823904

Open for food noon to 2.30 (2 Sun), 7 to 11 &
Closed Mon; Sun D

Originally a staging point for coaches travelling between Oxford and Bath, this charming village pub is now noted for its food. Soups are home made and the standard menu has grilled Alderley trout and coq au vin, as well as occasional pheasant and quail. Also there are daily specials, such as goulash with noodles or creamy fish pie, plus a good showing of vegetarian dishes: mushroom and walnut pâté, minted aubergine and rice timbale, lentil and celery lasagne. Beers from local breweries including Archers. Minimum charge £5.50 on Friday and Saturday evenings.

CHEDINGTON Dorset   map 2

Winyard's Gap [6/10]

TEL Corscombe (093 589) 244

Open for food 11.30 to 2.30 (noon to 2 Sun), 7 to
11 (10.30 Sun) & (also WC)
Closed Christmas Day

Superbly situated high up on the edge of
the Dorset Downs, in an area described in
Thomas Hardy's novels. The views are
superb, the old pub has plenty of
atmosphere and the food has some home-
cooked touches. Look for the deep-filled
pies: beef and vegetable with Guinness, or
turkey and mushroom, or gammon and
apple in cider. The menu also has Dorset
pâté, chicken with mushrooms in sherry
sauce, and steaks, as well as ploughman's,
kedgeree, and jacket potatoes. Barbecues
are held, weather permitting; there's a
skittle alley indoors. Eldridge Pope beers
on handpump.

CHICKSGROVE Wiltshire   map 2

Compasses Inn [6/10]

TEL Fovant (072 270) 318

Open for food noon to 2.30 (2 Sun), 7 to 11 &
Closed Tue

The thatched roof, low beams and high-
backed settles in the bar give this
handsome medieval pub a feeling of the
past. Farming implements hang on the
wall, and there's a mood of rural peace
about the place. Ploughman's comes with
a choice of thirteen cheeses, and the menu
also has big salad bowls, home-made steak
pie, omelettes, and steaks. Occasional
specialities have included walnut-stuffed
aubergine, and chicken stuffed with
asparagus and ham, plus seasonal game.
Wadworths 6X and Halls Harvest Bitter on
draught.

CHRISTCHURCH Dorset   map 2

Forum [5/10]

19 Saxon Square
TEL Christchurch (0202) 470555

Open 9.30 to 5 &
Closed Sun; Christmas Day and Boxing Day

Self-service vegetarian coffee-house,
decorated in stark white and icy blue with
classical columns. The food is self-service
and it is healthily wholefood: spinach and
cheese salad, vegetable bake, carob
brownies, flapjacks. All-day breakfasts;
children's menu.

CLANFIELD Hampshire   map 2

Bat & Ball [6/10]

Broad Halfpenny Down, Hambledon Road
TEL Hambledon (070 132) 692

Open for food noon to 2 (1.45 Sun); 7 to 10
& (also WC)
Closed Christmas Day, Boxing Day D

Cricket matches were first played on Broad
Halfpenny Down in the 1750s, and in its
early days this classic Hampshire pub
served as pavilion and clubhouse. Today it
is the setting for hearty food such as home-
made pies, steak and kidney pudding,
curries, and massive mixed grills. There
are also salads and vegetarian dishes such
as peanut bake, quiche, and vegetable
lasagne. More expensive dining-room.

CORSCOMBE Dorset   map 2

Fox [6/10]

TEL Corscombe (093 589) 330

Open for food noon to 2 (1.30 Sun), 7.15 to 10
(9.45 Sun)
Closed Mon L; bank hols

Landlord Stephen Marlow doesn't go in for
fast food. Dishes take time to prepare, and
almost everything is made on the
premises, from mayonnaise and salad
dressings to sweets. Fish from West Bay is
used for dishes such as sea-food omelette,
or plaice with lemon and ginger sauce.
Soups might include Stilton and walnut,
there's local farmhouse Cheddar in the
ploughman's, plus vegetarian options such
as mushroom and cauliflower cheese.
Lunch is a bit cheaper than dinner. Beers
from Devenish and Eldridge Pope. Children
can play on the lawn opposite the pub.

CORTON Wiltshire — map 2

Dove Inn [7/10]

TEL Warminster (0985) 50378

Open for food noon to 2, 7 to 9.30 &
Closed Sun D; Mon; 2 weeks mid-Jan

A cottagey Victorian pub that puts the
emphasis on food. Simple cold snacks
range from chilled gazpacho or smoked
beef with dill cucumbers to vegetarian
quiche or a wedge of turkey pie packed
with celery, walnuts and apricots. Specials
and hot dishes show some flashes of
colour: broccoli and orange soup, pork and
vegetables cooked in rosé wine with
cranberries, as well as haddock kedgeree
and savoury mince with marrow. Puddings
are worth exploring: try treacle tart with
walnuts, granny's lemon pud, or apricot
and almond crumble. Ushers Best tapped
from the cask. No children.

DEVIZES Wiltshire — map 2

Bear Hotel [6/10]

Market Place
TEL Devizes (0380) 2444

Open for food noon (10.30 Sun) to 2, 7 to 11 &

This is the home of Devizes Pie – an
extraordinarily complicated brawn cooked
in pastry. It has survived since the
nineteenth century and appears on the
menu in the Lawrence Rooms,
accompanied by pickled egg and Urchfont
beer mustard. Also on the buffet menu are
salads with home-cooked meats, Scotch
salmon, and raised pies such as chicken
with apricot topping, pork with tarragon
and apple, plus casseroles, hot-pots, scone-
topped cobblers, and curries. There are
also old-fashioned hot puddings such as
jam roly-poly, spotted dick and Chester
pudding. Simpler snacks like bacon buttys,
ploughman's and triple-decker sandwiches
are served in the bar. More expensive
restaurant meals. Beers from Wadworths,
the town's own brewery.

DORCHESTER Dorset — map 2

Bridge Between [7/10]

8 High East Street
TEL Dorchester (0305) 68438

Open noon to 2.30, 5 to 10 (10.30 to 10.30 end
July to beg Sept)
Closed Sun

The menu changes summer and winter in
this open-minded wholefood restaurant.
The aim is to serve meat and vegetarian
dishes side by side, with no clash of
loyalties. On the one hand there might be
lamb curry, beef ragout with celery and
walnuts, and turkey casseroled with
olives, capers and dried fruit; on the other,
Tibetan buckwheat roast, tofu burgers, or
spinach, mushroom and pasta pie. At
lunch-time there are also filled jacket
potatoes; in the evening there are fondues.
Sweets are home made.

Potter In [5/10]

19 Durngate Street
TEL Dorchester (0305) 68649

Open 10 to 5 &
Closed Sun; bank hols; Christmas Day and
Boxing Day

Rosalind Armstrong's wholefood snack
bar puts the emphasis on natural
ingredients, salads and simple vegetarian
dishes, with one meat speciality each day.
Asparagus pancake has been good.
Everything is cooked on the premises,
including rolls and cakes.

EASTLEIGH Hampshire — map 2

Piccolo Mondo [6/10]

1 High Street
TEL Eastleigh (0703) 613180

Open noon to 2.30, 6.30 to 11 (midnight Thur,
Fri and Sat) & (also WC)
Closed Sun; bank hols

A useful place for a quick pizza. For around
£3 you can choose from a range of
toppings. Also on the menu are pasta
dishes and a few more expensive items
such as fried calamari with salad.
Drinkable Italian house wine.

EAST MEON Hampshire   map 2

The George [6/10]

Church Street
TEL East Meon (073 087) 481

Open for food noon to 2, 7 to 10
Closed Christmas Day

A very popular, crowded pub that serves
good-value lunches of crab salad, quiches,
and home-made pies, such as rabbit or
steak, kidney and oyster in beer. Char-
grilled steaks are also served at the bar.
More expensive evening meals in the
restaurant. Beers from Friary Meux, Gales
and Wadworths. No children.

EVERLEIGH Wiltshire   map 2

Crown [6/10]

TEL Collingbourne Ducis (026 485) 223

Open for food 11 (noon Sun) to 2.30 (2 Sun),
6 to 12
Closed Christmas Day

Built in the seventeenth century as a
manor dower-house, this attractive inn
still has a traditional atmosphere and a
sense of history. The style is easygoing,
convivial and old-fashioned – particularly
in the lounge. Jim Earle is keen on fresh,
local produce and often catches his own
trout. Best-seller from the bar menu is
home-cooked Wiltshire ham with free-
range egg and chips; there are also big
bowls of soup, burgers, and smoked Avon
eel with salad. Daily lunch-time specials
might include hot ham, or steak and
kidney pie, and there's French onion soup
every Saturday. More expensive
restaurant. There's a family room with a
piano, as well as a walled garden for
children. Wadworths beers.

FIDDLEFORD Dorset   map 2

Fiddleford Inn [6/10]

TEL Sturminster Newton (0258) 72489

Open for food 11 to 2.30, 6.30 to 10
& (also ladies WC)
Closed Christmas Day D and Boxing Day

This one-time brewery has new owners
who are moving the menu towards weekly

changing bistro-style dishes. Fiddleford
pancakes – with all kinds of fillings from
seafood to chicken and mushroom – are
still a speciality. So are the real ales from
Gales, Hook Norton, Wadworths, the
Wiltshire Brewery and more. The garden
has a play area for children.

FORDINGBRIDGE
Hampshire   map 2

Coffee & Cream [6/10]

26 High Street
TEL Fordingbridge (0425) 54149

Open 10 to 5.30, 7.30 to 9.30
Closed D Mon to Thur

Vivienne Davies has moved down the road
to larger premises and has introduced a
no-smoking garden room. Her continental-
style tea-room still serves excellent
espresso and cappuccino to go with triple-
decker sandwiches, salads, and hot snacks
such as chicken and mushroom vol-au-
vent or macaroni cheese. Jacket potatoes
get all kinds of fillings, from savoury
mince to smoked mackerel with mandarin
oranges and mayonnaise. Home-made
waffles and ice-cream to finish. Three-
course evening meals are £7.50. Unlicensed,
but bring your own wine in the evenings
(20p corkage).

GREAT WISHFORD
Wiltshire   map 3

Royal Oak [6/10]

TEL Salisbury (0722) 790229

Open for food noon to 2, 7 to 9.45, plus 3.30 to 6
Sun to Fri spring and summer & (also WC)
Closed Christmas Day

Very much a pub for all the family, and
sympathetic to changes in the licensing
laws. The menu is long and tells all in
great detail (down to the brand of rice used
in various dishes). There are cold platters
with home-baked bread, puff-pastry pies
such as pork and scrumpy, steaks,
specialities ranging from creole veal to
burgundy beef, plus an increasing
emphasis on seafood. Completing the
picture are omelettes, burgers, pizzas, and
jacket potatoes. The owners use a flexible

pricing policy, offering cheaper dishes on Mondays and Tuesdays; they also stay open for afternoon teas in spring and summer. Ushers beers.

LACOCK Wiltshire   map 2

Red Lion [8/10]

High Street
TEL Lacock (024 973) 456

Open for food noon to 2, 7 to 10 (9 Sun) &
Closed Christmas Day and Boxing Day

Agricultural implements line the walls of this cavernous, higgledy-piggledy pub that might once have been a school or a brewery. Now it stands in a village within striking distance of the M4. The menu is old-English country cooking with some cottagey touches: game terrine with crab-apple jelly, a brace of giant sausages with locally produced Urchfont mustard; beef pie laced with Guinness; bubble and squeak. Vegetables are good and there's bread-and-butter pudding to finish. Wadworths beers on handpump.

MALMESBURY Wiltshire   map 2

 Vine Tree [6/10]

Norton
TEL Hullavington (066 63) 654

Open for food noon to 2, 7 to 10.30 &
Closed Tue

This small pub, licensed since 1863, packs a lot of atmosphere into a small space – from polo mementoes to a log fire. Along with guest beers and the excellent local ale, there is an intelligent blackboard menu of steaks, jacket potatoes, pies, and salads, plus some occasional oddballs, like goose or shark. All the cooking is done on the premises. There is a large garden with children's playground at the back.

MARLBOROUGH Wiltshire   map 2

 Bentley's Wine Bar [8/10]

7 Kingsbury Street
TEL Marlborough (0672) 54776

Open noon to 2, 7 to 9.45 &
Closed Sun; bank hols; 2 weeks Sept

A beautifully restored old building with open fireplaces and beams everywhere. The dining-room is like a tiny bistro. Nigel and Jane Worral's enterprise shows in the light lunch menu, which is aimed at business people and shoppers. Everything is home made and streets ahead of the average wine-bar offerings: smooth chicken liver and herb pâté with redcurrant sauce; cream of broccoli soup; crab and avocado salad with orange mayonnaise; garlic-baked poussin with onion and smoked bacon sauce. More expensive evening meals. The wine list includes ten by the glass.

Polly Tea Rooms [8/10]

26–27 High Street
TEL Marlborough (0672) 52146

Open 8.30 (9 Sun) to 6 (7 Sat and Sun) &
Closed Christmas Day to 27 Dec; 1 Jan

The best traditional tea-shop in Wiltshire, and a classic of its kind. It has all the expected trappings, from low beamed ceilings to flowery crockery, and the backbone of the menu is excellent home baking: scones and bread, cakes, gateaux and pastries. From breakfast onwards there's a range of genuine home-cooked food without frills. Lunch brings soup, fish mousse, and honey-baked gammon, backed up by specials such as salmon and spinach roulade, chicken and apricot plaite, or red pepper and tomato hot-pot with herb bread. Excellent coffees and teas, wine by the glass. Take-aways.

MARSHWOOD VALE
Dorset   map 1

Shave Cross Inn [6/10]

TEL Broadwindsor (0308) 68358

Open for food noon to 1.30 (1.15 Sun), 7 to 9.30 &
Closed Mon (exc bank hols)

Surrounded by the beautiful countryside of the Marshwood Vale, this fourteenth-century thatched inn is remote, friendly and welcoming. Excellent ploughman's comes with decent cheese and farmhouse butter; Dorset pâté and sausages are made especially for the pub; and there's fresh crab, lobster, and strawberries in season.

Dorset beers from Hall and Woodhouse, Devenish and Eldridge Pope. Family room and adventure playground for the children.

MIDDLE WALLOP
Hampshire   map 2

Fifehead Manor [7/10]

TEL Andover (0264) 781565

Open noon to 2.30 & (also WC)
Closed 1 week at Christmas

This ancient Hampshire manor-house scores heavily with its history and setting. It makes an ideal spot for a relaxed bar lunch. The short menu always has seasonal soups, from mange-tout or carrot and coriander in summer to vegetable and lentil or barley broth in winter. Sandwiches are filled with home-cooked beef, honey-roast ham, or smoked chicken, and there are ploughman's with salads and freshly baked rolls. Three-course set lunch in the dining-room is £7.50 for dishes such as chicken with peanut and chilli sauce or spiced lamb with aubergines. Afternoon cream teas are £3.50, and there are more expensive dinners.

MINSTEAD Hampshire   map 2

Honeypot [5/10]

TEL Southampton (0703) 813122

Open 10.30 to 5.30
Closed Nov to Feb

Honey Pot cream teas are big attractions in this little tea-room. The Queen Bee is the full works with scones, a choice of jams, butter or clotted cream and a pot of tea; the Drones version is just bread and jam or honey with tea. Light lunches feature home-made soup, salads, and club sandwiches plus a hot dish. From 7.30pm, Wednesday to Saturday, the place becomes the Honeysuckle Cottage Restaurant.

PETERSFIELD Hampshire   map 2

Folly Wine Bar [7/10]

Folly Market
TEL Petersfield (0730) 64088

Open noon to 2.30 (2 Sun), 6 (7 Sun) to 10.30
Closed Christmas Day

A huge converted barn with high rafters, bare floorboards and wooden tables. The menu is typical of an enterprising wine bar, with deep-fried mushrooms and tomato dip, kidneys bonne femme with brown rice, and stuffed mussels. A number of Mexican dishes have been added and there are always vegetarian specialities. Bread comes in big hunks, cheese are ripe and the coffee is strong. Children's menu available on request. Above-average wines.

PLUSH Dorset   map 2

Brace of Pheasants [6/10]

TEL Piddletrenthide (030 04) 357

Open for food 11.30 (noon Sun) to 2, 7.30 to 10

This thatched pub started life as a pair of sixteenth-century cottages and the village forge. It is now one of the most attractive hostelries in the area. Inside are beams, antiques and inglenooks. Seasonal game and char-grilled steaks supplement the bar menu, which has French onion soup laced with brandy, smoked mackerel pâté with lemon and gooseberry sauce, and lambs' kidneys cooked with tomato and basil. There are also specials and lunch-time dishes as as noisettes of lamb with rosemary butter. Bass and Hancocks beer on draught. Family room and garden.

POOLE Dorset   map 2

Chez Christian's [6/10]

73 Commercial Road,
Ashley Cross, Parkstone
TEL Parkstone (0202) 744316

Open noon to 2, 7 to 10 & (also WC)
Closed Sat L; Sun

Monsieur Christian serves unpretentious bistro food in this French café. Main dishes centre on the charcoal grill, which delivers rump steak and lamb chops as well as tuna, swordfish, and shark. To start there's seafood salad or mushrooms à la grecque; to finish there are ice-creams or apple tart.

NEW ENTRY Inn a Nutshell [6/10]

27 Arndale Centre
TEL Poole (0202) 673888

Open 9.30 to 5
Closed Sun; bank hols

No-smoking vegetarian café at the back of
the shopping centre. The menu is international, taking in mushroom Stroganoff,
oatmeal and cheese roast, vegetable
lasagne and African pilaff. Salads are
interesting and there are also home-baked
cakes and puddings such as barm brack
and treacle tart.

PORTSMOUTH Hampshire   map 2

Palash Tandoori [7/10]

124 Kingston Road, North End
TEL Portsmouth (0705) 664045

Open noon to 2.30, 6 to 12.30 (1 Fri and Sat,
11.30 Sun) ⅋ (also wc)
Closed Christmas Day

One of the most avidly reported Indian
restaurants in southern England, and
rightly so as the cooking is good value and
well above the usual curry-house average.
The décor is all pine tables and wood-clad
walls, with candles and flowers on the
tables. The menu holds few surprises, but
there are recommendations for the
tandooris and karahi dishes, also specialities, such as moghlai chicken with cream
and almonds, mint gosht, and spicy
chicken zelfarji. Set meals begin at £6.25
a head.

Pizza House [6/10]

14 Hilsea Market, London Road
TEL Portsmouth (0705) 695542

Open 7 to 11.30 (midnight Fri and Sat) ⅋
Closed Sun; Christmas Day, Boxing Day and
1 Jan; bank hols

Pizzas and pasta dishes are the cheapest
bets in Giuseppe and Massimo's informal
trattoria. There are eleven toppings for the
pizzas, from Marinara with shellfish to
Massimo with salami, olives and
mushrooms. Pasta is cooked al dente, and
big bowls of minestrone come with home-
made rolls. Full meals can take the bill
into double figures. House wines by the
carafe.

POWERSTOCK Dorset   map 2

NEW
ENTRY   ## Three Horseshoes [9/10]

TEL Powerstock (030 885) 328

Open for food noon to 2.30, 7 to 10 ⅋ (also wc)
Closed Mon

At the head of a beautiful Dorset valley,
with gardens overlooking the village. The
Fergusons put the emphasis on local fish,
game, and home-grown vegetables, and the
bar menu shows the full range. Cream of
cauliflower soup or grilled sardines with
garlic butter might be followed by grilled
Torbay sole, scallops in white wine, or
poached brill. To balance this there might
be calves' liver and bacon with Madeira
sauce, or aubergine bake. Cheeses are from
Dorset and Somerset; bread is baked at
Maiden Newton. More expensive
restaurant meals.

ROMSEY Hampshire   map 2

White Horse Hotel [6/10]

Market Place
TEL Romsey (0794) 512431

Open 12.30 to 2, 7 to 10 (9 Sun) ⅋ (also wc)

Good-value set lunches are served in this
hotel, now part of THF. Two courses can
be had for under £5; beef and venison
casserole with crisp fresh vegetables might
be followed by fresh fruit salad. There are
also bar snacks of sandwiches and jacket
potatoes. Children's menu.

SALISBURY Wiltshire   map 2

NEW
ENTRY   ## Harper's [9/10]

7 Ox Row, The Market Square
TEL Salisbury (0722) 333118

Open noon to 2, 6.30 to 10 (10.30 Sat)
Closed Sun L; Christmas Day and Boxing Day

'Real food is our speciality' say the
Harpers, who run this family-oriented
upstairs restaurant. Lunch is the best
value, with robust dishes such as beef
goulash, roast marinated poussin with
lemon and lime sauce, plus vegetarian
bake. There's gutsy soup or ratatouille to
start, and treacle tart or chocolate mousse

to finish. The three-course 'shoppers' special' is a Saturday bargain at £4.50; cheaper snacks are also available. Dinners are more expensive, but still good value at around £10 a head. House wines by the glass.

Haunch of Venison [6/10]

TEL Salisbury (0722) 22024

Open 10 to 2.30, 6 to 11 summer (10.30 winter)
Closed Sun D Oct to May

Salisbury's most ancient pub still has some echoes of a medieval alehouse, with its flagstone floors, exposed beams and boisterous atmosphere. Downstairs there is decent pub grub; home-made soups, savoury pies, such as chicken or steak and kidney, savoury pancakes and the like. Venison, naturally, appears on the menu in the more expensive Dickensian dining-room upstairs. Courage beers on draught; wine by the glass.

Hob Nob Coffee Shop [5/10]

The Kings House, 65 The Close
TEL Salisbury (0722) 332151

Open 10 to 4 (4.30 July and Aug, plus 2 to 4.45 Sun July to Aug) & (also WC)
Closed Sun; Oct to beg Apr

The coffee-shop attached to the South Wiltshire Museum is great value for light snacks and cakes. Ploughman's, filled rolls, and vegetarian soup (summer only) are backed up by good home-made cakes: apple crumble cake, date slice, raspberry buns, oat and raisin crunchies. Special set lunches for a minimum of four people can be ordered a week in advance: the choice is mainly vegetarian, from croustade of courgette or pasta and vegetable bake to pizzas and salads.

Just Brahms [8/10]

68 Castle Street
TEL Salisbury (0722) 28402

Open 11 to 2, 7 to 10 (10.30 Fri and Sat)
Closed Sun; bank hols

Stephen Hamson has done great things for Salisbury by opening this smart, youthful

wine bar-cum-bistro. Best value for cheap eaters is the single course menu, which has fresh pasta, galette of aubergine with tomato and yoghurt, casserole of fresh vegetables in puff pastry, alongside crêpes, open smoked-fish sandwiches, and steak and mushroom pie. The main menu is more ambitious, and full meals can take the bill into double figures. Dishes are in the modern vein of duck breast and mange-tout salad, beef fillet with three mustards; and tournedos of veal with chive and herb sauce. Six house wines by the glass.

Mainly Salads [6/10]

18 Fisherton Street
TEL Salisbury (0722) 22134

Open 10 to 5
Closed Sun

This modest vegetarian café gets very busy: there's no room for prams or pushchairs on Saturdays. The long display counter has a good showing of salads, plus hot dishes served from big tins and flan cases. Tomato, vegetable and lentil soup is a hefty purée, and the spiced nut loaf has been good. Morning coffee and afternoon teas are served with cakes. Take-aways. Unlicensed.

Michael Snell Tea Rooms [6/10]

8 St Thomas's Square
TEL Salisbury (0722) 336037

Open 9 (8.30 Sat) to 5.30 &
Closed Sun; bank hols

Michael Snell's skill is as a baker and pâtissier and high-quality cakes are served in the tea-room attached to his shop. The menu also has quiches, flans, and salads, plus hot lunch dishes such as beef curry. To finish there are real home-made ice-creams and sorbets. The children's menu steers clear of burgers and fish fingers. Coffee is freshly percolated. Unlicensed.

Mo's [7/10]

62 Milford Street
TEL Salisbury (0722) 331377

Open noon to 2.30, 5.30 (6 Sun) to 11.15
(midnight Fri and Sat)
Closed Sun (Jan and Feb); Sun L Mar to Dec;
Christmas Day and Boxing Day

The restaurant has a brightly lit exterior
near to the main shopping centre, and it
gets lively in the evenings. The emphasis
is still on a mixture of burger and bistro,
taking in barbecued spare ribs, chilli, and
steak and kidney pie on the way. Finish
with knickerbocker glory or treacle tart.
One-course business lunches are a new
feature, and there's a mini-menu for
children. Milk shakes, Colt 45 or
Wadworths 6X to drink. Take-aways.

Stoby's [6/10]

Market Place
TEL Salisbury (0722) 21950

Open 10 (5 Sun) to 10
Closed Christmas Day and Boxing Day

A long-established fish and chip shop in a
black-and-white painted building. There
are views of the market square from the
old bow windows. Upstairs is a long room
with bare brick walls and rows of pews and
tables down one side. Generous portions of
fish and chips are served with good peas,
bread-and-butter, and a big mug of tea.
Take-aways downstairs. Unlicensed.

SEAVIEW Isle of Wight   map 2

Seaview Hotel [7/10]

High Street
TEL Seaview (0983) 612711

Open noon to 2, 7.30 to 9.30 & (also wc)
Closed Sun D

Excellent, family-run Victorian hotel very
near the beach. The Haywards support
local fishermen and food producers,
gearing their menus to supplies. At lunch-
time there's a good trade in bar snacks,
which can range from pizzas and lasagne
to sauté scallops or lobster salad. More
expensive restaurant meals, including a
two-course set lunch for £7.50. Children
over four are welcome.

SHANKLIN Isle of Wight   map 2

Cottage [6/10]

8 Eastcliff Road
TEL Shanklin (0983) 862504

Open noon to 2 &
Closed Mon; mid-Feb to mid-Mar and Oct to
mid-Nov

An elegant pink restaurant in a
picturesque village about ten minutes
from the sea. Fixed-price lunches are good
value at £5.50 for dishes such as roast lamb
with rosemary, and braised beef with
mushrooms. Evening meals are more
ambitious and more expensive. No
children.

SOUTHAMPTON
Hampshire   map 2

Alice's [6/10]

16 Carlton Place
TEL Southampton (0703) 225503/220480

Open 11 to 11 (11.30 Fri and Sat)
Closed Sun; Mon D; bank hols; Christmas to
New Year

In a quiet street slightly out of the town
centre is this American/Mexican brasserie
serving excellent burgers and chocolate
fudge cake in a setting of stripped pine and
old American ads. The menu flashes its
way through guacamole, barbecued ribs,
double hot-dogs, enchiladas, and club
sandwiches, with steaks and salads for
good measure. Ice-cream sundaes and
pecan pie to finish. Milk shakes, beers and
wine by the jug or glass.

La Brasserie [7/10]

33-34 Oxford Street
TEL Southampton (0703) 35043/221046

Open noon to 2, 6 to 11.30 & (also wc)
Closed Sun

Southampton's Oxford Street is
fashionable and upwardly mobile. This
smart, pink brasserie follows the trend.
Stay with the fixed-price menus to eat
cheaply (lunch £6, dinner £6.50). The
quality of the cooking shows in the good
sauces, tender meat and lightly cooked

vegetables. Start with creamy pea soup garnished with strips of lettuce, before beef bourguignonne, escalope of veal with lemon, or breast of chicken stuffed with prawn mousse. Finish with crème brûlée or oranges in Grand Marnier. The *carte* is more showy and will take the bill well into double figures.

Kohinoor [7/10]

2 The Broadway, Fortswood
TEL Southampton (0703) 582770

Open noon to 2.30, 6 to midnight ᕒ (also WC)
Closed Christmas Day and Boxing Day

Rated as the best Indian restaurant in Southampton – along with its offshoot Kuti's (see entry). The décor is blue and grey, and the menu moves through good birianis, lamb pasanda and karahi gosht. Finish with kulfi, and drink lager.

NEW ENTRY Kuti's [7/10]

70 London Road
TEL Southampton (0703) 221585/333473

Open noon to 2.30, 6 to midnight ᕒ

Some of the most adventurous Indian food in Southampton is served at this comfortable pink and grey restaurant in the town centre. Lunch is an excellent buffet – £5.75 for as much as you can eat. The menu has some unexpected starters, including bhel-pooris, dahi vada and an assorted tiffin with lots of savoury snacks, before typical North Indian tandoori dishes and curries. There are good reports of the rogan josh, thick dhal, spinach and bhindi bhaji. Good-value thalis are another feature; the vegetarian Gujerati version is £6.25. Start your meal with a drink of chaas, diluted lassi which can be spiced Bombay-style with ginger, fresh coriander, cumin and fried mustard seeds. Finish with kulfi or gulab jamun. Kingfisher beer. Related to the Kohinoor (see entry above).

Lunch Break [5/10]

321–323 Shirley Road, Shirley
TEL Southampton (0703) 772713

Open 11 (9 Sat) to 3 ᕒ (also WC)
Closed Sun; bank hols

A little café attached to one of Pauline and Tony Butler's excellent bread shops. Look for the hot dishes, such as liver and bacon or beef layer pie, which are served with vegetables, salads, or baked potatoes. Cakes and snacks are also available. Unlicensed.

NEW ENTRY Maxwells [6/10]

1st Floor, East Street Shopping Centre
TEL Southampton (0703) 30831

Open 9.30 to 5 ᕒ (also WC)
Closed Sun; bank hols

This used to be Trugs, a bright airy self-service restaurant on the first-floor of a shopping precinct. New owners have changed the name and offer a good balance of vegetarian and meat dishes. There's a salad bar (£1.95, including bread), soups are well made, and the choice of home-made dishes ranges from sailor's curry, and chicken and mushroom pie, to prawn chowder, and cauliflower cheese. Sweets include walnut pie and ice-creams. Wine by the glass.

Pearl Harbour [7/10]

86A–88A Above Bar Street (first floor)
TEL Southampton (0703) 39833/225248

Open noon to midnight

After seven years this is still a useful Chinese restaurant offering some decent Cantonese cooking in a relaxed, spacious setting. Westernised set lunches are very cheap, but it's worth going for the freshly made dim-sum and one-plate meals, such as noodle soup with roast pork or fried beef ho fun with chilli and black-bean sauce. Otherwise the long menu ranges from deep-fried boned duck with minced prawn to bean curd and mixed meat hot-pot. Minimum charge £5 in the evening.

Piccolo Mondo [6/10]

36 Windsor Terrace
TEL Southampton (0703) 36890

Open 10 to 8 (7 Mon) ᕒ
Closed Sun

Pizzas are baked the Neapolitan way in this bustling little place. They are crisp round the edges, soft in the middle and topped with plenty of good things. There's minestrone, too, plus meaty lasagne and a few pasta dishes. Strong espresso, wine by the glass. Sandwiches available as take-aways.

SOUTHSEA Hampshire   map 2

Barnaby's Bistro [8/10]

56 Osborne Road
TEL Portsmouth (0705) 821089

Open noon to 2.30, 6 to 11 &
Closed Sun L; Christmas Day, Boxing Day and
1 Jan

Only the ice-cream is not home made in Colin Herbert's cheerful bistro with red cloths and art exhibition posters on the walls. Menus change seasonally and standard dishes, such as chilled avocado, cucumber and yoghurt soup, roast rack of lamb with mint jelly, and char-grilled baby chicken with Dijon mustard, are backed up by fresh seafood and vegetarian specialities along the lines of tagliatelle with tomato, celery and toasted almonds, or stuffed aubergine with rice. A new feature is a cheap menu of lunch-time specials: £1.65 pays for cauliflower cheese and salad or seafood risotto or blue cheese and cress quiche. Children's portions half-price. House wines by the glass, plus cocktails.

Colombo's [6/10]

12 Clarendon Road
TEL Portsmouth (0705) 755291

Open noon to 2.30, 5 to 11 (noon to 11 Sat; 6 to
10.30 Sun) &
Closed Christmas Day, Boxing Day and 1 Jan

A small, family-run business serving honest food with an Italian flavour. Pizzas are the mainstay – the quattro staggione is popular. Otherwise the menu has minestrone with garlic bread and interesting pasta dishes such as fettucine with butter, garlic and basil, or baked macaroni with bolognese sauce, Mozzarella and salami. Good espresso and cappuccino; wine by the glass.

Country Kitchen [6/10]

59A Marmion Road
TEL Portsmouth (0705) 811425

Open 10 to 6
Closed Sun

The emphasis is on wholefoods and vegetarian dishes in this cheerful restaurant opposite Waitrose, and the menu also has at least one vegan meal each day. Pâtés and pizzas have been added to a list that takes in quiches, filled jacket potatoes, and salads, plus specials and soups. The home-made cakes and fruit crumbles are good, too. Unlicensed, but there is a big selection of teas.

Mayfair Chinese Restaurant [6/10]

96 Castle Road
TEL Portsmouth (0705) 733353

Open 5 (2 Sun) to 2 &
Closed Christmas Day and Boxing Day

Seafood, Cantonese and Pekinese specialities share the limelight in this Chinese restaurant. Prices are reasonable, quality is high, and the place is open well into the early hours. Good dishes have included hot-and-sour soup, deep-fried seaweed, and bean curd stuffed with minced prawns.

Midnight Tandoori [6/10]

101 Palmerston Road
TEL Portsmouth (0705) 822567

Open noon to 2.30, 6 to 12.30 (1.30 Fri and Sat)
Closed Christmas day

A new team is maintaining standards at this reliable Indian restaurant. The menu doesn't stray far from the curry-house staples, but there are good reports of the samosas, chicken tikka masala, and vegetable dishes. Mint gosht – a favourite with several Hampshire restaurants – is one of the specials. The choice of good-value set meals includes a vegetarian spread for £5.70. Drink Kingfisher beer.

Rosie's Vineyard [7/10]

87 Elm Grove
TEL Portsmouth (0705) 755944

Open noon to 2 (Sun only), 7 to 11 (10.30 Sun and
Sept to May)
Closed L Mon to Sat; Christmas Day to 29 Dec;
1 and 2 Jan

This lively wine bar has a pergola covered
'wine garden' where barbecues are held on
Friday and Saturday evenings. Around £5
pays for fish brochette, steaks, or pork
kebabs with salads. The main menu is
typical bistro-style, ranging from stuffed
mussels and taramosalata to chicken
Seville with tagliatelle, seafood pancakes,
and beefsteak and Guinness pie. Sweets
include chocolate rum pot and Dutch
apple pie. Wine by the glass.

STEEP Hampshire   map 2

Harrow Inn [6/10]

TEL Petersfield (0730) 62685

Open for food 10.30 to 2.30 (noon to 2 Sun),
6 (7 Sun) to 10.30
Closed Christmas Eve

This tiny pub in the middle of nowhere
doesn't encourage crowds or publicity; it
isn't built for droves of weekend visitors.
Even so, it has its virtues, notably simple
home-made food, including big bowls of
soup, home-made Scotch eggs, home-
cured ham in sandwiches, and ploughman's, plus hot dishes such as baked
marrow. Flowers and Whitbread beers in
barrels behind the bar, cider, and wine by
the glass. No children.

SWINDON Wiltshire   map 2

Mamma's Kitchen [6/10]

122 Victoria Road
TEL Swindon (0793) 22558

Open noon to midnight &

Unfussy neighbourhood trattoria selling
some of the best-value Italian food in
Swindon. Big pizzas are the main
attraction, with a choice of five for under
£3. Otherwise there are massive portions
of pasta (second helpings are compli-
mentary) as well as home-made soups,
prawns with garlic, and more expensive
steak and chicken dishes. Open right
through the day for snacks, tea and coffee.
House wine by the tumbler. Pizza and
pastas to take away.

TARRANT MONKTON
Dorset   map 2

Langton Arms [6/10]

TEL Tarrant Hinton (025 889) 225

Open for food 11.30 to 2.30 (noon to 2 Sun), 6 to
11 (7 to 10.30 Sun) & (also WC)

Seventeenth-century thatched pub by the
village church. Bar food is a simple choice
of lentil and onion soup, steak and kidney
pudding, mushrooms florentine, and
chocolate mousse, backed up by steaks
and daily specials. On Monday nights
there are cheap three-course French meals
for around £5; Tuesdays and Fridays are for
pizzas; Wednesday is curry night; and
there are Chinese specialities on Thursday
evenings. More expensive restaurant. Bass,
Marstons Pedigree and Wadworths 6X on
handpump.

UPPER FROYLE Hampshire   map 2

Hen & Chicken [6/10]

TEL Bentley (0420) 22115

Open for food 10.30 to 2.30, 6 to 10.30 (11 Fri
and Sat) &

Once the haunt of horse-dealers and hop-
pickers, this sixteenth-century coaching-
inn now caters for all the family. The
Buttery Bar has a good choice of food from
omelettes, black pudding with bacon and
kidneys, curried chicken, and steaks to
fish moussaka and poached salmon. The
coconut treacle tart is good, too. There are
three-course Sunday lunches for £6.95 and
more expensive meals in the attached fish
restaurant. Beers might include representatives from Hall and Woodhouse or
Brakspears.

UPTON GREY Hampshire   map 2

 Hoddington Arms [8/10]

TEL Basingstoke (0256) 862371

Open noon to 2, 7.30 to 9.30

Ian Fisher and his wife are keen on fresh ingredients – especially fish – and offer daily changing blackboard specials in their spick-and-span village pub. Best value is at lunch-time, when there might be Dutch pea soup, moules marinière (with fresh Brixham mussels), Tuscan pasticcio with home-baked bread, and poached rabbit stew. The standard menu also has ploughman's, tarragon chicken, and mixed grill. More expensive dishes are served in the evening. Seventeen wines; Courage beers on draught.

WARMINSTER Wiltshire   map 2

Chinn's Celebrated Chophouse [6/10]

12–14 Market Place
TEL Warminster (0985) 212245

Open 10 to 2.30 &
Closed Sun; Christmas Day and Boxing Day; bank hols (exc Good Friday); 2 weeks Oct

The Pickfords no longer open in the evening, but concentrate their efforts on morning coffee and light lunches. Soup is made from good stock, and there are grills, ploughman's, and sandwiches in the middle of the day. Finish with local cheese, fruit pies, or sticky gateaux. Home-made cakes and scones. Children's menu.

Jenner's [6/10]

45 Market Place
TEL Warminster (0985) 213385

Open 9.30 to 5.30 &
Closed Sun Oct to Easter; Christmas Day to 1 Jan

Wholemeal vegetarian restaurant with a country air, pine furniture and rustic pottery. Start with home-made soup (though virtually a meal in itself), before vegetable and pulse lasagne, vegetable crumble, or egg mayonnaise salad. Old-fashioned fruit crumbles (banana and nut is a favourite) and bread-and-butter pudding come with cream or yoghurt as requested, but there are lighter ice-creams or sorbets too. Dark, no fat, low-calorie

fruit cake comes with a large hunk of butter on top. Unlicensed. A branch has opened at The Black Swan Arts Centre, Frome, Somerset.

WEST BAY Dorset   map 2

Riverside Restaurant & Café [7/10]

TEL Bridport (0308) 22011

Open 10.30 to 7 (8 Sat) & (also WC)
Closed Nov to Feb

For twenty years this café has been serving a mixture of excellent seafood, grills and fry-ups. The emphasis is now firmly on local fish, with daily specials taking in grilled red mullet, John Dory, and scallops, as well as real fish and chips. Alternatives are café staples such as bacon, egg and chips, omelettes, burgers, and pizzas. Home-made apple pie with clotted cream or 'last of the summer' pudding to finish. Wine by the glass.

WEST BEXINGTON Dorset   map 2

Manor Hotel [8/10]

Beach Road
TEL Burton Bradstock (0308) 897616

Open noon to 2, 7 to 10 (10.30 Sat) & (also WC)
Closed Christmas Day D

Set half-way down the hillside, this old-fashioned manor overlooks the great seventeen-mile stretch of Chesil Bank. Excellent snacks are served in the beamed cellar bar, where basics such as whitebait, meat curry, and chilli con carne are overshadowed by interesting specials. Look for the monkfish provençale, fricassee of veal, local West Bay scallops with bacon and cream, and 'gravad trout' (marinated like salmon). Vegetables are plentiful. More expensive restaurant meals. Beers from Eldridge Pope, Palmers and Wadworths.

WEST LULWORTH Dorset   map 2

Castle Inn [6/10]

Main Street
TEL West Lulworth (092 941) 311

Open for food 11 to 2.30 (2 Sun), 7 to 10.30 (11 Fri and Sat) & (also wc)
Closed Christmas Day D

An attractive thatched inn within walking distance of Lulworth Cove. There are good snacks in the bar, including a fine selection of crisp salads, well-filled rolls and specials such as shepherd's pie or cheese and onion bake. In summer there are barbecues in the garden. Devenish beers on handpump. No children.

WEYMOUTH Dorset   map 2

Sea Cow Bistro [7/10]

7 Custom House Quay
TEL Weymouth (0305) 783524

Open noon to 2, plus 7 to 9.30 July to mid-Sept & (also ladies wc)
Closed Sun; Christmas and New Year

An established harbourside bistro, well known for its good-value lunches. The price (£5.95) includes a selection from the smorgasbord cold table, which has an excellent choice of fish, meat, and salads including herrings in sweet mustard sauce, smoked mackerel, pastrami, and pizza. This can be followed by a hot dish such as lamb in rich onion gravy with a choice of potatoes and vegetables. The attached coffee-shop offers snacks through the day in summer, and there's a more expensive restaurant, open all year in the evenings Monday to Saturday, and for Sunday lunch.

Sibleys [7/10]

67 The Esplanade
TEL Weymouth (0305) 782196

Open 10 to midnight (11 Sun) &
Closed weekdays mid-Jan to mid-Mar

This continental-style restaurant now has tables on the pavement overlooking the pedestrianised shopping precinct. The wine bar has good-value food along the lines of mushroom and garlic pâté, cream

of chicken soup with brown rice, lasagne, jacket potatoes with smoked fish and prawn sauce. The adjoining restaurant, with Georgian bow windows overlooking the sea, offers slightly more ambitious dishes such as fresh pasta, interesting local seafood and unusual sweets, including blueberry pancakes. As well as a creditable wine list there's farmhouse cider, Samuel Smiles 'natural lager', perry, and organic rosé.

WHERWELL Hampshire   map 2

Mayfly [6/10]

TEL Chilbolton (026 474) 283

Open for food noon to 2 (1.45 Sun), 7 to 9 &

A sprawling stone pub idyllically situated near Wherwell on the banks of the River Test, with tables out on the river bank for summer evenings. The menu is short and to the point: cold cuts, quiches, a fine showing of salads, and some good-looking cheeses. There are also hot dishes, such as tandoori chicken, and a few puddings. Flowers and Whitbread Strong Country bitter on handpump.

WINCHESTER Hampshire   map 2

Cellar Peking [6/10]

Jewry Street
TEL Winchester (0962) 64178

Open noon to 2, 6 to 11 (11.30 Fri and Sat) &
Closed Christmas Day and Boxing Day

The name aptly describes this Chinese restaurant: the dining-room is in a basement and the menu emphasises Pekingese dishes. It is stylishly in vogue, with pink décor, mirrors and a menu that takes in twice-cooked pork with peppers, chicken with cashew nuts, and bang-bang chicken. Crispy wun-tun makes a good starter; glazed toffee apples are a favourite finish. Special Peking and Szechuan feasts for around £10 a head.

South East

Kent

Surrey

Sussex

ADDINGTON Kent   map 3

Angel Inn [6/10]

TEL West Malling (0732) 842117

Open for food noon to 2, 7 to 9.30 &
Closed Sun; Christmas Day D

A whitewashed seventeenth-century
village pub overlooking the green. There
are fresh fish dishes on Thursday and
Friday, otherwise the menu ranges from
kidneys in red wine and Lancashire hot-
pot to apple pie with custard.

ADDLESTONE Surrey   map 3

Cricketers [6/10]

32 Rowtown
TEL Weybridge (0932) 42808

Open for food noon to 2 (2.30 Sat, 1.45 Sun), 6 to
10 & (also WC)
Closed Sun D

Daily specials and vegetarian dishes
supplement a standard menu in this
friendly, comfortable pub. Look for celery
and cashew-nut risotto, vegetable quiche
and chilli as well as hot BLTs, jumbo
kippers with wholemeal bread, and brunch
fry-ups of bacon, sausage, eggs, tomatoes
and chips. Sunday lunch is a roast. There
are plans to operate a supper licence (food
until 3pm, then up to midnight every
evening except Sunday).

ALFRISTON East Sussex   map 3

Drusilla's Thatched Barn [7/10]

Drusilla's Corner
TEL Alfriston (0323) 870234

Open 10.30 to 5 & (also WC)
Closed Nov to Mar (exc Sun to mid-Dec and in
Feb and Mar)

Drusilla's is a family attraction. It boasts a
zoo, bakery, gift shop, pottery and
children's play barn. It is also home to the
English Wine Centre and has a pretty
thatched cottage restaurant. From the
bakery come cakes, soda bread, shortbread
and much more. The lunch menu is strong
on vegetarian dishes, such as tomato and
asparagus flan, as well as local recipes:
Sussex pie is sausagemeat and onions

wrapped in pastry. Children are offered
home-made soup, cottage pie and salad or
jacket potato for about £1. Beers, ciders
and English wines to drink.

ASHFORD Kent   map 3

Flying Horse Inn [6/10]

Boughton Aluph
TEL Ashford (0233) 20914

Open for food 10 to 2.30, 6 to 11 & (also WC)

Fifteenth-century village inn on the
Pilgrim's Way, with a rose garden and
views of the cricket green. Bar food centres
on a range of cold cuts and salads,
supplemented by roasts, home-made pies,
such as turkey and ham, plus apple pie,
and fruit flans. Courage beers on draught.

ASHTEAD Surrey   map 3

Curry House Tandoori [6/10]

71A The Street
TEL Ashford (037 22) 77495/77432

Open noon to 3, 6 to 11.30 (midnight Fri and
Sat) & (also WC)

Useful middle-of-the-road curry house
with a standard menu, big portions and
reasonable prices for the area. The range
includes all the familiar tandooris and
tikkas (including a mixed grill for about
£6), plus curries, ranging from chicken
Madras and prawn patia to vegetable
biriani. Drink lager or wine. There is an
identical branch, called The Curry House
Tandoori 2, at 1 Cheam Road, Ewell,
Surrey (TEL 01-393 5528/0734).

BENENDEN Kent   map 3

King William IV [6/10]

The Street
TEL Cranbrook (0580) 240636

Open for food 11.30 to 2.30, 6 to 11
Closed Christmas Day D

A tiny, low-ceilinged pub, and enormously
popular – so expect a crowd and go early if
you want a table. The short menu can take
in crab croquettes, duck pâté and beef
Stroganoff, with a nod to vegetarians in the
mushroom quiche, vegetable curry, and

baked stuffed aubergines. Shepherd Neame beers; wine by the glass. Children welcome in the beer garden.

BEXHILL-ON-SEA
East Sussex   map 3

Trawlers [6/10]

60 Sackville Road
TEL Bexhill-on-Sea (0242) 210227

Open 11.30 to 1.45, 5 to 8.45 (7.45 Mon)
Closed Sun; Christmas Day, Boxing Day and 1 Jan

Fresh fish is delivered daily from around the country to ensure quality in this fish and chip restaurant and take-away. The menu usually has cod, haddock, skate, huss and plaice – with jumbo-sized portions available for an extra 60p. Children's menu. Unlicensed.

BIDDENDEN Kent   map 3

Claris's Tearoom [6/10]

TEL Biddenden (0580) 291025

Open 10.30 to 5.30
Closed Mon

An archetypal old-fashioned tea-room attached to a craft shop. The Winghams offer home-made soup, salads and things on toast, as well as a good showing of home-made cakes: their speciality is a cake made with pure orange juice and Cointreau topped with Jersey cream. Otherwise look for the walnut bread with apricot preserve and the hot bread pudding. Cream teas are £1.60. Unlicensed.

Ristorante da Claudio [6/10]

West House, 28 High Street
TEL Biddenden (0580) 291341

Open noon to 2.30, 7 to 10.30 &
Closed Sun, Mon; 1 week Jan; 1 week after Easter; 2 weeks end Aug

Have a starter of a dish of home-made pasta at lunch-time in Claudio Covelli's attractive trattoria. Soup is made from stock, and sweets include ice-cream and sorbets. Full meals can take the bill into double figures. House wine is under £5 a bottle.

Three Chimneys [8/10]

TEL Biddenden (0580) 291472

Open for food 11 to 2, 6.30 to 10 (noon to 1.30, 7 to 10 Sun)
Closed Christmas Day and Boxing Day

One of the best pubs in Kent, serving excellent home-cooked food in a classic setting of dried hops, beams and old settles. It is one of a dying breed. The short, regularly changing menu is chalked on a blackboard, and might feature mushrooms à la grecque, chicken in red wine and green pepper sauce, veal goulash, or aubergine and tomato pie. Soups are enterprising and terrine comes with home-made chutney. Real ales from Adnams, Godsons, Marstons and Harveys, among others, plus Biddenden cider. Garden room for families.

BRIGHTON East Sussex   map 3

Al Duomo [6/10]

7 Pavilion Buildings
TEL Brighton (0273) 26741

Open noon to 2.30, 6.30 to 11.30 &
Closed Sun; Christmas Day

Noisy, boisterous, no-frills trattoria close to the Royal Pavilion. The menu is a successful formula of giant pizzas with lots of toppings and good-value pasta dishes backed up by minestrone, well-dressed salads, and creamy sweets.

Al Forno [6/10]

36 East Street
TEL Brighton (0273) 24905

Open noon to 2.30, 6.30 to 11.30
Closed Mon; Christmas Day

Related to Al Duomo (see above). The style is the same in this long-established Italian restaurant on two floors. Most of the action takes place downstairs, where the pizza oven and coffee-making machines keep running.

Allan Johns [5/10]

8 Church Street
TEL Brighton (0273) 683087

Open 10 (9 Sat, 9.30 Fri, 10.30 Sun) to 5.30 (3
Sun, 6 Fri and Sat) &
Closed Christmas Day and Boxing Day; bank
hols

A seafood bar in the old style, with a few
checked-cloth tables at the back. The
main trade is for take-aways, but there are
platters of cockles, mussels, prawns and
crab, as well as bowls of jellied eels and
whelks. Sandwiches are freshly made on
brown bread and there are one or two hot
dishes, including jacket potatoes and cod
and chips. Unlicensed.

Billabong [6/10]

34 Hampton Place
TEL Brighton (0273) 774386

Open 10.30 to 6
Closed Mon (exc bank hols), Tue

Functional café specialising in croissants
with all kinds of fillings. The menu has
some unusual ideas, such as artichokes
with Gruyère, spicy spinach laced with
chilli, aubergines with garlic, or smoked
ham. Alternatively there's ratatouille,
bacon and beans on toast, or pasta with
French bread. Unlicensed.

NEW ENTRY | Chilka [8/10]

58 Preston Street
TEL Brighton (0273) 27343

Open 6.30 to 11.15 & (also WC)
Closed 2 weeks Feb to Mar, May to June,
Oct to Nov

The opening times may be restricted, but
this is one of the most interesting Indian
restaurants in the South of England. It is a
genuine Bengali eating place, where the
cooking is done to order and the menu is
far removed from the standard fare of
most curry houses. Mr Ghoshal is
knowledgeable, friendly and cares about
his food. Local fish is a feature: halibut is
cooked with fresh coconut and lemon.
Duck vindaloo is powerfully infused with
red wine and lemon grass, and the skill

shows in spicy koftas, kurmas and
excellent breads. Minimum charge is £5,
but the place offers excellent value.

Clarence Wine Bar [6/10]

Clarence Yard, Meeting House Lane,
The Lanes
TEL Brighton (0273) 720597

Open noon to 2.15, 6 to 10

Spanish-style building with an enclosed
courtyard, transformed into a popular
wine bar-cum-brasserie. The menu takes
in anything from grilled sardines with
tarragon or deep-fried mushrooms to beef
and ale pie and pork chop with apple
sauce. Banoffi pie is a popular sweet. Wine
by the glass. Children welcome in the
courtyard.

Food for Friends [9/10]

17A–18 Prince Albert Street, The Lanes
TEL Brighton (0273) 202310

Open 9 (11.30 Sun) to 10 &

The Lanes is overrun with eating places of
every description, but this informal
vegetarian café is the pick of the bunch.
Queues are long and the mood is laid back,
but the food is worth waiting for. Many
ingredients, including fruit, vegetables,
flour and tofu, are from local suppliers.
There are lots of salads, excellent bread
and eclectic dishes ranging from
Indonesian spring rolls or stir-fried
vegetables to kidney bean and courgette
goulash. Indian food on Monday evenings;
Mexican dishes on Tuesdays. Drink
French cider, apple juice or wine. A new
pâtisserie has opened round the corner at
41 Market Street.

Latin in the Lane [7/10]

10 Kings Road
TEL Brighton (0273) 28672

Open noon to 11 &

Ercole Cappai's neighbourhood Italian
restaurant is now open right through the
day. It still serves some of the best home-
made pasta in town, but the menu has
expanded to take in pizzas (served from

noon to 6), as well as an all-day buffet with salads. The best bets for more substantial meals are the plainly cooked fresh fish dishes, such as grilled dover sole or grey mullet. House wine is £4.80 a bottle.

Market Café [5/10]

19 Circus Street
TEL Brighton (0273) 608273

Open 11pm to 11am (9am Sat, 6am Sun) &
Closed bank hols; Christmas

The best place to eat in Brighton in the early hours. This all-night café opposite the vegetable market serves egg and chips, sausage, bacon, fried bread and black pudding in various combinations. A full blow-out should cost around £2, plus 50p for a big mug of tea or coffee. Unlicensed.

Melrose [6/10]

132 Kings Road
TEL Brighton (0273) 26520

Open noon to 11 &
Closed end Dec to early Feb

Excellent café by the West Pier serving gigantic grilled sole and plaice as well as fried fish and big steaks. Lunch of roast beef or chicken is under £3. The owner is Cypriot and this shows in the calamari, shish kebabs and moussaka. Apple pie, gateau or trifle for sweet.

Mock Turtle [8/10]

4 Poole Valley (off East Street)
TEL Brighton (0273) 27380

Open 10 to 6
Closed Sun and Mon; 2 weeks in autumn; Christmas

The best old-style tea-room in Brighton. It is tucked away in a lane leading to the bus station, but the place is full of atmosphere. Home-made cakes are displayed in the window, and a dresser is loaded with preserves, lemon curd, fruit cakes and gingerbread. Lunches might feature fish or home-made sausages with bacon. Afternoon tea comes with two-inch-high scones stuffed with cream and home-made jam.

The room is tiny, but there are now seats outside for fine weather. Unlicensed.

Pie in the Sky [6/10]

87 St James's Street
TEL Brighton (0273) 692087

Open noon to 2.30, 6.30 to 11.30 (noon to 11.30 Sat and Sun) &
Closed Christmas Day, Boxing Day and 1 Jan

Good fun for hungry kids. The staple menu of deep-dish pizzas, ice-creams and cheesecakes has been boosted with five different pastas and the same number of sauces. From Sunday to Thursday, customers can eat their fill for £2.60. Coffee, Coke and lager to drink.

Pizza Express [7/10]

22 Prince Albert Street, The Lanes
TEL Brighton (0273) 23205

Open noon to midnight &
Closed Christmas

A Sussex branch of the highly rated pizza chain (see London entry).

BURHAM Kent   map 3

Golden Eagle [6/10]

80 Church Street
TEL Medway (0634) 668975

Open for food 11 to 2.30, 6 to 11 (noon to 2, 7 to 10.30 Sun) & (also WC)

New landlord Mr Forde and chef Marga Hui are carrying on where Chris and Chiu Blackmore left off. This out-of-the-way village pub still offers an enterprising menu of South-East Asian food, with a few Chinese overtones. Nasi goreng, Singapore mee hoon, sweet-and-sour duck with vegetables, and king prawn sambal are typical of the regularly changing menu. There's also a chef's special feast at £8.50 a head for spare ribs, then kung po king prawns, ginger chicken, kari kambing, beef with vegetables, and Balinese pork, followed by ice-cream or lychees. By contrast the beers are thoroughly English: Wadworths, Shepherd Neame, Goachers. Children welcome in the dining area.

CAMBERLEY Surrey   map 2

Pizza Express [7/10]

52 Park Street
TEL Camberley (0276) 21846

Open 11.30 to midnight 🚶
Closed Christmas Day

A branch of the highly rated pizza chain in and around the capital (see London entry).

 # Tithas [6/10]

31 High Street
TEL Camberley (0276) 23279/65803

Open noon to 2.30, 6 to midnight
Closed Christmas Day and Boxing Day

There are echoes of London's Last Days of the Raj in this dimly lit Indian restaurant on two levels, although prices are quite a bit cheaper. The menu is a mixture of North Indian and Bengali, taking in tandoori lamb chops, chicken jalfrezi and lamb korma. Finish with kulfi, and drink lassi or spiced tea.

CANTERBURY Kent   map 3

NEW ENTRY # Cogan House [8/10]

53 St Peter's Street
TEL Canterbury (0227) 472986

Open 10.30 to 10.30
Closed Mon; Christmas Day, Boxing Day and 1 Jan

The oldest house in Canterbury has been turned into an English brasserie serving food twelve hours a day. Inside, the history and the décor contrast with the modern, forward-looking style of the food. The menu ranges from adventurous Cumbrian air-dried ham with tomato and shallot salad, or lamb chops with orange and samphire, to nut roast, and ploughman's with English cheeses. To finish there are home-made sweets, including summer pudding with clotted cream. Have one course or a full meal; there's a set menu at £7. English wines and real ales to drink, as well as local apple juice.

County Hotel Coffee Shop [6/10]

High Street
TEL Canterbury (0227) 66266

Open 10.30 to 11 🚶

All-day coffee-shop attached to one of Canterbury's popular hotels. At lunchtime and in the evening there are vegetarian dishes, such as fresh green tortelloni with ricotta and tomato sauce, or walnut, celery and coleslaw salad, as well as a cold buffet and sandwiches. Full afternoon tea is £3.20 for toasted muffins, cucumber sandwiches and cake, plus a pot of tea.

George's Brasserie [8/10]

71–72 Castle Street
TEL Canterbury (0227) 65658

Open 10 to 10 (10.30 Fri and Sat) 🚶
Closed Sun

The alternative to Cogan House (see above) and just as popular. This all-day brasserie is a long, narrow, upstairs room with pictures and posters in the bar, and a blackboard menu. Typical dishes are roast rack of lamb with apricot sauce, salmon with ginger and spring onions, and chorizo sausage with peperonata. Cheeses include sheeps' and goats' and there are old-fashioned sweets, such as apple crumble or bread-and-butter pudding. A dish of the day is £3; the cheapest set menu is £5.90. House wine is £3 per half-litre.

Il Vaticano [7/10]

35 St Margaret Street
TEL Canterbury (0227) 65333

Open 11 to 11 (noon to 10 Sun) 🚶
Closed Christmas Day and Boxing Day

Serves the best fresh pasta in Canterbury. Five kinds are made on the premises and served with a choice of nine sauces, from funghi, carbonara and vongole to prawns with mushrooms in garlic sauce or veal in cream and sherry sauce. There are a few starters, such as minestrone or carpaccio, plus Italian ice-creams to finish. Drink

Birra Peroni, aqua minerale or just a glass of wine.

Millers Arms [6/10]

Mill Lane, St Radigands
TEL Canterbury (0227) 452675

Open for food 12.30 to 2, 6.30 to 9

Very popular, traditional inn across the road from the River Stour. The food is in keeping, with steak and oyster pie, rabbit pie and Somerset braised pork on the bar menu, alongside chicken in wine sauce and chilli con carne. There's a more expensive restaurant. The hotel breakfasts are staunchly patriotic, with locally smoked kippers, bubble and squeak, and smoked haddock with poached egg. Beers from Wadworths and Marstons.

Sweet Heart of Canterbury [7/10]

Old Weavers House, 2–3 Kings Bridge
TEL Canterbury (0227) 458626

Open 9 to 6 &
Closed 2 weeks Jan

Admirable coffee-house that is part old English, part German/Swiss. The place stakes its reputation on the quality of its cakes and pâtisserie – plum torte, red plum flan, Kentish apple pie. There are also quiches, savoury croissants, and German sausages. Vegetables are organic, salt is kept to a minimum and artificial flavourings are eschewed: the only tinned item is, apparently, Bockwurst. The owners say that the vegetarian dishes are starting to outsell those containing meat. From July to September there's a buffet in the evening in the newly opened Old Weavers restaurant attached to the coffee-house. Good choice of teas and wine by the glass.

CHICHESTER West Sussex   map 2

Clinchs Salad House [7/10]

14 Southgate
TEL Chichester (0243) 788822

Open 8 to 5.30
Closed Sun, bank hols

Some of the best-value vegetarian food in the area is served at Alison Ellis's daytime restaurant. It is good for a cheap lunch of, say, carrot and coriander soup, mushroom florentine, or nut roast with cucumber sauce. Mixed bowls of salad are enterprising, and there's home-cooked ham for meat eaters. Gooseberry and hazelnut upside-down cake or redcurrant and raspberry cheesecake to finish. The owners have recently opened an evening restaurant serving similar food at 13 Southgate.

COBHAM Surrey   map 3

Plough [6/10]

Plough Lane, Downside
TEL Cobham (0932) 62514

Open for food noon to 2 (1.45 Sun), 5.30 to 9.30 & (also WC)

Comfortably modernised, centuries-old pub on the outskirts of town. Home-made pies and daily specials such as beef and mushrooms in red wine appear alongside jacket potatoes and ploughman's. There's also a Sunday carvery. Courage beers, modest wines.

CRANLEIGH Surrey   map 3

Bricks [6/10]

Smithbrook Kilns, Horsham Road
TEL Cranleigh (0483) 276780

Open 8.30 to 4.30 (2 Fri, Sat, Sun), plus 7.30 to 9.45 Fri and Sat &

Small, informal restaurant serving home-cooked food from a daily-changing menu. Choices might range from parsleyed gammon or picnic pies to beef and prune hot-pot. Seasonal puddings. Open for morning coffees and afternoon teas; more expensive evening meals on Friday and Saturday. Wine by the glass.

La Scala [6/10]

High Street
TEL Cranleigh (0483) 274900

Open noon to 2, 6.30 to 11
Closed Sun and Mon; Christmas Day and Boxing Day; Aug

Stay off the fillet steak and sole and it's possible to have three courses plus a drink for around £8 in this popular, good-value trattoria. The huge antipasto hors d'oeuvre is almost a meal in itself. There are also big home-made pasta dishes, such as fettuccine with mushrooms and cream, four kinds of pizza, plus inexpensive veal and chicken specialities. House wine is £5.15 a bottle.

DANEHILL East Sussex　　　map 3

Coach & Horses [6/10]

School Lane
TEL Chelwood Gate (082 574) 369

Open for food noon to 2 (1.45 Sun), 7 to 9 &
Closed Sun D and Mon D; Christmas Day D; Boxing Day

New owners have updated, rather than modernised, this classic Sussex pub and have converted a stable block into a small eating area. The food is home cooked and reliable: soups, hummus with pitta bread, lamb cutlets with good fresh vegetables, treacle tart and apple crumble. Harveys on handpump, plus guest beers; excellent house wine. Children's room.

DEAL Kent　　　map 3

Going Dutch [6/10]

144 High Street
TEL Deal (0304) 360075

Open 9 to 4.30 (8.30 to 5 Sat)
Closed Sun

A spick-and-span Dutch coffee-house specialising in decent snacks, such as tomato soup with meatballs, smoked Dutch sausage, salads and 'uitsmijter' (open sandwiches topped with fried eggs). Dutch fruit flan, coconut cake, and croissants go well with tea or coffee. Unlicensed.

DOVER Kent　　　map 3

Moonflower [6/10]

32–34 High Street
TEL Dover (0304) 213812

Open 11.30 to midnight

Long opening hours and a creditable range of Cantonese and Pekingese food make this family business one of the most useful Chinese restaurants in Kent. Downstairs is the all-day café and take-away; upstairs is the more formal restaurant, which offers shredded roast duck with bean sprouts, king prawns in black-bean sauce, as well as Peking duck, crispy roast belly pork, and old-style chop suey, and chow mein. Set meals begin at £6.50 a head.

EASTBOURNE East Sussex　　　map 3

Bosworth's Wine Bar [7/10]

8 Bolton Road
TEL Eastbourne (0323) 23023

Open noon to 2, 6 to 10
Closed Christmas Day and Easter Day

Formerly Mike's, this town-centre wine bar has cool grey and salmon pink décor, with cane chairs and wall-mounted globe lamps. The menu is short, straightforward and changes regularly. Standard dishes are outnumbered by unusual ones. Char-grilling is a feature – taking in burgers and lamb steak in green peppercorn sauce; otherwise there might be taramosalata, cauliflower creole, leek and ham au gratin, or chicken breast in blue Brie and cucumber sauce. The well-chosen wine list is a short tour round most major wine producing areas. Children welcome in the garden.

Qualisea [6/10]

9 Pevensey Road
TEL Eastbourne (0323) 25203

Open 11.30 to 8 &
Closed Sun

Still the best fish and chip shop in Eastbourne. On its day, it can deliver first-rate fish fried in thin crisp batter and served with excellent chips. The choice is cod, haddock, plaice or roe, backed up by egg and chips, sausages, and chicken. A sit-down meal of fish and chips with bread and butter costs around £1.50. Drink tea, or there is white wine by the glass.

EASTLING Kent   map 3

Carpenters Arms [6/10]

TEL Eastling (079 589) 234

Open for food 11.30 to 2.30 (noon to 1.30 Sun),
7 to 10 (9 Sun) &

A typical steep-roofed Kentish pub with
brick and timberwork and white clap-
boarding. Inside are rough oak beams and a
vast fireplace with restored bread ovens.
Hot home-made soups come with chunks
of brown bread and the menu also has
well-tried favourites, such as beef in ale,
ham and eggs, steak, mushroom and oyster
pie, plus good old-fashioned sweets:
treacle tart, spicy bread pudding and glazed
apple flan. Shepherd Neame beers on
handpump. Children welcome in the
supper room.

EGHAM Surrey   map 3

NEW ENTRY   Jack's [6/10]

19–20 High Street
TEL Egham (0784) 35492

Open 11.30 to 2, 5 to 11 (11.30 Fri and Sat)
& (also WC)
Closed Christmas Day and Boxing Day

After twenty years in business, this is still
one of the best fish and chip shops in
Surrey. The old décor has been replaced by
stripped pine floors and plastic flowers,
but the food is as good as ever. Prime cuts
of fish are served with thickly cut firm
chips, and the choice includes haddock,
cod, plaice, and huss. A sit-down lunch or
supper of fish and chips plus bread and
butter is £2.25. Take-aways. Drink tea, a
glass of wine or a pint of beer.

ESHER Surrey   map 3

NEW ENTRY   Greek Vine [7/10]

The Green, Claygate
TEL Esher (0372) 65125

Open noon to 3, 7 to 11 & (also WC)
Closed Sat L; Sun; bank hols; Christmas Day to
31 Dec

Smarter than some Greek tavernas, with
cane-backed chairs, white-tiled floors and
Aegean murals. Plastic vines creep over

the pergolas. The place is high on
atmosphere, families love it, and the food
is good value. Meze at £7.95 a head is a
good introduction to the menu, with its
cold dips and starters, salads and main-
course dishes. Souvla – new season's lamb
on the bone, marinated in white wine and
char-grilled with oregano – is a speciality.
House wine is £5.75 a bottle; retsina is £6.

EWELL Surrey   map 3

Taste of Bengal [6/10]

The Broadway, Stoneleigh
TEL 01-393 0024

Open noon to 2.30, 5.30 to 11 & (also WC)
Closed Christmas Day and Boxing Day

Good-value thalis for about £6 supplement
a standard menu of birianis, dhansaks and
vindaloos in this neighbourhood curry
house. Specialities include chicken cooked
with minced meat and spices, jeera
chicken with cumin seeds, and karahi
dishes. Drink lassi or lager.

EWHURST Surrey   map 3

Windmill Inn [6/10]

Pitch Hill
TEL Cranleigh (0483) 277566

Open for food noon to 2.15, 7 to 10.15 &
Closed Christmas Day

Fine views are one good reason for visiting
this woodside pub. On a clear day the
panorama stretches across the South
Downs to the coast. Food is simple and
home cooked, with the emphasis on fresh
ingredients. Fish is collected every week
from the Selsey boats, and there is game in
season. The standard menu has sausage
and mash, curries with poppadums,
Bombay ducks and chutneys, rare roast
beef salads, and plates of smoked salmon.
King and Barnes and Youngs beers on
handpump. Children welcome in the
porches and gardens.

FITTLEWORTH West Sussex   map 3

Swan [6/10]

Lower High Street
TEL Fittleworth (079 882) 429/242

Open 8am to 11pm (10 to 10.30 Sun)

An ancient tile-hung pub dating from the fourteenth century. Inside there are paintings galore as well as a unique collection of bottle-openers and policemen's truncheons. Food in the bar is above average. Interesting soups, such as tomato and tarragon or chilled watercress and pear, share the bill with curries, salads, savoury pies, and vegetarian specialities such as spiced vegetables with nuts and rice. Sardines in sea salt is a good fish dish, and sweets might feature ginger-and-treacle pudding. Sunday lunch is £7.50. More expensive restaurant meals. Beers from Gales and Ushers.

FIVE OAKS West Sussex   map 3

NEW ENTRY Lannards [7/10]

Okehurst Lane, near Billingshurst
TEL Billingshurst (040 381) 4626

Open noon to 2.30, 7 to 9.30 & (also WC)
Closed Mon L; Tue D and Sun

German-born Hartmut Seidler runs this small country restaurant attached to an art gallery. Customers can browse and look at the pictures between courses. Light lunches might include cauliflower soup, lasagne, and salmon and prawn quiche. Steak and kidney pie is good, too. Main courses come with fresh vegetables and everything is prepared on the premises, including the bread. Afternoon teas and more expensive evening meals. Glüwein is served in cold weather.

FOLKESTONE Kent   map 3

India [8/10]

1 Old High Street
TEL Folkestone (0303) 59155

Open noon to 3, 6 to 11.30 &
Closed Christmas Day and Boxing Day

Ali Ashraf's cool Indian restaurant now rates as the best in the South-East and can match some of the finest in London. The setting is unpromising – at the back of town near the cinema and the amusement arcades – but the cooking is subtle and imaginative. It has been called 'Nouvelle Indienne' – in fact it's an original mixture of French and Bengali. Set meals begin at around £7 a head for onion pakora, tandoori chicken, rogan josh, prawn biriani, dhal, mixed vegetable curry plus nan and poppadum. Tikkas are excellent, bhajias are crisp and there are a few dishes for Francophiles such as salade niçoise and poulet provençale. Cheap lunches are £3.95. Drink Kingfisher beer or Veena – Indian wine.

Pullman Wine Bar [6/10]

7 Church Street
TEL Folkestone (0303) 52524

Open noon to 2 &
Closed Sun

The panelled bars have a railway theme and the atmosphere is rather like a pub with wine. Pizzas and kebabs have been added to a menu that stays with old-style dishes, such as three-egg omelettes, spaghetti bolognese, fish and chips and baked pork with pineapple. Short wine list.

FULKING West Sussex   map 3

Shepherd & Dog [6/10]

TEL Poynings (079 156) 382

Open for food noon to 2 (1.45 Sun), 7 to 9.30 & (also WC)
Closed Sun D; Christmas Day and Boxing Day

Two converted cottages in a tiny village at the foot of the South Downs, once a haunt of shepherds on their way to sheep fairs. Lunch consists of simple dishes, such as freshly made soup, ploughman's, and steak and kidney pie. The evening menu moves into the realms of feuilleté of salmon and prawns. Beef and Guinness pie and roast rack of lamb with apricot sauce are top of the popularity stakes. Tamplins or Ushers Best on handpump, as well as guest beers. No children.

GOMSHALL Surrey   map 3

Gomshall Mill [5/10]

TEL Shere (048 641) 2433

Open 10 to 5.30 &
Closed Mon; Christmas Day and Boxing Day

The restored mill is now a tourist attraction, combining a pottery, gallery and tea-shop. Local watercress appears as soup or in sandwiches with cold ham; otherwise the menu ranges from scrambled eggs on toast to almond cake and fruit flans. Unlicensed.

HARRIETSHAM Kent   map 3

Ringlestone Inn [6/10]

TEL Maidstone (0622) 859207

Open for food noon to 2, 7 to 10
& (also WC, 1 step)
Closed Christmas Day

An ancient pub deep in the Kent countryside, not far from the Pilgrims' Way. Inside it is all history, with thick stone walls, inglenooks and timbers from old Thames barges. Savoury pies are a speciality: beef and beer, lamb and apricot, and pork and pear have all featured on the menu. There's also a hot and cold buffet every day. Plenty of real ales, including Adnams, Fremlins and Ringlestone Bitter.

HASTINGS East Sussex   map 3

Brant's [6/10]

45 High Street
TEL Hastings (0424) 431896

Open 10 to 4.30 (earlier in winter)
Closed Sun; Wed in winter; Wed pm summer; bank hols

This feels more like a neighbourhood wholefood place in a small provincial town, rather than in a brassy seaside resort. The menu is quite short, but everything is fresh and made on the premises, and prices are low. Look for the home-made soup, quiches, flans, and nut loaf. Salads in summer, baked potatoes in winter. Drinks range from bottled water to elderflower wine. Take-aways.

NEW ENTRY | Porters Wine Bar [7/10]

56 High Street, Old Town
TEL Hastings (0424) 427000

Open noon to 2, 7 to 10 &

This used to be Briefs, but new owners have revamped the menu and given the

place a bistro feel. The choice of dishes changes regularly and portions are generous: excellent aubergine fritters come with garlic mayonnaise, and other dishes range from deep-fried Brie to beef and Guinness pie. There are also vegetarian specialities, such as stuffed courgettes, celery and Stilton quiche, and macaroni cheese. Hot chocolate fudge pudding to finish. Wine by the glass. There is a tiny, romantic terraced patio at the back of the wine bar where children are welcome.

JEVINGTON East Sussex   map 3

Eight Bells [6/10]

TEL Polegate (032 12) 4442

Open for food 11 to 2 (noon to 1.30 Sun), 6.30 (7 Sun) to 9.30 & (by arrangement)
Closed Christmas Day

Six-hundred year old village pub well supported by locals. The bar food has fish and chips, prawn quiche, and smoked mackerel pâté, supplemented by specials such as cauliflower cheese or turkey pie. Local produce is often for sale in the bar. Courage beers. No children.

LAMBERHURST Kent   map 3

Down [5/10]

TEL Lamberhurst (0892) 890237

Open 9.30 to 5.30 &
Closed Mon; Christmas Day, Boxing Day and 1 Jan

The china matches the old beamed style of this bow-windowed tea-room with a corner shop and craft centre attached. Light lunches of soup, pâtés, quiche, or ham ploughman's are good value. There's a choice of seven set teas – featuring home-made scones, lardy cake, Apfelstrudel, or honey and walnut loaf – for around £2. Eat in the garden on warm days. Unlicensed.

LEWES East Sussex   map 3

Pattisson's [7/10]

199 High Street (School Hill)
TEL Lewes (0273) 472727/473364

Open noon to 2.15; 7.30 to 9.15
Closed Sun; Mon D; 10 days Christmas;
bank hols

On a part of the High Street known locally
as School Hill. The Pattissons serve
unpretentious home-cooked dishes, and
lunches are good bets for cheap eating. A
bowl of home-made soup, plus a choice
from the cold table, is £4. Alternatively
there is a short list of daily specials, such
as ox-tail stew, grilled lamb cutlets and
kidney, or lamb and aubergine provençale.
There's usually a fresh fish dish, too. Bread
and ice-creams are home made. More
expensive evening meals.

Ronnie's Wine Bar [7/10]

197 High Street
TEL Lewes (0273) 477879

Open 10 to 3, 6 to 11 (7 to 10.30 Sun) & (also wc)
Closed Sun L; Christmas Day and Boxing Day

Formerly Mike's, this flashy wine bar has
been taken over and renamed by one of the
partners, Veronica Pink. The décor is
trendy and brassy; the menu is short and
to the point, taking in excellent home-
made taramosalata, accurately cooked
steaks, char-grilled swordfish, and a
lunchtime vegetarian dish, such as mixed
bean casserole. Salads come with good
herby French dressing. Better than average
wines.

Sussex Kitchen, Pelham Arms [6/10]

High Street
TEL Lewes (079 16) 6149

Open 12.30 to 1.30, 7 to 9.30 & (also wc)
Closed Sun

The snack bar attached to this comfortable
old inn serves a short menu of home-
cooked dishes. Home-made soup, such as
cauliflower or carrot, is reliably good, and
there's praise for the special steak and
kidney pie, chicken casserole with olives
and mushrooms, and Sussex seafood
platter. The menu also has escalope of
veal, fillet steak, and sole with wine and
asparagus sauce. Meringues or chocolate
pot to finish. House wine is £4.95 a bottle.

Trumps [7/10]

19–20 Station Street
TEL Lewes (0273) 473906

Open noon to 2 (3 Sun), 7 to 11 (11.30 Sat)
Closed L Thur and Sat; Wed; 26 to 30 Dec

Cheapest options in Neil McGown's tiny
sixteenth-century restaurant are daily-
changing specials from the à la carte
menu. Typically there might be sauté
chicken livers with madeira and pink
peppercorns in pastry, baked banana
wrapped in bacon with curry mayonnaise,
and summer pudding with cream. Two
dishes should leave change from £5. More
expensive set menu. House wine by
the glass.

LIMPSFIELD Surrey   map 3

Limpsfield Brasserie, Old Lodge [8/10]

High Street
TEL Oxted (0883) 717385

Open noon to 3, 6 until late & (also wc)
Closed Sun D, Mon L, Sat L

A high-profile brasserie in the converted
bar of the prestigious restaurant. The aim
is to offer three courses for around £10 – or
a single dish for less than a fiver. The all-
day menu has daily soups (such as celery
and mushroom), duck pâté with orange
and Grand Marnier, grilled calf's liver and
bacon, cold poached salmon with sorrel
mayonnaise. Fillets of sole with white
wine and madeira sauce flavoured with
anchovy is classical but works well.
Honey is from the restaurant's own hives;
puddings include fruit flans and sorbets.
Fourteen wines, plus house wines by
the glass.

MAIDSTONE Kent   map 5

Pizza Express [7/10]

83 Week Street
TEL Maidstone (0622) 53162

Open noon to midnight &
Closed Christmas Day

A branch of the highly rated pizza chain based mainly in the capital (see London entry).

Pye Peppers [6/10]

90 Week Street
TEL Maidstone (0622) 672089

Open 11 to 2.30, 6 to 11 (11 to 11 Sat) &
Closed Sun; bank hols

This used to be Mr Jones's Pie Shop, but the owners re-vamped the décor and changed the name. The menu still features hearty traditional pies, such as chicken and chestnut, or pork, plum and celery. There are cold joints, smoked fish and salads, plus jacket potatoes as snacks. A range of pâtisserie may soon be added to the menu. Reasonably priced wines or stout by the jug. No children.

Russett [5/10]

34 King Street
TEL Maidstone (0622) 53921

Open 9 to 5, 7 to 10 &
Closed Sun; Mon D and Tue D

New owner Michael Clark has extended the vegetarian menu in this former baker's shop and sandwich bar, and now caters for vegans. The menu is in the style of mushroom and Brazil-nut pâté, pizza pie, and French onion flan, with American-sounding sweets such as old Orleans orange pie.

OCKLEY Surrey   map 3

NEW ENTRY Cricketer's Arms [6/10]

Stane Street
TEL Oakwood Hill (030679) 205

Open for food 10.30 (noon Sun) to 2, 6 to 10.30

Twelve kinds of home-made pie are the speciality in this old pub with flagstone floors and cricket memorabilia. Each day at least four appear on the menu: perhaps lamb and redcurrant, rabbit and apple, pigeon, or chicken and mushroom, all served with fresh vegetables. Otherwise there's home-made soup, locally cured ham and one or two more expensive

specialities, such as lamb cutlets with tarragon cream.

PENSHURST Kent   map 3

NEW ENTRY Spotted Dog [6/10]

Smarts Hill
TEL Tunbridge Wells (0892) 870158

Open for food noon to 1.45, 7 to 9.45

The great thing about this tiled and weatherboarded pub is its view. It stands on a steep hillside overlooking miles of open country around the Medway Valley and Penshurst Place. The pub is also very old and was first licensed in 1520. Food is an extensive range of very light snacks and better-than-average pub grub, including cheese platters, ploughman's, Dorset crab salad, and specialities such as baked avocado stuffed with seafood and smoked chicken. There are also colourful daily dishes along the lines of lamb pasanda, Indonesian baked chicken, and seafood ragout. Salads come with home-made vinaigrette or mayonnaise. More expensive restaurant. Fremlins beer on handpump.

POLEGATE East Sussex   map 3

Polegate Fisheries [6/10]

31 High Street
TEL Polegate (032 12) 3157

Open 11.45 to 2, 5 to 9.30 &
Closed Sun

For twenty years, 'Nicky' has been frying top-quality fish and chips in this highly rated, no-frills chippie. These days he uses groundnut oil, which produces light, crisp results. A sit-down meal of fish and chips, tea, bread and butter, is £1.80. Unlicensed.

RAMSGATE Kent   map 3

Anne's Pantry [6/10]

8 Albion Hill
TEL Thanet (0843) 593287

Open noon to 3, 6 to 10 &
Closed Mon (exc bank hols and in July and Aug)

A three-course meal for £5.50 is the big scoring point here. The emphasis is on home cooking, so costs can be kept down. Tuna and tomato salad or vegetable soup might be followed by seafood and mushroom vol-au-vent, roast topside of beef or escalope of turkey Holstein – each served with a different selection of vegetables. Finish with apple pie and custard, strawberry mousse or chocolate gateau. Wine by the glass.

ROCHESTER Kent — map 3

Casa Lina [6/10]

146 High Street
TEL Medway (0634) 44993

Open 9 to 10 &
Closed Sun and Mon; bank hols; 1 week at Christmas; last 2 weeks Sept

Family-run pizzeria offering seventeen kinds of freshly cooked pizza from noon onwards. They are made from scratch, generously topped and baked in a genuine pizza oven. There are also some pasta dishes on the menu. Open for breakfast, morning coffee and grills. Children very welcome at lunch-time.

SEAFORD East Sussex — map 3

Hole in the Wall [6/10]

Pelham Yard, High Street
TEL Seaford (0323) 893785

Open for food noon to 2, 7 to 10 &

Steak, kidney and mushroom pie, beef and beer casserole, and Lincolnshire sausages with cauliflower cheese are the best bets in this cosy town-centre pub. The bar menu also has ham and eggs, fish pie, ploughman's, and club sandwiches. Two-course set lunches in the restaurant are about £4. Steaks are the main attraction in the evening. Children welcome in the dining-room.

SELLING Kent — map 3

White Lion [6/10]

The Street
TEL Selling (022 785) 211

Open for food noon to 2.30, 7 to 10
Closed Christmas Day

This three-hundred-year-old inn is famous for its traditional beef pudding and steak, kidney and mushroom pie, both served with mounds of fresh vegetables. A new attraction is the cold buffet, which features quiche, roast joints, and seafood with plenty of help-yourself salads. Sandwiches, ploughman's and things with chips complete the picture. More expensive restaurant meals. Real ales from Greene King and Shepherd Neame.

SHAMLEY GREEN Surrey — map 3

Red Lion [7/10]

TEL Guildford (0483) 892202

Open for food noon to 2 (1.30 Sun), 7 to 10
& (also WC)

Pleasant pub on the village green renowned for the generosity of its bar food. Quantity sometimes comes before quality, but the choice is varied and much of the food is home made. Typically there might be great bowls of soup such as ham and lentil, big salads, pies, and roast meats as well as dishes such as home-baked ham and eggs or curried cottage pie. Ind Coope Bitter and Burton Ale on draught. No children.

SHERE Surrey — map 3

Asters Tea Shop [5/10]

TEL Shere (048 641) 2445

Open 10.30 to 5.30 (6 Sat and Sun) &
Closed Tue

Jean Watson has taken over this thriving tea-shop, has changed the name (it used to be Mumfords) and extended the opening hours. She has also abandoned fried foods and white bread. The menu is a short selection of omelettes, salads, cakes, and scones. Afternoon teas are popular. Wine by the glass.

STONE Kent — map 3

Ferry Inn [6/10]

TEL Appledore (023 383) 246

Open for food 10.30 to 2.30, 6 to 11 (noon to 2, 7 to 10.30 Sun) &

Well named, as this seventeenth-century pub is on the site of the old ferry. Food is home cooked, dishes often come straight from the oven, and portions are generous. Typically there might be chicken liver pâté, spiced country chicken, ratatouille and pork casserole. Beers from Courage. No children.

THREE LEGGED CROSS
East Sussex   map 3

Bull [7/10]

TEL Ticehurst (0580) 200586

Open for food 11.30 to 2, 7 to 10 & (also WC)
Closed Sun D

There are six centuries of history inside this classic English country pub, with its low beams, flagstone floors and solid wooden tables. Lunchtime bar food is in keeping with the décor: hearty turkey and vegetable soup, big steak sandwiches, omelettes and specials such as chicken in cider or gammon glazed with mustard and brown sugar. Evening meals are a bit more ambitious – and it's best to book – taking in rack of lamb with rosemary and garlic or veal escalope with tarragon sauce. Four-course Sunday lunch is £6.95. Bass, Harveys and Shepherd Neame on handpump.

TICEHURST
East Sussex   map 3

Plantation Tea Company [6/10]

1 High Street
TEL Ticehurst (0580) 200015

Open 9 (10 Sun) to 5.30 & (also WC)
Closed Mon (exc bank hols)

New owners Melvyn and Michelle Vinall have extended the menu in their tea-shop-cum-restaurant. There are now main meals of steak and mushroom pie, quiche, honey-roast gammon, and pizza with three vegetables. Home-made cakes and pastries still feature along with afternoon cream teas. Unlicensed.

TONBRIDGE Kent   map 3

Office Wine Bar [8/10]

163 High Street
TEL Tonbridge (0732) 353660

Open for food noon to 2, 7 to 9.30 &
Closed Sun; bank hols

The best wine bar in Tonbridge is in a beamed sixteenth-century building on two floors. Much of the menu changes each day, and it tries to be a bit unusual. Starters or snacks might include spicy Malayan prawns with coconut cream, fresh ravioli with mushroom, tarragon and tomato sauce, or pastrami and tomato salad. More substantial dishes could range from cold smoked loin of pork with apple sauce and red pepper salad to hot salmon koulibiac or beef with sour cream and horseradish. Sweets are equally adventurous. Half a dozen house wines by the glass.

TUNBRIDGE WELLS
Kent   map 3

Downstairs at Thackeray's [9/10]

85 London Road
TEL Tunbridge Wells (0892) 37559

Open 12.30 to 2.30, 7 to 10.30
Closed Sun; Mon; Christmas

Once the home of the novelist William Makepeace Thackeray, this green-and-white clapboard house is set back from the road almost next door to the Conservative Club. Upstairs is classy and expensive; downstairs is cheaper and more flexible, but quality is just as good. Best value of all is the three-course set lunch for £5.90. Excellent dishes have included fresh noodles with spinach and banana, marinated beef with yoghurt and mint, shin of veal with green peppercorn sauce. Vegetables are flawless; sticky toffee pudding with butterscotch sauce is an outstanding sweet. Short, sensibly chosen wine list with good house red.

La Galoche, Mount Edgecumbe Hotel [6/10]

The Common
TEL Tunbridge Wells (0892) 26823

Open noon to 2, 7 to 10 &

This wine bar attached to one of the town's hotels is set in a cave cut from the local sandstone. It's a fun place with a varied hotch-potch of a menu that takes in carrot soup, salmon koulibiac, Dover sole, spicy avocado bake, and chicken in Pernod. Salads are fresh and vegetables lightly cooked. Sweets are seasonal and fruity. Children under twelve are not normally welcome, except on Saturday mornings (known as 'crêche morning').

NEW ENTRY Rag-a-Muffins [5/10]

25 Mount Pleasant Road
TEL Tunbridge Wells (0892) 25893

Open 9.30 to 5.30 &
Closed Sun

Rather unusual – a pine-furnished café specialising in American bran muffins, which are baked on the premises. There are eleven different flavours (from apricot to chocolate and orange), served with butter, whipped cream or Loseley ice-cream. Soup is home made, chilli is pungent, and there are savoury croissants and filled puff pastries at lunch-time. Unlicensed. Take-aways.

Royal Wells Inn [7/10]

Mount Ephraim
TEL Tunbridge Wells (0892) 23414

Open for food 12.30 to 2.30, 6.30 to 10.30 &
Closed Sun; bank hol Mon D; Christmas Day and Boxing Day

The emphasis is on cooked-to-order specialities at this architecturally impressive eighteenth-century hotel across from the common. The range of dishes is an international mixed bag of Hungarian pork goulash, lamb kebab with chilli in French bread, fried Camembert with cranberry sauce, and steaks. On show there's a cold buffet (including home-made

raised pork pie) and a few other dishes such as pea soup or toad-in-the-hole. Ice-cream or baked jam roll to finish. More expensive restaurant menus.

WESTERHAM Kent   map 3

Henry Wilkinson [6/10]

26 Market Square
TEL Westerham (0959) 64245

Open noon to 2.30, 7.30 to 10.30 (11 Fri and Sat)
Closed Sun; Christmas Day and Boxing Day; Good Fri; Aug bank hol

Useful town-centre wine bar with pine tables and prints on the walls. The food is simple and home made, ranging from hot avocado and crab or chicken and mush-room pie to blackboard specials, such as beef chasseur. Sandwiches and jacket potatoes are also available at lunch-time. Drinkable house wine.

WESTFIELD East Sussex   map 3

Casual Cuisine [7/10]

Church Lane, Westfield Village
TEL Hastings (0424) 751137

Open noon to 2, 6 to 9.30
Closed Mon and Tue; Sun D; Christmas Day, Boxing Day; 2 weeks Jan

The Symonds' informal farmhouse bistro offers eclectic cosmopolitan cooking and an ever-changing menu. It roams around the world for Bulgarian baked aubergines, Algerian lamb meatballs with apricot sauce, Egyptian beef with okra, and wholewheat Stilton pancakes from nearer home. The hundred-strong wine list is in the same style, and there are some unusual teas.

WEYBRIDGE Surrey   map 3

Gaylord [6/10]

73 Queens Road
TEL Weybridge (0932) 42895/55325

Open noon to 2.30, 6 to 11.30 & (also WC)

Three set meals offer the best value in this stylish stockbroker-belt curry house. The vegetarian thali (£5.95) includes three kinds of vegetables, onion bhajia, raita, pilau rice and puri. Also look for the special tandoori mix at £7.95. Otherwise the menu is standard North Indian, with karahi dishes, lamb pasanda and tandoori chicken masala as specialities.

WHITSTABLE Kent   map 3

Birdies [7/10]

Harbour Street
TEL Whitstable (0227) 265337

Open 7pm to 10.30pm, plus 12.30 to 3 Sun &
Closed Tue and Wed

The menu changes regularly in this relaxed, up-market bistro, and two courses plus wine should leave change from £10. Chicken and vegetable terrine, marinated anchovies or home-made soup might precede mutton with apricots and almonds, jambon dijonnaise, or an oriental special of chicken, prawns and beef with water-chestnuts, bamboo shoots and bean sprouts. Main courses come with vegetables. House wine by the bottle.

Pearsons Crab & Oyster House [6/10]

Sea Wall
TEL Whitstable (0227) 272005

Open 10 to 2.30, 6 to 11

The 'new' Pearsons Arms stands opposite the original site of the company of Free Fishers and Dredgers of Whitstable. Seafood is still the main attraction – local oysters, freshly boiled crabs and lobsters from the tank, cockles, and specials such as grilled sole. Steaks are available for meat eaters. Simple food in the nautical downstairs bar; more extensive menu in the upstairs dining-rooms. Flowers and Fremlins beer on handpump.

WINCHELSEA East Sussex   map 3

Winchelsea Tea Room [5/10]

Hiham Green
TEL Rye (0797) 226679

Open 2.30 (noon Sat and Sun) to 6 &
Closed Mon, Fri (exc bank hols); end Oct to Mar

Victorian-style tea-room behind an antique shop. The décor is all lacy tablecloths and old-fashioned china crockery, and the emphasis is on home-baked cakes, toasted cheese scones, crumpets, and savouries such as Welsh rarebit. Lunch (Saturday and Sunday only) brings home-made soup, quiche, and filled jacket potatoes.

WOKING Surrey   map 3

Village Green [6/10]

Pyrford Road
TEL Byfleet (093 23) 51835

Open noon to 2.30, 5.30 (7 Sun) to 10.30 & (also WC)
Closed Christmas Day

Despite the name, this is actually a leisure centre with a good choice of food in the bar. Salads naturally dominate and in keeping with the fitness theme there's now a Health Slim menu stating the calorie content of each dish. For those who are less health-conscious there's turkey curry, chilli or lasagne. Barbecues in summer.

WROTHAM Kent   map 3

Bull Hotel [6/10]

TEL Borough Green (0732) 883092

Open for food noon to 2, 7 to 10 &

On the site of a fourteenth-century hospice on the Pilgrims' Way, this hotel now has an atmosphere of sedate, old-fashioned comfort. The bar food is to the point: huge hot beef sandwiches with coleslaw on thick rye bread, cottage pie, local sausages and chips, risotto, and lasagne. Five real ales include Bass, Greene King and Youngs, among others. More expensive restaurant.

Central

Bedfordshire

Berkshire

Buckinghamshire

Hertfordshire

Oxfordshire

ABINGDON Oxfordshire   map 4

Lambert's [6/10]

13 Bath Street
TEL Abingdon (0235) 32211

Open 9.30 to 2, 6.30 to 9.30 & (also wc)
Closed Sun

Set lunches are good value in this converted butcher's shop named after Daniel Lambert, the legendary 52-stone giant from Leicester. To start there might be cream of mushroom soup or fresh salmon mayonnaise before grilled fillet of plaice, lasagne, or sauté of beef Diane. The price of £5.60 includes two courses plus coffee. Sweets, such as brown-bread ice-cream or apple and orange crumble, are extra. House wine is £1.20 a glass. More expensive dinners.

ADDERBURY Oxfordshire   map 4

White Hart [6/10]

Tanners Lane
TEL Banbury (0295) 810406

Open for food noon to 2, 7 to 10
Closed Christmas Day

New owners are highlighting the food in this small seventeenth-century pub, and have recently opened a separate dining-room by popular demand. There's not a chip in sight, but the short menu of freshly cooked dishes can include celery and Stilton soup, beef bourguignonne, and prawn curry, with apple and raspberry pie or lemon mousse to finish. Real ales. No children.

ALDBURY Hertfordshire   map 4

Valiant Trooper [6/10]

Trooper Road
TEL Aldbury Common (044 285) 203

Open for food 12.30 to 2, 7.30 to 9 & (also wc)
Closed Sun D and Mon D

The Trooper is actually two eating places. Simple snacks are served in the bar, along with a fine selection of real ales. More formal meals are available in Trooper's – a separate restaurant in a converted barn attached to the pub. Mid-week lunches are

£7.95 for, say, pasta salad or sauté mushrooms, then pork fillet provençale or beef carbonnade, followed by a home-made sweet or cheese. Dinners will take the bill over £10 a head.

AMERSHAM
Buckinghamshire   map 4

King's Arms [6/10]

High Street
TEL Amersham (0494) 726333

Open for food noon to 2.15, 6.30 to 9 &
Closed Christmas Day

An impressive half-timbered hostelry with all the trappings: old beams, antique settles and a big inglenook fireplace. Straightforward bar food is beef and Guinness pie, risotto, and vegetarian lasagne, backed up by the usual sandwiches, salads, and ploughman's. Weekday lunches in the separate restaurant offer three courses for £7.50, along the lines of cream of lettuce soup, venison sausages with mushroom sauce, chocolate pot with Cointreau. Ind Coope beers and wine by the glass.

Willow Tree [7/10]

Market Square, Old Amersham
TEL Amersham (0494) 727242

Open 10 to 5, plus 7.30 to 10 Wed to Sat &
Closed Mon; 5 days at Christmas

Usefully situated in the Market Square and open all day for snacks and meals. Lunch has the best bargains, with dishes such as beef with celery, orange and walnuts, fresh salmon terrine, and barbecued chicken, as well as home-made pizzas. Vegetarians do well with hot avocado with Mozzarella, spinach and quails' egg roulade, and broccoli and cheese flan. Sweets are the home-made kind. More expensive evening meals. Wines by the glass, including elderflower.

ASCOT Berkshire   map 2

Jade Fountain [6/10]

38 High Street, Sunninghill
TEL Ascot (0990) 27070

Open noon to 2, 6 to 10.30
Closed 25 to 27 Dec

A smart and consistent Chinese restaurant serving creditable food to the well-heeled locals and golfers from nearby Wentworth. Prices are reasonable, although to keep the bill under £10 a head it pays to go in a party. Hot and sour soup, sizzling lamb with spring onions, and steamed Dover sole are typical of the menu.

ASHWELL Hertfordshire   map 5

Bushel & Strike Inn [6/10]

Mill Street
TEL Ashwell (046 274) 2394

Open for food noon to 2.30, 6.30 to 11 (10.30 Sun) & (also WC)
Closed Christmas Day and Boxing Day

This genuine old village inn stands right opposite the impressively huge church. Inside there are open fires and a fine buffet laid out on the central table. Cold roast pork and whole fresh salmon are the main attractions, backed by unusual salads served with home-made mayonnaise. Hot dishes include home-made soup, steak and kidney pie served with roast or jacket potatoes and other vegetables, and grills. Good old-fashioned sweets to finish. Charles Wells beers.

AYLESBURY
Buckinghamshire   map 4

Bottle and Glass [6/10]

Gibraltar
TEL Aylesbury (0296) 748488

Open for food noon to 2.30 (2 Sun), 6 to 11 &
Closed Sun D

A fifteenth-century beamed pub five miles from Aylesbury on the A418, towards Thame. Simplest choices from the menu are all kinds of open sandwiches and salads: Brie, pear and apple, egg and anchovy, prawn and coleslaw. The main menu changes every two weeks. Hot dishes might include almond chicken, beef and venison pie, or fillet of pork in cream and peach sauce. There's always a vegetarian choice, such as mushrooms in Dijon mustard sauce. A special menu has

been introduced for the garden and patio extension.

NEW ENTRY Hampers [6/10]

56 Kingsbury Square
TEL Aylesbury (0296) 23487

Open 9 to 4.30 (5 Sat) &
Closed Sun

A useful restaurant at the back of a long-established delicatessen. Food is reasonably priced and much of it is local: bread comes from a small bakery, cakes are made in a nearby village. The simple menu has home-made soup, such as celery, smoked salmon pâté, and fidget pie, as well as vegetarian dishes along the lines of cauliflower cheese or broccoli and walnut quiche. The choice of cakes and pastries ranges from baklava to bread pudding. To drink there's a good selection of teas and coffees, as well as wine by the glass.

NEW ENTRY Seatons [7/10]

Market Square
TEL Aylesbury (0296) 27582

Open noon to 2.30, 7 to 10 &
Closed Sun; Mon D; bank hols

This wine bar/bistro with a Georgian-style bay window and bare wooden décor is the most popular lunchtime eating place in Aylesbury. The menu is enterprising for the area, taking in spinach and lentil pâté, tomato and Mozzarella salad with basil vinaigrette, fillet of pork with Stilton and walnuts, and courgettes stuffed with almonds, thyme and tomato. The mixed seafood platter is a plate of smoked salmon, prawns, tuna, anchovies and crab pâté with all kinds of salad ingredients, plus interesting dressings such as cucumber and mint. There are also special open sandwiches. Pecan pie is a good sweet. Related to the Bottle and Glass (see entry). No children.

BALDOCK Hertfordshire   map 5

NEW ENTRY Zeus [7/10]

20B High Street
TEL Baldock (0462) 893620

Open 6 to 11 (11.45 Fri and Sat)
Closed Sun

Free and easy Greek restaurant in a gastronomic desert. It is good fun but not the place for an intimate meal, as you eat cheek-by-jowl with your neighbours. Hummus and taramosalata are above average; kebabs and other main courses are prepared from good-quality meat. The separate vegetarian menu is worth supporting: fasoladka (Cyprus beans casseroled with carrots, celery and potatoes) and melindzanes stofourno (baked aubergines with courgettes and peppers) have both been recommended. Good-value meze. Drinkable Greek and Cypriot wines.

BANBURY Oxfordshire   map 4

Cromwell Lodge [6/10]

North Bar
TEL Banbury (0295) 59781

Open noon to 2, 7 to 9.30
Closed Sun D

A thriving town-centre hotel in a converted eighteenth-century school. At lunchtime (Monday to Saturday) there's a good choice of decent bar food, including plenty of salads and sandwiches, plus hot dishes such as lamb curry, pork, apricot and ginger pie, and macaroni cheese. The hotel is also renowned for its summer barbecues, which operate whatever the weather. Steaks, tandoori chicken, kebabs and trout all find their way on to the grill. Three-course Sunday lunch is £6.95. More expensive restaurant menu. Hook Norton beers.

BARLEY Hertfordshire   map 5

Fox and Hounds [6/10]

TEL Barkway (076 384) 459

Open for food noon to 2.30, 6 to 10.30 (10 Sun)
& (also WC)

First licensed in 1795, this village pub in the high street has undergone a face-lift. A new dining-room has been added and there are plans for a conservatory eating area, too. But the old local atmosphere of skittles and dominoes remains. The

extensive menu has good helpings of steak and kidney pie with an impressively risen puff-pastry crust, decent jacket potatoes and a range of dishes from pork vindaloo to rabbit casserole. The choice of real ales includes home-brews and guest beers.

BEACONSFIELD
Buckinghamshire   map 2

China Diner [7/10]

7 The Highway, Station Road
TEL Beaconsfield (049 46) 3345

Open noon to 2.30, 6 to 11.30 (12 Fri and Sat) &
(also WC)
Closed Christmas Eve to Boxing Day

The boldly revamped décor of dark blue venetian blinds and ceiling fans is more Hollywood than China. This is one of the best Chinese restaurants in the area, with a menu of Pekingese and spicy Szechuan dishes. Regional set banquets are £10.50 a head, otherwise go in a crowd and choose from hot-and-sour soup, crispy aromatic duck, chicken with almonds and yellow-bean sauce, and hot chilli bean curd with mince. There is a branch at 310 Uxbridge Road, Hatch End (TEL 01-421 3130).

BEDFORD Bedfordshire   map 5

Park [6/10]

98 Kimbolton Road
TEL Bedford (0234) 54093

Open for food 11 to 2.30 (2 Sun)

The four-square, black-and-white painted building dominates the top end of a wide leafy boulevard. Go through the tiny arched doorway into the bar, which is all exposed brickwork, bare floors and old timbers. Cheese is the main attraction, although the huge choice now owes more to the commercial creamery than the farmhouse dairy. The standard lunch is three cheeses plus pickles and locally baked bread. There are also home-made pies, pâtés and soups. Charles Wells beer.

Santaniello's Pizzeria [6/10]

Newnham Street
TEL Bedford (0234) 53742

Open noon to 2, 6 to 11.30
Closed Mon

In a tiny back-street off Bedford's main shopping area. The pizzas are good for a quick snack and there's also spaghetti, lasagne, and chicken salad. Decent coffee, good cheap house wine. Two courses and a drink will leave change from a fiver.

BERKHAMSTED
Hertfordshire   map 5

Cook's Delight [8/10]

360–362 High Street
TEL Berkhamsted (044 27) 3584

Open 9 to 9 &
Closed Mon to Wed; Christmas Day

Since 1981 Rex Tyler and his South-East Asian wife have stuck to their principles and developed this delicatessen/ alternative bookshop/tea-room and restaurant into the most uncompromising vegetarian eating place in Hertfordshire. There's no sugar or salt on the tables, and much of the food is now vegan. During the day there are scones, salads, organic vegetable terrines, buckwheat quiches and casseroles; the only concessions to flesh-eaters are fish and turkey. On Thursday and Friday evenings there are Malaysian platters: £4.50 pays for as much as you can eat of vegetable curry, stir-fried vegetables and brown rice (an extra 95p will buy a bowl of miso or pumpkin soup). Saturday features four-course South-East Asian dinners for £12 a head; Sunday lunch is a macrobiotic platter for £4.50. The list of ingredients now runs to over thirty types of organic produce. Some people still prefer to sit right by the kitchen, although there are now more tables upstairs and the sheltered garden is delightful.

BOTLEY Oxfordshire   map 4

Tong San [7/10]

20 The Square
TEL Oxford (0865) 248230/726414

Open noon to 2 (1 to 2.30 Sun), 6 to 11.45 &
Closed Christmas Day to 27 Dec

Raymond Mak's small Chinese restaurant is rated as one of the best in the area. The cooking is Pekingese with a few Cantonese overtones, and specialities range from Peking duck and sizzling dishes to barbecued quail and stir-fried mussels in black-bean sauce. The rice cooked in lotus leaves is worth trying. Good-value set lunches start at £4.50. A new branch, The Dragon Inn, has recently opened in Burford.

BRACKNELL Berkshire   map 2

Oscar's [7/10]

South Hill Parks Arts Centre, Bagshot Road
TEL Bracknell (0344) 59031

Open noon to 2, 6.30 to 10 & (also WC)
Closed Sun, Mon; Christmas Eve for 10 days

The Arts Centre is in a lovely old house, and the restaurant is handy if visiting the Wilde Theatre. There are pre-theatre snacks as well as a full menu taking in stuffed vine leaves, chicken couscous, and vegetarian moussaka supplemented by specials such as calf's liver with avocado and orange sauce, or pan-fried skate with prawns and capers. At lunchtime there are snacks in the bar, and the restaurant becomes a pizzeria. Interesting new British cheeses, such as Coverdale and Cornish Yarg, plus a decent list of more than eighty wines.

BRIGHTWELL BALDWIN
Oxfordshire   map 4

Lord Nelson Inn [7/10]

TEL Watlington (049 161) 2497

Open for food noon to 2, 7 to 10 & (also WC)
Closed Mon (exc bank hols)

A modernised seventeenth-century pub in a quiet lane opposite the village church. Food is the major attraction, and the bar menu has salads of home-made pâté, prawn and sweet pear, or roast sirloin of beef, as well as prawn risotto, home-made steak and kidney pie, and chilli con carne topped with crispy bacon. To finish there are home-made fruit pies and cheesecakes. More expensive restaurant meals. Beers from Brakspears. No children under seven. Snacks only on Sunday evenings.

Central

BROOM Bedfordshire   map 5

| NEW ENTRY | **Cock** [6/10] |

23 High Street
TEL Biggleswade (0767) 314411

Open for food 10.30 to 2.30, 6 to 11 & (also wc)

Known locally as 'the pub with no bar'.
Greene King beers are served straight from
the cask in a little wood-panelled room a
few steps down from the main drinking
area. It is rather like being in an old house
that serves alcohol. The front room is for
table skittles. Food is simple, cheap and
nourishing, with the emphasis on huge
portions of excellent cheeses served with
local crusty bread and relishes.
Alternatively there is good ham carved off
the bone, and a few simple sweets.

BUCKINGHAM
Buckinghamshire   map 4

| NEW ENTRY | **Dipalee Tandoori** [6/10] |

18 Castle Street
TEL Buckingham (0280) 813151/813925

Open noon to 2, 6 to 11 (11.30 Fri and Sat) &

A town-centre curry house with a typical
Indian atmosphere. Tables are in booths
divided by vertical green and yellow
fluorescent tubes. The menu has all the
familiar North Indian tandoori dishes and
curries, from chicken tikka to onion
bhajias, birianis and lamb pasanda. Mango
or pistachio-flavoured kulfi to finish.
Prices are reasonable.

BURFORD Oxfordshire   map 4

Bull Hotel [6/10]

High Street
TEL Burford (099 382) 2220

Open noon to 2, 6.30 (7 Sun) to 9.30 &

Burford has its share of old hostelries. This
fifteenth-century coaching-inn has a good
choice of bar meals, taking in home-made
pâté, game pie, and apple pie. There are
sometimes fresh mussels in season as well
as vegetarian dishes, such as tomato and
cashew nut roast with parsley sauce.
There are plans to introduce a carvery and

cold table in 1988. Real ales from
Wadworths and decent house wine by the
glass.

CHIPPING NORTON
Oxfordshire   map 4

Nutters [7/10]

New Street
TEL Chipping Norton (0608) 41995

Open 10 to 6 (5 Nov to Apr) &
Closed Sun and Mon; Christmas Day to 27 Dec

Elizabeth Arnold was a health and
relaxation therapist before setting up this
little restaurant specialising in healthy
eating. She follows the NACNE guidelines,
producing dishes that are low in saturated
fat, salt and sugar, but high in dietary fibre,
protein and vitamins. However, the food
isn't clinical, and it's not exclusively
vegetarian. Alongside broccoli in
mushroom sauce, ratatouille, and
courgettes with peanut sauce, might be
beef with Guinness and mushrooms,
paprika chicken, and baked cod Mornay.
Soup and fish pâtés are served with
wholemeal rolls or oatcakes, while sweets
are deliberately low in calories, despite
their names: fresh raspberry meringue,
strawberry crumble, blackcurrant
cheesecake. As well as wines and lager,
there are herb teas and home-made
lemonade.

CLANFIELD Oxfordshire   map 4

Clanfield Tavern [6/10]

TEL Clanfield (036 781) 223

Open for food noon to 2, 6 to 10 &
Closed Christmas Day

This sturdy seventeenth-century
coaching-inn serves good-value bar food.
Eat in the comfortable carpeted lounge,
which has a log fire in winter. A standard
menu always features ploughman's,
sandwiches (including hot beef or
Oxfordshire sausage), home-made chicken
liver pâté, and steakburgers. Look for the
daily specials, which might include deep-
fried garlic mushrooms, breast of chicken
stuffed with asparagus, and grilled lemon
sole. Three-course business lunches are

£7.25. More expensive restaurant meals. Real ales from Hook Norton and Morlands.

CLIFTON HAMPDEN
Oxfordshire   map 4

Barley Mow [6/10]

TEL Clifton Hampden (086 730) 7847

Open for food noon to 2 (1.30 Sun), 7 to 10 &
Closed Sun D; Christmas Day, 1 Jan

A famous thatched Thames-side pub, whose history goes back several centuries. In the bar, help yourself to interesting pies, such as venison and bacon, as well as various salads. There are also hearty casseroles and thick slabs of meat carved off hot joints. Portions are generous. Ushers beers.

CROPREDY Oxfordshire   map 4

Brasenose Inn [6/10]

TEL Cropredy (029 575) 244

Open for food 11.30 to 2.30, 6 (7 Sat) to 11
Closed Sun

The most useful local stopping place on the Southern Oxford Canal. Lunch is a blackboard menu of freshly made soups, pies, garlic mushrooms, and dishes such as liver and bacon casserole. Grills and steaks feature in the evening. Sweets range from raspberry meringue to treacle tart. Draught Bass and good-value wines.

CUMNOR Oxfordshire   map 4

Bear and Ragged Staff [6/10]

Appleton Road
TEL Oxford (0865) 862329

Open for food noon to 2, 7 to 10 &

A well-cared-for sixteenth-century pub within striking distance of Oxford. Bar food centres on a choice of salads plus a blackboard listing hot stews, pies and casseroles. Gateaux, fruit pies, and cheese for afters. Morrells beers. More expensive restaurant.

DEDDINGTON Oxfordshire   map 4

Kings Arms [7/10]

TEL Deddington (0869) 38364

Open for food noon to 2, 7 to 10.30 & (also WC)

The food at Anthony Hutton's sixteenth-century coaching-inn is 'traditional English fayre' with a meaty flavour. Rabbit, ale and mushroom pie, stuffed lambs' hearts, home-made faggots, and grilled pork chop with Oxford sauce are typical of the style. Otherwise there's chicken casserole, trawler pie, or prawn and crab salad. Sunday roast is £6.50 (children's portions half-price). Halls Harvest Bitter, Marstons Pedigree and Ind Coope Burton Ale on draught.

EAST ILSLEY Berkshire   map 2

Crown and Horns [6/10]

TEL East Ilsley (063 528) 205

Open for food 10.30 to 2.30 (noon to 2 Sun), 6 to 11
Closed Sun D

A gem of a pub with occasional puppet shows and poetry readings to distract the drinkers. Inside there are beams, outside there are trees. The range of bar snacks takes in everything from fish and chips to home-made pies. Excellent real ales might include Arkells, Morlands, Wadworths and Theakstons.

ETON Berkshire   map 2

Eton Wine Bar [8/10]

82–83 High Street
TEL Windsor (0753) 854921/855182

Open noon to 2.30, 6 to 10.30 & (also WC)
Closed Christmas, Easter Sun

A perfect model for any aspiring wine bar. The food is home-made, seasonal and adventurous. Particularly good are the savoury mousses and stuffed pancakes, such as fresh salmon, trout with courgettes, or a cold version filled with apple, pear and vanilla cream. There are also unusual soups, quiches and salads. The wine list is admirable, with plenty of decent drinking for under £10. Handy for Windsor theatre.

FORTY GREEN
Buckinghamshire   map 2

Royal Standard of England [6/10]

TEL Beaconsfield (049 46) 3382

Open for food 10.30 to 2.30, 5.30 to 11 (noon to 2, 7 to 10.30 Sun) ♿ (also WC)

One of the oldest and most historic pubs in England. The ancient beams and uneven floors are reminders that parts of the building date from the eleventh century. A fine spread of food is laid out in the bar: cold pies, crab in season, assorted salads, and sandwiches. There's also a big choice of cheeses, which are often served with home-made chutneys. To go with the food there are real ales, including Marstons and Eldridge Pope.

FRILSHAM Berkshire   map 2

Pot Kiln [6/10]

TEL Hermitage (0635) 201366

Open for food noon to 1.45, 7 to 10 ♿

This feels like a genuinely old pub, tucked away down country lanes in a Berkshire backwater. The tables outside overlook fields. A short menu of bar food has hot filled rolls, cottage pie, curry, and very good chicken pie served hot with salad, to go with draught Morlands and Arkells beers.

FYFIELD Oxfordshire   map 4

White Hart [6/10]

TEL Frilford Heath (0865) 390585

Open for food 10.30 to 2.30, 6 to 11 (noon to 2, 7 to 10.30 Sun)

There's plenty of history in this converted fifteenth-century almshouse with high timbered roof and minstrels' gallery. The bar food is straightforward, but there are some good touches: soup comes with home-baked bread, pigeon is casseroled, and there's a range of savoury pies, from

chicken and mushroom to fisherman's. Steaks, roast chicken, and chilli con carne complete the picture. Real ales from Morlands, Theakstons and Wadworths, among others. More expensive restaurant.

GORING-ON-THAMES
Oxfordshire   map 2

Coffee Pot [6/10]

3 Goring Arcade
TEL Goring-on-Thames (0491) 872485

Open 9 (noon Sun) to 5.30 ♿

A useful, prettily laid out restaurant in a shopping arcade near the car-park. Sunday lunch is still a great attraction, with its excellent, well-hung roasts and fresh vegetables. Snacks are served all day, and the owners are planning to open for simple evening meals of lasagne, chicken casserole and the like. The restaurant is now licensed.

HAMBLEDON
Buckinghamshire   map 2

Stag & Huntsman [6/10]

TEL Henley-on-Thames (0491) 571227

Open for food noon to 2 (1.45 Sun), 7 to 10 ♿ (also WC)
Closed Sun D; Christmas Day

Mexican dishes dominate the menu in this old-fashioned Chiltern pub. There are familiar-sounding dishes as well as unusual ones, such as puerco verde – pork served on a bed of corn chips. The menu also features plenty of English pub stalwarts, from home-made soup and quiche to chicken pie. Stilton or home-made ice-cream to finish. Real ales from Brakspears, Wadworths and Eldridge Pope. Children welcome at lunch-time.

HAMSTEAD MARSHALL
Berkshire   map 2

White Hart [6/10]

TEL Kintbury (0488) 58201

Open for food noon to 2 (1.45 Sun), 7 to 10 (9 Sun) ♿
Closed Christmas Day

Deep in the Berkshire countryside about two miles from the A4, between Newbury and Hungerford. The Aromandos have given the pub an Italian flavour, especially in the food. As well as pasta there is good fresh fish from Billingsgate, pastries and home-made sweets, such as crème caramel. The caraway-seed bread is good too. Reasonably priced wines as well as real ales.

HEMEL HEMPSTEAD
Hertfordshire   map 5

NEW ENTRY Gallery Coffee Shop and Brasserie [7/10]

Old Town Hall Arts Centre, High Street
TEL Hemel Hempstead (0442) 42827

Open 10 to 4.30
Closed Sun; 2 weeks Sept

The coffee-shop-cum-brasserie on the first floor of the Arts Centre is suitably decorated with prints and photos on the walls, and lacy cloths on the tables. The menu is chalked up on an old teacher's blackboard and easel, and the food has a strong vegetarian bias: watercress and leek soup, Mozzarella, tomato and avocado salad, baked stuffed aubergines, as well as coronation chicken with nut and rice salad. Sweets include delectable strawberry cheesecake, green grapes with yoghurt cream, or hazelnut and mango meringue. Teas, coffee and house wine by the glass. Open in the evening for theatregoers.

Jade Lotus [6/10]

119 Marlowes
TEL Hemel Hempstead (0442) 52748

Open noon to 2, 5.30 (6 Sun) to 11.30 &
Closed Christmas Day and Boxing Day

There has been a Chinese restaurant on this site since the early 1960s. The original, the Hong Kong, was Hemel Hempstead's first chop-suey house. The present restaurant has moved with the times and offers a fashionable mix of Pekingese dishes plus a few reminders of the past, such as sweet-and-sour king prawns and chicken with bean sprouts.

Otherwise there are sesame prawn toasts, dumplings, sizzling lamb with spring onions, and deep-fried oysters. Weekday set lunches start at £3 for beef and green peppers in black-bean sauce or roast duck with char siu pork, plus soup, rice and coffee.

HIGH WYCOMBE
Buckinghamshire   map 4

George and Dragon [7/10]

West Wycombe
TEL High Wycombe (0494) 23602

Open for food noon to 2 (1.30 Sun), 6 to 10
Closed Sun D

A fine old coaching-inn on the main street of a district in High Wycombe. The extensive bar menu has some enterprising touches and home-made pies are a speciality: not only chicken, but also Cumberland sweet lamb (with beer, rum, apples and dried fruit), and sole with grapes. There's also marinated salmon with mustard sauce, smoked mackerel with gooseberry and horseradish sauce, and home-made game pâté. Steaks and lamb cutlets for meat-eaters, baked avocado with crab, or spinach and blue cheese pancakes for vegetarians. Oldfashioned, home-made sweets.

HOUGHTON CONQUEST
Bedfordshire   map 5

Knife and Cleaver [7/10]

TEL Bedford (0234) 740387

Open for food 11.30 to 2, 7 to 9.30 (10 Sat)
Closed Sun; bank hols

Fillets of sole with crab mousseline, filo pastry cases filled with vegetable purées, and hot caramel pears suggest that this seventeenth-century pub has transformed itself into a restaurant with a bar. Any Gallic flourishes are balanced by sturdy English stalwarts, such as steak, kidney and oyster pie, or roast rack of lamb. Full meals would take the bill into double figures, but it's possible to have just one course. Best value are dishes such as braised quails with almonds and grapes, or wholemeal croustade with courgettes, walnuts and cheese. House wine is £5.20 a bottle.

HUNGERFORD
Berkshire   map 2

Galloping Crayfish [8/10]

The Courtyard, 24 High Street
TEL Hungerford (0488) 84008

Open for food 10 to 10 & ground floor bar only
(also WC)

The story is that Henry VIII was so fond of the crayfish from the River Kennet that messengers collected supplies from what is now the Dundas Arms (at Kintbury, see entry) and galloped with them back to London whenever the King fancied a few for his supper. Hence the name of this new bistro/wine bar in a courtyard next to the Hungerford Wine Company. Good ingredients are used for a menu that features freshly made soup (perhaps asparagus), deep-fried Brie with home-made tomato chutney, spicy lamb balls in pitta bread. Main courses, such as roast rack of lamb, mushroom Stroganoff, or trout stuffed with tomato and basil, come with excellent vegetables. There are also club sandwiches, steak baguettes, and salads. Impressive wines include twenty by the glass. Morning coffee comes with croissants and brioches, afternoon tea with sandwiches and Danish pastries.

INKPEN Berkshire   map 2

Swan Inn [8/10]

Lower Inkpen
TEL Inkpen (048 84) 326

Open for food noon to 2, 7 to 9.30 &
Closed Mon (exc bank hols); Sun D

This village pub has undergone a transformation. The setting is pure English – heavy beams, trestle tables in the garden, fine walking country all round – but the menu has moved east. Esther Scothorne is from Singapore and her cooking is first-rate South-East Asian backed up by some better than average pub grub. Go in a party and order a range of dishes, such as beef satay, thom yam soup flavoured with tamarind, lemon grass and nam pla (fermented fish sauce), lamb rendang, and

deep-fried chicken with cashew nuts, plus Singapore noodles and dill-flavoured rice. In more familiar territory there is good chicken liver pâté, quiche, lamb cutlets, and beef and venison pie. Ice-creams, gateaux and mousses to finish. The same menu operates in the bar and restaurant. House wine £4.50 a bottle.

KINTBURY Berkshire   map 2

Dundas Arms [6/10]

Station Road
TEL Kintbury (0488) 58263

Open for food noon to 2 & (also WC)
Closed Sun

A young, boisterous atmosphere pervades the bar, and crowds spill out onto the canal towpath on fine days. The Dalzell-Pipers serve good cheap lunches of hummus, potted shrimps, cold curried chicken with salad, and gammon, egg and chips. Beers from Ushers and Morlands. More expensive meals in the elegant dining-room.

LANE END Buckinghamshire   map 4

Peacock [6/10]

Bolter End
TEL High Wycombe (0494) 881417

Open for food noon to 2 (1.15 Sun), 7 to 10 &
Closed Sun D; Christmas Day, Boxing Day and 1 Jan

Bolter End is a small dot on the map, about a mile north-west of Lane End on the B482. Janet Hodge does the cooking in this cheerful pub and is renowned for her double-decker sandwiches. Sausages and burgers come from the local butcher and the menu also roams around for coq au vin, steak and kidney pie, and satay. Home-made sorbets or treacle tart to finish.

LEIGHTON BUZZARD
Bedfordshire   map 4

| NEW ENTRY | Akash Tandoori [6/10] |

60 North Street
TEL Leighton Buzzard (0525) 372316

Open noon to 2.30, 6 to 12

This brightly lit, glass-fronted restaurant is rated as one of the best in the neighbourhood. Inside, the décor is shades of pink with coloured lights in the ceiling. The standard menu has good shish kebabs, mushroom bhajis, and the usual range of curries and tandoori dishes. Decent portions, reasonable prices.

Swan Hotel [6/10]

High Street
TEL Leighton Buzzard (0525) 372148

Open noon to 2.30, 7 to 9.30 & (also WC)
Closed Boxing Day and 1 Jan

This impressively refurbished hotel provides good-value bar food in a town short on decent eating places. The menu is strong on sandwiches (plain or toasted), there are jumbo rolls filled with sausages, triple-decker club sandwiches, and 'bargees' buttys' filled with steak, fried onions and tomatoes. There's also a special dish of the day. Set lunch in the smart dining-room is £8.50, but dinners will take the bill well into double figures.

LEY HILL Buckinghamshire   map 4

Swan Inn [6/10]

nr Chesham
TEL Chesham (0494) 783075

Open for food noon to 2, 6.30 to 9
Closed Sun D; Christmas Eve to Boxing Day

New landlord Jeff Steers has changed very little in this busy old pub. Its reputation for good home-cooked food is as solid as the old beams and big fireplace in the bar. A bowl of soup with a hunk of wholemeal bread makes a filling snack, otherwise the menu takes in lunchtime specials such as beef and onion pie, or chicken in white wine sauce. Evening dishes range from curried prawns to liver and onions or steak with garlic butter. Ind Coope beers on draught; house wine £4 a bottle.

LONGWORTH Oxfordshire   map 4

Blue Boar [6/10]

TEL Oxford (0865) 820494

Open for food noon to 2 (1.45 Sun), 7 to 10
Closed Christmas Day

An out-of-the-way village local with long refectory tables on the flagstone floors. Well-hung steaks are served with chips and mustard, otherwise the blackboard menu has garlic prawns, wholemeal pizzas, and beef and Guinness pie. Children welcome at lunch-time.

LUTON Bedfordshire   map 5

Casa Bianca [6/10]

26 Chapel Street
TEL Luton (0582) 27916

Open 11am to 2am &

A town-centre trattoria-cum-wine bar with black beams and a ceramic-tiled floor. Food is cooked in full view of the customers, and it's possible to have one course or a full meal. Pasta, pizzas and salads are the mainstays, and sweets are freshly made each day. House wine is £4.95 a bottle.

Man Ho [7/10]

80 Dunstable Road
TEL Luton (0582) 23366

Open noon to 2, 6 to 11
Closed Sun

John and Cora Lau's smart restaurant has earned a good local reputation as a family eating place and children are accommodated happily. Meals can easily break the £10 barrier but are nonetheless good value for the area. The menu is mainly Peking and Szechuan, and set feasts begin at £9 a head. Otherwise choose from the menu, which ranges from crispy lamb and sizzling beef with ginger and spring onion, to seafood, in the shape of Kung Po prawns, deep-fried oysters, and steamed sea bass.

MAIDENHEAD Berkshire   map 2

Jack of Both Sides [6/10]

81 Queen Street
TEL Maidenhead (0628) 20870

Open for food noon to 2 & (also WC)
Closed Sun

A busy town-centre pub serving honest lunchtime bar food. Around £2 pays for, say, cottage pie, a roast, liver and bacon casserole, or steak and kidney pie. There's also home-made soup in winter. Wethereds and Flowers beers, plus guest brews; wine at 95p for a big glass.

MAIDENSGROVE
Oxfordshire   map 2

Five Horseshoes [7/10]

TEL Nettlebed (0491) 641282

Open for food noon to 2 (1.30 Sun), 7 to 10 &
Closed Sun D; limited Mon L; Christmas Day D

This seventeenth-century pub is out on its own, past a big common down the Stonor road from Henley. Prices can seem a bit high for a snack lunch, but the menu has some interesting items, from avocado and walnut pâté to seafood lasagne and stir-fried beef with vegetables. The Stilton soup is renowned and there are more expensive specials, such as poached wild salmon with wine and tarragon. Barbecues on Thursday evenings and Sunday lunchtimes in summer. Children can play in the garden. Brakspears beers.

NEWBURY Berkshire   map 2

Bacon Arms [6/10]

Oxford Street
TEL Newbury (0635) 31822

Open for food noon to 2, 7 to 9.30 (7.30 to 10 Fri and Sat) &
Closed Sun (wine bar)

This seventeenth century coaching-inn has a wine bar with French posters on the wall and a menu dominated by good charcoal-grilled meat and fish, from chicken tikka and butterfly lamb chops to salmon. Alternatively, there are decent bistro favourites such as cream of watercress soup and pork goulash with rice; there's also a choice of salads. Afternoon teas are served from Monday to Saturday. The separate carvery offers more expensive roast lunches and à la carte meals in the evening. House wine by the glass or bottle.

NEWPORT PAGNELL
Buckinghamshire   map 4

Glover's Wine Bar [6/10]

18 St John Street
TEL Newport Pagnell (0908) 616398

Open 11.30 to 2.30, 6.30 to 11
Closed Sun and Mon; Christmas to New Year

A useful wine bar in an area where decent eating places are thin on the ground. The cold buffet has a promising spread of pies, quiches, gammon, smoked Cumberland sausage, and plenty of salads. Hot dishes take in home-made soup, hot ratatouille with garlic bread, prawn provençale, and spaghetti bolognese. A glass of Muscadet is £1.05.

OXFORD Oxfordshire   map 4

Browns [9/10]

5–9 Woodstock Road
TEL Oxford (0865) 511995

Open 11 (noon Sun and bank hols) to 11.30 & (also WC)
Closed Christmas Eve to Boxing Day

Like the Bodleian Library, Browns is an Oxford institution. It is light-hearted, inimitable and has an extraordinary buzz. The potted palms, the hanging plants, and the waiters in their long aprons are all part of the place and part of its attraction. The food is casual, with big helpings of pasta, salads, grills, and pies backed up by pub-style specials, such as leg of lamb with Oxford sauce. A pianist plays in the afternoon. Croissants for breakfast, toasted muffins for tea. To drink there are snazzy cocktails, imported beers and good-value wines.

Crypt [7/10]

Frewin Court (off Cornmarket)
TEL Oxford (0865) 251000

Open 11.30 to 2.30, 6 (7 Sat) to 10.30 (11 Fri and Sat)
Closed Sun; bank hols

An out-of-town representative of Davy's chain of London wine bars. The old-style Dickensian atmosphere is a good antidote to the frantic mood of most pubs in Oxford. Chicken and chestnut pie is the speciality and the menu is stoically patriotic, with lamb steaks, plates of smoked salmon, rare roast beef salads, and apple pie. Sausage in a crusty roll makes a good snack. Creditable wines by the glass or bottle, as well as naturally aged, strong lager by the jug.

Fasta Pasta [7/10]

3 Little Clarendon Street
TEL Oxford (0865) 57349

Open 10 to 11 (1 to 10.30 Sun) & (also WC)
Closed Christmas Day, Boxing Day and 1 Jan

The best place for fresh pasta in Oxford. The green and white shop with little garden tables sells a range of sauces, such as pesto, alfredo, and bolognese, to go with the spaghetti and tagliatelle. There's also a dish of the day, such as ravioli with cream and tomato. Good sorbets; drinkable house wine. Take-aways.

Fellows Brasserie [7/10]

37 St Clements
TEL Oxford (0865) 241431

Open 11 to 11 &

Some say that Fellows is a clone of Browns (see entry), but it has its own pace and style. The plants, the newspaper rack near the coffee machine, and the mirrors look familiar, and the waiters are slick. New owner Michel Sadones has steered the menu towards Mediterranean fish soup, warm salad of chicken with orange dressing, pork chop with mustard sauce, lamb kebabs, and pasta specials. There are also plates of cheese, burgers, and steaks. Cocktails, imported beers and house wines from £1 a glass. Michel Sadones has also reopened the old Michel's Bistro at 146 London Road, Headington, Oxford, as Café Français, where the cheapest option is set lunch at £7.45.

Go Dutch [6/10]

18 Park End Street
TEL Oxford (0865) 240686

Open 6 (noon Sat, Sun and bank hol Mons) to 11
Closed Christmas to New Year; Easter Sun

This pancake house makes a good alternative to the railway station buffet across the road. The place feels authentically Dutch, and pancakes are made the traditional way. All kinds of savoury ingredients can be mixed and matched: smoked bacon, cheese, green pepper, salami, mushrooms. Try spooning Stroop – a sweet cane sugar syrup – over them. Sweet versions are just as varied, otherwise there is Dutch apple pie or ice-cream concoctions with fruit, nuts and liqueurs. A second, unlicensed, branch at 43 St Clements is useful for lunch.

Munchy Munchy [9/10]

6 Park End Street
TEL Oxford (0865) 245710

Open noon to 2.30, 5.30 to 9.40 &
Closed Sun and Mon; 2 weeks Aug, 3 weeks Dec to Jan; bank hols

Ethel Ow describes her little café as an 'Indonesian and Malaysian origin food bar', which sums it up precisely. She serves a brilliantly idiosyncratic version of South-East Asian home cooking with an amazing range of flavours and ingredients. Each day there are half a dozen main dishes, such as spicy lamb with turmeric and lemon grass in sour-cream sauce, stuffed chicken with fresh apricots, cardamom, cloves, mace and apricot brandy, king prawns with fenugreek, cumin and fresh mango purée. Order at the counter, then sit at one of the pine tables. Plates are piled high with rice, and dishes come in separate bowls. To finish there are tropical fruits or exotic ice-creams. Unlicensed, but you can bring your own. No children under six on Friday and Saturday evenings, when the place is full to bursting. The restaurant may be closed from July to September for renovation.

Museum of Modern Art [6/10]

30 Pembroke Street
TEL Oxford (0865) 722733

Open 10 (2.30 Sun) to 5 & (also WC)
Closed Mon; bank hols

The ground-floor gallery stages some of the most exciting and innovative art exhibitions in Oxford. Downstairs in the white-walled basement there is good cheap food to be had: excellent home-made soups, imaginative salads, ice-creams, and substantial wedges of good cakes. Unlicensed.

Oxford Bakery and Brewhouse [8/10]

14 Gloucester Street, Gloucester Green
TEL Oxford (0865) 727265

Open 10.30 to 2.15 (noon to 1.45 Sun) & (also WC)
Closed Christmas Day, Boxing Day and 1 Jan

Beer and bread are natural companions. This enterprising pub-cum-bakery produces a fine choice of both. From the casks come a range of home-brewed beers of different strengths, and from the ovens an extraordinary selection of breads, including red pepper and onion, apple and cinnamon, apricot and walnut, as well as rye, caraway seed and wholemeal. These go well with inventive salads, locally smoked Chewton Mendip cheese, a version of guacamole with apples and walnuts, and home-made moules marinière quiche. There are also hefty sandwiches.

St Aldate's Coffee House [6/10]

94 St Aldate's
TEL Oxford (0865) 245952

Open 10 to 5
Closed Sun; bank hols

Owned by St Aldate's church and run in conjunction with the church bookshop. The atmosphere is comfortably sedate, with dark polished tables, upholstered settees and panelled walls. Home-baked cakes and scones are served through the day, while at lunch-time there are jacket potatoes, salads and dishes such as chicken curry. Vegetarians are well catered for with, say, vegetarian cottage pie. Clotted cream teas are a new feature. Unlicensed.

Wykeham [5/10]

15 Holywell Street
TEL Oxford (0865) 246916

Open 10 (noon Sun) to 5.30 &
Closed 23 Dec to 8 Jan; Sun in vacations

The most popular traditional café in the city. All the usual plain and toasted sandwiches, various ploughman's, and cakes to go with a pot of tea or a cup of coffee. Home-made scones are first rate and soup is free of animal fats. There's a patio for sunny days. Unlicensed.

PANGBOURNE Berkshire   map 2

Copper Inn [8/10]

Church Road
TEL Pangbourne (073 57) 2244

Open for food 12.30 to 2, 7.30 to 9.30 &
Closed D Fri to Sun

This upmarket, modernised eighteenth-century inn is now part of the Fine Inns Group, whose policy is to provide English food using English ingredients. In practice the enterprising bar menu shows the British theme more strongly than the classy dining-room. Potted Cornish crab, oak-smoked sea trout, and Cumberland 'macon' (mutton cured like Parma ham) with spiced oranges, share the bill with warm salad of oyster mushrooms and home-cured bacon, or grilled fillet of cod with garlicky creamed spinach. An heroically patriotic mixed grill has black pudding, Cumberland sausage, bacon, mushrooms and free-range eggs on a Staffordshire oatcake for £3.95. Sunday lunch is a traditional roast.

NEW ENTRY | King Charles Head [6/10]

Reading Road
TEL Checkendon (0491) 680268

Open for food noon to 2, 7 to 10 & (also WC)
Closed Sun D

A brick-built pub set in leafy woods a couple of miles north-east of Pangbourne. Blackboard specials, such as seafood crêpes or lamb with orange and ginger, supplement the familiar list of pâté, lasagne, and steak and kidney pie. Trout 'smoked to an old Norwegian recipe' comes with salad containing a little of everything – from peanuts and red cabbage to peaches and pineapple. Good range of beers, including Adnams, Theakstons, Bass and Ruddles. No children.

READING Berkshire   map 2

Corner Café [5/10]

51 Vastern Road
TEL Reading (0734) 507272

Open 7 to 4 (7.30 to noon Sat)
Closed Sun, bank hols; Christmas Eve to Boxing Day

A no-frills corner café serving hefty fried breakfasts, as well as sausage, chips and beans, burgers, and steak and kidney pudding with mash. Coffee and tea come in mugs. Cheap, down-to-earth, and a better bet for a plate of food than the nearby railway station buffet.

Mama Mia [6/10]

11 St Mary's Butts
TEL Reading (0734) 581357

Open noon to 2, 6 to 10 &
Closed Sun; bank hols

Pizzas and pasta dishes are the cheapest bets in this unpretentious bistro. The house special is a twelve-inch diameter pizza loaded with ham, mushrooms, tomatoes and plenty of cheese. There are also salads, soups, and dishes such as Mozzarella in carrozza (layers of cheese and ham with mushrooms, baked in a shallow earthenware dish). About twenty wines.

Wine Butts [6/10]

61 St Mary's Butts
TEL Reading (0734) 509363

Open noon to 2.30, 6 to 10.30
Closed Sun and Mon; bank hols

A handy town wine bar with church pews and stripped pine tables. The menu offers good value for dishes such as tuna lasagne, home-made chicken and mushroom pie, and vegetarian salad. A three-course meal

can be had for around £6 a head. House wine by the glass.

ST ALBANS Hertfordshire   map 5

NEW ENTRY # Alban Tandoori [7/10]

145 Victoria Street
TEL St Albans (0727) 62111

Open noon to 2.30, 6 to 11 (11.30 Fri and Sat)

St Albans has more than its share of creditable curry houses. This smart place close to the station wins the vote for quality and value; it is also the only one to serve decent vegetarian thalis. The standard menu has excellent tandoori chicken, as well as aloo chat, prawn dhansak and mutton mhoglai. Service is careful and attentive. Must book for evening meals.

Garibaldi [7/10]

62 Stanhope Road
TEL St Albans (0727) 65537

Open noon to 3, 5 to 10.30 (noon to 10.30 Sat) & (also WC)
Closed Sun; bank hols; Christmas Day, Boxing Day and 1 Jan

Still the best bet in St Albans for cheap Italian food. This down-to-earth café near the station has Formica-topped tables and precious little décor, but the pasta dishes are excellent and there are great home-made pizzas and well-cooked veal and fish dishes. Excellent zabaglione to finish. One dish and a glass of house wine will leave plenty of change from £5.

Garibaldi Pub [6/10]

61 Albert Street
TEL St Albans (0727) 55046

Open for food noon to 2 (1.45 Sun, 2.15 Sat), 6.30 to 9.30
Closed Sat D and Sun D

A busy Fullers pub, up a side street away from the town, serving good beer and fresh, home-cooked pub grub to match: turkey and mushroom soup; gutsy mince and kidney hot-pot; trout with mussel and orange stuffing; authentic moussaka in a big dish, beef pie laced with ESB; chunky cakes of sausagemeat wrapped in bacon and topped with slices of black pudding. Vegetables are superb: big earthy potatoes in their skins, whole carrots roughly peeled and scrubbed, perhaps fresh spinach. Salads centre on a huge basin of fresh all-sorts. The London Pride and ESB are kept in top condition. Children are happily accommodated inside and out. The conservatory is a no-smoking area.

 ## Marmaris [6/10]

128 London Road
TEL St Albans (0727) 40382

Open noon to 3, 6 to 12
Closed Sun L; Christmas Day and Boxing Day

St Albans' first Turkish restaurant is in a converted curry house on the London Road. Inside it is cheery and close-packed and brightens up a dull part of town. Good starters such as stuffed aubergines or spinach with yoghurt and garlic, set the scene for stuffed vine leaves, karisik kebab, shish kebab and moussaka. Good value business lunches during the week are £4.95. Drinkable house red is £5.75 – otherwise pay an extra 50p for Turkish.

NEW ENTRY | La Province [7/10]

13 George Street
TEL St Albans (0727) 52142

Open noon to 2.15 (3.30 Sun), 7 to 10.15
Closed Mon; Sun D, 2 to 12 Jan

In a steep winding street in an historic part of the town with lots of half-timbered and higgledy-piggledy buildings. New owners have turned it into a good-value bistro with a French accent. Inside it is pink and beamed with a Parisian Peggy Lee on tape and sylph-like waitresses. Straightforward cheap lunches take in French onion soup, salads, calf's liver with bacon, and chicken provençale. Slightly more expensive evening menu in the mould of rack of lamb, and pork fillet with Calvados. Dark, strong coffee; drinkable house wine.

Pizza Express [7/10]

11–13 Verulam Road
TEL St Albans (0727) 5300

Open 11.30 to midnight
Closed Christmas Day

A Home Counties branch of the highly rated pizza chain (see London entry).

SHIPTON-UNDER-WYCHWOOD
Oxfordshire   map 4

Lamb Inn [7/10]

TEL Shipton-under-Wychwood
(0993) 830465

Open for food 12.15 to 2 (noon to 1.30 Sun), 7 to 10 &

Locals and visitors support this centuries-old Cotswold pub set back off the road. The blackboard bar menu is patriotic – asparagus soup, potted shrimps, roast garlic lamb, Cotswold pie, treacle tart. Buffet lunches include ham cut in thick slices, new potatoes in their skins, pasta salad, marinated mushrooms and the like. Sunday roasts are served in the beamed dining-room. Hook Norton and Wadworths real ales. No children.

Shaven Crown [6/10]

TEL Shipton-under-Wychwood (0993) 830330

Open for food noon to 2 (1.30 Sun), 7 to 9.30 (9 Sun)
Closed Christmas Day

The soaring stone walls, the church roof timbers and the medieval courtyard are part of the attraction in this historic inn. The name refers to the time when the place was a retreat for monks from the nearby monastery. Cheap meals in the Buttery Bar take in chicken liver pâté, steak sandwiches, curried prawns, and vegetarian options such as mushroom and walnut pancake. Finish with home-made ice-cream or treacle tart. More expensive restaurant meals.

SOUTH LEIGH Oxfordshire   map 4

NEW ENTRY | Mason Arms [6/10]

TEL Witney (0993) 2485

Open for food 11 to 2, 6.30 to 10 & (also WC)
Closed Mon (exc bank hols)

An ancient thatched pub that has earned a good reputation for its food and drink. Home-cured salt beef is served in salads and sandwiches or with vegetables. There's a good range of ploughman's as well as seafood pancakes, lasagne, and trifle to finish. Beers include Glennys Bitter, brewed locally in Witney. There are picnic tables under the trees in the garden.

SPEEN Buckinghamshire   map 4

| NEW ENTRY | **Atkins** [9/10] |

The Old Plow Inn, Flowers Bottom
TEL Hampden Row (024 028) 300

Open for food noon to 2 (1.45 Sun), 7 to 10
Closed Sun D and Mon D

Gerald and Frances Atkins have transformed this Chiltern roadside inn into one of the finest eating places in the Home Counties. It still feels like a village local, and the range of bar food shows off Frances Atkins' talents, as well as catering to a local demand for simple pub grub. Lasagne, club sandwiches, and jacket potatoes are ever popular, but the real interest is in the specialities: risotto, home-made pasta, duck pasties with apricots, spinach roulade – all of which are served with salad. There's also a soup, such as leek and apple, with garlic bread, and fine puddings, ranging from almond tart to fresh fruit soufflés. Decent wines, plus beers from Morlands, Brakspears and Fullers. Restaurant meals are outside this book's price range, but there is now a set menu for £12.50 served in the bar, which is a bargain at this level. Children welcome in the garden.

STANFORD DINGLEY
Berkshire   map 2

Farmer's Table [7/10]

TEL Bradfield (0734) 744369

Open noon to 2, 8 to 10.30, plus 3 to 6 Sun
& (also WC)
Closed Sun (exc 3 to 6)

The small farm is noted for its Jersey cream and asparagus. It also serves as a village shop, and the cowshed has been spruced up and converted into an informal restaurant (bookings only). All kinds of options are available, from Sunday teas and harvest suppers to Christmas dinners. During May and June there are highly popular asparagus suppers, and on three evenings a week there are set meals for under £10. The first person to book always chooses the main meat course, which is flanked by, say, jumbo asparagus with hollandaise, and a choice of sweets plus cheese and coffee. To drink there are English wines, or you are welcome to bring your own.

Old Boot Inn [6/10]

TEL Reading (0734) 744292

*This pub was sold as
we went to press.*

STANTON HARCOURT
Oxfordshire   map 4

Harcourt Arms [8/10]

TEL Oxford (0865) 882192/881931

Open for food noon to 2, 7 to 10
Closed Christmas Day

George Dailey's hospitable, creeper-covered inn is more of a restaurant than a pub, with prices and food to match. There are three candlelit dining-rooms and a menu that includes anything from spinach and bacon salad to poached breast of chicken with cream and apricot sauce. Choose carefully to keep the bill in single figures: a bowl of mussels, excellent-quality fish and chips, smoked haddock crumble on a bed of spinach, or the renowned grilled king prawns with garlic bread and mayonnaise. At the bar you can also get steak sandwiches, BLTs, and ploughman's. House wine is £5.50, otherwise drink Wadworths 6X.

STEWKLEY Buckinghamshire   map 4

| NEW ENTRY | **Swan Inn** [6/10] |

High Street North
TEL Stewkley (052 524) 285

Open for food 12.15 to 2, 7 to 9.30 & (also WC)
Closed Sun

Colin Anderson serves the beer and his
wife cooks the food in this popular pub at
the end of the village street. The simple
menu has ploughman's, salads,
Cumberland sausages, and a few intriguing
dishes, such as trout mousse wrapped in
smoked salmon. There are also big steaks,
curries, and pies. Home-made Paris-Brest
is a good sweet. Courage beers.

STONY STRATFORD
Buckinghamshire   map 4

| NEW ENTRY | **Old George** [6/10] |

Watling Street
TEL Milton Keynes (0908) 562181

Open for food noon to 2, 7 to 10
Closed Sat L; Sun D

Excellent roast lunches are served in the
beamed bar of this gentrified old inn, parts
of which date from the fifteenth century.
The joint of the day is concealed beneath
the silver dome of a carving trolley; a hefty
loin of pork is perfectly cooked with
crunchy, crisp crackling, and served with
good roast potatoes, fresh runner beans
and ratatouille, plus stuffing and gravy, for
£3.65. Otherwise there are grills, salads,
ploughman's and dishes of the day. Family
Sunday lunches are £6.95 (children under
five £3.50). More expensive restaurant
menu. Beers from Hook Norton and
Charles Wells.

TRING Hertfordshire   map 4

Kings Arms [6/10]

King Street
TEL Tring (044 282) 3318

Open for food 11.30 to 2.15 (noon to 1.45 Sun),
7 to 10
Closed Christmas Day D, Boxing Day D

Vicky and John Francis are real-ale
campaigners and a regularly changing list

of brews is chalked up on a blackboard:
Adnams, Wadworths 6X, Archers,
Shepherd Neame . . . the list changes from
week to week. To go with the beer there
are hot beef sandwiches with onions and
gravy, home-made burgers, soup, big
'crusties', and specials, such as minced
beef and onion pie topped with wholemeal
pastry. Big fry-ups are served as Saturday
brunch. Children are welcome in the
garden.

TURVEY Bedfordshire   map 4

Ye Three Fyshes [6/10]

TEL Turvey (023 064) 264

Open for food 11.30 to 3, 5.30 to 11 &

Giant crusty rolls are the main attraction
in this seventeenth-century village pub by
the River Ouse. The 'Dynamic' version
(£2.50) is filled with steak, onions, melted
cheese and fried egg. The basic bar menu
also has a couple of vegetarian dishes, such
as mushroom and mung bean biriani. Real
ales include Marstons and the local brew
from Banks and Taylors; there's also West
Country farmhouse cider on draught.

WARFIELD Berkshire   map 2

Cricketers [6/10]

Cricketers Lane
TEL Winkfield Row (0344) 882910

Open for food 10.30 to 2.30 (noon to 2 Sun),
6 to 11 & (also WC)
Closed Sun D

The setting is pure England – a converted
hunting-lodge in Windsor Great Park, full
of beams and wooden settles – but the food
in this busy country pub is international.
The menu roams around for Moroccan
lamb, beef Stroganoff, and Mexican tacos,
taking in pâté, salads, and steaks on the
way. On Monday night there are curry
extravaganzas with all kinds of meat, fish
and vegetable dishes, plus nan bread and
poppadums. Greek evenings centre on dips
and grilled swordfish steaks. Brakspears
and occasional guest beers.

WATERPERRY Oxfordshire   map 4

Waterperry Teashop [5/10]

Waterperry Horticultural Centre
TEL Ickford (084 47) 226

Open 10 to 5.30 (4.30 Oct to Mar) & (also WC)
Closed Christmas and New Year

The garden centre is a renowned complex
of nurseries and glasshouses some nine
miles east of Oxford. Home baking is
much in evidence in the tea-shop, which
offers everything from lemon cake to pear
frangipane and shortbread. Quiches and
salads make good light lunches. Wine by
the glass. Eat outside on the lawn when
the weather allows.

WATFORD Hertfordshire   map 5

 # Flower Drum [7/10]

16 Market Street
TEL Watford (0923) 26711/21811

Open noon to 3, 7 to 11.30 &

The revamped décor has all the colours of
a cocktail bar: bright blue venetian blinds,
yellow door-frames, metallic grey
paintwork in the dining-room. The
cooking is a fashionable provincial blend
of Pekingese and Szechuan, and the
bargains are the set lunches. Two or more
can eat for around £6.50 a head from a set
menu that offers beef satay, seaweed with
dried scallops, chilli broth dumplings,
kung po chicken, rice and tea. Full meals
from the menu are likely to break the £10
barrier. Dim-sum lunches on Sunday for
£6.80.

WATTON-AT-STONE Hertfordshire   map 5

George and Dragon [8/10]

High Street
TEL Ware (0920) 830285

Open for food 12.15 to 2, 7.15 to 10 & (also WC)
Closed Sun; Christmas Day, Boxing Day
and 1 Jan

Some of the finest bar meals in
Hertfordshire are served at this beamed
pub-cum-restaurant. Seafood is the
highlight, with the huge plate of hors
d'oeuvre containing a bit of everything.
Otherwise the menu features deep-fried
Brie with gooseberry sauce, steak in a bun,
Barnsley chop, or coq au vin with a quartet
of vegetables, plus specials, such as duck
leg with chestnut sauce. Smoked salmon
is cured in the village. Greene King beers
on draught or house wine by the carafe.
More expensive meals in the dining-room.
No children.

WINDSOR Berkshire   map 2

The Punter [6/10]

Thames Street
TEL Windsor (0753) 865565

Open noon to 3, 6 to 11 (7 to 10.30 Sun) &
Closed Christmas Day and Boxing Day

The emphasis is on good-value home
cooking in this informal restaurant. Thick
soups, savoury pies in individual dishes,
and roast duck all feature; spinach
pancake stuffed with duxelles of
vegetables and mushrooms is a best seller.
The bargains are the full lunches for less
than £7, and two-course Sunday evening
meals for £5.95. Dinners can be more
expensive.

WITNEY Oxfordshire   map 4

Country Pie [7/10]

63 Corn Street
TEL Witney (0993) 3590

Open 10.30 to 2.30 (noon to 2 Sun), 7 to 9.45 &
Closed Mon; Sun D

Home cooking and excellent value for
money are the attractions at this
sixteenth-century building near the
Buttercross. Home-made pies are a feature,
along with hearty dishes such as liver and
bacon, or pork chop with apple sauce. A
mighty mixed grill of lamb chop, liver,
sausage, bacon, mushrooms and tomatoes
is £4. Vegetarians do well with Spanish
omelette, spinach and lentil roulade, or
vegetable pie with nut pastry. Snacks and
home-made cakes are also available.
Evening meals are slightly more
expensive.

WOBURN Bedfordshire   map 4

Black Horse [6/10]

Bedford Street
TEL Woburn (052 525) 210

Open for food noon to 2.30, 6 to 11 (noon to 2,
7 to 10.30 Sun) & (also WC)
Closed Christmas Day

Handy for a snack during an outing to
Woburn Park and Abbey. The bar menu
has quiche and jacket potatoes at one end
of the price scale and steaks at the other. In
between there are burgers, cauliflower
cheese, and pitta bread filled with tuna
salad. Lunchtime extras include home-
made soup, Brixworth pâté, smoked
mackerel and a mini grill. Full meals in
the restaurant may take the bill over £10 a
head. Marstons beers.

WOODSTOCK Oxfordshire   map 4

Feathers Hotel [7/10]

Market Street
TEL Woodstock (0993) 812291

Open 12.15 to 2.30, 3.30 to 5.30 &

The Garden Bar of Gordon Campbell-
Gray's sedate, old-fashioned hotel serves
fine light lunches. There are some
adventurous touches, such as deep-fried
monkfish coated with hazelnuts, but
simpler dishes, such as baked ham and
salad, are just as good. A special vegetarian
menu is always available. Afternoon tea is
an elegant affair, with home-made scones,
shortbread and cakes plus a pot of either
tea or coffee.

King's Head [6/10]

Park Lane
TEL Woodstock (0993) 812164

Open for food noon to 2, 6 to 10 & (also WC)

Reputedly the oldest pub in Woodstock,
and a good choice for bar food. Filled jacket
potatoes are the speciality of the house,
with a choice of twenty-one fillings, from
savoury mince to sweetcorn and egg.
Otherwise there are dishes served on a
wooden platter – anything from
Highwayman's Hoard (chicken leg, ham,
salad, bread and butter) to Squire's Relish
(half a roast guinea-fowl with mushroom
sauce and all the trimmings). All dishes
are available to take away.

YATTENDON Berkshire   map 2

Royal Oak [9/10]

The Square
TEL Hermitage (0635) 201325

Open for food 11 to 2.30, 5.30 to 10.30 &

The Smiths have turned this fine village
hostelry into one of the best eating places
in Berkshire. It is still the local pub, but
that is only part of the story. Richard
Smith's cooking is excellent and the range
of bar food shows the enterprise, British
spirit and flair of the kitchen. The menu
has fish soup, chicken terrine with watercress and tarragon, and kidneys and black
pudding with herb mustard sauce, alongside crab salad, home-cured ham, rump
steak with rösti, and grilled wild salmon.
Ploughman's come with a range of
cheeses. Puddings are the likes of rice
pudding, plum crumble, and hot apricot
pancakes. Bin-end wines are £2 a glass,
or there is real ale at £1 a pint. More
expensive meals in the formal dining-
room.

West Midlands

Hereford & Worcester

Shropshire

Staffordshire

Warwickshire

West Midlands

ABBEY DORE
Hereford & Worcester   map 6

Abbey Dore Court Gardens [6/10]

Abbey Dore Court
TEL Golden Valley (0981) 240279/240419

Open 11 to 6 &
Closed Wed; 1 Nov to mid-Mar

Sarah Sage maintains the National Sedum and Euphorbia Collections in this country house with a walled garden. The stables have been converted into a tea-room and a new conservatory has been added for extra seating. Her own herd of Jersey cows produces the milk, cream and butter for the cream teas and milk shakes. There are wholemeal rolls with home-made pâté and cheeses, as well as sponge and fruit cakes. Yoghurt-based fruit parfaits and Japanese wine berry flan are served with Jersey cream, too. Suppers by arrangement. Unlicensed.

ACTON SCOTT Shropshire   map 6

Working Farm Museum Café [5/10]

Wenlock Lodge
TEL Church Stretton (0694) 6306/6307

Open 10 to 4.30 (5.30 Sun and bank hols)
& (also WC)
Closed Nov to Mar

The museum demonstrates life on a Shropshire farm before the Industrial Revolution, and the little self-service café serves simple food for visitors. Dishes are cooked on the premises and there are seasonal specialities and old-fashioned recipes from time to time. Soup, salads and rolls are backed up by Shropshire fidget pie, butter bean pie or beef stew with dumplings. Unlicensed.

BEWDLEY
Hereford & Worcester   map 4

Pack Horse Inn [6/10]

High Street
TEL Bewdley (0299) 403762

Open for food 11 to 2.30, 6 to 11 (10.30 Sun) &
Closed Christmas Day

Tucked away in an inconspicuous part of town, just up the road from the River Severn. Inside there are beams, a hotch-potch of assorted bric-à-brac, stone floors, and old newspapers pasted to the ceiling. Food is simple and good value: jacket potatoes with fillings, omelettes with salad, lasagne with garlic bread and Forester's Pie with vegetables. Ansells, Tetleys and Ind Coope Burton Ale on draught. Children welcome in the back room.

BIRMINGHAM
West Midlands   map 4

Acropolis [6/10]

608 Bristol Road, Selly Oak
TEL 021-471 4696

Open noon to 2, 5.30 to 11.30 (12 Fri and Sat)
& (also WC)
Closed Sun; Christmas Day and Boxing Day

A little taverna in a busy suburb of Birmingham. Andreas Ktori and his wife cook authentic Greek kebabs, dolmades, afelia and stifado, with hummus and pastourma to start, and baklava with Greek coffee to finish. Meze (for two people) is under £7 a head. Unlicensed, but you can bring your own wine. Take-aways from the shop next door.

Adil [8/10]

150–154 Stoney Lane, Sparkbrook
TEL 021-449 0335

Open noon to midnight (1am Thur to Sat)

The best café in Sparkhill, serving some of the most uncompromising Indian food in Birmingham. There's not much décor, no cutlery, and menus are tucked under the transparent table-tops. Meals begin with a dish of minty yoghurt laced with chilli and topped with sliced onions. Highlights are the superb balti dishes, cooked and served in huge blackened metal pans. Vegetables are fresh from Asian shops in the neighbourhood: spinach, mustard leaf, tinda. Breads are outstanding: tandoori chapatis are actually huge steaming hot roti the size of dinner plates, while a single 'large' nan is enough bread for four people. Unlicensed, but there's an off-licence next door. Adil 2 is a smaller branch with a smaller menu, at 130 Stoney Lane.

Los Andes [9/10]

806 Bristol Road, Selly Oak
TEL 021-471 3577

Open noon to 2, 7 to 11.30 &
Closed Sun

After four years, the most authentic Latin American restaurant in the country has moved down the road to a converted curry house overlooking a massive red-brick Sainsbury. The gutsiness and subtlety of the cooking prove that there's more to South American food than Tex-Mex and tacos. Here are dishes from Brazil, Peru and Chile, as well as Mexico. Look for the superb casseroles, such as feijoada (a Brazilian dish of pork, chorizo, smoked ham and red beans spiked with cumin seeds), the empanadas de horno (pastries filled with minced meat, sultanas and olives), and the vegetarian chipahauzu (baked vegetables and cheese topped with sweetcorn purée). The atmosphere is as full-blooded as the food.

Beaufort Bar, Plough and Harrow Hotel [6/10]

Hadleigh Road, Edgbaston
TEL 021-454 4111

Open for food noon to 2 & (also WC)

Before the war, half a pint of beer cost sixpence in this elegant Victorian hotel. Since then it has maintained its rather overpowering expense-account image. But lunch in the Beaufort Bar is a different story. Here it is possible to eat well and cheerfully for under £5. The cold buffet has massive portions of game pie with salads and home-made mayonnaise, and there are decent hot pies, too, served with three vegetables. Also look for the casseroled liver, bacon and onions, or pork steaks portugaise. Sweets are from the trolley. Wine by the glass. Arrive before 12.30 to be sure of a seat.

Bobby Browns in Town [6/10]

Burlington Passage, New Street
TEL 021-643 4464

Open noon to 3, 6 to 11 &
Closed Sun L

The vaulted cellar is right in the centre of Birmingham, a couple of minutes' walk from New Street Station. It is busy, noisy and cosmopolitan especially at lunchtime, when there are good-value meals for around £5. Soups such as carrot and orange with garlic bread might be followed by navarin of lamb, goulash, or beef and Guinness pie. A glass of wine is included in the set price. Full meals from the main menu can take the bill into double figures.

Café Papillon [7/10]

14 Fletchers Walk, Paradise Place
TEL 021-200 1504

Open 10 to 7.30 (9.30 to 5 Sat)
Closed Sun

One of the new eating places in the Paradise Place development. Inside it looks like a pine furniture shop, with round tables, wheelback and Windsor chairs, a dresser and a wardrobe, plus an old upright piano. Through the day there are croissants, French onion soup, quiches and snacks. French bread is baked on the premises and some sweets are home made. Good-value lunches are the likes of mushroom soup, roast lamb and chocolate mousse; evening meals centre on bistro favourites such as beef bourguignonne and chicken with tarragon and yoghurt sauce. Wine is served with meals.

NEW ENTRY Casa Paco [6/10]

7 Fletchers Walk, Paradise Place
TEL 021-233 1533

Open noon to 2.30, 6.30 to 10.30 (11 Fri and Sat) &
Closed Sun; Sat L

A boisterous new bodega in one of the most enterprising developments in the centre of Birmingham. At lunch-time it buzzes, and it's the place for a dish of paella and a bottle of San Miguel beer. Lunch dishes are reasonably priced at £2.65 for, say, chicken in a garlicky tomato sauce, Pinchito Moruno (Moroccan kebabs on rice) or Andalucian fish. There's plenty of oil and garlic with the vegetables. The full menu is a more expensive mix of Spanish and Continental. The waiters are flamboyant and the taped music clicks with castanets. Basic wines.

Chung Ying [9/10]

16–18 Wrottesley Street
TEL 021-622 5669/1793

Open noon to midnight (11 Sun) &
Closed Christmas Day

The pick of Birmingham's Chinese restaurants, offering some of the best-value food in the city. A huge menu of over three hundred dishes pulls no punches: the kitchen delivers bold, full-blooded Cantonese food with some finer touches but no compromise to western tastes. Best value of all is the list of almost forty dim-sum: superb steamed dumplings; huge crispy spring rolls; green pepper stuffed with prawn meat; Chinese sausage buns. For a substantial meal add minced chicken and glutinous rice steamed in lotus leaves. Cheapest meals from the full menu are impressively big one-plate rice and noodle dishes – the brilliance is in the ingredients and the fresh, vivid flavours. Otherwise it's worth experimenting with ox-tripe and pickled cabbage, stewed lamb with dried bean curd, or grilled eel ball with black-bean sauce. Tea is free.

College of Food and Domestic Arts [7/10]

Summer Row
TEL 021-235 2753

Open noon to 2, 7 to 9 &
Closed Sat and Sun; Fri D; college vacations

The training restaurant places emphasis on 'traditional styles of food production and service'. The set menus are tailored to the market as well as the curriculum, and meal prices are extraordinary: £5 at lunch-time, £7.50 in the evening. A typical menu

might include avocado with Stilton, or kidney soup, before navarin of lamb, poached turbot with hollandaise, or fillet of beef with horseradish. To finish there might be bananas flambé with rum, coupe Malmaison, or a soufflé.

NEW ENTRY Days of the Raj [8/10]

51 Dale End
TEL 021-236 0445

Open noon to 2.30, 7 to 11.30 &
Closed Christmas Day and Boxing Day

The best Indian lunches in Birmingham are served at this restaurant underneath the back of Tesco. The place adds another dimension to Indian food in the city and its new-wave style is a world away from the local red-flock curry houses and the cafés of Sparkhill. The upstairs dining-room is an elegant mix of rattan and cane furniture, pink linen and faded photos of the Raj. Lunch is a daily changing hot buffet: perhaps tandoori chicken drumsticks, gobi gosht, chicken pasanda, dhal masala, saffron pilau rice and nan. The all-in price of £5.50 pays for as much as you can eat. Dishes are arranged in a row of big metal bain-maries. Queue up and wait to be served. More expensive evening meals.

NEW ENTRY Forbidden City [8/10]

36 Hurst Street
TEL 021-622 2454/3668

Open noon to 11.45 & (also wc)

The biggest Chinese restaurant in Bir-mingham and also one of the best. The front entrance is in Hurst Street, the back in Wrottesley Street. Between the two is one huge, sprawling, flamboyant dining-room full of noise and colour. For cheap eating there's a menu of around forty dim-sum (served until 6pm) with one or two unusual items, such as minced carp balls and chicken wrapped in dried bean curd. Also good value are the one-plate rice and noodle dishes (listed on the separate menu of chef's specialities). Above the restaurant is the vast China Palace casino.

Hawkins [6/10]

King Edward Building,
205–219 Corporation Street
TEL 021-236 2001

Open 11 to 3, 6 to 10.30 (11 Sat) & (also WC)
Closed Christmas Day and Boxing Day

The unmistakable semi-circular frontage of this vast café-bar faces Aston University and the place is a very popular student haunt. The atmosphere and décor are big pluses. The cooking is based on 'impinger technology', which combines convection with microwave, and every dish on the menu is bar-coded for faster service. Light meals are filled baguettes, potato skins, tacos and soups. More substantial items range from chicken and Mozzarella in puff pastry to baked courgettes with minced lamb. To drink there are champagne cocktails, wines and coffees.

Horts Wine Bar [6/10]

17–18 Edgbaston Shopping Centre,
Harborne Road, Edgbaston
TEL 021-454 4672

Open noon to 2.30, 5.30 to 10.30 (11 Fri; 7 to 11 Sat, 7 to 10.30 Sun)
Closed Christmas Day and Boxing Day; bank hol Mons

One of the busiest wine bars in Birmingham, especially at lunch-time, when it fills up with office workers and shoppers. Food centres on salads with good fish and roast meats, plus a few bistro-style dishes. The new champagne and port bar has a wide selection of vintage and non-vintage ports and champagne by the glass or bottle. No children.

Ho Tung [7/10]

308 Bull Ring Centre
TEL 021-643 0033/0183

Open noon to midnight & (also WC)

Right by the Bull Ring shopping centre, this smart Cantonese restaurant offers good value at lunch-time. The cheapest dishes are also the best: one-plate meals, based on rice and noodles, show off the quality of the roast meats, offal and

seafood, and there are authentic hot-pots, too. The range of around thirty dim-sum is excellent and more interesting than the westernised businessman's lunch. Flashing fairy lights give the place the mood of a night-club; there's live entertainment on Saturdays.

Loon Fung [7/10]

37–41 Pershore Street
TEL 021-622 7395/5056

Open noon to midnight & (also WC)

One of the new arrivals in Birmingham's growing Chinatown. Inside it is elegant, and the style is aimed at Westerners, but the food makes few compromises. The Cantonese origins show in the menu of over thirty dim-sum, which are prepared by a separate chef. Most items are either steamed or deep fried, from prawn dumplings and ox-tripe buns to yam croquettes. On Sundays the kitchen offers that great Cantonese speciality, roast suckling pig. The menu – 235 dishes – has some one-plate rice and noodle dishes for cheap eaters.

Milan Sweet Centre [6/10]

191 Stoney Lane
TEL 021-449 1617

Open 9 to 8

This spotless corner shop is the best Indian sweet centre in Birmingham. It has an enormous range of savoury snacks – not only pakoras and vada but also stuffed pickled chillies in a coating of besan flour, and whole potatoes with a sandwich filling of spinach, herbs and spices. It is one of the few that sells samosas in their raw state. Cooking is done in a small kitchen at the back, where the snacks are freshly fried in huge blackened pans. Pickles come free of charge: onions in a sharp, spicy sauce; minced carrot in yoghurt. There are also breads and a wide selection of sweetmeats. Take-aways only. There is a branch at 238 Soho Road, Handsworth.

NEW ENTRY Pearce's Shellfish [5/10]

209 Market Hall, Bull Ring
TEL 021-643 3929

Open market hours (approx. 9 to 3)
Closed Sun

The little bar attached to the stall sells bowls of cockles, whelks and shrimps – whatever is in season. There are also jellied eels, prawns and dressed crab to eat there or take away. For a luxurious market snack have some oysters – three for £1 as we go to press. Condiments, including cayenne pepper and, occasionally, bread are provided. George Smith, the Original Crab King, at 201 Market Hall has a similar range of snacks. These shellfish bars are at the other end of the spectrum to places such as Sweetings and Bentleys in London.

Plaka [7/10]

204 Lightwoods Road, Warley
TEL 021-429 4862

Open 6.30pm to midnight
Closed Sun; Christmas Day and Boxing Day

The well-known city-centre taverna has moved to a converted corner shop in Smethwick. The new premises are brighter than before, otherwise very little has changed. The food is authentic Greek-Cypriot and meze are excellent value at £8.75 a head (minimum two people). The menu has dips, kebabs, dolmades, stifado, kotopoulo (casseroled chicken with savoury potatoes) and kalamarakia (deep-fried baby squid). Children's portions half-price. Greek wines are under £5 a bottle.

Rajdoot [7/10]

12–22 Albert Street
TEL 021-643 8805/8749

Open noon to 2.30, 6.30 to 11.30 & (also wc)
Closed Sun L

A useful place for an upmarket Indian lunch in the centre of Birmingham. The décor is extravagant, the waiters wear full Indian costume, and some dishes are garnished with edible silver leaf. The set

menu (£5.50) might feature tandoori chicken and a small nan, before bhuna gosht or fish masala with dhal and rice, plus sweet and coffee to finish. The main menu is more expensive, with a minimum charge of £6.50. An old-style alternative to Days of the Raj (see entry).

Royal Al-Faisal [6/10]

140 Stoney Lane, Sparkbrook
TEL 021-449 5695

Open noon to midnight & (also wc)
Closed Christmas

Larger than most of the Indian cafés in the Sparkhill area, with seats for over two hundred. The menu centres on a big range of balti dishes, from mince with aubergine to chicken with dhal, to fish with mushrooms. Look also for the balti vegetables – spinach, mustard leaf, lotus roots. Breads are up to standard and there are colourful barfi, halva and kulfi to finish. Unlicensed, but bring your own.

NEW ENTRY Rustie's Caribbean Restaurant [7/10]

69 Hurst Street
TEL 021-622 4137

Open noon to 11.30 & (also gents wc)

TV's Rustie Lee has moved her restaurant to the heart of Birmingham's Chinatown. A cheap, bistro-style menu is available at lunch-time and for pre-theatre suppers (5.30 to 7pm). Dishes such as Caribbean soup, saltfish fritters, chilli pot and suckling pork ribs are served with potato fries, salad or savoury rice. Between 3 and 5pm there are Caribbean high teas for £1.95. More expensive evening meals.

Salamis Kebab House [7/10]

177–178 Broad Street, Edgbaston
TEL 021-643 2997/5169

Open 6pm to 1am
Closed Sun

Birmingham's original Greek taverna opened as a café and take-away in 1948 and became a full restaurant in 1971. It's no longer the cheapest place in the city, but the food is genuine and the atmosphere is helped along with music and dancing. Best bets are the three-course set menus at £8.50, which centre on kotopoulo, stifado, keftedes and the like. Otherwise there are good meze for two or more at £9.75 a head. House wine is about £5 a bottle.

NEW ENTRY | La Santé [7/10]

182–184 High Street, Harborne
TEL 021-426 4133

Open 7 to 10 (10.30 Fri and Sat)
Closed Sun, Mon

An informal vegetarian off-shoot of Michelle's, above the well-known bistro. It is not only Birmingham's first vegetarian French restaurant, but also one of the few creditable vegetarian restaurants of any kind in the city. The décor is all pine and lace, and the good-value menu has pâté clamarti (green pea) with pitta bread, cassoulet provençale, brochette of vegetables with herb sauce and brown rice. Leeks are cooked in white wine, wrapped in a sheet of bean curd and deep-fried. Unlicensed, but you can bring your own, otherwise drink teas or tisanes. Occasional live music.

NEW ENTRY | Satay House [8/10]

92 Hurst Street
TEL 021-622 1313

Open noon to 2.15, 6 to 11.45
Closed Sun; Mon L

An idiosyncratic café serving a mixture of South-East Asian and Chinese fast food. There's no kitchen, just an open cooking area, with a big chopping block and counter at the front, and woks, charcoal grills and a deep-frier at the back. The dining-room looks like a transformed pub, with rough plastered walls, uneven beams painted grey, and pink cloths on the tables. The short menu has excellent smoky satays, also stir-fried dishes, one-plate meals and crispy duck, as well as a couple of sizzling specialities and steaks. Drink Chinese tea or bring your own wine.

Shah Bagh [6/10]

26 Bristol Street
TEL 021-622 2407

Open 6pm to 4am

The least ostentatious and most useful of a cluster of old-style Indian restaurants along Bristol Street. The small ground-floor dining-room looks more like a little trattoria with dim red lighting, unmatching blue check tablecloths and candles in Chianti bottles. Portions are big and flavours full-blooded. The menu includes all the usual curry house staples – the chicken dhansak is a winner – plus tandooris and balti dishes. Useful for a late-night curry after a work-out at the nearby Dome disco.

NEW ENTRY | Thai Paradise [7/10]

Paradise Street, 31 Paradise Circus
TEL 021-643 5523

Open noon to 3, 6 to 1 &

Birmingham's first Thai restaurant is in an arcade of shops and offices not far from the town hall and the Holiday Inn. Set lunch is a cheap introduction to the menu: £4.95 pays for, say, excellent pork satay with a blistering peanut sauce and a miniature salad, then Thai chicken curry or stir-fried beef with chillies plus rice, followed by ice-cream or lychees. Otherwise go in a crowd, invest ten pounds and explore the full menu of soups, salads, and dishes such as crab claws with basil leaves and chillies. Drink Singha Thai beer or Chinese tea.

NEW ENTRY | Wild Oats [6/10]

5 Raddlebarn Road, Selly Oak
TEL 021-471 2459

Open noon to 2, 6 to 9 &
Closed Sun, Mon; Christmas and New Year

One of the few genuine vegetarian cafés in Birmingham, handily placed for the University. The décor is brown, with bare tables, plain wooden chairs, rustic pottery – even a brown menu. To match this the kitchen offers brown, rather than green cuisine – old-style wholefood dishes with plenty of pulses and grains. The day's choice might include tomato and lentil soup, bean lasagne, leek and cheese flan and damson crumble. Unlicensed.

NEW ENTRY — Wild Thyme [7/10]

422 Bearwood Road, Bearwood
TEL 021-420 2528

Open noon to 2, 6 to 10
Closed Sun, Mon; Christmas and New Year

Related to Wild Oats (see above) but more of a restaurant than a café. The style is upmarket, with alcoholic cocktails alongside herb teas, and a garden for al-fresco eating. Prices are higher too, but still good value for cashew nut pâté, stuffed peppers with sesame sauce, or French mushroom tart. The menu changes daily, but there are always enterprising salads and healthy sweets such as banana and apple crunch. Wine is £4.25 a bottle.

BRIDGNORTH Shropshire   map 4

Old Colonial [7/10]

3 Bridge Street, Low Town
TEL Bridgnorth (074 62) 66510

Open 5.30 to 12.30 (1 Fri and Sat)

A smart Indian restaurant in a 350-year old, half-timbered building. Laura Ashley fabrics, cane chairs and fresh flowers suggest something more than the average curry house, and the cooking is up to the mark. Tandooris and creamy kormas are recommended, and aloo bhartha (mashed potatoes with onions, green chillies and coriander) is an unusual speciality. Set-meal prices range from £6 for the vegan Tagore's choice and £7 for vegetarian Brahmin's choice, up to £9.80 for the Viceroy. Drink Kingfisher lager – or Indian tea.

BRIMFIELD
Hereford & Worcester   map 4

Roebuck [9/10]

TEL Brimfield (058 472) 230

Open for food noon to 2, 7 to 10 (9.30 Sun)
& (also WC)
Closed Mon; Sun D; Christmas Day and Boxing Day; 1 week Oct, 2 weeks Feb

Orders are taken at the bar and the menu is chalked up on a blackboard. The Roebuck bar menu is the best choice for cheap eaters, particularly for those who arrive without booking when the dining-room is busy. Pigeon casseroled in red wine, chicken pie laced with local Dunkerton's cider, lamb and apricot pie, and vegetable filo pastries with pine kernels, herbs and oats give a foretaste of Carole Evans' inventive cooking. Ploughman's come with Shropshire Blue or Chewton Mendip Cheddar, locally baked bread, home-made chutney and pickled onions. Full meals from the adventurous Poppies restaurant menu will take the bill into double figures.

BROADWAY
Hereford & Worcester   map 4

Collin House [7/10]

Collin Lane
TEL Broadway (0386) 858354

Open noon to 1.30 & (also WC)

Bar lunches are served by the fireside in the lounge or out in the garden of this beautiful seventeenth-century Cotswold hotel. English dishes top the bill: celery and lovage soup; Kentish sausages with spicy red cabbage; wild rabbit with bacon, tarragon and cider; grilled sprats. Sweets are patriotically traditional, in the shape of steamed syrup sponge with custard; bread-and-butter pudding, and home-made damson ice-cream. Four-course Sunday lunch is £9.50. More expensive dinners.

Goblets Wine Bar, Lygon Arms [7/10]

High Street
TEL Broadway (0386) 852258

Open noon to 2.30 (2 Sun), 6 (7 Sun) to 9.30 (10 Fri and Sat) & (also WC)
Closed 10 days at Christmas

A wine bar attached to the famous Cots-wold hotel in one of the most photo-graphed villages in Britain. The menu has interesting main dishes for around £4, such as chicken breast stuffed with herbs, or lamb noisettes in creamy mint sauce. Start with courgette and ham bake or avocado filled with creamed smoked trout, and finish with peach and hazelnut meringue or baked bananas in puff pastry with chocolate sauce. No children.

BROUGHTON HACKETT
Hereford & Worcester   map 4

March Hare Inn [6/10]

TEL Upton Snodsbury (090 560) 222

Open for food 11 (noon Sun) to 2, 7 to 10 &
Closed Christmas Day

An old established black and white pub with a good range of bar food. Cold dishes are pâté, salads and sandwiches, hot ones range from grilled trout or seafood vol-au-vent to chicken curry and sirloin steaks. Barbecues are held on the terrace, and there's a separate restaurant. Real ales include Springfield and Hook Norton Bitter. Wines by the glass.

BURSLEM Staffordshire   map 7

High Lane Oatcakes [5/10]

599 High Lane
TEL Stoke-on-Trent (0782) 810810

Open 2pm to 6pm Tue; 8am to 6pm Mon;
7am to 6.30pm Fri; 7am to 6pm Sat; 7am to
11.30am Sun
Closed Mon, Wed

Oatcakes are Staffordshire's most famous local speciality. This small, family-run terraced house produces excellent examples with all kinds of savoury fillings – bacon, eggs, sausage, cheese, onion, ham and so on – and there are plans for a vegetarian version, too. Prices range from 22p for cheese to 34p for a full house.

CAREY Hereford & Worcester   map 4

Cottage of Content [6/10]

TEL Carey (043 270) 242

Open for food 11.30 to 2, 6.30 to 10 (noon to 2, 7
to 9.30 Sun)
Closed Christmas Day

When the original labourers' cottages were built on this site in 1485, it was a condition that a cider and ale parlour should be maintained in one room, and the house has been licensed ever since.

There's plenty of space for eating – in the bar, two small dining-rooms and a converted barn. The menu is home-made soup with crusty bread, vegetable crumble, free-range chicken, home-cured ham, quiche, plus chilli, curries and cottage pie. Hook Norton, Flowers and guest beers.

CLAVERLEY Shropshire   map 4

Crown Inn [6/10]

High Street
TEL Claverley (074 66) 228

Open for food noon to 2, plus 7 to 9 Thur, Fri
and Sat
Closed Sun; Christmas Day and Boxing Day

Parts of the pub date from 1580, and there are echoes of the past in the old beams, oak timber frame and old-fashioned settles. The food is home-made steak and kidney pie, home-cured ham with salad, big steaks and daily specials. Children's portions are half-price. Hansons beers on draught. Family room.

CLUN Shropshire   map 6

Old Post Office [8/10]

9 The Square
TEL Clun (058 84) 687

Open noon to 2
Closed Sun and Mon; Feb; D Nov to Mar

The restaurant is a converted village post office in the heart of Houseman country. Martin Pool has been joined in the kitchen by Pam Linnett (ex-Effy's, Hereford) and they specialise in high-class country cooking based on local produce. Children are welcome at lunch-time, when bills can be kept in single figures for dishes such as pasta carbonara, smoked fish and cheese roulade with sorrel sauce, pigeon terrine and ham salad. More adventurous main dishes might include lamb cutlets provençale with redcurrant sauce or Gruyère profiteroles with pea and mint purée and a tomato and whisky sauce. More expensive dinners.

Sun Inn [6/10]

TEL Clun (058 84) 277/599

Open for food noon to 2, 6 (7 Sun) to 9.30 &

Home-grown ingredients are a feature of
the bar food in this fifteenth-century
village pub. Snacks are simple soups, local
sausages, quiches, salads and sandwiches,
backed up by international specials, such
as Moroccan chicken or genuinely spiced
curried beef. Beers include Davenports and
locally brewed Woods. No children.

COVENTRY West Midlands   map 4

 A-Roma Snack Bar [7/10]

70 Barker Butts Lane
TEL Coventry (0203) 594124

Open 9.30 to 3 &
Closed Sun

A brilliant café and snack bar attached to
the Quo Vadis (Coventry's best Italian
restaurant). The atmosphere is an unlikely
mix of Midlands and Mediterranean, but it
works. There's not much décor – just half
a dozen tables, a cappuccino machine, a
cabinet of cooking utensils and shelves of
bottles. The short menu is extraordinary
value for money: a big dish of spaghetti
bolognese, plus a glass of house red and a
cup of coffee, is currently £2.60. Also
available are seafood salads, omelettes and
minestrone, plus big toasted sandwiches of
tuna and Italian beans. Full English
breakfasts are £2.95.

 Cottage Teashop & Gallery [6/10]

1–3 Ryley Street
TEL Coventry (0203) 23642

Open 10 to 5.30, 8 to 11.30 Fri and Sat &
(also wc)
Closed Sun; Christmas; bank hols

Probably the most genteel spot in
Coventry for light lunch or afternoon tea.
It feels more like a tea-shop in a rural
market town than an industrial city. The
menu has a full range of snacks, things on
toast, locally made sausages and home-
made cakes and pastries. Lunches might
feature home-made chicken and bacon pie
and plum crumble. Grills on Friday and
Saturday evenings (bookings only).

Friends Corner [7/10]

547–549 Foleshill Road
TEL Coventry (0203) 686688/689962

Open noon to 3, 6 to 12 & (also wc)
Closed Sun

The most interesting and best-value
Indian restaurant in Coventry is a mile and
a half out of the city, opposite the General
Wolfe pub. The proprietors' links with
Kenya show in the animal skins and African mementoes on the walls. The style is
idiosyncratic home cooking with flavours
you won't find in most curry houses. The
kitchen cooks to order, so the pace can be
slow. Look out for the long list of starters,
including fried fish masala, bhajia maru
(potato skins with gram flour), and spicy
meat rolled in a paratha, as well as lamb
with bitter melon, quail with spinach,
dhal masoor, and roti mukki (an unusual
corn-flour chapati). Set lunch is £4.

Herbs, Trinity House Hotel [9/10]

28 Lower Holyhead Road
TEL Coventry (0203) 555654

Open 6.30 to 9.30 &
Closed Sun; bank hols; 10 days at Christmas

Since 1982 Robert Jackson has developed
this lively restaurant in a mundane hotel
into one of the very few decent vegetarian
eating places in the West Midlands. He has
succeeded by offering good value and by
steering clear of stodgy wholefoods. The
menu now has a couple of meat and fish
dishes, but the vegetarian specialities are
still the most interesting, and the most
popular: black-eyed bean and carrot
terrine; timbale of parsnips with Dijon
mustard vinaigrette; cashew-nut and
sweet pepper loaf with pineapple and
coconut sauce. Main dishes are served
with jacket potatoes and unusual salads,
such as bean sprout, Chinese leaf and
water chestnut in soy vinaigrette. Sweets
are indulgent, though soya ice-cream
appears from time to time. To drink try
English elderflower or blackcurrant wine.
Children welcome for early evening meals.

Ostlers [6/10]

166 Spon Street
TEL Coventry (0203) 26603

Open 11 to 10.30 (7 Sun) (11.30 Fri and Sat) &
Closed Sun L; bank hols

Jean Jinks and Suzanne Nobes have made a
great success of this beamed bistro in the
historic suburb of Spon. Inside are bare
brick walls, low-beamed ceilings, green
check tablecloths, and a staircase in the
centre. Food is served through the day and
best bets are the house specials: home-
cooked crock-pot of moussaka, cod
provençale, chicken casserole and
vegetable goulash. Hot garlic bread is
worth the extra 75p. There are more
expensive steaks and roasts among the
main courses. House wine is 90p a glass.

DORRINGTON Shropshire   map 6

Country Friends [8/10]

TEL Dorrington (074 373) 707

Open noon to 2, 7 to 9 &
Closed Sun; Mon L

Charles and Pauline Whittaker's black-
and-white timbered building is best
known for its highly rated restaurant, but
bar meals offer a taste of the kitchen's
impressive style. Home-made ravioli filled
with broccoli and served with blue cheese
sauce has echoes of the dining-room
menu, and the choice of snacks extends to
baked peach with cheese and herb stuffing,
hot chicken mousse with madeira sauce,
Stilton doughnuts, and sweet pickled
herrings. There are also soups and toasted
sandwiches. House wine is about £5 a
bottle. Bar food is not available in the
evening if the restaurant is busy.

EATHORPE Warwickshire   map 4

Auberge-Inn, Eathorpe Park Hotel [7/10]

Fosse Way
TEL Marton (0926) 632245

Open 7.30 to 11
Closed Sun to Tue

Eathorpe Park is a grand Victorian Gothic
hotel just off the ancient Fosse Way. The
Auberge-Inn is its youthful offshoot – a
basement bistro serving wholefood and
vegetarian dishes with an international
flavour. The menu relies on organically
grown fruit and vegetables and naturally
reared meat where possible, and takes in
tomato and cognac soup, broccoli and
almond pancakes, cauliflower and nut
curry, sweet-and-sour leeks with fried rice,
and tandoori fish. Sweets are the likes of
fruit syllabub or nectarine brûlée. Better
than average bistro wines.

EVESHAM
Hereford & Worcester   map 4

Cedar Restaurant, Evesham Hotel [7/10]

Cooper's Lane
TEL Evesham (0386) 49111

Open 12.30 to 2, 7 to 9.30 &
Closed Christmas Day and Boxing Day

The house was built in 1540 as a manor,
and given Georgian symmetry in the early
years of the eighteenth century. Today it is
a fine country hotel, run with great good
humour by the Jenkinson family. The
lunchtime buffet is excellent value at £5
for its array of cold meats, salads, quiche,
sausages and baked potatoes. Otherwise
have just a bowl of soup or choose from
dishes such as choux pastry fritters, grilled
sardines with provençale sauce, or pork
and sausage kebabs. Steaks and grilled
Dover sole are available for those who
want to splash out. More expensive
dinners. The wine list spans the world in
flamboyant style.

Scottie's Bistro and Wine Bar [6/10]

9 Port Street
TEL Evesham (0386) 6946

Open noon to 2, 7 to 10.30 & (also WC)
Closed Mon; Sun in winter

Norman Banford has maintained standards
at this wine-bar-cum-bistro full of
Victoriana. Steaks have been added to a
menu that also includes moussaka,

chicken and tomatoes in wine sauce, plus home-made soup and pâtés (such as tuna and tomato). The comprehensive wine list includes house red at 85p a glass.

FOWNHOPE
Hereford & Worcester   map 4

Green Man [6/10]

TEL Fownhope (043 277) 243

Open for food 10 to 2.30, 6 to 11 ♿

A classic Herefordshire timber-framed inn, only half a mile from the River Wye. In the lofty beamed lounge bar there's a good choice of pub grub, including home-made soup with wholemeal bread, steak sandwiches, lasagne and ham salad. There's a hot roast on Sundays, plus a cold carvery. Beers from Hook Norton, Marstons and Sam Smiths.

FROGHALL Staffordshire   map 7

NEW ENTRY ## Wharf [7/10]

Foxt Road
TEL Ipstones (053 871) 486

Open 11 to 5.30 ♿
Closed Mon; Oct to Easter

Bill and Peggy Young run horse-drawn narrowboat trips on the Caldon Canal and have converted a derelict two-hundred-year-old warehouse into an all-purpose eating house. Inside are brick walls, varnished beams and Staffordshire Blue quarry-tiles on the floor. During the day the place functions as a café, serving simple snacks and light meals. Everything is home-made, from the bread, pizzas, quiche and gateaux, to savoury pies such as cheese and onion, turkey and egg, or sausage. As well as afternoon teas, there are buffet lunches during the week (with plenty of choice for vegetarians) and in the evening the place becomes a more expensive formal restaurant.

HANLEY Staffordshire   map 7

G. Leese Oatcakes [5/10]

134 Chell Street
TEL Stoke-on-Trent (0782) 261899

Open 6 (noon Sun) to 6
Closed Mon to Wed; 2 weeks July

A long-established bakery well known for its Staffordshire oatcakes, which are made to a special family recipe. Filled with bacon, cheese or sausage they make a cheap take-away snack. The shop also sells plain or currant pikelets, rather like crumpets cooked without restraining metal rings. Unlicensed.

HEREFORD
Hereford & Worcester   map 4

Cathedral [6/10]

Church Street
TEL Hereford (0432) 265233

Open 10.30 to 8 (3 Mon, 9.30 Fri and Sat), plus noon to 4 Sun in summer ♿ (also WC)
Closed Mon D; Sun in winter

Handily placed, just a cobbled street away from the cathedral. On the ground floor is a beamed dining-room serving traditional English stalwarts such as roast beef, steak and kidney pie, and apple pie. On Friday and Saturday evenings, international dishes are served in the cellar bistro. Modest wines.

Effy's [8/10]

96 East Street
TEL Hereford (0432) 59754

Open noon to 2, 7 to 9.30
Closed Sun, Mon

This small timbered cottage in a row not far from the cathedral is a civilised spot for a decent lunch. New owners the Chichesters now offer a set meal at £7.50, or you can have just a main course of, say, pork vindaloo, chicken with tarragon, or pasta with cream cheese and walnuts, for £3.50. The full menu has dishes such as hot goats' cheese tartlets with seakale sauce, pigeon breasts in garlic butter and chocolate mousse with Cointreau.

Gaffers [7/10]

89 East Street

Open 10 to 4.30
Closed Sun

A first-rate wholefood café in a converted organic greengrocer's shop. The menu is short but effective: soup with brown bread, hot quiches served straight from the oven, pizzas, vegetarian burgers and fresh, original salads. Genuine lemon cheesecake to finish. The café has its own jewellery workshop and a small paved garden for outdoor eating. Unlicensed.

NEW ENTRY Nutters [6/10]

Capuchin Yard (off Church Street)
TEL Hereford (0432) 58171

Open 10 to 4.30
Closed Sun; bank hols

This used to be Fodder. The town-centre vegetarian café has new owners but little else has changed. Wholemeal pizzas are made on the premises; most other items are obtained from another source. The short menu has spring rolls, curried vegetable pie, quiches, and ploughman's with hummus. Salads are cheap, fresh and good; brown rice and bean sprouts have been excellent. To finish there are Thayers ice-creams, pears in red wine, or vanilla soya dessert. Farmhouse cider or wine by the glass.

KENILWORTH
Warwickshire   map 4

Ana's Bistro [8/10]

121–123 Warwick Road
TEL Kenilworth (0926) 53763

Open 7 to 10.30
Closed Sun, Mon; 1 week Easter, 3 weeks Aug

The best value in Kenilworth. This first-rate bistro is in a beamed basement beneath the Restaurant Diment. The short menu is to the point: home-made soup, pâté, steaks and lasagne are backed up by daily specials, such as suprême of chicken in courgette and mint sauce, lamb's liver and smoked bacon, escalope of pork with ginger and spring onion sauce. Home-made sweets take in German applecake, Caribbean trifle and strawberry Pavlova. No bookings, so be prepared to take pot luck or queue. House wine is £4.95 a bottle.

George Rafters [6/10]

42 Castle Street
TEL Kenilworth (0926) 52074

Open noon to 2, 7 to 10.30 (12.30 to 3, 7 to 10 Sun)

Not far from Kenilworth Castle, and popular with all ages. The restaurant has Landseer prints on the walls and candles on the tables. The home-made vegetable soup is well reported, and other good dishes have included guacamole, beef and mushroom pie, and lasagne. Raspberry mousse with Cointreau and chocolate crunch cake are decent sweets. Modest wines. Full meals in the evening can take the bill beyond £10 a head.

LEAMINGTON SPA
Warwickshire   map 4

NEW ENTRY Piccolino's [6/10]

9 Spencer Street
TEL Leamington Spa (0926) 22988

Open noon to 2.30, 5.30 to 11 (11.30 Fri; noon to 11.30 Sat)
Closed Christmas Day and Boxing Day

A branch of the highly popular restaurant in Warwick (see entry). The menu has the same range of interesting, well-topped pizzas and pasta dishes, backed up by antipasto, salads and steaks. House wine by the glass or carafe.

Regency Fare [6/10]

72 Regent Street
TEL Leamington Spa (0926) 25570

Open 9 to 6
Closed Sun; bank hols

This all-day restaurant has been established in Leamington for more than twenty years, and still serves big helpings of home-cooked food at bargain prices. For a quick snack there are filled jacket potatoes, stuffed pancakes, omelettes and quiche. Otherwise prices range from around £3 for shepherd's pie to £6 for grilled steak or poached salmon, with duckling vol-au-vent, roast beef, and chicken breast cooked with tarragon and wine, in between. Main courses come with plenty of well-timed vegetables. Lavish, old-fashioned sweets. Twenty-five per cent discount for children. Wines are £1 a glass.

LEDBURY
Hereford & Worcester   map 4

NEW ENTRY | Applejack Wine Bar [7/10]

44 The Homend
TEL Ledbury (0531) 4181

Open noon to 2.30 (noon to 2 Sun), 7.30 to 10
Closed Christmas Day, Boxing Day and 1 Jan

An old, white-plastered building with dormer windows, on one of the main roads through Ledbury. Downstairs is the wine bar – a small room with bare floorboards and pews. The menu leans towards vegetarian dishes, with dishes containing lots of ingredients: avocado special is boosted with cheese, black olives, peanuts and raisins. A quartet of Greek-style dips includes excellent home-made blue cheese purée, guacamole, hummus and taramosalata with raw vegetables. Otherwise the menu has red-bean lasagne, cannelloni stuffed with cream cheese, sesame chicken, and devilled spare ribs. A similar menu is served in the raftered barn restaurant upstairs. House wines by the glass.

NEW ENTRY | Market Place [6/10]

1 The Homend
TEL Ledbury (0531) 4250

Open 9 to 5.30 (9.30 to 5 in winter), plus 7.30 to 10.30 Thur to Sun ⅋
Closed Sun in winter

Right in the centre of town, opposite the famous timber-framed Market Hall. During the day, the attractive room with hops on the counter, spindle-backed chairs and flower prints on the walls sells good-value dishes with a vegetarian bias. Cakes, scones and cheesecake are home-made and quite healthy. Lunch dishes range from beef bourguignonne or sweet-and sour chicken to spicy lentil and tomato soup, curried mushrooms and haricot beans, and nut roast with salad. Four evenings a week (Thursday to Sunday), the place becomes a

simple Italian restaurant with a conventional menu. Herefordshire apple juice, cider and wine by the glass.

LICHFIELD Staffordshire   map 4

Scales [6/10]

Market Street
TEL Lichfield (054 32) 24526

Open for food noon to 2.30 ⅋
Closed Christmas Day, Boxing Day and 1 Jan

Home-made pies and roasts are the best bets in this town-centre pub. The former might include turkey and ham, rabbit, or chicken and mushroom as well as steak and kidney; the latter is usually a choice of pork, beef and lamb with vegetables and all the trimmings. Soup comes with a hunk of crusty bread. On the cold table look for the Scotch eggs and coleslaw – both of which are made on the premises. Bass and M&B Springfield bitter on draught. A conker competition is held in the public bar every October.

LONG COMPTON
Warwickshire   map 4

Manor House [6/10]

Main Road
TEL Long Compton (060 884) 218

Open 10.30 to 12, 3 to 5, 7 to 9 ⅋
Closed Sun D; Jan, Feb

Sunday lunches are the main attraction in the Empsons' modest eighteenth-century manor-house. A full meal of home-made soup, slices from a roast joint with all the trimmings and a sweet from the trolley, can be had for £6.50. Otherwise there's a range of set dinners from around £7 a head. A cold table is laid out in the second dining-room. Morning coffee comes with home-made cakes, and there are cream teas in the afternoon.

MALVERN
Hereford & Worcester   map 4

Enigma [6/10]

Worcester Road
TEL Malvern (068 45) 3289

Open 11.30 to 2.30, 5.30 to 9.30 (10.30 to 10.30 Sat; noon to 9.30 Sun) & (also WC)
Closed Mon D

Once the Promenade Restaurant, this lofty dining-room still has lingering echoes of its past. Simple snacks are served through the day, more substantial meals in the evening. The home-made cottage pie, grilled trout and vegetables are notably good, and the chips are real. There's now a separate vegetarian menu. Wine is around £4 a bottle.

MUCH BIRCH
Hereford & Worcester   map 4

Old School House [7/10]

TEL Golden Valley (0981) 540006

Open All year, by arrangement

Rita Ayers runs this converted school-house as a guest-house, but cooks meals for non-residents if given twelve hours' notice. She likes to discuss menus in advance. Typically there might be leek and potato soup and Stilton and port pâté before roast lamb with apricot stuffing or chicken in white wine and tomato sauce. Vegetables are seasonal and sweets range from chocolate and walnut mousse to raspberry gateau. Three courses plus cheese and coffee can be had for £5.50. Unlicensed, but guests are welcome to bring their own (no corkage).

MUCH WENLOCK
Shropshire   map 4

George and Dragon [6/10]

High Street
TEL Much Wenlock (0952) 727312

Open for food noon to 2, 7.30 to 9.45
Closed Sun D and Mon D

Brian and Eve Nolan's sixteenth-century pub is handy for visitors to Ironbridge and its museums. Lunches are served in the beamed bar; evening meals in the bistro-style dining-room. The style is good home cooking: pea and ham soup; hummus and tabbouleh with pitta bread; beef in beer; chicken in mead and cream sauce. Fish is fresh each day, and there's local Shropshire Blue in the ploughman's. Sticky toffee

pudding is a favourite sweet. Full evening meals may take the bill over £10 a head. Live music on Sundays. Marston's, Hook Norton and guest beers on draught, plus a short wine list.

Scott's [6/10]

5 High Street
TEL Much Wenlock (0952) 727596

Open 10 to 5 &
Closed Wed, Sept to Easter; first week Jan

Scott's is a wholefood shop as well as a café and you sit surrounded by shelves of beans and pulses. The food is mainly vegetarian, though there are meat and fish dishes too. Home-made vegetable soup comes with locally baked bread, and the menu might also include bean lasagne, macaroni cheese and various salads. The cakes are good too; only the gateaux are bought in. Pints of beer as well as tea and coffee to drink.

OMBERSLEY
Hereford & Worcester   map 4

Kings Arms [6/10]

TEL Ombersley (0905) 620315

Open for food 12.15 to 2.15, 6 to 9.30 (9 Fri and Sat) &
Closed Sun

The building dates from 1411, and the old blackened beams and timber and the inglenook fireplace are reminders of its past. Chris and Judy Blundell offer a good choice of home-made food; some say their steak and kidney pie is the best in the neighbourhood. The menu also features mixed seafood pâté, spicy kedgeree, grilled salmon, and turkey and leek pie. More vegetarian dishes are now available. Children over six are welcome inside until 8pm. Bass and Springfield Bitter on draught.

OSWESTRY Shropshire   map 6

Good Companion Wine Bar [7/10]

10 Beatrice Street
TEL Oswestry (0691) 655768

Open noon to 3, 6 to midnight &
Closed Sun L and Mon L

New owners Gordon and Marjorie Tipton are putting the emphasis on food in this atmospheric wine bar. The décor is all oak beams, pine furniture rescued from an old chapel, and parquet floors. Light comes from gas lamps, heat from a pot-bellied stove. The menu ranges from spicy prawns and tomatoes with pitta bread, or Shropshire fidget pie with baked potato and salad, to chilli con carne. Ice-creams are home made. Good choice of inexpensive wines.

ROSS-ON-WYE
Hereford & Worcester   map 4

 Meader's [7/10]

1 Copse Cross Street
TEL Ross-on-Wye (0989) 62803

Open 10 to 2.30, 7 to 9.30
Closed Sun; Mon D; Christmas Day and Boxing Day

Andras and Sally Weinhardt sold their house to set up this restaurant. He cooks and she looks after the front of house. The menu is a mix of English staples, vegetarian dishes and Hungarian specialities. During the day, the place is a self-service café offering home-made pâté, vegetable curry, wholemeal pizzas and things with chips. There is also Hungarian bean soup, layered cabbage with little dumplings, and goulash with rice. Helpings are generous and prices affordable. In the evening it becomes a candlelit restaurant with a fixed-price menu at £8.50. Hungarian wines and fruit brandies, as well as local Dunkerton's cider.

Wine Bar [7/10]

24 High Street
TEL Ross-on-Wye (0989) 67717

Open 11 to 2, 7 to 10 &
Closed Christmas Day and Boxing Day

The mood is casual in Alan Bennett's candlelit wine bar-cum-bistro, and the food is eclectic. The short menu can take in spicy Persian lamb, Greek kebabs,

Swedish beef with rice and Creole shrimps. There's always an interesting soup, such as smoked bacon and lentil, or tomato, celery and apple, plus a good range of savoury crêpes. Vegetarians do well with courgette, tomato and Parmesan bake or tagliatelle with walnuts and garlic. To go with the food there's a list of some fifty good-value wines; house wine is 80p a glass. Children are welcome, but not in the bar area.

RUGBY Warwickshire   map 4

NEW ENTRY **Dilruba** [6/10]

155 Railway Terrace
TEL Rugby (0788) 74478

Open noon to 2.30, 6 to 12.30 (1.30 Fri to Sat) &

A good-value curry house only a few minutes' walk from the station. The dining-room is a standard mix of regimented rows of high-backed chairs and flock wallpaper, but the service is courteous and the food tastes authentic. Chicken dhansak is thick and pungent, bhindis are fresh, and chapatis come steaming hot to the table. Cheap weekday lunches are £2.50. For Indian snacks, rather than full meals, see entry for Shaheen Pan and Sweet Centre.

Pepper's Coffee House

25 Sheep Street
TEL Rugby (0788) 61819

*This restaurant was sold
as we went to press.*

Shaheen Pan and Sweet Centre [5/10]

88 Craven Road
TEL Rugby (0788) 68181

Open 8.30am (10 Sun) to 9pm
Closed Mon (exc bank hols)

The best local bet for authentic Indian snacks. There are usually piles of little meat or vegetable samosas on the counter, as well as pakoras, tandoori chicken, chickpea curry and occasional extras, such as shami kebabs, kachori and bateta vada. Fruit juices, kulfi and a whole range of sweets and cakes are also available. Paan leaves are wrapped around seeds and pulses displayed in stainless steel bowls. The best choice is at weekends. Take-aways only. Unlicensed.

RYTON-ON-DUNSMORE
Warwickshire   map 4

Ryton Gardens [8/10]

TEL Coventry (0203) 303517

Open 10 to 5.30 & (also WC)
Closed Christmas Day and Boxing Day

Five years ago, a National Centre for Organic Gardening would not have got off the ground, let alone starred in an eight-part TV series. Ryton Gardens has changed all that. Under the direction of Alan Gear, this twenty-two-acre site has succeeded in stating the case for pesticide-free cultivation, laying out the evidence for all to see. The gardens grow the produce, and the modern open-plan café serves the results. As the slogan says, 'this is food you can trust'. The menu is deceptively simple: soup (perhaps fennel and lemon, or thick pea) is cooked in a big pan; quiches and pizzas come fresh and hot from the oven behind the counter. Salads show off the sheer flavour of the ingredients, and there can be surprises – such as rocket and dandelion in February. Bread and rolls are first rate, eggs are from the free-ranging hens in the gardens, and there are plans to serve naturally reared meat. A new feature is the fascinating list of a dozen organically produced wines. The rating is for the food *and* the enterprise.

SELLACK
Hereford & Worcester   map 4

Lough Pool Inn [6/10]

TEL Harewood End (098 987) 236

Open for food noon to 1.45, 7 to 9.45 & (also WC)

Paul and Karen Whitford offer better-than-average pub food in this black and white tiled cottage nestling in a dip in the hills. The menu has sausage and chips, curry, and chilli con carne, but these stalwarts are outnumbered by enterprising dishes, such as pork with apricot and brandy sauce, lamb in black cherry sauce and trout stuffed with prawns or crab. For vegetarians there is a mixed platter, as well as cheese and walnut pâté or pasta with tomatoes, mushrooms and red wine. Ice-creams make a good finish. Bass and Springfield Bitter on draught. No children.

SHIPSTON-ON-STOUR
Warwickshire   map 4

White Bear [8/10]

High Street
TEL Shipston-on-Stour (0608) 61558

Open for food noon to 1.45, 6.30 to 9.30 & (also WC)

Still very much the local pub, although Hugh and Suzanne Roberts now concentrate most of their energies on their new venture at the Fossebridge Inn (see Fossebridge, South West). Bar food is well above average and menus are eclectic. Veal with white wine and peaches, fillet of beef with black-bean sauce, and smoked haddock and spinach lasagne rub shoulders with liver and onion casserole or steak and kidney pie. To start there might be carrot and coriander soup or pork and chicken liver terrine with apricot relish; to finish, spiced plum pie or raspberry brûlée. More expensive restaurant meals. Bass and Springfield Bitter on draught, wine by the glass.

SHREWSBURY Shropshire   map 6

Delanys [8/10]

St Julians Craft Centre, St Alkmonds Square
TEL Shrewsbury (0743) 60602

Open 10.30 to 4
Closed Sun

The original branch of this colourful vegetarian restaurant is still going strong in the historic church vestry. The brilliant-green PVC tablecloths and blue chairs set the tone for celery and lentil burgers, cauliflower paprika, and chickpea casserole. The food is exclusively vegetarian and vegan, using organic produce wherever possible. The philosophy extends to the fruit juices, yoghurt drinks and organic wines. A new branch has recently opened in an oak-panelled pub in Wyle Cop, Shrewsbury (TEL Shrewsbury (0743) 66890).

Good Life [6/10]

Barracks Passage, Wyle Cop
TEL Shrewsbury (0743) 50455

Open 9.30 to 3.30 (4.30 Sat) &
Closed Sun; bank hols; Christmas and New Year

A tiny wholefood restaurant in a restored fourteenth-century building in an historic part of the town. The menu is basic home cooking – excellent cakes, pastries and flans, soup with wholemeal bread, quiches and nut roast, plus a daily hot dish and plenty of salads. Decent coffee, wine by the glass.

Old Police House [7/10]

Castle Court (off Castle Street)
TEL Shrewsbury (0743) 60668

Open 10 to 1.45, 7 to 9
Closed Sun, Mon; Christmas Day and Boxing Day

Lunches are good value in this converted police station and county jail. The real bargain is the Family and Tourist menu (two courses for £4.95, three courses for £5.95), which might include tomato and orange soup, quail eggs on a salad, or smoked trout, before spiced fillet steak and Guinness pie, pan-fried chicken with lemon and nuts, or vegetarian moussaka. To finish there are English puddings or farmhouse cheeses. The businessmen's menu is more ambitious, though still good value at £8.95, but dinners will take the

bill well into double figures. Morning coffee is served until noon.

Raven Bar, Just Williams [6/10]

62–63 Mardol
TEL Shrewsbury (0743) 57061

Open 11 to 2.30 (noon to 2 Sun), 7 to 10 &
Closed Christmas Day

One of Shrewsbury's oldest timber-framed buildings has been turned into a restaurant complex serving good-value wine bar food. The range is filled jacket potatoes, chilli con carne, burgers and quiches, plus lasagne and lamb chops. Good choice of beers and imported lagers. The Pengwern Hotel, Longden Road (also owned by the Williams), has an identical menu, plus barbecues and slightly longer opening hours (TEL Shrewsbury (0743) 3871/65387).

STOKE LACY
Hereford & Worcester   map 4

| NEW ENTRY | **Plough Inn** [7/10] |

TEL Bromyard (0885) 3658

Open for food noon to 2, 7 to 10

In the middle of nowhere, on the main A465 from Bromyard to Hereford. The pub is next door to the Symonds Cider and English Wine Company Shop and the two share a car-park. Norman and Janet Whittall run the place enthusiastically, with plenty of emphasis on interesting, good-value food. The bar menu steers clear of most of the pub clichés, offering instead deep-fried Brie, home-made gravlax, and massive portions of spiced lamb with apricots, salmon tart or vegetable and cashew casserole. Sweets include home-made ice-creams (damson or greengage or brown-bread), plus treacle tart and chocolate roulade. Traditional three-course Sunday lunch is £5.50. Restaurant meals may take the bill into double figures. Greenall Whitley beers.

STONE Staffordshire   map 7

La Casserole   [6/10]

6 Oulton Road
TEL Stone (0785) 814232

Open 7.30 to 11 Tue to Fri   ♿ (also WC)
Closed Christmas Eve to Boxing Day

From Tuesday to Friday there are light
suppers in this restaurant. The style is
flexible and the price depends on what you
choose. It's possible to eat for around £5 a
head, but even two or three courses plus
coffee shouldn't come to more than £10.
The range includes soup, stuffed
vegetables, curry and spare ribs.

STOURBRIDGE
West Midlands   map 4

French Connection   [7/10]

1–3 Coventry Street
TEL Stourbridge (0384) 390940

Open 10.30 to 4.30, 7 to 11
Closed Sun; D Mon to Thur; bank hols

Allen and Janet Weston opened this casual
café/bistro as an offshoot of their excellent
French delicatessen. Through the day
there are croissants with coffee or tea, but
most interest centres on the lunch menus.
For a cheap snack there's chicken and
apple salad, home-made pâté, or French
smoked ham with tomato and onion salad,
all served with real French bread. Three-
course set menus offer bistro staples, such
as rabbit with mustard, trout in white
wine, or pork provençal. On Friday and
Saturday there are set dinners for around
£10 a head. Wine by the glass.

High Street Tandoori   [7/10]

74 High Street
TEL Stourbridge (0384) 395092/379714

Open 6 to midnight (1 Fri and Sat)
Closed Christmas Day

Serves the best conventional curry-house
food in the area. The setting is a bay-
windowed Victorian building with old-
style floral designs and paintings on the
walls, and fresh flowers on the tables. The
mixed tandoori special is very good value,

otherwise the menu has decent chicken
tikka masala, lamb pasanda and vegetable
pilau. The onion bhajias make an excellent
starter, and there are exotic fresh fruits to
finish. Under twelves eat for half price.

Mr Dave's   [6/10]

15 High Street, Lye
TEL Lye (0384) 891353

Open 6 to 11.30 (12.30 Fri and Sat)   ♿
Closed Sun

Several new Indian cafés have opened in
Lye in recent months, but Mr Dave's still
rates as the best value and quality. The
balti dishes and breads are as good as
anything produced in the Sparkhill district
of Birmingham. Otherwise the menu has a
few tandooris, birianis and kormas for
good measure, plus authentic Indian
sweets. Take-aways. Unlicensed, but you
are welcome to bring your own – 'in
moderation', say the owners.

STOURPORT-ON-SEVERN
Hereford & Worcester   map 4

Severn Tandoori   [7/10]

11 Bridge Street
TEL Stourport (029 93) 3090

Open noon to 2.30, 6 to 11.30   ♿ (also WC)
Closed Christmas Day

A smart, comfortable curry house with
courteous, helpful waiters. Tandooris are
the best choice, but the menu also has
good vegetable biriani, meat madras and
specialities such as chicken makhani and
lamb pasanda. To finish try kulfi or patty
shapta (sweet pancake). Cheap business
lunches for around £4. Drink lassi or lager.

STRATFORD-UPON-AVON

Slug and Lettuce   [7/10]

38 Guild Street
TEL Stratford-upon-Avon (0789) 299700

Open for food noon to 2, 6 to 10 (noon to 1.30,
7.15 to 9.30 Sun)
Closed Christmas Day, 31 Dec and 1 Jan

A boisterous modern pub in an old
building, with a taste for bistro food. The

menu is colourful and spicy: mushrooms à la grecque, chilli con carne, black pudding with mustard sauce, chicken breasts stuffed with avocado and garlic. Dishes come with plenty of fresh bread or salad. There are a few sweets, otherwise try Brie with fresh fruit. Good house wine at around £5 a bottle. Hook Norton and Arkells bitter on handpump.

South Warwickshire Catering College [7/10]

The Willows North, Alcester Road
TEL Stratford-upon-Avon (0789) 292117

Open 12.30 to 2.30, 7 to 10 & (also WC)
Closed Sat and Sun; Wed and Fri D; college hols; during exams

The training restaurant offers such good value that lunches are booked up to six weeks ahead, and dinners up to ten weeks. A four-course lunch can be had for as little as £3.50 for, say, omelette aux fines herbes, pasta, then pork viennoise followed by a sweet and coffee. Dinners, from £6.50, might be anything from a Caribbean evening to a Russian banquet – depending on the tutors and the syllabus.

STUDLEY Warwickshire   map 4

Peppers [7/10]

45 High Street
TEL Studley (052 785) 3183

Open 12.30 to 2.30, 6.30 to 11.30 &
Closed Sun L; Christmas Day and Boxing Day

A very smart high-street Indian restaurant with fine crockery and polished furniture. The £8 minimum charge may deter the really dedicated cheap eater, but there is a useful vegetarian thali for £5.55 and a special version for £8.95, which pays for bhuna king prawn masala, lamb pasanda, chicken tikka masala, bhuna keema, mushroom pilau and masala kulcha.

SUTTON COLDFIELD
West Midlands   map 4

Wyndley Leisure Centre [5/10]

Clifton Road
TEL 021-354 9281

Open 10 to 4 & (also WC)
Closed Christmas Day

The self-service cafeteria overlooks the badminton courts and is popular with families, business people and fitness freaks. The lunchtime salad bar is good value with its choice of quiches, pizzas, chicken, sausages and rissoles to go with all kinds of salads. There's also one hot dish each day.

UPTON-UPON-SEVERN
Hereford & Worcester   map 4

Old Bell House [6/10]

9 New Street
TEL Upton-upon-Severn (068 46) 3828

Open 9.30 to 5.30 (11 Sun; noon Mon)

Angela and Terry Mason's bow-windowed café is in a seventeenth-century building in a quiet side street of the town. The menu is familiar tea-shop fare, but it is good value and all the cakes and scones are home-made. A full breakfast fry-up is under £2; cream teas are £1.50. The range also includes soup, salads and sandwiches. Wine and sherry by the glass.

WARLEY West Midlands   Map 4

La Copper Kettle [7/10]

22 High Street, Blackheath, Rowley Regis
TEL 021-561 3434

Open noon to 2, 7 to 10
Closed D Sun to Wed; Sat L; bank hols

Related to Michelle Vale's restaurants in Harborne, Birmingham. The spacious dining-room has a choice of light snacks, including minute steak and chips, omelettes, burgers, and various salads, from beef to niçoise; there's also croque monsieur. Three-course business lunches are £4.20 and a dish of the day, such as cod provençale, roast pork or beef Stroganoff is £2.60. More expensive evening meals.

WARWICK Warwickshire   map 4

Bar Roussel [6/10]

62A Market Place
TEL Warwick (0926) 491983

Open noon to 2.15, 7 to 9.45
Closed Sun L; 25 and 26 Dec

The most useful wine bar in a town well-endowed with all kinds of eating places. Menus change each day, and there's a good choice, from tsatsiki with pitta bread, quiches, cold joints and salads to hot dishes, such as beef carbonnade or chicken in lemon, white wine and mushroom sauce. Good selection of cheeses, plus home-made sweets such as treacle tart. No children.

Piccolino's [6/10]

31 Smith Street
TEL Warwick (0926) 491020

Open noon to 11 (11.30 Fri and Sat; 10.30 Sun)

The best place for pizzas and pasta dishes in Warwick. Dough for the pizzas is kneaded in view and there are eighteen toppings – from Speedy Gonzales (Mozzarella, Gorgonzola and tomatoes) to Red Hot Mamma (with ground beef and chillies). Eight pasta dishes take in everything from tortellini alla crema to gnocchi with peas in tomato sauce. House wine is 85p a glass.

Zaranoff's [7/10]

16 Market Place
TEL Warwick (0926) 492708

Open noon to 2, 7.30 to 10.30
Closed Sun, Mon; 4 days at Christmas

Unlike any other restaurant in the area. Joseph Zaranoff used to be a heavyweight wrestler and this bizarre dining-room is lined with photos of great men of the ring. There are posters, press cuttings and books everywhere. The music might be weighty extracts from *The Ring* and food comes on strange, peasant-style pottery plates. The menus are unexpected and global, the wine list is huge, and two great dishes are loaded up with rare cheeses. Go for lunch to keep the bill in single figures. The choice could be anything from Transylvanian goulash or rabbit couscous to filo pastry pie with wild mushrooms. The Zaranoffs are devoted to the search for rare recipes, good ingredients and local

suppliers. The whole set-up is more about food than cooking.

WEOBLEY
Hereford & Worcester   map 6

NEW ENTRY Jule's Cafe [9/10]

Portland Street
TEL Weobley (0544) 318206

Open 9am to 10pm (L noon to 2.30, D 7.30 to 10) & (also WC)

Julian and Juliet Whitmarsh moved from the Radnor Arms, Llowes to this one-time bakery in a fine timbered building. During the day it is a café. Light lunches might feature home-made minestrone with crusty home-baked bread, anchovy and onion tart, terrines, spiced herring fillet with aïoli, and substantial dishes, such as paprika beef with spinach noodles and sour cream. Fresh pasta comes from a firm in Abergavenny and might appear as tagliolini with mussels. Through the day there's an excellent selection of cakes and pastries. Dinners are more expensive.

WHITMORE Staffordshire   map 7

Mainwaring Arms [6/10]

TEL Whitmore (0782) 680851

Open for food 5.30 to 8 &
Closed Sun; Christmas Day

One of the most pleasant and useful food pubs in the Keele area. This old coaching-inn has its share of oak beams and log fires, plus a maze of interconnecting rooms. Cold meats, pies and salads are laid out on a table, and there are hot dishes, such as cottage pie, goulash and lasagne. Real ales from Boddingtons, Davenports and Marstons. Food in the evening only.

WHITNEY-ON-WYE
Hereford & Worcester   map 6

Rhydspence Inn [6/10]

TEL Clifford (049 73) 262

Open 11 to 1.45, 7 to 9.45 &

Peter and Pamela Glover have taken over the reins at this well-known converted drovers' inn and cider house. Bar food is one of its many attractions, and the menu stays with simple dishes such as Salcombe smokies, Devon farm sausages in natural skins, potted shrimps, and home-made pasties. Soup is from the stock-pot, and ploughman's comes with English farmhouse cheeses. More expensive restaurant meals include spit-roast duckling and seafood thermidor. Beers from Hook Norton and Robinsons, cider from Dunkertons. Children welcome until 8pm.

WOLVERHAMPTON
West Midlands   map 4

NEW ENTRY Beverley House [6/10]

3–4 Cleveland Street
TEL Wolverhampton (0902) 28968/22666

Open noon to 2, 5 to midnight &
Closed Sun L

The most useful place for Chinese food in Wolverhampton is this well-established restaurant under Security House and the Unemployment Offices. Lunch is excellent value at £3.25 for a Chinese soup followed by, say, Szechuan beef, Singapore chow-mein or ho-yu-gai-po (chicken cooked in batter and served with Chinese roast pork and vegetables). All dishes come with egg roll and fried rice, and the price includes a sweet. The full menu is an expensive mixed bag of Cantonese, Pekingese and Szechuan dishes with a few South-East Asian specialities and chop-suey house stalwarts for good measure. Set meals begin at around £8 a head.

Bilash [7/10]

2 Cheapside
TEL Wolverhampton (0902) 27762

Open noon to 2.30, 6 to 12.30 (1.30 Fri and Sat)
Closed Sun L

The most favourably reported of Wolverhampton's curry houses is this modest restaurant off the main thoroughfare, right opposite the tiered brickwork of the Civic Centre. Best value is at lunch-time, when there are set meals served buffet-style from a battery of metal dishes: £4.40 pays for, say, onion bhajia, chicken curry, cauliflower bhaji, rice and nan. The full menu is standard North Indian, balti specialities are served from little black karahi dishes, and thalis are £5.10. Drink lassi or Kingfisher beer, or try Indian champagne at £12 a bottle.

WOOLHOPE
Hereford & Worcester   map 4

Butchers Arms [7/10]

TEL Fownhope (043 277) 281

Open for food 11.30 to 2.15 (noon to 1.45 Sun), 7 to 10
Closed Christmas Day

Rabbit and bacon pie cooked in local cider is the speciality in this half-timbered fourteenth-century inn by a stream. The simple bar menu also has bowls of home-made soup, prawn pots with garlic mayonnaise and salads. Moussaka and lasagne come with hunks of crusty bread; ploughman's includes home-made apple chutney. The vegetarian trend shows in mushroom biriani with dhal and wholemeal cheese, onion and herb quiche. Hook Norton and Marston's beers on draught.

WORCESTER
Hereford & Worcester   map 4

Food for Thought [7/10]

20 Mealcheapen Street
TEL Worcester (0905) 29537

Open 7am to 4pm
Closed Sun

Superb breakfasts are just one of the attractions at this chic little restaurant above a delicatessen. Through the day there's an international choice of dishes, from fresh pasta and Mexican specialities to pizzas, samosas and quiches. Three-course lunches of, say, soup, steak and kidney pie plus a sweet, are around £3.50. To drink there are wines from nearby vineyards, as well as cider and beer.

Heroes [6/10]

26–32 Friar Street
TEL Worcester (0905) 25451

Open noon to midnight (11.30pm Sun) &
Closed Christmas Day; Boxing Day and 1 Jan

The setting is Elizabethan but the food in
this inviting, lively restaurant is up to the
minute. All kinds of steaks, kebabs,
burgers, pizzas and Mexican dishes are on
offer, with plenty of options for
vegetarians. Start with deep-fried
Camembert or chicken wings in barbecue
sauce, and finish with maple-nut sundae or
hot chocolate mint cake. From 5pm to
7pm Monday to Thursday, and all day
Sunday, meals for under-thirteens are half
price.

Hodson Coffee House [6/10]

100–101 High Street
TEL Worcester (0905) 21036

Open 9.30 to 5.30 &
Closed Sun; bank hol Mons; Christmas Day and
Boxing Day

Handily placed between the cathedral and
the guild-hall, this lively coffee shop and
pâtisserie feels very Parisian, with tables
out on the pedestrian precinct. Cakes,
pastries and quiches are freshly baked;
there's also a range of omelettes, various
salad platters and jacket potatoes with
different fillings each day. Hot buttered
tea-cakes go well with a cup of freshly
ground Viennese coffee. Wine by the glass.

East Midlands

Derbyshire

Leicestershire

Northamptonshire

Nottinghamshire

ASHBOURNE Derbyshire   map 7

Ashbourne Gingerbread Shop [5/10]

26 St John Street
TEL Ashbourne (0335) 43227

Open 8.30 to 5.30 (5 Mon to Wed) &
Closed Sun; Wed from 2pm Oct to Apr

This bakery, founded in 1805, has been in the same family for a hundred years. The shop sells all kinds of home-baked breads, tarts, cakes and gateaux, but the star is the gingerbread, which comes in the form of small, rectangular, crisp biscuits. The full range can be sampled in the beamed café, which also serves high-quality burgers, jacket potatoes, salads and sandwiches. Cream teas are popular. Unlicensed.

ASHBY DE LA ZOUCH
Leicestershire   map 7

Mews Wine Bar [7/10]

8 Mill Lane Mews
TEL Ashby de la Zouch (0530) 416683

Open 9.30 to 2.30, 6 to 11 &
Closed Sun

Menus are changed daily to please the regular customers in this popular wine bar-cum-restaurant. Lunch is the best option for cheap eaters, when there are soups (such as tomato and spring onion), salads and main courses, ranging from roast sirloin of beef to rabbit with peaches in red wine sauce. Sweets are mostly old favourites, such as bread-and-butter pudding, gooseberry charlotte, and treacle tart with custard. Wines include Hugh Rock's elderflower. Suppers are more expensive.

La Zouch [6/10]

Kilwardby Street
TEL Ashby de la Zouch (0530) 412536

Open noon to 2, 7 to 10 &
Closed Sun D; Mon; first week Jan, first week July

Geoff and Lynne Utting's little restaurant right in the middle of town is popular for its excellent-value lunches. Two-course meals (£2.50 to £3.50) might range from smoked haddock with parsley butter or quiche Lorraine and salad to lemon sole provençale or beef and vegetable pie. Start with soup or mushroom and lemon salad, and finish with a sweet from the trolley or good Stilton from the Leicestershire cheeseboard. More expensive evening meals.

ASHBY ST LEDGERS
Northamptonshire   map 4

Olde Coach House Inn [6/10]

TEL Rugby (0788) 890349

Open for food noon to 2, 7 to 9.30

A rambling old stone farmhouse with all the ingredients of a good country pub for the family. Log fires burn in the deliberately rustic bars. The buffet is a perennial attraction, with its array of cold joints, pies, seafood and big bowls of salad. There are also savoury hot-pots, such as turkey cooked with vegetables, beer and herbs. A hot carvery in winter offers roasts and home-made pies. Bank holiday entertainments are a feature, with anything from morris dancing to pantomimes. More expensive restaurant. Real ales from Ruddles, Marstons and Flowers.

BADBY
Northamptonshire   map 4

Windmill Inn [6/10]

Main Street
TEL Daventry (0327) 702363

Open for food noon to 2.30, 7 to 10.30 & (also WC)

One of the most useful family pubs in the area. There's a children's room with a pool table, a sloping field at the back for sunny days and a separate dining-room in a huge raftered barn. Best bets from the menu are the home-made soup with garlic bread, black pudding with horseradish sauce, omelettes, and locally caught trout. Pizzas come in different sizes and there are reasonably priced steaks. Well-kept Hook Norton beer on draught.

BAKEWELL Derbyshire   map 7

Aitch's Wine Bar [7/10]

4 Buxton Road
TEL Bakewell (062 981) 3895

Open 11.30 to 2.30, 7 to 11 ఉ (also WC)
Closed Sun L in winter

This grade II listed building has been
turned from a derelict garment factory into
a lively wine bar with potted palms, a
terracotta-tiled floor and church pews for
seating. The food is international: tandoori
chicken; beef and Guinness pie;
ratatouille niçoise; spanokopitas with
Greek salad and pitta bread. Also look for
specials, such as Cantonese chicken,
marinated red snapper and stuffed lemon
sole with orange butter. Five house wines
by the glass. Children welcome until
7.30pm.

Green Apple [7/10]

Diamond Court
TEL Bakewell (062 981) 4404

Open 11 to 2, 7 to 10, plus 3 to 5 Wed to Sun in
summer ఉ
Closed Sun; Mon D; Tue D

Down a narrow alley, with a courtyard
decked with flowers; on fine days there are
tables and chairs outside. The little dining-
room has flowers too, and a good-value
lunch menu: just over £5 will pay for two
courses, such as carrot and coriander soup
followed by stuffed marrow or home-made
chicken and mushroom pie. To finish
there might be Derbyshire treacle tart.
House wine is £4.70 a bottle. More
expensive evening meals.

Old Original Bakewell Pudding Shop [5/10]

The Square
TEL Bakewell (062 981) 2193

Open 9 to 6 (5 Mon to Fri in winter)
Closed Christmas Day and Boxing Day

The famous puddings are still made by
hand to the original 120-year-old recipe,
though the whole process is a closely
guarded secret. The upstairs, licensed
restaurant sells them, along with good-

value meals of fish and chips, grills, roasts
and café snacks. Full breakfasts and
afternoon teas are available, and there's a
set lunch for £5.50. Mini-menu for
children.

BRACKLEY Northamptonshire   map 4

Brackley Tandoori [6/10]

8 Banbury Road
TEL Buckingham (0280) 704814

Open noon to 2.30, 6 to 11.30 (12 Fri and Sat) ఉ
Closed Christmas Day

A handy curry house near the centre of the
town. The menu is the familiar
assortment of tandooris, dhansaks,
birianis and the like, backed up by a decent
selection of vegetables and side dishes.
Thalis are good value. Related to the
Dipalee Tandoori, Buckingham (see entry,
under Central England).

CHESTERFIELD Derbyshire   map 7

Mr C's [7/10]

71 Low Pavement, The Pavements
TEL Chesterfield (0246) 207070

Open 8 to 2.30, 6 to 10 Mon to Fri, Sun; 8am to
10pm Sat ఉ (also WC)

This restaurant might be mistaken for a
Victorian pub, with its polished
mahogany, mirrors and brass light-fittings.
Mr C (Colin Payne) presides benevolently.
The menu is unpredictable and changes
often: fish soup with saffron might rub
shoulders with cauliflower cheese or
Yorkshire pudding. Main courses are big:
Spanish omelette made with free-range
eggs, calf's liver lyonnaise, steak chasseur,
plus renowned fish and chips. Lamb might
appear as Greek kleftiko or as roast leg. A
summertime special of salmon and
strawberries is £5.95. Breakfasts and
snacks are also available. Wines by the
glass.

CRICK Northamptonshire   map 4

Edwards of Crick [6/10]

The Wharf
TEL Crick (0788) 822517

Open 10.30 to 6 ర (also w c)

Richard Coleman and Hermione Ainley run a narrowboat business as well as this restaurant in a converted wharf building by the banks of the canal. Downstairs is an informal, all-day café with red chairs, bright curtains and a simple menu of robust, restorative food. A three-course meal of, say, vegetable soup, devilled seafood, or chicken and mushroom pie with well-timed fresh vegetables, then ice-cream or plum fool, can be had for around £5. Salads might feature brawn or Arbroath smokies. Call in at any time for coffee or tea and scones. Wines by the glass. Upstairs is a more expensive restaurant specialising in English cooking.

DAVENTRY
Northamptonshire   map 4

Huffadine's [6/10]

10 Sheaf Street
TEL Daventry (0327) 702222

Open 9 to 4.30 ర
Closed Sun; bank hols

A handy coffee-shop in a town devoid of decent eating places. Inside are dark wooden settles, flowery fabrics and pretty china crockery. Cakes, scones and sweets are home made, savouries include quiches, pizzas and omelettes, and there is an all-day fried breakfast for £2.20. Coffee beans are ground on the premises, orange juice is freshly squeezed, and there's a choice of twenty teas as well as wine by the glass. The owners operate a local delivery service.

DERBY Derbyshire   map 7

Ben Bowers [7/10]

13 Chapel Street
TEL Derby (0332) 365988

Open noon to 2, 6.30 to 10 (11 Fri and Sat)
Closed Sat L and bank hols L; Sun D; Christmas Day and Boxing Day

Chapel Street runs between Cathedral Road and King Street (the main A6, running north to Matlock). The main attraction in the oak-panelled restaurant is the set lunch (£5.25 for three courses).

Start with soup or deep-fried mushrooms, before roast chicken and bacon, peppered beef, or home-made cannelloni, and finish with fruit pie, trifle or chocolate mousse. More expensive evening meals have an international flavour, with the emphasis on fish from the market. Cheaper meals and snacks are also available in the Blessington Carriage on the ground floor.

Bennetts Coffee Shop [6/10]

Irongate
TEL Derby (0332) 44261

Open 8.30 to 4.30 (4.15 Sat) ర
Closed Wed; Sun; Christmas Day, Boxing Day and 1 Jan

A coffee-shop in a long-established department store. Tables are set out on balconies round the well of an elegant staircase with Ionic columns; there are cane chairs and a pleasant 'garden' atmosphere. Substantial dishes are the likes of beef, kidney and onion pie, seafood gratin, chicken curry, and spinach and walnut lasagne. Otherwise there is home-made soup, pâté, pizzas and ploughman's, plus plenty of good-looking cakes. Unlicensed.

Lettuce Leaf

21 Friar Gate
TEL Derby (0332) 40307

*This restaurant was sold
as we went to press.*

EAST HADDON
Northamptonshire   map 4

Red Lion [7/10]

TEL Northampton (0604) 770223

Open for food 12.30 to 2, 7 to 9.30 ᴅ (also wc)
Closed Sun D; Christmas to New Year

Home-cooked bar lunches are served in this old thatched pub in a quiet village. For a light meal there might be choux buns filled with fish pâté, Welsh rarebit, or trout and broccoli quiche, as well as soup from the stockpot. Braised steak and onions, roast lamb, and moussaka are for those with bigger appetites. Vegetables and salads come in great piles. Puddings are traditional stalwarts, such as treacle sponge or Queen of Puddings. Charles Wells beers. More expensive restaurant meals.

EMPINGHAM Leicestershire   map 4

White Horse [7/10]

ᴛᴇʟ Empingham (078 086) 221/521

Open for food 8am to 11pm ᴅ (2 steps; also wc)

The seventeenth-century court-house is now a well-dressed country inn near the dam on Rutland Water. Robert and Andrew Reid get their trout from the reservoir, vegetables are from the family farm, and they butcher their own meat. Steak and kidney pie is a renowned bestseller, saddle of lamb is decorated with leeks and spring onions, and the Suffolk casserole has been good. Otherwise the bar menu features home-made lasagne, vegetarian burgers, stir-fried chicken and veal fricassee. There's a lot of cream in the sweets. The pub opens for morning coffee and croissants at 8am, and afternoon teas are available from 3.30pm. More expensive restaurant meals.

EYAM Derbyshire   map 7

Miners Arms [6/10]

Water Lane
ᴛᴇʟ Hope Valley (0433) 30853

Open for food 12.30 to 1.30, 7.30 to 9.15
Closed Mon; Sun D

A seventeenth-century pub in an ancient and historic village a couple of miles from Chatsworth. Inside its past is preserved in the fireplaces, the beams and the original inn-stone over the front door. Three-course lunches are a bargain at £3.95, for,

say, vegetable soup, then roast beef or chicken croustade with sweetbreads and mushrooms, followed by home-made sherry trifle or chocolate roulade. Dinners are more expensive. No children.

FOTHERINGHAY
Northamptonshire   map 5

Falcon Inn [8/10]

Main Street
ᴛᴇʟ Cotterstock (083 26) 254

Open for food 12.30 to 2, 6.45 to 9.45
(7 to 9 Sun) ᴅ
Closed Mon

This village pub is so popular that you need to book two weeks ahead for Friday and Saturday. No wonder, when a meal for two can cost as little as £10. Have just a cup of coffee or a bowl of soup, or try something more substantial such as moussaka, pigeon and ale pie, roast duckling with oranges and almonds, or courgettes Parmesan. There are grills too, and sweets such as blackcurrant cheesecake or coffee and walnut fudge pie. Beers from Greene King or house wine at £4 a bottle.

GLOSSOP Derbyshire   map 7

Gingers [7/10]

36 High Street West
ᴛᴇʟ Glossop (045 74) 63174

Open 11 to 4 (10 to 5, 7.30 to 9.30 Sat)
Closed Tue, Sun

A thriving vegetarian café in a converted slaughterhouse. Lunches and daytime snacks are cheap and satisfying, with the emphasis on colourful salads, jacket potatoes, meatless burgers (made with peanuts, beans and vegetables), and quiches. More expensive on Saturday evenings, but still good value for dishes such as mushroom biriani, Chinese leaves with pineapple and walnut stuffing, and vegan vegetable terrine. Sweets range far and wide: apple strudel; Caribbean lime pudding; Indian rice pudding flavoured with rosewater. Unlicensed, but bring-your-own. Take-aways.

HARRINGTON
Northamptonshire   map 4

Tollemache Arms [6/10]

TEL Kettering (0536) 710469

Open for food 11.30 to 2, 6.30 (7 Sun) to 10.30

An attractive thatched pub with old
stonework outside and rejuvenated
woodwork inside. It has been in the same
hands for the last fifteen years, and
continues to offer good value. Choose from
chicken liver pâté; fillet steak sandwich
with chips; seafood platter of prawns,
smoked mackerel, fresh salmon and
cockles; steak and kidney pie. Charles
Wells beers.

HARTINGTON Derbyshire   map 7

Jug & Glass [6/10]

Ashbourne Road
TEL Hartington (029 884) 224

Open for food 11 to 4.30, 7 to 10 (noon to 2, 7 to
9.30 Sun) & (also WC)

High up on a lonely road overlooking the
moors into Staffordshire and Cheshire.
The star turn at this hospitable pub is the
'carve your own joint' special meal. Given
twenty-four hours' notice, the kitchen will
do a big roast rib of beef, loin of pork or leg
of lamb with all the trimmings. The party
is presented with the meat and they carve
their own (any left over is wrapped up to
take home). With starters, puds and coffee,
the price is £6.75. The menu also has
ploughman's, grills, and more expensive
dishes such as escalope viennoise or
chicken with almonds. Excellent choice of
real ales: Marstons, Theakstons, Ruddles,
Mansfield and more.

HAYFIELD Derbyshire   map 7

Kinder Kitchen [7/10]

3–5 Church Street
TEL New Mills (0663) 47321

Open 10 to 5 (6 Sun), plus 6.30 to 9.30 Fri and
Sat &
Closed Mon to Wed

At lunch-time this stylish café in a
beautiful Pennine village serves good

three-course meals along the lines of apple
and parsnip soup, spinach and lentil
quiche, and banana rum waffle. On Friday
and Saturday evenings it turns into a
bistro, but dinners can still cost under £10
a head. The owners care about ingredients
and care about cooking, too. Dishes can be
bought from a display freezer to take away.

HULLAND Derbyshire   map 7

Black Horse [6/10]

TEL Ashbourne (0335) 70206

Open for food noon to 2, 7 to 9.30 & (also WC)
Closed Sun D and Mon D; Christmas Day

An extensive cold buffet is the attraction
in this whitewashed pub. There are cold
joints, quiches and all kinds of serve-
yourself salads in bowls. As well as the
lettuce and tomato, there might be
mashed potato with sage, broad beans with
sweetcorn, cucumber with dill.

LAMPORT
Northamptonshire   map 4

Lamport Swan [6/10]

Harborough Road
TEL Maidwell (060 128) 555

Open for food noon to 2, 7 to 10.30 & (also WC)
Closed Sun D; Christmas Day D

The pub gets its name and logo from
Lamport Hall, just across the road. Star of
the bar menu is gigantic fish and chips
served in newspaper, otherwise there is
home-made soup, prawn, apple and celery
cocktail, savoury pies (including pigeon),
and dishes such as liver and bacon
casserole. Vegetarians can eat well on
mushroom Stroganoff, or vegetable curry.
Sunday roast lunch is £6.95.

LANGHAM Leicestershire   map 7

Noel Arms [6/10]

1 Bridge Street
TEL Oakham (0572) 2931

Open for food noon to 2, 6.45 (7 Sun) to 10 &
Closed Christmas Day D

A handsome converted farmhouse north of
town on the A606. The cold buffet, with

its array of cold joints and salads, is the highlight, but there are also soups, pâté, grilled trout, and dishes such as turkey and ham fricassee. Ruddles beers, draught cider and wine by the glass. More expensive restaurant.

LEA Derbyshire
map 7

Coach House [6/10]

TEL Dethick (062 984) 346

Open 10.30 to 10.30 (6 Sun) & (also WC)
Closed Mon

The old farm buildings include a diary used for making ice-cream and soft cheese. There's also a tea-room serving wholesome lunchtime meals and snacks, from Welsh rarebit and devilled mushrooms to plaice poached in white wine, lasagne, and steak and kidney pie. The owners say the only commercial items are the frozen breaded scampi. More expensive restaurant meals include pasta dishes and grills. Take-aways from the farm shop.

LEICESTER Leicestershire
map 4

Acropolis [7/10]

270 Loughborough Road
TEL Leicester (0533) 663106

Open 6.30 to 11 & (also WC)
Closed Sun; 1 week Jan, 2 weeks July

Mr Menicou's family-run Greek restaurant, a mile or so out of the city centre, still offers excellent-value authentic food. The Acropolis special of pork kebabs, two sheftalia and two dolmades with rice and salad is a best seller. Avgolemono soup is good, too. Charming atmosphere. Greek-Cypriot wines.

Bobby's [8/10]

154 Belgrave Road
TEL Leicester (0533) 660106

Open noon to 10.30 (11 Fri and Sun; 11.30 Sat)
& (also WC)
Closed Mon (exc bank hols)

Serves the best Indian vegetarian food in Leicester. Mr Bhagwanji Lakhani and his family specialise in snacks and superb-value thalis. The standard price is £3.20 and on Fridays there's a special version including a yoghurt-based curry, pilau rice, mixed vegetables, puris, sweets, farsan, pickles and far-far. There are curries with all kinds of vegetables, snacks such as samosas and pani puris, and some obscure items: dhokla is chickpea flour, yoghurt, coriander, chillies and sesame seeds, deep fried; patis are round cakes filled with peas and coconut; dhebra are made from millet flour, spinach and sesame seeds. There's also a big choice of sweetmeats to take away. Unlicensed.

Bread and Roses [6/10]
NEW ENTRY

70 High Street
TEL Leicester (0533) 532448

Open 10 to 4
Closed Sun and Mon; 1 week at Christmas, 2 weeks July

A wholefood/vegetarian café beneath a radical bookshop. There's a strong Middle Eastern and East European bias to the food, which includes lots of salads, beans and grains. As well as hummus with pitta bread and vegetarian goulash, the short menu has ful medames and bulgur with lentils. Unlicensed, but there's a good choice of herb teas and fruit juices, plus barley cup to drink. Take-aways.

Chaat House [6/10]

108 Belgrave Road
TEL Leicester (0533) 660513

Open noon to 9
Closed Tue

One of the best Indian vegetarian cafés on Belgrave Road. It specialises in chaat – snacks famous in the Bombay area. There are good samosas, hollow pani puri filled with chickpeas and sauce, bhel puri and masala dosai. Sweets are barfi, gulab jamun and several kinds of kulfi. Unlicensed, but there's lassi or mango milk shake to drink.

NEW ENTRY | Curry Fever [7/10]

139 Belgrave Road
TEL Leicester (0533) 662941

Open noon to 2.30, 6 to 11.30 (12 Fri and Sat) &
Closed Mon; Sat L and Sun L

More of a restaurant than most of its
neighbours on Belgrave Road. The style is
idiosyncratic home cooking with some
unusual dishes, such as burning hot pili-
pili chicken, as well as karahi specialities,
masalas and birianis. A bowl of lamb
masala with enough for six is £18.60. The
vegetarian thali has two vegetables, dhal,
raita, plain rice, puri and a sweet for £4.70.
Minimum charge of £5 at peak times.

Farringdon's Wine Bar [7/10]

29 Market Street
TEL Leicester (0533) 556877

Open 10 to 2.30, 5.30 to 11 & (also WC)
Closed Sun; Mon D and Tue D; bank hols

An old favourite for business lunches in
Leicester. The style is traditional and
sedate, with dim lights, dark panelling and
a long row of tables running the length of
the room. Most dishes are pre-cooked,
then given a burst in the microwave,
which works more successfully with
turkey risotto, lasagne and roast lamb than
with beef Wellington or vegetarian quiche.
Excellent home-made stuffing and real
gravies are a big plus. There are also salads,
hefty steak sandwiches, and fondues. More
expensive evening meals in the cellar
restaurant.

Joe Rigatoni [7/10]

St Martin's Square
TEL Leicester (0533) 533977

Open noon to 2.30, 6.30 to 11 & (also WC)
Closed Sun; Christmas Day, Boxing Day
and 1 Jan

Some of the best pizzas and pasta dishes in
Leicester are served in this colourful place
in a revamped pedestrian piazza. The walls
are yellow, and there are pink tablecloths
on the marble-topped tables. The menu
also has good pancakes and omelette

dishes, and there are half-price portions for
children.

Panda [7/10]

215 Fosse Road North
TEL Leicester (0533) 538628

Open noon to 2, 6.30 to 11.30 (12 Fri and Sat) &
Closed Sun

A separate vegetarian menu is a new
feature at this creditable Chinese
restaurant. Choose from good-value dishes
such as vegetarian wun-tun soup, seaweed,
mushrooms in oyster sauce, or spiced bean
curd roll. The main menu has a mix of
Cantonese and Pekingese specialities,
from braised crab with ginger and spring
onion or lemon chicken to Peking duck
and fried shredded chilli beef. Set meals
start at £7.95 a head.

NEW F'NTRY | Rise of the Raj [7/10]

6 Evington Road
TEL Leicester (0533) 553885

Open 12 to 2.30, 6 to 12 & (also WC)

Leicester has one of the largest Asian
communities in the country, and more
than fifty Indian eating places within the
bounds of the city. Mostly they are
flamboyant, old-style curry houses dating
back to the 1960s, or small vegetarian
cafés and sweet-centres. Rise of the Raj, on
the outskirts of the prosperous suburb of
Evington, has more in common with new-
wave Indian restaurants in London, with
its pink and burgundy décor, list of
cocktails and selective menu of tandooris
and curries. It is one of the few in the city
to offer an in-vogue non-vegetarian thali:
£6.95 pays for shish kebab, tandoori
chicken, rogan josh, murgh makhani, sag,
raita, Basmati rice and nan. There's a
minimum charge of £5.95, but it's possible
to eat well for around £8.

NEW ENTRY | Talkies [6/10]

210 Narborough Road
TEL Leicester (0533) 546690

Open 8 to 6 (4 Sat; 10 to 3 Sun) & (also WC)

The most interesting café in Leicester is about a mile out of the city centre. It is decorated with old photos of movie stars and movie adverts. There's an amazing range of food on offer: mixed grill is chop, sausage, bacon, liver, egg, steak, chips and peas for £3.50; a roast with three veg is £2.25; there are all kinds of fillings for jacket potatoes, from ravioli to mushy peas, plus cobs at knock-down prices. One of the owners is Asian, so the curries are authentic and served with genuine Basmati rice, chutneys and poppadums. Licensed.

Tesco [6/10]

Beaumont Leys
TEL Leicester (0533) 355838

Open 9 to 7.30 (8.30 Fri) & (also WC)
Closed Sun

Still one of the cheapest places to eat in Leicester, with main courses averaging £1.50. The restaurant is part of the supermarket and serves baked potatoes, chicken and mushroom pie, macaroni cheese and decent coffee. Seasonal treats include fresh strawberries and hot-cross buns. Unlicensed.

Vivek [7/10]

144 Walnut Street
TEL Leicester (0533) 553031

Open 6pm to 11.30pm & (also WC)
Closed Christmas Day

This no-frills curry house is slightly off the beaten track, in a terraced row not far from the Royal Infirmary. The short standard menu is split between tandooris and curries, with good reports of boti kebab, butter chicken tikka masala, rogan josh and aloo gobi. The cover charge pays for a poppadum and pickles.

Water Margin [8/10]

76–78 High Street
TEL Leicester (0533) 516422/24937

Open noon to 11.30 &

The most authentic Cantonese restaurant in Leicester and the only one that stays open through the day for cheap dim-sum. The list includes char-siu buns, meat and rice steamed in lotus leaves, beef balls and paper-wrapped prawns. One-plate rice and noodle dishes are also good value – the barbecued pork is as good as anything in Soho or Manchester Chinatown. The short menu also takes in crispy duck, stuffed bean curd with vegetables, and king prawns in Szechuan sauce. Set dinners start at £14 for two. Tea is 35p and orange segments come at the end of the meal. One of the owners, Philip Chan, has recently opened another Water Margin, at 72 Burton Road, Derby (TEL Derby (0332) 364754).

LITTLE LONGSTONE
Derbyshire   map 7

| NEW ENTRY | Packhorse Inn [6/10] |

TEL Great Longstone (062 987) 471

Open for food noon to 2, 6 to 9.30
Closed Christmas Day D

This historic Peak District pub has just celebrated two hundred years as licensed premises. There's a collection of beer taps on the walls of the pine bar, but main interest centres on Sandra Lynne Lythgoe's huge baps – spread with dripping and stuffed with thick hunks of roast beef, or packed with roast pork, apple sauce and crackling. Otherwise there are good-looking pies, soups and casseroles, as well as lasagne with a pretty salad including sliced avocado and strawberries. Meat is reared locally and well hung, which makes all the difference. Marstons Pedigree in top condition.

LITTON Derbyshire   map 7

| NEW ENTRY | Red Lion Inn [8/10] |

TEL Buxton (0298) 871458

Open for food noon to 1, 7 to 8.45 &
Closed 2 weeks Sept

A quaint eighteenth-century pub on the White Peak, overlooking the village green. Inside it is a bit like a Victorian chop-house, with three little snugs, oak beams, panelling and prints. Eating is the main business of the day, and the enterprising menu is a mix of solid traditional British and French bistro cooking. There are good soups, such as pistou, or ham, lentil and pea, followed by a strong showing of roasts, from rib of beef and pheasant to veal in sherry, lemon and thyme, or duckling with ginger and pineapple sauce. Otherwise there might be cassseroled woodpigeon, poached salmon with butter and dill or Barnsley chop. Puddings are old favourites – spotted dick, jam roly-poly, apple crumble. Booking advisable.

LONG EATON Derbyshire   map 7

Steam Boat Inn [6/10]

Trent Lock, Sawley
TEL Long Eaton (0602) 732606

Open for food 12.15 to 2.30, 7.15 to 9.30
Closed Christmas Day D

Handily placed at the junction of the Erewash Canal and the River Trent. Home-brewed beer is the latest attraction, and the bar snack menu has no-nonsense, filling food, such as home-made soup, crab mousse, chicken Kiev, and curry, with gateaux or cheese to finish. A three-course set menu puts it all together for £4.45. More expensive meals in the ground-floor restaurant, including a carvery.

LOUGHBOROUGH
Leicestershire   map 7

 Dizzi Heights [6/10]

27 Biggin Street
TEL Loughborough (0509) 262018

Open 10 to 5 Tue to Sat, plus 7 to 10.30
Fri and Sat
Closed Sun; bank hols

Started by the owner of the nearby healthfood shop, this pine-furnished, self-service restaurant offers modest vegetarian food at knockdown prices. Minted tomato and split pea soup has plenty of fresh ingredients, homity pie (potato, garlic and onion with a cheese topping) has a wholemeal pastry base, and fresh fruit trifle is wholemeal, too. On Friday and Saturday evenings there are good-value candlelit dinners along the lines of garlic mushrooms, layered nut roast with red wine sauce, and fresh fruit salad. Three courses can be had for around £6. Flour is

organically produced, bread is home baked, and eggs are free range. To drink there are teas, as well as elderflower wine.

 Hong Kong Fountain [7/10]

14 Bedford Square
TEL Loughborough (0509) 216216

Open noon to 2, 6 to 11.30 (12 Fri and Sat)
Closed Sun L

A stylish Chinese restaurant on the first floor above some shops. Best bets for cheap eaters are the set meals: two people can eat for about £7 a head from dishes such as chicken and sweetcorn soup, sweet-and-sour pork, lemon chicken, and 'wandering dragon' (a mixed bag of pork, chicken and king prawns with vegetables) plus fried rice and tea. Meals from the main menu can take the bill into double figures. Related to the Paper Tiger, Lutterworth (see entry).

Koh-i-Noor [7/10]

29–33 Nottingham Road
TEL Loughborough (0509) 214660

Open noon to 2.30, 6 to 12.30 (1.30 Fri and Sat)
   (also WC)
Closed Christmas Day

Within walking distance of the station, this smartly decked-out Indian restaurant continues to offer good value. The long menu has all the usual tandooris and curries, but the cooking is authentic. Thalis – including a vegetarian version – begin at about £7 per person, and there's a set dinner for two at £20 (the price includes a bottle of wine).

LUTTERWORTH
Leicestershire   map 4

Paper Tiger [7/10]

27 Church Street
TEL Lutterworth (045 55) 56244

Open noon to 2, 6 to 11 (11.30 Thur,
Fri and Sat)
Closed Sun L

A highly popular Chinese restaurant in a small market town. The cooking is an up-to-the-minute blend of Pekingese and Cantonese specialities, and set meals are good value. For around £10 a head there are banquets (minimum four persons), which include hot-and-sour soup, crispy aromatic duck, kung po prawns, crispy shredded beef with carrots and chilli, chicken with yellow-bean sauce, fillet steak with chilli and black-bean sauce, plus rice, vegetables and tea.

MANSFIELD
Nottinghamshire   map 7

Pizzeria la Bella Napoli [7/10]

59 Leeming Street
TEL Mansfield (0623) 652376

Open noon to 2.30, 6 to 11.30 (12 Fri and Sat) &

Some of the best pizzas in the neighbourhood are served at this popular, family-run pizzeria. There's a choice of fourteen toppings, from margherita to marinara, or you can mix and match any ingredient to order. The menu also has a good showing of pasta dishes, pancakes, and Italian-style burgers, plus more expensive meat and fish specialities. Children's portions available on request, also take-aways.

MARKET HARBOROUGH
Leicestershire   map 4

Taylor's Fish Restaurant [6/10]

10 Adam & Eve Street
TEL Market Harborough (0858) 63043

Open noon to 2, 5 to 10 & (also wc)
Closed Sun; Christmas Day, Boxing Day and 27 Dec

Dating from 1902, this is reputedly the second oldest fish and chip shop in the world. Downstairs is the take-away and self-service cafeteria; upstairs is a restaurant-cum-coffee shop with bare brickwork, beamed ceilings and obliging waitresses. Eight types of fish, and scampi, come with proper chips, genuine mushy peas, plus pickles and a pot of tea if you want. Also on the menu are pies, pizzas and salads, plus scones, toasted teacakes and apple pie. The shop also sells fresh wet fish, which is a good sign. Wines by the glass, as well as beer and cider.

MATLOCK Derbyshire   map 7

Riverside [6/10]

1C Dale Road
TEL Matlock (0629) 56061

Open 9.30 to 5.30 (9.30 Fri and Sat; 2.30 Sun to Thur in winter)
Closed Christmas and New Year

This friendly basement wine bar has a splendid terrace overlooking the River Derwent. All the food is home cooked and the range might include carrot and orange soup, seafood pasta, and stuffed marrow with rice. Goulash comes with salad, bread and butter. Good sweets, such as chocolate pudding on a biscuit base. There are plans for summer barbecues and jacket potatoes in winter. Evening meals Friday and Saturday. Wine by the glass.

NASSINGTON
Northamptonshire   map 5

NEW ENTRY Black Horse Inn [7/10]

TEL Stamford (0780) 782324

Open for food 11.30 to 2.30, 6.30 to 11 & (also wc)
Closed Christmas Day D and Boxing Day D

There's a homely feel to this seventeenth-century black and white pub on the main road through the village. The emphasis is on food and tables are laid out for eating. The menu is an enterprising mix of toasted steak sandwiches, spaghetti carbonara and beef Stroganoff, supplemented by devilled crab, pork fillet in Marsala and apples, and stir-fried chicken with shrimps and bean sprouts. Blackboard specials are mainly fish: pan-fried shark steak, whole lemon sole, lobster salad. Spices and herbs are used adventurously. Good fresh vegetables; home-made sweets. Adnams beer; Bulgarian house wine.

NEWARK Nottinghamshire   map 7

Gannets [7/10]

35 Castlegate
TEL Newark (0636) 702066

Open 10 to 4.30
Closed Sun; bank hols; Christmas week

Hilary Bower's self-service restaurant overlooks the River Trent and the castle ruins. The menu has a strong vegetarian slant, which means walnut, mushroom and basil pâté, seaweed roulade, and stuffed beefsteak tomato, as well as bobotie, American chicken pie and meatballs in tomato and celery sauce. Salads are imaginative: pasta, mange-tout and pepper, or baby tomato with basil, sorrel and yoghurt. Coffee, tea and cakes are available through the day. Wines by the glass.

Old Kings Arms [6/10]

Kirkgate
TEL Newark (0636) 703416

Open for food noon to 2.15 (1.45 Sun), 7 to 10 (10.30 Fri and Sat)
Closed Sun D and Mon D; Christmas Day

An unspoilt town pub just a few minutes' walk from the castle ruins. Chris Holmes is a former chairman of CAMRA and keeps the range of Marstons beers in good condition. The same care goes into the food, which has home-made specials, such as sausage and mash, carbonnade of beef, vegetable curry and cottage pie, alongside ploughman's salads and sandwiches. Trad. jazz on Monday nights.

NORTHAMPTON
Northamptonshire   map 4

Buddies Food Factory [6/10]

Old Mission School, Dychurch Lane
TEL Northampton (0604) 20300

Open noon to 2 (11.30 to 2.30 Sat), 6 to 10.30 (11 Fri and Sat) ♿
Closed Sun; bank hols

The old mission school now preaches the gospel of jazzy American-style food amid décor of hanging Mickey Mouses and plastic space-rockets. The menu features 'mountain' salads, New York-style ribs, tuna and swordfish steaks, and burgers served with salad, relish and a choice of dressing. Milk shakes and ice-cream to follow. American wines and beers to drink. A second branch, the L A Café just down the road at 30 St Giles Street (TEL 0604 36608), promises West Coast cooking.

Kingsley Coffee House [6/10]

6A Kingsley Park Terrace
TEL Northampton (0604) 713320

Open 9.30 to 3
Closed Sun; bank hols

Philip and Diane Walton's daytime coffee-house-cum-restaurant offers great value for home-cooked snacks and lunches. Two courses and a drink can be had for just over £3. The menu always features a home-made pie, such as fish, or steak and kidney, along with quiche, lasagne, a roast and salads, Main courses come with plenty of fresh vegetables and a jug of gravy where appropriate. Sweets are old faithfuls, such as strawberry crumble and custard. Strong coffee; wine by the glass.

Luigi's [6/10]

50 Wellingborough Road
TEL Northampton (0604) 28621

Open noon to 2, 6.30 to 12 (7 to 11 Sun) ♿ (also WC)

Pizzas and pasta dishes are the cheapest options in this small, cosy trattoria just out of the town. There are five toppings for the pizzas and half a dozen pastas, from lasagne bolognese to tagliatelle napolitano. Take-aways available. More expensive veal, chicken and steak dishes are for eating in only.

Napoleon's [7/10]

9 Welford Road, Kingsthorpe
TEL Northampton (0604) 713899

Open noon to 2, 7 to 10 ♿
Closed Sun; Tue D; Sat L

Northampton's version of a typical French bistro is in a pair of converted shops on the outskirts of town. Best value is the £6.50 set lunch menu, which might include French onion soup or avocado salad, before beef bourguignonne or chicken provençale. The sweets trolley has featured home-made bread-and-butter pudding and cold orange and lemon soufflé. Button mushrooms in puff pastry is a good choice from the main menu. Decent house wine at £6.90 a litre.

 New Phipps Brasserie, Derngate Centre [6/10]

19–21 Guildhall Road
TEL Northampton (0604) 26222

Open noon to 2.30, 6 to 10.30
Closed Sun; D in Aug

This Victorian-style wine bar/brasserie attached to the theatre is a warehouse conversion with black painted metal columns, pink ceiling and potted plants dotted about. Behind the small food counter is a tiny kitchen for basic work and microwaving. Cold dishes, such as duck and orange pie, roast beef or turkey and chestnut pie come with a small selection of fresh salads. Hot dishes are the likes of steak and mushroom pie with notably good pastry, roast gammon with vegetables, or double lamb chop cooked with rosemary. Basic wines.

Sunargaon [6/10]

38 Bridge Street
TEL Northampton (0604) 32032

Open noon to 2.30, 6 to 12.30 (1 Fri and Sat) &
Closed Sun L; Christmas Day D

Serves some of the best-value and most authentic North Indian food in Northampton. It is friendlier and more chatty than some neighbouring curry houses. There are few surprises on the menu – apart from a couple of balti dishes and mochommom chicken (with green beans, egg and tomato) – but the flavours are genuine and prices reasonable. There's also a good range of tandooris and tikkas. Meat thali is £6.50, the vegetable version £5.75. Drink lager.

Sun Rise [7/10]

18 Kingsley Park Terrace
TEL Northampton (0604) 711228

Open noon to 2, 5.30 to 11.30 & (also WC)

Still the best place to eat Chinese food in Northampton. The décor is smart, service is spot on and the menu has a long run of Pekingese and Cantonese specialities, from paper-wrapped chicken to beef with black-bean sauce and deep-fried scallops. Chef's specials include several hot-pots as well as fried squid with chilli-salt and prawn balls. Set lunches are £3; set dinners for two or more start at £8 a head for the likes of pancake roll, sweet-and-sour chicken, beef with oyster sauce, fried king prawn with cashew nuts, and fried rice.

Tesco [6/10]

Weston Favell Centre
TEL Northampton (0604) 413261

Open 9 to 8 (6 Sat) &
Closed Sun; Christmas Day and Boxing Day

The largest supermarket in Europe, with all kinds of amenities, including a cinema and a sports centre. The useful all-day restaurant has a good carvery and salad bar. Rolls and doughnuts are freshly baked on the premises. Very reasonable prices. Wine by the glass.

NOTTINGHAM
Nottinghamshire   map 7

Ben Bowers [7/10]

128 Derby Road
TEL Nottingham (0602) 413388

Open noon to 2, 7 to 10.15 (10.45 Fri and Sat) & (also WC)
Closed Sat L; Sun; Christmas Day and Boxing Day

Ben Bowers was, apparently, a well-travelled coachman and the eclectic menu roams around the world for inspiration. Best value are three- or four-course set-price lunches (£5.95 and £6.50), which can take in roast breast of pigeon from England, chicken paprika from Hungary, rolled beef escalopes with madeira sauce from Bavaria, and vegetarian vol-au-vent from Hawaii. More expensive à la carte menu. Betty's Bar in the basement offers cheaper lunchtime snacks during the week, along the lines of lasagne, minute steak dijonnaise, chilli and roast turkey, as well as various cold platters.

Café Punchinello [6/10]

35 Forman Street
TEL Nottingham (0602) 411965

Open 8.30am to 10pm
Closed Sun; bank hols

As the Soup Kitchen, this café was a useful source of cheap food in Nottingham. The name has changed, the place is smarter than it was, but the quality and value for money are still good. Through the day there are light meals of moussaka, haddock in cream and egg sauce, quiche, plus vegetarian versions of shepherd's pie or goulash, and specials such as kidneys and mushroom casserole. The more extensive evening menu begins at 7.30pm, with broad beans à la grecque, chicken with ginger, beef in burgundy and pork with honey and orange.

Café Royal [7/10]

27–33 Market Street
TEL Nottingham (0602) 413444

Open 10.30am to 11pm (noon to 10.30 Sun) &
(also WC)
Closed Restaurant Sun

A converted porticoed building on the corner of Market Street and Upper Parliament Street. Snacks and simple dishes are available all day in the café bar. Upstairs is the restaurant, with a wide-ranging menu taking in Camembert fritters, salade niçoise, burgers, and chicken with apples and calvados. Vegetables are cooked al dente. Basic wines. Children are welcome in the restaurant but not the bar.

Chand [7/10]

26 Mansfield Road
TEL Nottingham (0602) 474103

Open noon to 2.30, 5.30 to 12.30 &
Closed Christmas Day

Handily placed just up the road from the massive Victoria shopping centre. The menu at this small, prettily decorated curry house reads more authentically than many in Nottingham. There are Persian and Kashmiri-style dishes among the

tandooris, bhunas and vindaloos, with forthright spicing and plenty of garlic and herbs. Three-course weekday lunches are very good value at around £3, otherwise a thali for two is £10.10. There's a minimum charge of £6.50 on the full menu, but it's easy to eat well for under £8.

NEW ENTRY | Lidio's [6/10]

2 Kings Walk
TEL Nottingham (0602) 473767

Open noon to 2, 6.30 to 11.30 (7 to 11 Sun)
Closed Sun L

Some of the best-value Italian food in Nottingham is served in this trattoria in an alley just off the main square. Set lunch is exceptional value at just over £3 for starters such as minestrone or spaghetti bolognese, before lasagne, chicken cacciatore, steak pizzaiola or escalope of veal milanese; the price also includes a sweet. The main menu has pizzas from around £2.20 and main-course pasta dishes from £3.

NEW ENTRY | Mr Shing's [7/10]

148A Mansfield Road
TEL Nottingham (0602) 587209

Open noon to 2.30, 5.30 to 11.30 (noon to 11.30 Sun)

On the first floor above the Inkap Chinese supermarket. This is one of the new breed of Chinese restaurants in Nottingham, and is particularly useful for its range of rice and noodle dishes, from roast duck with rice to beef ho fun with black-bean sauce, or Singapore vermicelli. Otherwise the 150-strong menu has some interesting bean curd dishes and classic Cantonese seafood specialities, such as steamed eel or crab with ginger and spring onions, as well as fashionable sizzling dishes and birds' nests. Set dinners start at £8 a head. Open all day Sunday.

NEW ENTRY | Ocean City [8/10]

100–104 Derby Road
TEL Nottingham (0602) 475095

Open noon to 11.45 & (also WC)

The best place in Nottingham for lunchtime dim-sum. It is within striking distance of the University and is a favourite with Chinese students. The full menu moves between old-style Cantonese dishes, such as steamed eel with crispy pork, lemon chicken and stuffed duck, and in-vogue sizzling monkfish with chilli and black-bean sauce or fillet steak in a bird's nest. Evening meals, when there's a minimum charge of £7.50, can break the £10 barrier.

 ## Sagar [6/10]

473 Mansfield Road, Sherwood
TEL Nottingham (0602) 622014

Open noon to 2.30, 5.30 to 12.30
Closed Christmas Day

Well out of the city centre in the suburb of Sherwood. This elegant, Regency-style curry house is related to Chand (see entry). Local opinion is divided about the merits of the two places, but there is certainly authentic, good-value food to be had here. The menu is North Indian curries, birianis and tandooris. Thalis begin at £6.50 a head for makhani kofta, chicken or prawn kurma, mixed vegetables, mushroom bhaji, nan, and rice. Drink lassi or lager.

 ## Shogun [8/10]

95 Talbot Street
TEL Nottingham (0602) 475611

Open noon to 2, 7 to 12
Closed Sun

Nottingham's first Japanese restaurant and one of only a handful in the North of England. The setting is a monolithic converted brick warehouse facing the Derby Road, with a blue pennant across the door. Set lunches are an interesting way of spending £5: the menus feature vegetable tempura, tonka-tsu and egg, gyudon (slices of beef sirloin cooked in a sauce with onions), and chicken katsu (deep fried, with a dipping sauce). The price includes rice, salad, soup and dessert. Set dinners start at £10 (£8 for vegetarians) or there is a range of sashimi, sukiyaki, shabu-shabu, and other classics. Drink tea, saké or plum wine.

Staropolska [7/10]

King John's Arcade, 13–15 Bridlesmith Gate
TEL Nottingham (0602) 502672

Open 11am to 3.30pm
Closed Sun

A modest daytime café in an alley not far from the city centre. The ground floor has little pine tables, bare floors and yellow paintwork, with posters and advertisements covering every inch of the walls. As well as a good choice of cakes there are lunchtime specials with a wholefood slant: aubergine and lentil bake, swede and Cheddar pie, spinach and cheese pasta. In the evening, authentic Polish meals are served with colourful costumes, live music and chilled vodka. Prices are reasonable, though a dinner bill is likely to be in double figures.

Ten [8/10]

10 Commerce Square, Lace Market
TEL Nottingham (0602) 585211

Open noon to 3, 5.50 to 12
Closed Sun, Mon

One of the many nineteenth-century warehouses in Nottingham that have been turned into restaurants. Ten is vegetarian by persuasion. During the day there are cheap, enterprising snacks, such as tofu and red pepper pâté with pitta bread, falafel, cauliflower thermidor and stuffed aubergines, plus baked potatoes and savoury herb waffles with toppings. Also look for the home-prepared baked beans. Evening meals bring together eclectic, meatless dishes and classical sauces: baby marrow stuffed with rice, chestnut purée, tarragon and redcurrants comes with a crème de Cassis sauce; nut cutlets are served au poivre or Diane; broccoli soubise topped with carrot puree and fresh basil gets a vermouth sauce. Three courses can be had for under £10. House wine is £4.50 a bottle.

OLD DALBY Leicestershire   map 7

Crown Inn [7/10]

Debdale Hill
TEL Melton Mowbray (0664) 823134

Open for food 10 to 2.30, 6 to 11 (noon to 2, 7 to 10.30 Sun) &

A fine country pub that feels like a private house, with cosy rooms, log fires and Windsor chairs. The bar menu makes interesting reading, with the emphasis on adventurous home-cooked dishes. Black pudding and apple with mustard sauce, lamb's liver and sausage kebabs, and carbonnade of beef rub shoulders with stuffed tomatoes topped with thyme butter, pasta and seafood salad, and game in red wine sauce. There are also wholemeal sandwiches, Welsh rarebit, and a special Crown lunch – a glorified ploughman's of Melton Mowbray pork pie, ham and Stilton, plus all the trimmings. Good choice of real ales. More expensive restaurant meals.

OVER HADDON Derbyshire   map 7

Lathkil Hotel [6/10]

TEL Bakewell (062 981) 2501

Open for food noon to 2, 7 to 9

Spectacular panoramic views of the Peak District are a big plus at this old-fashioned hotel. Buffet lunches include salads and filled cobs as well as hot dishes, such as steak, kidney and oyster pie, lamb curry, and beef and mushroom casserole. Evening meals take in steaks, stuffed turkey breast, and courgette and mushroom lasagne. Smoked Lathkil trout is good and there is local Stilton, too. Beers from Wards and Darleys. Bookings only on Sunday evenings.

PLUMTREE
Nottinghamshire   map 7

Perkins Bar Bistro [9/10]

Old Railway Station
TEL Plumtree (060 77) 3695

Open noon to 2, 7 to 9.45 &
Closed Sun; 1 week at Christmas

The derelict railway station has been turned into an excellent bar-cum-bistro serving first-rate food. The cooking centres on a short blackboard menu taking in laverbread with bacon, casseroled wood pigeon, goujons of plaice with aïoli, and mutton and mint sausages, all served with plenty of fresh vegetables. Lunch is a bit cheaper than dinner. On summer evenings, visitors can sit outside on the platform and wait for their meal. Decent coffee and drinkable house wine at £4.40 a bottle.

ROTHLEY Leicestershire   map 7

Red Lion [6/10]

TEL Leicester (0533) 302488

Open for food 12 to 2, 6.30 to 10 & (also WC)
Closed Christmas Day

Otherwise known as the Halfway House, this seventeenth-century inn is geared to food. The weekday cold buffet lunch is an impressive array of roast joints and salads, otherwise the bar menu has mushrooms and bacon in garlic butter, char-grilled burgers, steak and kidney pie laced with Burton Ale, and Barnsley butterfly lamb chops. Sunday lunch is £6.95 (£3.95 for children). The more expensive restaurant has a full vegetarian menu and the itemised list of ingredients by each dish is revealing. A note says that the béchamel sauce 'consists of skimmed milk, modified starch, hydrogenated vegetable oil, wheat flour, onion, salt, flavourings, herbs and spices'. Ind Coope Burton Ale on draught; house wines by the glass.

SHARDLOW Derbyshire   map 7

La Marina [6/10]

134 London Road
TEL Derby (0332) 792553

Open noon to 2.30 (2 Sun), 7 to 10.30 (10 Sun) & (also WC)
Closed Mon

A bright and cheerful trattoria serving straightforward Italian food. Weekday business lunches are good value at £5.75 for, say, fresh minestrone, goujons of plaice, or lamb chops, followed by Italian cake. There's also a traditional Sunday lunch for the same price. Main course pasta dishes are the cheapest bets from the full menu. House wine is £5.20 a litre.

SILEBY Leicestershire   map 7

Bunter's [6/10]

19 High Street
TEL Sileby (050 981) 2532

Open 9 to 5.30 (2.30 Sat)
Closed Sun; 1 week July, 1 week at Christmas

Jackie Baum's licensed tuck shop is the casual alternative to the village's Old School House restaurant. Home-made burgers and pizzas are the mainstay, backed up by American-style cookies, fish pie, quiches and lasagne. Start the day with griddle pancakes served with egg, bacon and sausage. A three-course meal with wine can be had for as little as £3. Take-aways.

STRETTON Leicestershire   map 7

 Ram Jam Inn [8/10]

Great North Road
TEL Castle Bytham (078 081) 776

Open 7am to 11pm & (also WC)

Call it what you will: a 1980s coaching inn, a five-star transport café, or an alternative roadhouse, bang on the A1. The guiding spirit behind this venture is Tim Hart of Hambleton Hall and it shows in the quality of the ingredients and the imaginative menu, which has hot sausage sandwiches and burgers alongside a salad of mange-tout and sun-dried tomatoes. For sheer style it puts the chain pit-stops to shame. Choose a table in the restaurant or prop yourself up at the bar – the menus are similar. Breakfast is served until eleven in the morning; there is blackberry and apple pie with home-made custard at coffee time; for lunch try fresh fettucine, grilled pork ribs, or a hefty B L T. Unpasteurised Stilton comes from the Colston Bassett dairy. To drink there are real ales from Ruddles, as well as Murphy's Irish stout and some obscure Belgian beers – from Kriek with cherries to strong monastic Chimay – plus fresh orange juice and wine by the glass.

TIDESWELL Derbyshire   map 7

Poppies [8/10]

Bank Square
TEL Tideswell (0298) 871083

Open 6 to 11 &
Closed Mon

Polished oak tables, chapel chairs, dried flowers and a wooden staircase going nowhere set the tone in this thoroughly English village restaurant. Su Horsman's cooking is an enterprising mix of bistro and vegetarian. Potato, onion and herb broth with home-baked bread, ratatouille pancakes, and green lentil cutlets with spicy yoghurt and lemon sauce rub shoulders with pork steak in cider, American meat loaf with tomato sauce, and beef and mushroom pie. Seasonal sweets to finish. Children over ten welcome.

Tideswell Fish and Chip Shop [5/10]

Commercial Road
TEL Tideswell (0298) 871727

Open 11.30 to 1.30, 4 to 6, 8 to 12.30
Closed Sun; 4 to 6 Sat to Wed; L Mon to Thur; Christmas Day, Boxing Day and 1 Jan

A friendly neighbourhood chippie open for lunch, tea and supper. The fish is fresh and you can pick the piece you want and have it cooked to order. Very good value. Unlicensed.

THORPE MANDEVILLE
Northamptonshire   map 4

Three Conies

TEL Banbury (0295) 711025

*This pub was sold
as we went to press.*

TOWCESTER
Northamptonshire   map 4

New Bekash Tandoori [6/10]

100 Watling Street East
TEL Towcester (0327) 50505

Open noon to 2.30, 6 to 12
Closed Christmas Day and Boxing Day

A creditable North Indian curry house
with the added attraction of a wine bar
where samosas, tikkas and kebabs are
served as snacks. Otherwise the menu is a
familiar mix of tandoori dishes plus
kormas, dhansaks, rogan josh, vindaloos
and something even hotter, called sylhet.
Good value thalis and set meals. Drink
Kingfisher lager. The branch in Stony
Stratford is less impressive.

UPPINGHAM Leicestershire   map 4

Baines [5/10]

5 High Street West
TEL Uppingham (0572) 823317

Open 9 to 5 (1 Thur) &
Closed Christmas Day, 1 Jan

The Baines family are Uppingham's best-
known bakers, and they run a cottagey tea-
room next to their shop. There are prints
of wild flowers on the solid walls, and bare
pine tables. Macaroons are the best-sellers,
but a vast range of home-made cakes, tarts
and pies, including Battenburg cake and
jammy dodgers, is piled up on cake stands.
Excellent buttered toast goes well with a
pot of tea. Lunches are quiches and salads
for around £2. Unlicensed.

WALCOTE Leicestershire   map 4

Black Horse Inn [7/10]

TEL Lutterworth (045 55) 2684

Open for food 11 to 2.30, 5.30 to 11 (noon to 2,
7 to 9.30 Sun)
Closed Christmas Day

Michael Tinker and his wife serve very
creditable Thai food amid all the trappings
of a typical English village pub. The short
menu of specialities has a Thai mixed grill
and a range of Thai curries, as well as khau
mu daeng (marinated leg of pork with rice

and a chilli and ginger dip), and nuer phat
nam an hoi (sliced beef in oyster sauce).
There are also special Thai banquets at £8
a head for a minimum of four people (book
in advance). To drink there's Thai beer, as
well as English real ale. Children welcome
in the dining-room.

WEEDON Northamptonshire   map 4

NEW ENTRY # Narrow Boat Inn [6/10]

Watling Street, Stowe Hill
TEL Weedon (0327) 40536

Open for food 11 to 2.30, 6 to 11 (noon to 2, 6 to
10.30 Sun) & (also WC)
Closed Christmas Day; restaurant Tue L and
Wed L

This roadside pub is understandably
popular: out front is the A5, out back is the
Grand Union Canal. The landlord's wife is
Chinese and a major attraction is the
Chinese restaurant tacked on to the bar.
The chef from Hong Kong offers a
fashionable mix of Cantonese and
Pekingese specialities with a few South-
East Asian dishes for good measure. Set
meals for around £10 might feature prawn
satay, sizzling Cantonese steak, spare ribs
and pork with ginger and spring onion.
The pub also serves bar snacks such as
curries, chilli and dishes from the
restaurant menu, to go with the Charles
Wells beers. There's a high-raftered family
room as well as a big terrace and garden.

WELLINGBOROUGH
Northamptonshire   map 4

Magee's [6/10]

5–7 Queen Street
TEL Wellingborough (0933) 226051

Open noon to 2.30, 7 to 11 & (also WC)
Closed Sun L; Boxing Day

A bright, lively bistro with old metal
advertising signs on the walls and a
penchant for zany entertainments, such as
Cossack dancing. The menu goes over the
top with 'Cocklewarmers' and
'Bellybusters', but the food is well cooked
and fresh. Tomato soup or pork satay
could be followed by chicken and white
wine casserole with herb dumplings or a

hefty burger. There are also vegetarian dishes, such as oat and cauliflower bake.

Tithe Barn [6/10]

Burystead Place, Tithe Barn Road
TEL Wellingborough (0933) 78764

Open 9 to 4.30 & (also WC)
Closed Sun; Christmas Day and 1 Jan; bank hol Mons

In a grassy square between the shops and the car park. The menu has a good range: on the cold side are quiches, savoury pies and salads; on the hot there are robust dishes, such as macaroni cheese or corned beef hot-pot, plus filled jacket potatoes. Wine by the glass, as well as tea, coffee, juices and milk shakes. Tables outside.

WHITWELL Leicestershire   map 4

Noel Arms [6/10]

TEL Empingham (078 086) 334

Open for food noon to 1.45, 7 to 9.30
Closed Christmas Day

A two-hundred-year-old thatched pub a few hundred yards from Rutland Water. Fishermen come here for straightforward bar snacks of vegetable soup, liver and onions, home-made lasagne, and seafood pancakes. There's also a pie of the day, and ploughman's comes with fine Stilton. More expensive meals in the busy dining-room. Ruddles beers.

WILSON Leicestershire   map 7

Bull's Head [6/10]

TEL Melbourne (033 16) 2644

Open for food noon to 2.30 (2 Sun), 6 to 11
Closed Sun D and Mon D; Christmas Day

An oak-beamed pub with a solid local reputation for food. Big helpings of roast beef with Yorkshire pudding are a firm favourite; the steak and kidney pie is good; salads are plentiful. Otherwise the menu features home-made soup, salmon and crab in season, and the usual ploughman's and sandwiches. Sweets are gateaux and cheesecakes.

East Anglia

ABY Lincolnshire   map 8

Claythorpe Mill [7/10]

TEL Withern (0521) 50687

Open 10 to 5, 7 to 10
Closed Mon (exc bank hols); 29 Dec to Good Fri

This renovated mill is run by a Dutch
couple who smoke all their own fish and
meats. Peacocks roam in the gardens and
trout from a nearby farm swim in the river.
Lunches revolve around huge platters
loaded with all kinds of delicacies from
smoked eel to smoked chicken, served
with plenty of bread and butter. To finish
there are locally baked cakes or enormous
banana splits. Simple list of wines.

ALDEBURGH Suffolk   map 5

Aldeburgh Fish & Chip Shop [6/10]

226 High Street
TEL Aldeburgh (072 885) 2250

Open 11.45 to 1.45, 5 to 9
Closed Sun and Mon out of season

The best chippy in the area is in an old
brick building at the top end of the High
Street. Excellent local fish – especially cod
and plaice – is freshly cooked in light
batter and the chips are crisp and golden
brown. The shop also sells home-smoked
salmon (off-cuts as well as prime slices).
Long queues, but fast service. No tables, so
eat on the beach if weather allows.
Unlicensed.

 Regatta [7/10]

171 High Street
TEL Aldeburgh (072 885) 2011

Open noon to 2.15, 6.30 to 10.15 & (also WC)
Closed Sun L

This used to be Hammersley's. Peter Hill
and Sara Fox moved here from the Odds &
Ends Scullery in Hadleigh and have
quickly established their cheerful bistro as
one of the most popular eating places in
the neighbourhood. The décor has been
revamped and a big seascape mural now
dominates the scene. Cheapest and best

bets from the menu are the home-made
soups (such as cream of watercress) and
the fresh fish from the Aldeburgh boats,
which might appear as seafood crumble,
monkfish brochettes or grilled Dover sole.
Long wine list from Lay & Wheeler. Open
late and useful during the Aldeburgh
Festival.

Ye Olde Cross Keys Inn [6/10]

Crabbe Street
TEL Aldeburgh (072 885) 2637

Open for food noon to 2, 7 to 9 &
Closed Sun D

Still the best bet for a pub lunch in
Aldeburgh. The sixteenth-century pub has
a dark beamed bar as well as a long
gravelled patio/garden at the back, handy
for families with children. Local fish is a
feature of the long menu: crab salad in
summer, cod pie in winter. There's also a
good range of dishes for vegetarians, such
as marrow in cheese sauce. Adnams beers.

ARKESDEN Essex   map 5

Axe & Compasses [6/10]

TEL Clavering (079 985) 272

Open for food 12.15 to 2, 7 to 9.30
Closed Mon D

Food varies from day to day in the
restaurant of this thatched village pub. On
Tuesday there is fresh fish from Lowestoft,
on Wednesday, steaks, Thursday is hearty
English bangers and mash or lamb cutlets.
There's also a good-value Sunday lunch for
£6.50. Lunches in the bar include good
sandwiches and ploughman's, plus dishes
such as mushroom soup, roast lamb, and
salads. Greene King and Rayments beers.
Children welcome in the restaurant.

BILLERICAY Essex   map 5

Webber's Wine Bar [7/10]

2 Western Road
TEL Billericay (0277) 656581

Open 11.30 to 2, 6 (7 Mon) to 10.30 (11 Fri and
Sat) & (also WC)
Closed Sun; Christmas Eve D to 2 Jan; last week
July and first week Aug

Adventurous bistro food and well-chosen wines are the attractions in this split-level wine bar. Blackboard specials can take in anything from Arbroath smokie hot-pot or aubergine pâté to rabbit in elderflower wine or Indonesian beef. Puddings promise the 'ultimate chocolate cake', as well as fresh raspberries and strawberries in red wine. Cheeses are interesting: unpasteurised Brie, Coverdale, Taleggio. A Cruover machine means that fine wines can be dispensed by the glass.

BLAKENEY Norfolk   map 8

Drifters [7/10]

High Street
TEL Cley (0263) 740702

Open 10.30 to 2 (noon to 3 Sun), 7 to 10 &
Closed Mon

A reliable village restaurant just up the hill from the quay. The menu makes good use of local produce, from crabs, mussels and ham to additive-free ice-creams and sorbets made in the nearby village of Wiveton. Lunches are simple: home-made vegetable soup, potted shrimps, roast chicken, pasta. Evening meals are strong on old-style fish dishes: grilled whole plaice with parsley sauce, poached turbot, scallops Mornay. Otherwise there are steaks, roast guinea-fowl, and medallions of pork for meat eaters, and a special menu for vegetarians. Thirty wines include two from Norfolk vineyards.

BLICKLING Norfolk   map 8

Buckinghamshire Arms Hotel [6/10]

TEL Aylsham (0263) 732133

Open for food 10.30 to 2.30, 6 to 11 (noon to 2, 7 to 10.30 Sun)
Closed Christmas Day

Blickling Hall is just a stone's throw away from this civilised Jacobean inn. Nigel Elliott is a generous host, and his food is big platefuls of honest home-cooking. Soup comes from the stock-pot, big salads (including Cromer crab in season) are served with a great stick of French bread, and there are filling daily specials, such as

prawn risotto or steak and mushroom casserole. More expensive restaurant. Beers from Adnams and Greene King.

BOSTON Lincolnshire   map 8

Eagles [6/10]

54–56 Main Ridge
TEL Boston (0205) 64458

Open 11.30 to 1.30, 5 to 11 (10.30am to 11.30pm Sat)
Closed Sun, Mon

Downstairs is the take-away chippy, upstairs is the fish and chip restaurant. The place has been given a face-lift and a forty-seat extension has been added. There's also a new bar at the back serving food and drinks. Johnny Eagle still does the cooking and the fish is fresh from Grimsby. Lager is 90p a pint; house wine £3.40.

BRANCASTER STAITHE
Norfolk   map 8

| NEW ENTRY | Jolly Sailors [6/10] |

TEL Brancaster (0485) 210314

Open for food noon to 2, 7 to 9 (11 to 10 July and Aug)
Closed Christmas Day

Brancaster Staithe is the only EEC-recognised pollution-free harbour in England and Wales, and this two-hundred-year-old pub takes full advantage of it. The great attractions are big bowls of local mussels in winter, and cockles in summer. The former might be baked in garlic butter, the latter are usually served freshly boiled. Most of the bar food is home-made, from the soup (which can be served in a big mug to take away), macaroni cheese, and beef curry, to fish pie and lasagne. Tartare sauce is the real thing, too. Food is served right through the day during July and August. More expensive restaurant meals. Greene King beers, draught cider and wines by the glass.

BRANDON Suffolk   map 5

Collins [6/10]

50–52 High Street
TEL Thetford (0842) 811766

Open 11.45 to 2, 5 to 11 (noon to 7.30 Sun)
Closed Christmas Day, Boxing Day and 1 Jan

A cut above most fish and chip restaurants in the area. Food is cooked to order and portions are generous. There's a special three-course menu for around £5, and reduced prices for children and old-age pensioners. Sit and eat in comfort, or take away.

BRANDON CREEK Norfolk   map 5

Ship Inn [6/10]

TEL Brandon Creek (035 376) 228

Open for food 11 (noon Sun) to 1.45, 6 (7 Sun) to 9.45 & (also WC)
Closed Christmas Day and Boxing Day

An isolated riverside pub at the junction of the Great Ouse and the Little Ouse. There's no pool table or juke-box; instead the bar has an open fire, photographs of old Fenland scenes and corn-dolly shepherds' crooks above the bar. Food is a mixture of home-made soup, local ham, jacket potatoes, and vegetable crumble backed up by blackboard specials, such as kebabs with savoury sauce, seafood pie, and mixed grill. Barbecues every Sunday in summer, and regular entertainments such as morris dancing. Real ales. Children welcome (if eating) up to 8.30pm.

BRENTWOOD Essex   map 5

Pizza Express [7/10]

5 High Street
TEL Brentwood (0277) 233569

Open 11.30 to midnight &
Closed Christmas Day and Boxing Day

A branch of the highly rated pizza chain (see London entry).

BURNHAM MARKET
Norfolk   map 8

Fishes [8/10]

Market Place
TEL Fakenham (0328) 738588

Open noon to 2, 7 to 9.30 (9 winter) &
Closed Mon; Sun D, exc July to Sept; Christmas; last 2 weeks Jan

Gillian Cape's uncomplicated restaurant on the village green is still one of the best local options for fresh and home-smoked fish without frills. Scallops, skate, sole and sea-trout are from the North Norfolk boats, cockles and crabs are specialities, and oysters are from the restaurant's own beds. Salmon fish-cakes with baked potato or salad is a firm favourite, otherwise the menu has gravlax, seafood gratin and crab soup. Meat and poultry appear in the shape of smoked goose breast, and home-baked ham with fresh fruit. To finish there are home-made ice-creams and British cheeses, such as Lanark Blue or Cornish Yarg. House wine is £5.25 a bottle.

BURNHAM-ON-CROUCH
Essex   map 3

NEW ENTRY # Polash [7/10]

169 Station Road
TEL Maldon (0621) 782233

Open noon to 3, 6 to midnight &

A cut above the standard high-street curry house. The long menu holds no surprises, with its clusters of tandooris, Malays, dhansaks and birianis. Set menus for up to eight people begin at £8.95 a head, and the names are intriguing: Kipling's Favourites (for two) is chicken and mutton tikka, tandoori lobster masala, bhuna gosht, mushrooms, rice, fruit salad and coffee. There's a branch at 86 West Road, Shoeburyness, Essex (TEL Shoeburyness (037 08) 3989/4721).

BURY ST EDMUNDS
Suffolk   map 5

Mortimer's [7/10]

31 Churchgate Street
TEL Bury St Edmunds (0284) 60623

Open noon to 2, 7 to 9 &
Closed Sun; Sat L; bank hols; 23 Dec to 6 Jan

A useful fish restaurant with paintings of boats on its light-cream walls. At lunch-time there are specials, such as fish curry or kedgeree, for around £2.50, otherwise have a starter from the menu: crab pâté, gravlax, fish soup or Loch Fyne oysters. Main courses take in grilled whole grey mullet, steamed fillet of halibut on a bed of spinach, and baked monkfish provençale. Lobsters are from Felixstowe. Cream caramel and chocolate pot are good sweets. Drinkable house wines by the glass; the useful list has a small contingent from the New World. There's a new branch in Ipswich (see entry).

Owl and the Pussycat [6/10]

25 Abbeygate Street
TEL Bury St Edmunds (0284) 705703

Open 9.30 to 4.30, 7 to 10
Closed Sun; Mon D

The restaurant is on the first floor above a shoe shop and the entrance is round the corner from Abbeygate in Lower Baxter Street. During the day there are toasted sandwiches, pizzas and salads, with soup, quiches, and daily specials at lunch-time. Evening meals for under £10 a head centre on dishes such as chicken casserole, pork noisettes with calvados, and aubergine pie. The wine list includes some bottles from English vineyards.

Shapla Tandoori [6/10]

29 Mustow Street
TEL Bury St Edmunds (0284) 60819

Open noon to 2.30, 6 to 11.30 & (also WC)
Closed Christmas Day and Boxing Day

A reasonably priced local curry house not far from Angel Hill. Tandoori chicken and tikkas are recommended, and the menu has a full range of North Indian curries, plus omelette and chips for those who prefer something unspicy.

CAMBRIDGE
Cambridgeshire   map 5

| NEW ENTRY | **Browns** [8/10] |

23 Trumpington Street
TEL Cambridge (0223) 461655

Open 11 (noon Sun and bank hols) to 11.30 & (also WC)
Closed Christmas Eve to Boxing Day

It was almost inevitable that Browns — that buzzy centre of Oxford social life — would one day take Cambridge by storm.

The light-blues' version is in a converted Edwardian hospital, and has all the trappings of its mentor: hanging baskets, ceiling fans, waiters in long aprons and a jazzed-up American-style menu. Burgers, huge salads, hot sandwiches, and grills are backed up by daily specials, pasta, and pies. Cocktails, thick milk shakes and around twenty wines (most by the glass).

Catering Training Restaurant [6/10]

Cambridge College of Further Education, Newmarket Road
TEL Cambridge (0223) 357545/324455

Open noon to 2, 7 to 10 Tue and Thur (bookings only D) & (also WC)
Closed weekends and college hols

The Training Restaurant offers some of the best-value food in Cambridge. Cooking is done by the students under the supervision of chef-tutors and menus are tailored to the curriculum. Set lunch for around £3 centres on dishes such as boiled beef, roast lamb, or poached salmon. Dinners cost more, but it's easy to eat for under £10 a head. There are some decent wines, too. A big plus is the view over Midsummer Common and the college boathouses along the Cam.

Fitzbillies [6/10]

50 Regent Street
TEL Cambridge (0223) 64451

Open 9 (11 Sun) to 5 (6 Sat) &
Closed Sun end Sept to Easter

The tea-room attached to the young branch of Cambridge's most famous baker's and confectioner's sells the same fine range of breads, cakes and pastries as the shop. Chelsea buns are the most renowned speciality but there are also exotic ice-cream sundaes, filled rolls, pies, and a choice of a hundred teas and coffees. The famous chocolates are worth buying to take away. Unlicensed.

Free Press [7/10]

7 Prospect Row
TEL Cambridge (0223) 68337

Open for food noon to 2 & (also WC)

The best bar lunches in Cambridge are served in this tiny back-street pub. Every day there are fine-looking cold meats, pies, and salads, boosted by hot dishes such as macaroni cheese or minced beef bake with almonds and cheese. Hearty soups, such as curried apple, come with decent bread, and to finish there might be summer pudding or banana and ginger meringue. Greene King beers on draught.

Greenhouse, Eaden Lilley [6/10]

Market Street
TEL Cambridge (0223) 358822

Open 9.30 to 5 & (also WC)
Closed Sun; bank hols

The self-service restaurant on the first floor of the prestigious department store is still noted for its splendid lunchtime display of food. Salads are the mainstay of the menu, and there's an excellent array of sweets including summer pudding. The sandwiches are good, too.

Hobbs Pavilion [6/10]

Park Terrace
TEL Cambridge (0223) 67480

Open noon to 2.30, 7 (8.30 Thur) to 10.30
Closed Sun and Mon; mid-Aug to mid-Sept; Christmas Eve to early Jan; Good Fri and Easter Sat

The setting is a converted cricket pavilion bedecked with paintings by the proprietor Steven Will. The food is based around all kinds of filled pancakes: savoury versions range from pastrami with horseradish to smoked haddock with egg; sweet kinds include unlikely combinations such as sliced Mars bars with whipped cream. To drink there's real ale from Greene King, Aspall cider and a short list of wines.

Martin's [6/10]

Trumpington Street
TEL Cambridge (0223) 61757

Open 8.30 (9 Sat, 10 Sun) to 7.30 (5.30 Sat and Sun)
Closed Christmas Day, Boxing Day, 1 Jan; Good Friday

A very popular coffee-shop serving remarkably cheap lunches and snacks. Salads, chilli con carne, omelettes, pâté and jacket potatoes are all good value. The home-made cakes are excellent and the coffee is some of the best in Cambridge. A pleasant refuge during the long summer vac. Unlicensed.

Nettles [7/10]

6 St Edward's Passage

Open 9am to 8pm
Closed Sun

The best vegetarian food in Cambridge is served in this tiny restaurant close to St Edward's churchyard. It is so small that crockery has to be cleared by going out the back way and coming in through the front door. The choice of food takes in hot dishes, such as macaroni cheese, couscous, and savoury flans, as well as bowls of salad, wholemeal rolls, and scones. By four in the afternoon the counter can be depleted, but regulars flock in again at six when fresh supplies are brought down from the kitchen. The lack of space means that there's a brisk take-away trade. Unlicensed.

Pizza Express [7/10]

28 St Andrews Street
TEL Cambridge (0223) 61320

Open noon to midnight &
Closed Christmas

A provincial city branch of the highly rated pizza chain (see London entry).

Roof Garden, Arts Theatre [6/10]

6 St Edward's Passage
TEL Cambridge (0223) 355246

Open 9.30 to 8
Closed Sun; some bank hols; Christmas Day

The charming, plant-filled Roof Garden above the theatre is very popular with townspeople at lunchtime – and there are usually long queues for the buffet. Salads are the mainstay, backed up by quiches, local sausages, roasts, and a hot dish, such as curry. Vegetables are fresh. Afternoon teas are becoming more popular. Children's menu. Beer or wine by the glass. The Pentagon wine bar-cum-restaurant on the first floor was being redecorated as we went to press; when it reopens the emphasis will be on table service.

Shades [7/10]

1 King's Parade
TEL Cambridge (0223) 359506

Open 11.30 to 2.30, 6 to 11
Closed Sun; Christmas Day, Boxing Day and 1 Jan

On a corner overlooking King's College Chapel. The downstairs wine bar serves good chunks of cheese with wholegrain bread, as well as cold roast beef, seafood and salads. There are also a few daily dishes chalked on the blackboard, such as squid rings in batter or ham and asparagus quiche. Sweets are fruity. Enormous portions to go with modest wines. There's a small restaurant upstairs. Children welcome at lunch-time.

NEW ENTRY Upstairs [8/10]

71 Castle Street
TEL Cambridge (0223) 312569

Open 6.30 to 10.30
Closed Mon; 1 week at Christmas, 2 weeks Sept

The cheap eating scene in Cambridge has suddenly come to life and there are now alternatives to dining in college that won't break the bank. This cramped Middle Eastern/North African restaurant above Waffles (see entry) serves authentic and gutsy dishes: spicy Moroccan beef soup with lentils and chickpeas, huge portions of couscous, Armenian lamb with apricots, vegetarian tajine. Interesting meze to start and sweet crêpes to finish. Good Turkish coffee. It's possible to have a full meal for under £10, provided you don't go overboard with the Moroccan Tarik M'tir wine.

Waffles [6/10]

71 Castle Street
TEL Cambridge (0223) 312569

Open 6.30am to 11pm (noon to 3, 6 to midnight Sat, 9.30 to 2.30, 6 to 10 Sun)
Closed Mon

An old-style waffle house with a taste for Victoriana as well as honest cheap food. Savoury versions come topped with anything from asparagus and egg sauce to chicken créole. Sweet ones might have butter, maple syrup and cream, or spiced apple. On Sundays there's also an excellent breakfast. Drink tea, coffee or buttermilk; otherwise there are wines and beers.

CASTLE ACRE Norfolk   map 8

Ostrich Inn [6/10]

TEL Castle Acre (076 05) 398

Open for food noon to 2 (1.30 Sun), 7.30 to 10.30 (10 Sun)
Closed Christmas Day and Boxing Day

The only pub on the Peddars Way – the ancient trackway from Suffolk to the Wash. At lunch-time there are good cold platters and sandwiches (the Royal Ostrich double-decker is filled with crab and smoked salmon). Pâté and pizzas are home made, and other good dishes have included turkey kebabs and baked nut loaf. Greene King beers. Children's room.

CHAPPEL Essex   map 5

Swan Inn [6/10]

TEL Earls Colne (078 75) 2353

Open for food noon to 2 (1.15 Sun), 7 to 10.45 & (also WC)
Closed Christmas Day

The five-hundred-year-old pub by the River Colne has a courtyard for fine weather and a straightforward menu of bar snacks. Best bets are the home-made pies, the home-cooked ham, and the rare Scotch beef with chips. More substantial meals are served in the dining-room: the mixed grill is a massive plateful for £7.25. Large portions, good value. No children under 10 in the restaurant.

CHELMSFORD Essex   map 5

Melissa [9/10]

21 Broomfield Road
TEL Chelmsford (0245) 353009

Open 9 to 4
Closed Sun

Chelmsford's first vegetarian restaurant
and still one of the most enterprising in
Essex. Set lunches are wholefood classics,
such as tomato and potato soup, spinach
and cauliflower pancakes with mustard
sauce, and carob mousse. The dazzling
range of salads can run to almost twenty,
from grated courgette with ginger to
peach, cauliflower and curried peanuts.
Through the day there are filled baps,
jacket potatoes, quiches, and cakes.
Everything is home made, and many
ingredients are organically produced.
Take-aways, outside catering and freezer
foods are part of the enterprise. Herb teas,
barley cup or wine to drink.

CHELSWORTH Suffolk   map 5

NEW ENTRY   Peacock Inn [6/10]

The Street
TEL Bildeston (0449) 740758

Open for food noon to 2, 6.30 to 10.30
Closed Christmas Day

This magnificent timbered inn is in one of
Suffolk's prettiest villages, not far from the
parkland of Chelsworth Hall. Inside it is
historic, with a huge stone inglenook
fireplace and exposed Tudor brickwork.
The food includes some good home-made
dishes: vegetable soup with hunks of bread
from a local baker, pâtés (such as game or
trout), pies, and salads, as well as specials,
such as chicken curry, cod ratatouille, and
seafood Mornay. There are home-made
eclairs, too. The garden is delightful in
summer. Beers from Adnams, Greene King
and Mauldons. Jazz on Friday evenings.

CLARE Suffolk   map 5

Peppermill [6/10]

Market Hill
TEL Clare (0787) 278148

Open 11 to 4.30, 7 to 9.15
Closed Sun D; Mon

During the day, Roger and Julie Steele's
beamed restaurant is an informal tea-shop
serving pots of tea and home-made scones,
as well as light lunches of soup, omelettes,
jacket potatoes, and salads. To finish
there's bread pudding or home-made
cheesecake. More expensive restaurant
meals in the evening.

CODDENHAM Suffolk   map 5

NEW ENTRY   Duke's Head [7/10]

TEL Coddenham (044 979) 330

Open for food noon to 2, plus 7 to 9.45 Tue to Sat

Ron Cole is an enthusiastic cook at this
seventeenth-century village pub and
makes good use of local and fresh
ingredients. There are no chips or scampi
on the seasonally changing menus. Instead
there might be home-made lentil and
vegetable soup, Moroccan lamb tajine,
plaice stuffed with feta cheese, prawns and
almonds with saffron sauce, and treacle
tart. In summer there might be Greek and
Middle Eastern dishes such as hummus
and sheftalia; in winter the emphasis is on
cassoulet, hare in red wine and boiled
bacon with caper sauce. Also look for the
range of curries: Goan chicken, rabbit
vindaloo, rogan josh and Indonesian lamb.
Tolly Cobbold beers are tapped from
barrels behind the bar and there is wine
from East Anglian vineyards.

COGGESHALL Essex   map 5

White Hart [7/10]

Market End
TEL Coggeshall (0376) 61654

Open for food noon to 2.30 (also WC)
Closed Aug; 2 weeks at Christmas

This fine old coaching-inn is best known
for its classical, old-style restaurant and its
phenomenal wine list, but there are good-
value lunches in the buttery, too. Most
dishes are under £5 and the emphasis is on
fish – anything from poached Finnan
haddock to char-grilled swordfish. There
are also a few meaty offerings. Beers from
Adnams.

COLCHESTER Essex   map 5

 Bistro Nine [7/10]

9 North Hill
TEL Colchester (0206) 576466

Open noon to 2, 7 to 10.45 &
Closed Sun, Mon; 1 week after Christmas

Good for a cheap, satisfying lunch. The
bistro lives up to its name with red
gingham tablecloths and abstract
paintings on the wood-panelled walls.
Simplest dishes are often the best – baked
potato with garlic mushrooms, hot Sussex
smokies, steak, and trout. Other
specialities, such as a trio of mousses, can
be less successful. To finish there's superb
banana split topped with all kinds of fresh
fruit, treacle tart, or brown-bread ice-
cream. Evening meals are more expensive.
Wines by the glass.

Clowns [6/10]

61A High Street
TEL Colchester (0206) 578631

Open 11.30am to 10.30pm &
Closed Christmas Day and Boxing Day

A jumping burger joint popular with
students. The décor is jazzy, the music
loud. The menu is burgers, plus chilli con
carne, salads, barbecued pork, and home-
made chocolate brownies with cream. Half
a pound of pork sausages is £2.60; the
same weight of Scotch sirloin is £5.60. A
new branch has opened at 16 Falcon Street,
Ipswich (TEL Ipswich (0473) 230185).

Tillys [6/10]

Crouch Street
TEL Colchester (0206) 572780

Open 9.30am to 10.15pm & (also WC)
Closed Sun; bank hols; Christmas Day; 1 Jan

One of the most popular cheap eating
places in Colchester. It's open through the
day for sandwiches (the egg mayonnaise is
excellent), jacket potatoes, salads, quiches,
and pies. Dishes have jokey names: Turn
Over a New Beef is lasagne; Salmon
Chanted Evening is a triple-decker toasted
sandwich with smoked salmon, black

pepper and cream cheese. Cakes are baked
on the premises. Portions are massive.
More substantial evening meals. Tea by
the pot, wine by the glass.

 Wings, Mercury Theatre [8/10]

Balkerne Gate
TEL Colchester (0206) 46881

Open noon to 2, 6 to 10.45
Closed Sun; bank hols

The Campbells moved from Bistro Nine
(see entry) to take over this open-plan
restaurant attached to the theatre. Since
their arrival, standards have soared. Best
value of all is the fixed-price theatre menu
(£6.50 for two courses). Start with tomato
and orange soup and home-baked bread, or
fanned avocado, grapefruit and orange
salad, before chicken with ginger and
spring onion sauce, or vegetarian lasagne
with salad or perfectly cooked vegetables.
Sweets are worth the extra money –
especially the raw sugar meringues with
lemon sauce. Well chosen, reasonably
priced wines.

DISS Norfolk   map 5

Diss Coffee House/Thai Restaurant [8/10]

Norfolk House Yard, St Nicholas Street
TEL Diss (0379) 51580

Open 10 to 3 (4.30 Sat), plus 7 to 10 Thur to Sun
Closed Sun L; D Mon to Wed; Sun D Oct to Mar

The development of Norfolk House Yard
has benefited this pretty coffee-house with
pine furniture and cottagey flowers on the
tables. During the day there are sandwiches, savoury snacks, jacket potatoes
and omelettes, plus a special Thai dish at
lunch-time. Four evenings a week, the
place puts on full oriental costume and
becomes a Thai restaurant, with a menu of
around forty accessible and well-described
dishes. As well as satay and pu-jar (cakes of
minced beef and crabmeat with vinegared
cucumber and peanut sauce), there are
soups flavoured with lemon grass, curries,
lots of stir-fried dishes, Thai-style omelettes, rice, and noodles. Egg mayonnaise

and jacket potatoes are tacked on to the menu almost as an afterthought. Unlicensed, but bring your own wine.

DUNWICH Suffolk map 5

Flora Tea Rooms [6/10]

Beach Car Park
TEL Westleton (072 873) 433

Open 10 to 6 &
Closed 1 Dec to 1 Mar

The tea-rooms are actually a big converted hut on the beach, but people come from miles around for the first-rate freshly cooked fish and chips. The last of the Dunwich boats provide cod, plaice, sole and skate, which are done in a light, crisp batter. Scones, apple pies, doughnuts, cakes and rolls are made on the premises each day. Sit on the benches outside on the dunes if the place is packed. Unlicensed. Take-aways.

Ship Inn [6/10]

St James's Street
TEL Westleton (072 873) 219

Open for food noon to 2, 7.30 to 9.30 & (also WC)
Closed Christmas and 31 Dec

Once a great medieval port, Dunwich is now a tiny tourist village, famous because it is sinking into the sea. This whitewashed pub near the beach is the hub of the place and serves good food and drink for the visitors. At lunch-time there's home-made soup, cottage pie, ploughman's, and local fish and chips. The evening menu has trout pâté, mushrooms in batter with a curry dip, steaks, and crab in season. Adnams and Greene King beers on draught.

EARLS COLNE Essex map 5

 NEW ENTRY # Colne Valley Tandoori [7/10]

110 High Street
TEL Earls Colne (078 75) 3380/2983

Open noon to 2.30, 6 to 11.30

A very popular curry house, rated as one of the best in Essex. The long menu has all

kinds of tandooris, birianis, karahi dishes and curries, including first-rate lamb pasanda cooked with pistachios, almonds and cream. The vegetarian thali is good value at £5.95 for onion bhajia, mattar paneer, dhal, vegetable curry, raita, pilau rice and nan. Good-quality ingredients and distinctive spicing make the cooking better than average. Kulfi or fresh mango to finish.

EARL SOHAM Suffolk map 5

Victoria [7/10]

TEL Earl Soham (072 882) 758

Open for food 11.30 to 2.30, 5.30 to 11 (noon to 2, 7 to 10.30 Sun)

This is a pub that sticks to its principles. The landlord brews his own beer in a converted malthouse at the back and the food is honest home cooking, with a wholefood accent. There's always soup, as well as chilli with brown rice, undyed kippers, walnut and rice salad, and specials, ranging from tuna risotto to steak, kidney and mushroom casserole. Sandwiches are made with wholemeal bread from the local bakery. The owners plan to open a second pub, The Tram Depot, East Road, Cambridge, in spring 1988.

EASTON Suffolk map 5

White Horse [8/10]

TEL Wickham Market (0728) 746456

Open for food noon to 2, 7 to 9.30
Closed Sun and Mon D

Ian Chamberlain has moved from the Market Place, Framlingham (see entry), to work with David Grimwood in the kitchen of this enterprising village local. The bar food is ambitious and there's much use of local produce. East coast crabs, locally smoked trout, and shellfish appear on the buffet; fish stew is packed with squid, mussels, sea bream, grey mullet, and there are seasonal game dishes from raised pie to hare casserole with juniper berries. Chicken is cooked with mango sauce and there's an enterprising showing of vegetarian specialities, such as black-bean casserole flavoured with coconut and pineapple. More expensive restaurant meals. Tolly Cobbold beers on draught, plus a blackboard list of recommended wines, including half a dozen by the glass.

EDENHAM Lincolnshire   map 8

Five Bells [6/10]

Main Street
TEL Edenham (077 832) 235

Open for food noon to 1.45, 7 to 10 &
Closed Christmas Day and Boxing Day

A comfortably modernised old stone pub serving a mixture of bar-food stalwarts plus a useful showing of home-made dishes. Look for the chicken liver pâté, lasagne, stuffed green pepper with cheese sauce, and grills. Vegetarians can choose from pilaff of fruit and nuts, sweet-and-sour vegetables or vegetable curry. On Sundays a plate of roast beef with all the trimmings is £2.75. Sam Smith's beers on draught. There's a children's tree-house in the garden.

ELY Cambridgeshire   map 5

Peking Duck [7/10]

26 Fore Hill
TEL Ely (0353) 2948

Open noon to 2, 6 to 11
Closed Mon; Tue L

Peking and Szechuan restaurants have a habit of blossoming in unlikely places. The food here compares favourably to that in many similar restaurants in London. Peking duck is a speciality, but the menu also takes in dishes such as sesame prawn toasts, beef with spring onion, and Go Ta chicken. The mixed hors d'oeuvre is beautifully presented and the Szechuan prawns are spicy. Set dinners from around £6 a head.

EYE Suffolk   map 5

Dove House [6/10]

7 Lambseth Street
TEL Eye (0379) 870736

Open 10 to 6 (noon to 6 Sun) &
Closed Tue

A classic Suffolk-pink tea-shop serving traditional English snacks right through the day. Light lunches include home-made soup, pizzas, and dishes such as sausage plait with mashed potatoes, as well as salads. Sunday lunch is a roast. Morning coffee and afternoon tea are also available. Local apple juice and cider, as well as wine by the glass.

FAKENHAM Norfolk   map 8

Chadwicks Wine Bar [6/10]

2 Quaker Lane
TEL Fakenham (0328) 2032

Open 10.30 to 2.30, 6.30 to 11 &
Closed Sun; Mon D

This used to be Fishes' Wine Bar, but Miss Chadwick has bought the freehold and changed the name. The menu is a standard range of soup, pâtés and hors d'oeuvre, backed up by pies, honey-roast ham, smoked fish, and beef served with salads and new potatoes. Hot dishes range from beef bourguignonne to Dover sole. Wines by the glass.

FELIXSTOWE Suffolk   map 5

Yoyo's Bistro, Ordnance Hotel [6/10]

1 Undercliffe Road West
TEL Felixstowe (0394) 273427

Open noon (12.30 Sun) to 2, 7 to 10.30
Closed Sat L and Sun D; bank hols L

This rather sombre, 1930's-style hotel has a bright jazzy bistro in one wing, with bentwood furniture, pot plants and a light, airy atmosphere. The menu is international, taking in crab imperial from the USA, oriental-sounding chicken with plum sauce, Norfolk venison with apricot sauce, and Scottish finnan haddie pie. During the summer there's a lunchtime salad table for £4.95. Basic wines by the glass or carafe.

FOWLMERE Cambridgeshire   map 5

Chequers Inn [7/10]

TEL Fowlmere (076 382) 369

Open noon to 2, 7 to 10 &. (also WC)
Closed Christmas Day and Boxing Day

One of the Poste Inns group of upmarket
pubs, serving imaginative bar food in a
classy setting. This seventeenth-century
beamed hostelry seven miles from
Cambridge is a popular venue. The menu
has plenty of good things, such as crab au
gratin, ham and mushroom pancake, and
monkfish with bacon, as well as roast beef
and rack of lamb. Good soups, excellent
crisp vegetables, and home-made sweets
from the trolley. Tolly Cobbold beers.

FRAMLINGHAM Suffolk   map 5

Market Place [8/10]

18 Market Hill
TEL Framlingham (0728) 724275

Open 10 to 11.30, noon to 2, 3.15 to 5, 7 to 9.30
&. (also WC; 1 step)
Closed Sun and Mon; Christmas Day and
Boxing Day

Timothy Smart has taken over as chef at
this tiny cottage restaurant in the market
place. The cooking is modern with
strongly flavoured light sauces, eye-
catching presentation and touches of
Anton Mosimann in the swirls of colour
and visuals. Lunch is cheaper than dinner,
but both are excellent value for money.
The style shows in the delicate galantine
of salmon and sole poached in white wine
and dill sauce, the venison cutlet with
smoked bacon in port sauce, and chicken
quenelles with pink peppercorns.
Vegetarians are offered sauté field
mushrooms with brandy and risotto rice.
The walnut bread is superb and sweets
include excellent cinnamon and tayberry
ice-cream. Good Australian wines.

Wheelwright's [6/10]

Well Close Square
TEL Framlingham (0728) 724132

Open 10.30 to 5 &. (1 step)
Closed Sun; Wed (exc Aug)

Rosemary Western's simple family
restaurant is a good bet for cheap snacks
such as toasted sandwiches, ploughman's,
and burgers. She puts on a salad bar in
summer, with home-made quiches, meats,
smoked fish, and vegetarian dishes, and
there are more substantial meals to be had
from a menu of local steaks, casseroles,
pies, and curries. Good old-fashioned
puddings.

FRINTON-ON-SEA Essex   map 5

Casseroles [6/10]

7 Old Road
TEL Frinton-on-Sea (025 56) 4517

Open 9.15 to 5 (2 Wed) &.
Closed Sun and Mon; Christmas Day and
Boxing Day

This intimate restaurant-cum-tea-room is
one of the old school. The décor is
traditional and so is the food. Good-value
lunches (two courses for £3.80) can begin
with egg mayonnaise or avocado
vinaigrette, before roast rib of beef,
chicken normande or trout meunière.
Sweets reflect the other arm of this
business – the production of home-made
freezer foods. Unlicensed.

GAINSBOROUGH
Lincolnshire   map 8

Red Lion [6/10]

Redbourne
TEL Kirton Lindsey (0652) 648302

Open for food noon to 2.15 (2 Sun), 7.30 to 10
&. (1 step)

This Tudor-style hotel has its own
preserved fire station, complete with a fire
engine. To eat, there's a standard menu of
well-cooked food: home-made pâté, garlic
mushrooms, poached scampi, grills, and
specials, such as chicken chasseur or
peppered steak with creamy mustard
sauce. Tables outside, opposite the green.
Children welcome in the dining-room.

GESTINGTHORPE Essex   map 5

NEW
ENTRY # Pheasant [6/10]

TEL Hedingham (0787) 61196

Open for food noon to 2, 7 to 10.30 (also WC)

A down-to-earth local pub just out of the village on the Sudbury road. Inside, not much has changed since the 1930s and the atmosphere is old-fashioned. The menu has some interesting offerings, such as Jamaican bean pot, as well as macaroni cheese, fish pie, and decent home-made goulash with crusty bread. The ham ploughman's is good and meaty. Don't bother with the sweets. Beers from Greene King and Adnams, as well as Pheasant Ale from the Mauldon Brewery.

GRAYS Essex   map 3

R. Mumford & Son [6/10]

6–8 Cromwell Road
TEL Grays Thurrock (0375) 374153

Open 11.45 to 2.15 (3.15 Sat), 5.30 (5 Sat) to 11
Closed Sun; bank hols (exc Good Fri); Christmas Eve to 31 Dec

The Mumfords use only fresh fish from Billingsgate in this long-established fish and chip restaurant with a take-away next door. Sit-down prices vary from under £5 for rock, eel, cod, and plaice, to just under £8 for halibut and Dover sole. All come with lemon, parsley, peas, roll and butter. There are porterhouse steaks and chicken for meat eaters. Bottled beers and wine by the glass.

GREAT BARDFIELD Essex   map 5

 Vine [6/10]

TEL Great Dunmow (0371) 810355

Open for food noon to 2, 7.30 to 9.45
Closed Christmas Day and Boxing Day

Extensive modernisation has changed the face of this seventeenth-century pub in the centre of the village. But any lack of atmosphere is redeemed by big helpings of home-cooked food. The menu has lots of grilled and fried dishes, but country-style ham is the real thing, served with fried egg and piles of fresh, ungreasy chips. Steak sandwich is about a quarter of a pound of meat in a hunk of French bread, while the massive special of the day might be chicken hot-pot pie served with cauli-flower cheese and mashed potatoes. Ridleys beers. No children.

GREAT DUNMOW Essex   map 5

Gurr's [7/10]

81B High Street
TEL Great Dunmow (0371) 2358

Open 7.15am to 9.45pm
Closed Sun and Mon; Christmas Eve to 3 Jan

Next door to a fish and poultry shop of the same name. This is a restaurant devoted to the serious cooking of fresh fish delivered each day from Lowestoft and Billingsgate. On the standard menu there is seafood chowder, Arbroath smokie pâté, and fried squid with chips. Also look for the list of daily specials: monkfish provençale, skate (poached with black butter, or nobs, or middle), grilled sea bass, or whole plaice topped with prawns and cheese sauce, served with a trencherman's helping of carefully cooked fresh vegetables. Decent wines.

GREAT WALTHAM Essex   map 5

Windmill [6/10]

TEL Chelmsford (0245) 360292

Open for food noon to 2, 7 to 9.15
Closed Sun; bank hols; Christmas Day and Boxing Day

The style is upmarket and genteel and food is the order of the day in this comfortable Essex pub. The menu has its share of prawn cocktail and scampi and chips, but look for specials, such as smoked chicken with home-made coleslaw, steak, kidney and mushroom pie, or vegetable marrow stuffed with savoury mince. Adnams beer on draught. No children.

GREAT YARMOUTH
Norfolk   map 5

NEW ENTRY **Mastersons** [6/10]

113 Regent Road
TEL Great Yarmouth (0493) 842747

Open 11.30 to 8 (also WC)
Closed Christmas Day

The east coast has more than its share of good fish and chip shops and standards are high. The wet fish side of this business is a classic seaside fishmonger's, with old-fashioned signs and a big range, including home-smoked bloaters and sprats. Mr Masterson is a wholesale/retail fish merchant, and customers in the attached restaurant (open June to September, though the take-away is open all year) can pick their piece of fresh fish for frying. The choice is cod, plaice, haddock, skate, plus anything else that the markets can provide. Licensed for beer and wine.

Zaks Yankee Traveller [6/10]

36 King Street
TEL Great Yarmouth (0493) 857065

Open noon to 11.15 (4 to 10 Sun and bank hols)
Closed Christmas Eve to Boxing Day

Started more than ten years ago as a home-from-home for American oil-rig management, this busy diner has lost none of its popularity. Char-grilled burgers are the mainstay, but the menu takes in teriyaki beef brochette, chilli dogs, and Suffolk ham steaks served with corn and fries. Cocktails, beers and workaday wines.

HARLOW Essex   map 5

Upstairs Downstairs [6/10]

21–22 Post Office Walk, The High
TEL Harlow (0279) 414994

Open 11.30 to 2.30, 6 to 11.30
Closed Sun; Christmas Day and Boxing Day

Useful brasserie and restaurant in the heart of Harlow New Town. Best value is in the downstairs bistro that serves moules marinière with garlic bread, grilled pork and garlic sausage, and various ploughman's. Busy and friendly. The upstairs restaurant is more expensive. No children.

HARWICH Essex   map 5

Pier at Harwich [8/10]

The Quay
TEL Harwich (0255) 503363

Open noon to 2, 6.30 to 9.30 & (also WC)
Closed Christmas Day and Boxing Day

Cheap eaters should head for the Ha'penny Pier, the bargain fish and chip restaurant on the ground floor. The spacious, comfortable room is appropriately decorated with murals of Harwich's Victorian pier, and the menu has good fish pie and fried fishy centrepieces flanked by smoked haddock and mushrooms in cheese sauce, lemon cheesecake and ice-creams. Meaty alternatives include steak and lasagne. Three courses for children come to £2.25. The upstairs seafood restaurant also offers good value, though the bill is likely to be in double figures. Tea, coffee, wine by the glass and Adnams beer.

HEACHAM Norfolk   map 8

Norfolk Lavender [5/10]

Caley Mill
TEL Heacham (0485) 70384

Open 10.30 to 5.30 & (also WC)
Closed Oct to Easter; weekdays Easter to early May

Since 1932 Caley Mill has been the home of Norfolk Lavender, the only commercial grower and distiller of lavender in Britain. The Miller's Cottage tea-room serves all kinds of cakes and scones with fresh coffee and tea. Most of the baking is done on the premises. Cream teas are popular. Unlicensed.

HILDERSHAM
Cambridgeshire   map 5

Pear Tree [7/10]

TEL Cambridge (0223) 891680

Open for food 11.30 to 3

For a long while, the food in this country pub was one of the best-kept secrets in Cambridgeshire. Now the word has spread, but the cooking is as good as ever. The style is simple: big bowls of wholesome soup, such as split pea and smoked sausage, or lentil and vegetable; roasts; freshly baked pies; fish; and specialities such as genuine Welsh rarebit made with real ale. Fresh vegetables are always available, and to finish there's spotted dick or fruit crumble.

HOLYWELL Cambridgeshire map 5

Ye Olde Ferry Boat Inn [6/10]

TEL St Ives (0480) 63227

Open noon to 2 (2.30 Sat), 7 to 10 (10.30 Sat) &
Closed Christmas Day

This ancient thatched building was originally a monastic ferry-house for the Great Ouse. Fish and meat are brought up every week from the London markets and used for a range of bar food that includes Stilton and walnut pâté, sweet-and-sour turkey and duck, seafood pilaff, and steaks. There are also one or two curiosities, such as smoked wild boar, and venison burgers with green pepper and radish sauce. Beers from Adnams and Greene King.

HUNTINGDON
Cambridgeshire map 5

George Hotel [6/10]

George Street
TEL Huntingdon (0480) 432444

Open noon to 2, 7 to 9.30 &
Closed Sun L

A fine old coaching-inn with a galleried central courtyard and an elegant Georgian lounge bar. Lunchtime snacks always feature a pasta dish of the day, along with soups and casseroles; evening meals are omelettes, steaks, and pizzas. Afternoon tea is a sedate affair with sandwiches, hot buttered toast, pastries and cream cakes.

Old Bridge Hotel [7/10]

1 High Street
TEL Huntingdon (0480) 52681

Open 12.30 to 2.15 (2 Sun), 7.30 to 10.15
(7 to 10 Sun) &
Closed Christmas Day D and 31 Dec D

An upmarket hotel on the edge of town, with a nouvelle cuisine restaurant and a good range of bar food in the plant-filled Terrace Lounge. There are plenty of bargains, including Gruyère cheese and spinach fritters, pan-fried herring roes in herb and garlic butter, and jugged hare, as well as soup, pâté, and lasagne. Much of the interest centres on the buffet. Well-chosen wines by the glass. The garden runs to the river and there are tables outside.

ILFORD Essex map 3

Mandarin Palace [7/10]

559 Cranbrook Road, Gants Hill
TEL 01-550 7661

Open noon to 3, 6 to 12 (1 Fri and Sat) & (also wc)
Closed Christmas Day and Boxing Day

One of the better Chinese restaurants east of London. Lunches at £3.80 for three courses are a bargain and dishes such as sweet-and-sour pork or crispy duck are excellent. Otherwise there is a three-hundred-strong menu that runs with the fashion for Pekingese specialities, taking in a few Cantonese dim-sum snacks and classic fish dishes along the way. The vegetarian section is worth investigating (try the set dinner at £9.80 a head). Other set meals break the £10 barrier. There is a second branch in Essex – The Roding Restaurant, Market Place, Abridge – and another in Marbella.

IPSWICH Suffolk map 5

Marno's Food Reform [6/10]

14 St Nicholas Street
TEL Ipswich (0473) 53106

Open 10.15 to 10 (2.15 Mon to Wed) & (also wc)
Closed Sun; bank hols

This folksy vegetarian restaurant is run entirely by women and it feels homespun, with vases of fresh flowers, basketwork lamps and ethnic-looking clothes hanging up for sale. The food is self service and everything is home made. Good dishes have included hot and spicy chilli beans with rice, mushroom pie, and sweet-and-sour pancakes. To finish there's trifle, cheesecake or treacle tart. Wine, juices and coffee to drink. Best value at lunch-time.

Mortimer's on the Quay [7/10]

Wherry Quay
TEL Ipswich (0473) 230225

Open noon to 2, 7 to 9 (8.30 Mon) &
Closed Sun; Sat L; 24 Dec to 5 Jan; bank hols and day after

Kenneth Ambler moved from Mortimer's in Bury St Edmunds (see entry) to open this new branch in a converted quayside warehouse. The style is very similar, from the green and white décor and watercolour seascapes to the menu dominated by fresh fish. All kinds of simple dishes are on offer, such as potted shrimps, gravlax, Loch Fyne oysters, and smoked eel with horseradish sauce, as well as lunchtime specials, such as seafood risotto. Choose carefully to keep the bill in single figures. Useful wines including Abbey Knight from Suffok, as well as Greene King beers.

IXWORTH Suffolk   map 5

Pickerel Inn [7/10]

TEL Pakenham (0359) 30398

Open for food 11 to 2, 7 to 10 &
Closed Christmas Day

This impressive Elizabethan inn has been given a face-lift to highlight many of its finest features, which include historic panelling and an outstanding carved and beamed ceiling in the lounge and bar. There's continuing praise for Swedish-born Kerstin Burge's cooking. The Scandinavian influence shows in the excellent open sandwiches, and fish is a speciality: home-made gravlax, poached trout or salmon, fresh sardines, bowls of prawns with good brown bread. Meaty alternatives range from steaks to pork fillet with green peppercorn sauce, and there are hot bananas in rum or Dutch apple pie to finish. Greene King beers.

KERSEY Suffolk   map 5

Bell Inn [6/10]

TEL Hadleigh (0473) 823229

Open for food 11 to 2.30, 6.30 to 11 (noon to 2, 7 to 10.30 Sun & (also WC)
Closed Christmas Day D

Kersey is a beautiful village famous for its watersplash across the main street and for its well-preserved old buildings. This fine half-timbered pub is one of the most

impressive, with its carved black beams, latticed windows and upper floor. Bar food is a familiar selection, with good home-made pâté and ploughman's as well as salads and steaks. Sunday lunch is excellent value for interesting soups, hefty roasts, and home-made puddings. Adnams, Flowers and Wethereds beers on draught.

KING'S LYNN Norfolk   map 8

Crofters Coffee House [6/10]

The Fermoy Centre, 27 King Street
TEL Kings Lynn (0553) 773134

Open 9 to 5.30 (plus 6.45 to 11 and 2.45 to 5 Sun when theatre open)
Closed Sun when no performance

The coffee-house is in the Guildhall undercroft, and its walls are lined with interesting theatrical posters. Teas and coffees are served right through the day, along with sandwiches, savoury snacks and cakes. There are now more salads on offer, and the scones and quiches are wholemeal. Wine by the glass.

Riverside Rooms [8/10]

The Fermoy Centre, 27 King Street
TEL Kings Lynn (0553) 773134

Open noon to 2, 7 to 10
Closed Sun

Part of the Fermoy Centre, which also houses a theatre as well as a coffee-house (see Crofters). The restaurant is an old warehouse by the River Ouse, with beams, rafters and brick walls. Quick lunches include kidney-bean casserole with saffron rice, fisherman's pie, or Swiss omelette (with cheese, onion and potato) for under £2.50. Otherwise there are more expensive steaks, and dishes such as pork medallions with mustard sauce. Suppers are available when plays are running (minimum charge £3.50). House wine by the glass or litre.

LAXFIELD Suffolk   map 5

NEW ENTRY   # Kings Head [6/10]

TEL Ubbeston (098 683) 395

Open for food noon to 2, 7 to 9.45 &
Closed Mon (exc bank hols)

Known as the Low House, this Tudor pub is down behind the village church. Nothing has changed in the last two hundred years. There's no bar and no real counter: casks are kept in the back room. If you want to be served, bang your glass on the table and the landlord appears with a tray. The banging of glasses merges with the clatter of dominoes. Kippers have been a long-standing tradition here for many years, but the menu also has fresh fish, home-made game pie in season, and steamed puddings in winter. There are a few spicy items, such as gazpacho and enchiladas, but no scampi and no chips. Vegetables are fresh; goats' cheese and yoghurt are home made. Adnams beers and Suffolk cider are mulled in winter. Outside is a garden with a bowling green and a pets' corner.

LEIGH-ON-SEA Essex   map 3

Osborne Bros [5/10]

Billet Wharf, High Street
TEL Southend-on-Sea (0702) 77233

Open 10 to 6 Mon to Fri; 8 to 8 Sat and Sun (6 Oct to Easter)
Closed Weekdays Oct to Easter

Osborne Bros are rated as the best purveyors of cockles in Leigh-on-Sea. Their shop and stall is on the High Street overlooking the front, which is lined with more huts and stalls selling shellfish. As well as saucers of freshly boiled cockles, there are whelks, shrimps, jellied eels and prawns to have with a cup of tea. Some stalls specialise in crabs to take home. Unlicensed.

Simply Blues [6/10]

948 London Road
TEL Southend-on-Sea (0702) 712888

Open 6 to 11.15 &
Closed Christmas Day to 27 Dec

Lively, American-style restaurant with food from north and south of the border. Chowder, one-hundred per cent beefburgers, steaks, and sundaes are supplemented by tortillas, chilli, and nachos. Small menu for children.

LETHERINGSETT
Norfolk   map 8

King's Head [6/10]

TEL Holt (026 371) 2691

Open for food noon to 2, 6 (7 Sun) to 9.30 (9 Mon to Wed) & (also WC)

The garden leading down to a stream is one of the main attractions of this friendly old-fashioned pub, and there is now a barbecue at Sunday lunch-time (weather permitting). Stay with the home-made items on the simple bar menu: home-cooked ham, Cornish pasties, steak and kidney pie, and daily specials. There are also sandwiches, steaks, and salads (including local crab in season). Greene King and Tolly Cobbold beers on draught.

LINCOLN Lincolnshire   map 8

NEW ENTRY   # Browns Pie Shop [7/10]

33 Steep Hill
TEL Lincoln (0522) 27330

Open noon to 12.30, 6 to 10 (11.30 Fri and Sat)
Closed Mon D; Christmas Day to 1 Jan

Once famous as a guest-house frequented by Lawrence of Arabia, this sixteenth-century beamed building close to the cathedral is now a restaurant serving wholesome British food. The food centres on pies – steak and kidney, chicken and chestnut, pork, plum and celery. Most come with magnificently risen puff-pastry tops. There are big pies for grown-ups, little ones for children. Starters include a smooth chicken liver pâté, and to finish there are old-fashioned puds such as bread-and-butter pudding, treacle tart, and apple pie with custard. Morning coffee and afternoon teas in summer. Everards Bitter or wine to drink.

Crust [6/10]

46 Broadgate
TEL Lincoln (0522) 790436

Open 10.30 (noon Sun) to 2, 7 to 10 (11.15 Fri and Sat)
Closed Mon; Sun D

This old-fashioned restaurant, on the Roman road near the cathedral, attracts crowds of tourists and visitors. The food is as traditional as the beamed dining-room, and set lunches are excellent value. Cheapest of all is the £2.45 deal – which pays for home-made beef and vegetable broth, then poached haddock in cider sauce, grilled pork cutlet with fried onions, or braised chicken in mushroom sauce, with fruit pie or apple fritters to finish. Steaks and other evening meals are more expensive. The restaurant offers a booking service and late dinner for theatre- and cinema-goers.

Harvey's Cathedral Restaurant [7/10]

1 Exchequer Gate, Castle Square
TEL Lincoln (0522) 21886

Open noon to 2, 7 to 10
Closed Christmas Day D, Boxing Day and 1 Jan L

The wine's the thing at this big smart restaurant at the top of Steep Hill. Visitors to the nearby cathedral also call in for the special set lunch, which is excellent value at £4.95 for three courses. Salmon and cucumber soup or Brie tart might be followed by beef and Guinness pie, lamb curry, or stuffed marrow with provençale sauce. Sweets range from apple and raspberry meringue to chocolate nut sundae. A 'pay as you drink' policy means that you are only charged for what you actually consume. Lunches and dinners from the à la carte menus are more expensive.

Taj Mahal [6/10]

445–446 High Street
TEL Lincoln (0522) 21778

Open noon to 2, 5.30 to 12 ﹠ (also wc)
Closed Christmas Day

A popular town curry house with comfortable décor and a menu that does not stray far from chicken tikka, rogan josh and prawn dhansak. Vegetable thali is £6.95 for samosa, mushroom bhaji, vegetable curry, cauliflower bhaji, pilau rice, nan and poppadum. Other set meals begin at about £8, and there's a cheap

three-course business lunch for £2.95. Drink lager.

Wig & Mitre [7/10]

29 Steep Hill
TEL Lincoln (0522) 35190

Open for food 8am to midnight ﹠ (also wc)
Closed Christmas Day

Michael and Valerie Hope transformed this derelict antique shop in a fine fourteenth-century building into a pub that operates like a brasserie. It is open for food sixteen hours a day, right through the year. Prices in the downstairs bar are reasonable, and dishes are enterprising: goats' cheese on toast, avocado provençale with pasta, pork and ginger casserole, nectarine in plum sauce. Good fresh vegetables. Wine is the main attraction for drinkers, but there's also real ale on handpump.

LONG MELFORD Suffolk   map 5

NEW ENTRY **Black Lion Hotel** [8/10]

TEL Sudbury (0787) 312356

Open 12.30 to 2 (2.30 Sun), 7 to 9.30 (9 in winter)
Closed Mon and Sun D in winter

Luke and Amelia Brady have turned a rather down-at-heel pub into a country-style restaurant with rooms. There are plenty of interesting bargains for cheap eaters. The good-value lunch menu offers two courses for under £7: perhaps endive salad with crispy bacon, then grilled pork cutlet with madeira and peppercorn sauce plus fresh vegetables. Three-course Sunday lunch is £7. There are also light snacks, such as duck fillet salad with walnuts, smoked sprats with sweet dill sauce, or BLT sandwiches. House wines are £4.60 a bottle.

LOUGHTON Essex   map 5

Gardeners Arms [6/10]

103 York Hill
TEL 01-508 1655

Open for food 11 to 2.30
Closed Sun; bank hols

Well placed for good walks on the edge of Epping Forest. The food is hearty and substantial: steak, kidney and mushroom pie, lamb cutlets with tarragon and red wine sauce, seafood pancakes with brandy and mustard sauce. Salads come with home-cooked meats. Thick steak sandwiches for meat eaters; raw vegetables with mustard and mayonnaise dip for vegetarians. No children.

LOUTH Lincolnshire   map 8

Mr Chips [6/10]

17–21 Aswell Street
TEL Louth (0507) 603756

Open 11 to 11 &␣ (also WC)
Closed Sun

Three generations on, the Hagan family is still in residence at this fish and chip restaurant. Fresh fish in a light batter with decent real chips is the star of the show and the reason why people come here. There are cut-price meals for children. Vegetarian dishes are a new feature, and wine is available at 60p a glass.

MALDON Essex   map 5

Maldon Coffee Shop [6/10]

63 High Street
TEL Maldon (0621) 57146

Open 10 to 5 &␣ (also WC)
Closed Sun; bank hols

The best value in Maldon. This old-fashioned coffee-shop in a quiet alley off the high street serves interesting lunches along the lines of cream of spinach soup, celery and blue cheese quiche, or lasagne, then treacle tart or home-made ice-cream. Through the day there are toasted teacakes, scones and all kinds of cakes. Tables in the courtyard. Good coffee; wine by the glass.

Wheelers [7/10]

13 High Street
TEL Maldon (0621) 53647

Open 11.30 to 1.45, 6 to 9.30 &␣ (also WC)
Closed Sun and Mon

A long-established family business serving first-rate fish and chips. Portions are big and the choice can range from fresh cod and haddock to skate and Dover sole. Soups are home made and there are some good-looking sweets on the trolley, such as lemon meringue pie and Bakewell tart. Eat in the sixteenth-century beamed dining-room or take away.

MARCH Cambridgeshire   map 5

Acre [7/10]

TEL March (0354) 57116

Open for food 12.30 to 2.30 (4 Wed) &␣ (also WC)
Closed Sun

Mrs Charnock's bar lunches are as popular as ever, and regulars often phone in their orders to be sure of a meal. Favourites are the roasts, the pies, liver and bacon, sausage plait, and moussaka. Bread is good wholemeal and there's Greene King beer on draught.

NEWMARKET Suffolk   map 5

Jane's Wine Bar [7/10]

29 High Street
TEL Newmarket (0638) 668031

Open 10 to 4.30
Closed Sun; bank hols

This brightly decorated modern wine bar below an upmarket dress shop is a handy venue for a decent cheap lunch when shopping. Everything is made on the premises, from the breads, cakes, and pastries to the mayonnaise and vinaigrette. A bowl of soup with a hunk of bread is a bargain for just over £1, otherwise the menu has salads, omelettes, quiches, and daily specials such as spaghetti milanese. Filled jacket potatoes are served in winter. Wine by the glass.

Pablo's Cantina [5/10]

18 St Mary's Square
TEL Newmarket (0638) 660367

Open noon to 2, 5 to 10
Closed Mon; Sun L

Geoffrey Connelly has taken over from Paul Lawrence, but little else has changed at this little take-away. It still serves authentic dishes and tries to prove there's more to Mexican food than 'beans and hot sauce'. The menu has tacos, tostadas, burritos and chimichangas as well as chilli soup, enchiladas and flautas, plus burgers and ribs from north of the border. More vegetarian dishes are being introduced. Unlicensed.

NEWTON Cambridgeshire map 5

Queen's Head [6/10]

TEL Cambridge (0223) 870436

Open for food 11.30 to 2.30, 6 to 11 (noon to 2, 7 to 10.30 Sun)
Closed Christmas Day

Originally three nineteenth-century thatched cottages, this low-ceilinged country pub still has a traditional atmosphere. Bar food is an unpretentious mix of home-made soup, ploughman's, baked potatoes, and all kinds of sandwiches (including the Humphrey, filled with banana). In the evening and for Sunday lunch there are plates of cold roast beef, pâté, ham, and cheeses. Adnams beers. Games room for children.

NEWTON Lincolnshire map 8

Red Lion [6/10]

TEL Folkingham (052 97) 256

Open for food 11 to 2.30, 6 to 10 & (also wc)
Closed Sun D; Mon

John Power has been running this civilised village pub for twenty years. The cold carvery is still a major attraction, with its fresh salmon, pies, roasts and Lincolnshire specialities, such as stuffed chine and spicy sausages. Help yourself to as much salad as you want. Pâté and puddings are home made. Batemans beer on draught. The pub has its own squash courts as well as a patio garden. Children welcome up to 8.30pm.

NORTH ELMHAM Norfolk map 8

| NEW ENTRY | King's Head [6/10] |

Holt Road
TEL Elmham (036 281) 8856

Open for food 11 to 2.30, 7 to 9.30 & (also wc)

A large nineteenth-century coaching-inn on the main crossroads of this mid-Norfolk village. A set menu with dishes of the day lifts the food above the level of average pub grub: Cromer crab salad, mushrooms in garlic butter, pigeon and bacon with fresh vegetables, bread-and-butter pudding. Drinks include the full range of wines from the nearby Hicks & Don vineyard. More expensive restaurant meals.

NORWICH Norfolk map 8

| NEW ENTRY | Adriano's Trattoria [7/10] |

68 London Street
TEL Norwich (0603) 622967

Open 12 to 2.30, 6 to 11 &
Closed Christmas Day and Boxing Day

A good choice for authentic Italian cooking in the centre of Norwich. The décor is pure trattoria, with candles on the tables and posters on the walls. Best bets for a decent meal in single figures are the pasta dishes such as cannelloni and lasagne. There are also good salads such as apple, celery and walnut or tomato, and the cappuccino is first-rate.

Bombay [6/10]

9–11 Magdalen Street
TEL Norwich (0603) 666618/666874

Open noon to 3, 6 to midnight &

Oak-beamed ceilings are an unusual feature of this above-average Indian restaurant. Prices are reasonable and the menu includes specialities such as karahi meat, chicken jalfrezi and lamb pasanda, as well as tandooris, birianis, and dhansaks. Vegetarian set meals are £6 a head. Drink Kingfisher beer. There are branches at 43 Timber Hill and 15 Prince of Wales Road, Norwich, and at 1 Exchange Square, Beccles, Suffolk.

| NEW ENTRY | Brasserie l'Abri [8/10] |

Upper St Giles Street
TEL Norwich (0603) 633522

Open 8am to 1am &
Closed bank hols; 1 week Dec

Norwich needed a place like this – a stylish, seventeen-hours-a-day brasserie serving excellent food in a setting of cane chairs and potted plants. The décor feels French and the music is often as jolly as a fairground. Best bets from the menu are chilled cucumber and yoghurt soup, spinach salad with bacon, and the massive filled crêpes. There's a good cheeseboard, and for breakfast there are hot flaky croissants, plus the newspapers to read.

Mange-Tout [7/10]

24 White Lion Street
TEL Norwich (0603) 617879

Open 8 to 10.30 (10.30 to 4.30 Sun)

The style is slightly art deco and there are interesting photographs on the walls of Norwich's answer to a genuine French bistro. Snacks and hot and cold food are served right through the day. As well as hot French bread and croissants with fillings, there's charcuterie, a choice of salads and cheeses, plus various steaks. Specials of the day might range from beef ragout or kidneys Turbigo to a vegetarian dish. Interesting aperitifs, good house wine and decent coffee.

Morello's [7/10]

Orford Yard, Red Lion Street
TEL Norwich (0603) 616106

Open 9 to 5.30, 7 to 10 &
Closed Sun; Mon D to Wed D

New owners have made lots of changes to this restaurant just out of the city centre. Light meals are served through the day and lunches have a vegetarian bias, with dishes such as meatless lasagne, stuffed tomatoes, and stuffed peppers as well as chilli, and herb chicken with salad. Three evenings a week there are dinners with an Italian flavour: cheapest bets are the interesting pasta dishes; tagliatelle Bearzot comes with pork, paprika, peppers, tomatoes and sour cream. Wine by the glass.

 Sir Garnet Wolseley [6/10]

36 Market Place
TEL Norwich (0603) 615892

Open for food 10.30 to 2.30, 5.30 to 11
Closed Sun D

A fine historic pub, formerly two buildings, on the steep slope of the market. The downstairs bar gets packed with market workers and the ceiling is festooned with Norwich City football programmes. Upstairs is quieter, with busts of Sir Garnet and General Gordon and splendid views over the market. Decent pub lunches are Norfolk ham salad, bangers and mash with onions, plus local seafood, such as dressed Cromer crab or a fisherman's platter with fresh mackerel. Courage Directors and Best on handpump; wine by the glass.

Skippers [7/10]

18 Bedford Street
TEL Norwich (0603) 622836

Open noon to 3, 5.30 to midnight
Closed Sun; Christmas Day and Boxing Day; bank hols

Diane Skipper does the cooking in this cheerful, dimly lit restaurant. There are good cheap snacks and light meals such as macaroni cheese, and Black Forest ham salad. More substantial dishes come from around the globe: coq au vin; Moroccan lamb stew with oranges; steak and kidney pie. Long, varied wine list.

Zaks Family Diner [6/10]

Gurney Road, Mousehold Heath
TEL Norwich (0603) 47016

Open noon to 11.15
Closed Christmas Day and Boxing Day

An American family diner set in wooded parkland close to the centre of Norwich. The menu is identical to the original branch in Great Yarmouth (see entry): steaks, burgers, salads and so on.

ORFORD Suffolk   map 5

Butley-Orford Oysterage [8/10]

Market Hill
TEL Orford (0394) 450277

Open noon to 2.15, 6 to 8.30 & (also wc)
Closed Jan; 2 weeks Feb

The Pinneys' archetypal local-food café is a showcase for their enterprise as oyster-growers and fish-curers. The set-up couldn't be simpler: fish is from their own boats, oysters are grown in Butley Creek, and the smoking is done over oak using their own system. Stars of the show are the smoked fish – Irish salmon, cods' roe, eel, sprats – and the oysters themselves. Other items that require cooking – soup, pork and cockle stew, angels on horseback – don't have quite the same brilliance. Take-aways from the shop next door. Short, interesting wine list.

PAGLESHAM Essex   map 5

Plough and Sail [6/10]

TEL Canewdon (037 06) 242

Open for food noon to 2, 7 to 9.30 &
Closed Christmas Day and Boxing Day

The Paglesham oyster beds on the River Crouch date from Roman times and have recently been revived. This beamed and timbered seventeenth-century pub sells the harvest when there is an R in the month. Otherwise the menu features roll-mops, Barnsley chops, grills, and home-made cheesecake. Other good reasons for visiting this pub are the garden with its aviary and swings, the riverside walks and the old boatyards.

PETERBOROUGH
Cambridgeshire   map 5

India Gate [7/10]

9 Fitzwilliam Street
TEL Peterborough (0733) 46160

Open noon to 2.30, 6 to midnight (1am Fri and Sat) & (also WC)

This popular Indian restaurant offers good value and quality in an area not blessed with many decent cheap eating places. There are no surprises on the menu, which has the standard range of tandooris and North Indian curries, from chicken dhansak to methi gosht. Specialities include chicken chat masala (grilled fillet of chicken cooked with cream and nuts). Set dinner for two is £8.25 a head. The 'Call a Curry' service means that meals can be delivered to the door.

ROMFORD Essex   map 3

Moon House [7/10]

64 Victoria Road
TEL Romford (0708) 44303

Open noon to 2, 5 (6 Sun and bank hols) to midnight (12.45 Fri and Sat) & (also WC)
Closed Sun L; bank hols L

A little pink Chinese restaurant that serves old favourites, such as spare ribs in a sweet dark-red sauce and beef chow-mein, as well as more interesting items, for instance chicken with cashew nuts, and bean curd with mixed meats. Take-aways.

SAFFRON WALDEN Essex   map 5

Eight Bells [7/10]

Bridge Street
TEL Saffron Walden (0799) 22790/26237

Open for food noon to 2 (1.45 Sun), 6.30 (7 Sun) to 9.30 (10 Sat) &
Closed Christmas Day and Boxing Day

The competition for cheap eating in Saffron Walden is fierce, but this traditional pub-cum-restaurant on the edge of the town is very useful for good-value lunches or evening meals. The long bar menu has its share of ploughman's, pizzas and lasagne, but look for the daily specials, such as pan-fried herring roes in garlic butter, baked red mullet with orange, or charcoal-grilled lamb cutlets with fresh mint sauce. Gilded chicken is stuffed with prawns and appropriately coated in saffron sauce. Home-made sweets. Family room.

Old Hoops [7/10]

15 King Street
TEL Saffron Walden (0799) 22813

Open noon to 2.30, 7 to 10
Closed Sun and Mon

The upstairs dining-room of this three-hundred-year-old pub has the mood of a casual bistro, with posters and old metal advertising signs on the dark-green walls. Lunch is particularly good value, with dishes such as chicken and sorrel soup, lamb's liver with onion sauce, roast pork with cider and apples, and steamed treacle pudding. Dinners are more expensive and can move into the fanciful realms of breast of chicken with Bayonne ham and bananas.

Staircase Cellar [6/10]

21 High Street
TEL Saffron Walden (0799) 22226

Open 11 to 2

The beamed cellar beneath the Staircase Restaurant is popular for morning coffee and lunches and does a roaring trade with pre-booked parties. Star attractions are the pizzas – made from scratch and baked to order. Otherwise there are pasta dishes, four-egg omelettes, salads and jacket potatoes. More substantial offerings include grilled sirloin steak and wiener Schnitzel. Sorbets, ice-creams or blackcurrant cheesecake to finish.

Sue Eaton [5/10]

Lime Tree House, King Street
TEL Saffron Walden (0799) 22695

Open 9 to 5
Closed Sun; bank hols

The cafeteria is in the basement of the health and beauty clinic, so the food is predictably healthy, too. The bias is towards vegetarian and wholefood dishes and everything is home made, from soups, pâté, lasagne, crêpes and quiche, to all kinds of cakes and pastries. Meals are served in the cobbled courtyard when the weather allows.

SCOLE Norfolk map 5

Scole Inn [6/10]

TEL Diss (0379) 740481

Open for food noon to 2.30, 6 to 10 ♿ (also wc)

This striking seventeenth-century gabled mansion is one of the few pubs with a Grade I preservation listing, and is one of the most impressive hostelries in the region. Bar food is a choice of plough-man's, home-made pâtés (including Stilton, celery and port), and savouries such as mushrooms in garlic butter or chicken livers in herb butter. Also there's a big choice of salads and sandwiches, plus blackboard specials ranging from smoked haddock in cheese sauce to duck and lamb pie. More expensive restaurant. Adnams and Greene King beers on draught.

SCOTTER Lincolnshire map 8

Gamekeeper Inn [6/10]

40 High Street
TEL Scunthorpe (0724) 762035

Open for food 11 to 2.30, 7 to 10.30 ♿
Closed Christmas Day

The speciality here is a jumbo haddock which can be fried in batter, grilled, or poached in milk and butter, and served with chips or salad. Savoury and sweet pies are baked each day on the premises, and other dishes range from lasagne and quiche to liver and bacon. The menu of the day is exceptional value at £2.10 for a main course and either soup or sweet.

SNAPE Suffolk map 5

Golden Key [7/10]

Priory Road
TEL Snape (072 888) 510

Open for food noon to 2 (1.30 Sun), 6.30 (7 Sun) to 9
Closed Christmas Day

On the by-road from Snape to Aldeburgh, this genteel country pub serves some of the best bar food in the area. The décor is all scrubbed pine tables and large open fires, and the menu is home cooking: soups, pâtés, casseroles, roasts. There are daily specials, such as cottage pie, as well as steaks and lobster for those who want to splash out. Drink Adnams beer or Suffolk cider from James White's orchard.

SOHAM Cambridgeshire map 5

No 38 [6/10]

38 High Street
TEL Ely (0353) 721055

Open 9.30 to 5 (2 Wed, noon on Sat) ♿
Closed Sun; Christmas Day

Everything is home made in this small two-roomed café. Lunches are good value for bacon and mushroom or tomato soup before braised beef and vegetables, liver and bacon casserole, or chicken and vegetable pie. Sweets are old favourites, such as apricot and apple charlotte. Biscuits, cakes and scones come with morning coffee or afternoon tea. Wine is 80p a glass.

SOUTHEND-ON-SEA Essex   map 3

Pearl Dragon [7/10]

18 Eastern Esplanade
TEL Southend-on-Sea (0702) 613468

Open 12.30 to 11 (noon to 11 Sun) &

A well-established Cantonese restaurant right on the seafront. Outside is a gaudy neon sign and a pagoda-style awning; inside there are imitation dragons and green monsters. For an unexpected cheap seaside lunch try the dim-sum: around twenty different snacks, from stuffed bean curd rolls, beef cheung-fun or pork and king prawn dumplings, to sweet versions such as egg custard tarts, and water-chestnut paste. There is also a big choice of good value rice and noodle dishes for a filling meal. Set menus from around £8 a head.

Pipe of Port [7/10]

84 High Street
TEL Southend-on-Sea (0702) 614606

Open 11 to 2.30, 6 (7 Sat) to 11
Closed Sun; bank hols; Christmas Day and Boxing Day

An old-style basement wine bar with sawdust on the floor and a taste for traditional English wine-bar food: anchovy and Stilton toasts, smoked fish, rare roast beef with hot potatoes, and home-baked pies – such as chicken and chestnut, pork, plum and celery – as well as game or steak, kidney and mushroom. There are also salads, sandwiches and cocktail starters such as crab, corn and rice on a hunk of crusty bread. Plenty of wines and ports by the glass, and Bucks Fizz by the mug. No children.

Tomassi's [7/10]

9 High Street
TEL Southend-on-Sea (0702) 335589

Open 11.45 to 9
Closed Christmas Day and Boxing Day

The Tomassi family started making ice-cream in 1912, and their old premises (opened in the 1930s) was one of Southend's best-loved institutions. They have recently moved to a new site across the road and have expanded. The restaurant has English oak-clad walls, hand-made Italian tiles in the servery and rose marble in the entrance. As well as the famous ice-creams the menu offers home-made pies, Italian specialities and fresh fish.

Truffles [6/10]

159 Eastern Esplanade
TEL Southend-on-Sea (0702) 62299

Open 6 to midnight
Closed Sun

Food comes from north and south of the border in this lively American-style diner. From the north come barbecued ribs, steaks, and crispy potato skins; from the south, guacamole, tacos, burritos, and enchiladas. Burgers get all kinds of international toppings from Danish (with blue cheese) to Chinatown (with sweet-and-sour sauce). Cocktails, juices and milk shakes to drink. The owners are planning to open a wine bar in the basement.

SOUTHWOLD Suffolk   map 5

Crown [9/10]

90 High Street
TEL Southwold (0502) 722275

Open 10.30 to 9.45

Over the past two years the Crown has put Southwold back on the map. Its success story isn't just about the excellent modern restaurant, or the brilliant wines, or even the Sunday brunch. The whole package impresses because it proves that quality and value for money can go hand in hand. The place functions rather like an all-day, all-year country brasserie, although main meals are geared to the traditional times. Lunch and evening bar food show the style: warm salad of beef with sesame and soya, fillet of pork with tarragon and apples, duck breast with leeks and madeira, and above all superb fresh fish, ranging from roast monkfish with pink peppercorns to steamed cod with basil and tomato concasse. To finish there are English cheeses or sweets, such as ginger ice-cream. During the morning there are croissants with strong coffee, in the afternoon soup and savouries share the bill with cakes and scones.

NEW ENTRY | **Minivers** [7/10]

76 High Street
TEL Southwold (0502) 722537

Open 8 to 8 Jul to Oct; 10 to 6 Nov to June &
(also WC)
Closed 2 weeks Nov; 1 week at Christmas

Ruth Boyce used to cook at Mary's in Walberswick, and has brought her talents across the Blyth estuary to Southwold. The cottage restaurant has a natural history theme and little arrangements of dried flowers on the tables. Local produce is used for a simple menu that includes first-rate fresh fish with chips, curries with side dishes and poppadums, steak and kidney pudding, and vegetarian specialities, such as pasta and vegetable bake. Scones and cakes for afternoon tea, kippers, sausage and mash or poached eggs for high tea. Beer or wine by the glass.

Squiers [6/10]

71 High Street
TEL Southwold (0502) 723354

Open 9 to 5.15 &
Closed Tue

The best of Southwold's quota of tea-shops. The tables are at the back of a shop selling sweets, local mustards and all kinds of gastronomic souvenirs. The place is open all day, but highlights are the huge cooked breakfasts and lunches, which might feature home-made asparagus soup, fish pie with fresh vegetables, and a sweet. During the summer there are cream teas

with local strawberries or raspberries. Take-away sandwiches.

SPILSBY Lincolnshire   map 8

Buttercross [9/10]

18 Lower Market
TEL Spilsby (0790) 53147

Open 10 to 4.30, plus 7.30 to 10.30 Fri and Sat
Closed Tue and Sun; bank hols; Christmas week

Tim and Janette Boskett make everything from the wholegrain bread to the yoghurt and ice-cream in their bistro in a Georgian building. They buy organic fruit and vegetables and are developing their menus in line with current healthy eating trends. During the day they serve snacks – soup, sandwiches and scones, as well as cakes – to go with a range of teas and coffees. At lunch-time the main interest is now with the substantial blackboard specials, which can take in anything from potato and onion pancakes with sweet-and-sour sauce, ratatouille, and grilled trout with hazelnuts and orange, to stew and dumplings or hot game pie. There are special sweets too, such as bread-and-butter pudding or raspberry roulade. Young children are offered 90p-worth of home-cooked mince with vegetables. More expensive evening meals on Friday and Saturday.

STAMFORD Lincolnshire   map 8

George [8/10]

71 St Martin's
TEL Stamford (0780) 55171

Open for food noon to 2.30, 6.30 to 11 & (also WC)

There are some nine hundred years of history behind the doors of this famous coaching-inn. The spirit of hospitality and good food lives on, and today's visitors can sample the huge spread of cold joints and salads laid out in the garden lounge. As well as excellent roast beef and cold salmon, there are vegetarian dishes such as fruit and vegetable kebab or ravioli stuffed with spinach and ricotta cheese. For a larger outlay the menu also has steaks and lobster. Summer barbecues are held in the flower-filled courtyard. As well as decent beer there are some well-chosen Italian wines.

STOW BARDOLPH Norfolk   map 8

Hare Arms [6/10]

TEL Downham Market (0366) 382229

Open for food noon to 2, 7 to 10
Closed Sun; Christmas Day and Boxing Day

Bar food is now served at lunch-time and in the evening in this popular village pub. Seasonal fish and game find their way onto the menu, which can take in anything from Stilton and bacon soup with croûtons to coffee gateau and profiteroles. In between there might be chicken curry, cold duck and apricot pie, or pheasant and red wine pie. More expensive restaurant meals. Greene King beers on draught. No children.

UFFORD Cambridgeshire   map 5

Old White Hart [6/10]

TEL Stamford (0780) 740250

Open for food noon to 2, 6 to 8 ♭
Closed Sun and Mon; a few days at Christmas

New landlord Chris Hooton has taken over this well-kept stone inn with terraced gardens and a sunken patio for sunny days, and a big log fire in winter. The style of the food is robust home cooking: steak and mushroom pie, big rib steaks with salad and chips, spotted dick, and treacle roly-poly with custard. There are plans for barbecues in the garden on Thursday, Friday and Saturday nights. Real ale from Homes of Nottingham.

WALBERSWICK Suffolk   map 5

Potter's Wheel [7/10]

Village Green
TEL Southwold (0502) 724468

Open noon to 2, 7.30 to 9, Easter to Oct ♭
Closed Nov to April/Easter

Lesley Scott's restaurant is part of a gallery and shop selling pottery and paintings. Many ingredients are home grown or locally produced and they are used for simple family lunches with a vegetarian bias: gougère with ratatouille, nut and pea croquettes with blue cheese sauce, and pear cheesecake have all been excellent. Dinners are more elegant but the bill can still be around £10 for the likes of cucumber soup, jugged hare, and almond ice-cream. Local cider from James White as well as a limited range of wines.

WALTHAM ABBEY Essex   map 5

Shuhag Tandoori [6/10]

16 Highbridge Street
TEL Lea Valley (0992) 711436

Open noon to 3, 6 to 11.30 (midnight Fri and Sat) ♭

Shuhag means hospitality and the service lives up to the name in this reliable curry house. The cooking is North Indian, with the emphasis on tandooris and curries. Onion bhajias, vegetable curry, and chicken tikka have all been good.

WELLS-NEXT-THE-SEA
Norfolk   map 8

Crown Hotel [6/10]

The Buttlands
TEL Fakenham (0328) 710209

Open for food noon to 2, 7.30 to 9.30 ♭
Closed Sun D

The best choice for pub food in Wells, and a handy alternative to the Moorings (see entry). Bar lunches are straightforward but there are plenty of home-made dishes, from wholesome soup and chicken liver pâté to Norfolk pasties, prawn and tomato gougère, and good grills. Sandwiches and salads include crab in season. Marstons beers. More expensive restaurant meals.

Moorings [9/10]

6 Freeman Street
TEL Fakenham (0328) 710949

Open 12.30 to 2, 7.30 on ♭ (also WC)
Closed Wed; Tue D; Thur L; Christmas Eve to Boxing Day; first 3 weeks June; first 3 weeks Nov

Carla and Bernard Phillips have transformed this hundred and fifty-year-old building by the quay into a remarkable restaurant dedicated to local food. Fish is from the Wells boats, Norfolk black turkeys and venison come from Holkham Park, garlic sausages (for the cassoulet) and hams from a butcher in Dersingham, goats' cheese from a farm in Mattishall. Fungi, berries and marsh samphire are from the wild. This translates into an adventurous, eclectic menu that might include clam chowder, terrine of sea bass, or gratin of sea trout and crab alongside venison with Marsala, meatballs with mushroom sauce, or chicken with mustard and wine sauce. There are always vegetarian dishes, such as eggs and mushrooms in Brie sauce. Finish with unpasteurised English cheeses, locally made sorbets or fresh fruit with fromage blanc. Meals are excellent value: a main course plus one other dish at lunch is £6; three courses at dinner is £9.50. House wines are £4.50 a bottle.

WESTLETON Suffolk   map 5

Crown [6/10]

TEL Westleton (072 873) 273/239

Open for food noon to 2.15 ᗧ (also wc)
Closed Christmas Day, Boxing Day

This solid red-brick pub is a useful watering hole for people trekking round Minsmere bird reserve. Fresh fish is the star of the bar menu: Richard Price gets his supplies from the boats in Dunwich and Aldeburgh and travels to Cromer for crabs. In the bar the catch is usually fried or poached (it receives more elaborate treatment in the separate restaurant). Otherwise there are grills, pies, and salads, plus treacle pudding to finish. The children's menu plays safe with sausages, burgers, and ice-cream. Suffolk beers from Adnams and Greene King.

WEST MERSEA Essex   map 5

Mussett's Oyster Bar [6/10]

Coast Road
TEL West Mersea (0206) 382871

Open 9.30 to dusk (unless party booked) ᗧ

Marie Mussett – one of Britain's few female oyster merchants – has been joined by her son Redver and his wife in this classic seafood bar on the coast road. Oysters are the speciality but visitors can expect anything from smoked salmon and prawns to mackerel. The mixed seafood platter is popular, and it can be followed by melon in ginger wine or fresh fruit with local Jersey cream. From 8pm there are candle-lit dinners for parties up to twelve people. The Mussetts prefer customers for these to ring at least two hours in advance (or a full day, if they fancy lobster), as orders are cooked individually. Unlicensed, but bring your own wine if you have made a booking.

Willow Lodge [6/10]

108 Coast Road
TEL Colchester (0206) 383568

Open 12.30 to 2.30, 7 to 10.30 ᗧ (also wc)
Closed Mon (exc bank hols); Tue D

Built in 1840 as a sailmaker's, this pink, Tudor-style restaurant still maintains its maritime connections. The dining-room overlooks the sea, and the menu is biased towards local oysters and other seafood. The menu takes in everything from lobster soup with French bread to plaice and chips with tartare sauce.

WINTERTON-ON-SEA
Norfolk   map 8

Fisherman's Return [6/10]

The Lane
TEL Winterton-on-Sea (049 376) 305

Open for food 11.30 to 2 (noon to 1.30 Sun), 6.30 (7 in winter) to 9.30 ᗧ
Closed Christmas Day and Boxing Day

A classic Norfolk brick and flint pub not far from the dunes and the beach. It pays to stay with the home-made items on the menu: chilli con carne with pitta bread, fish pie, cottage pie, and the fisherman's omelette filled with bacon, onions and mushrooms. There are burgers, steaks, and salads, plus fruit crumble to finish. In winter, bowls of soup are served by the roaring fire. The back bar opens out onto the terrace and garden. Real ales include Ruddles and Steward and Patteson.

WITHAM Essex   map 5

Crofters [6/10]

25 Maldon Road
TEL Witham (0376) 511068

Open noon to 2, 7 to 10
Closed Sun D and Mon D

A good-value wine bar where chicken
Diane and broccoli au gratin rub shoulders
with liver pâté, quiche, and beef curry.
Steaks are cooked as requested: if you
want your fillet 'blue', that's the way it
comes. A starter and a sweet would make a
light meal for under £3. On Friday and
Saturday nights the new Garden
Restaurant offers a wider choice, but
prices are still reasonable. The wine list
has some decent drinking for around £7 a
bottle.

WIVENHOE Essex   map 5

Black Buoy [6/10]

Black Buoy Hill
TEL Wivenhoe (020 622) 2425

Open for food noon to 2, 7 to 10 & (also WC)
Closed Sun

Superb jacket potatoes are the star
attraction in this village pub a short walk
from the River Colne. They come with a
choice of ten fillings: from tuna and green
peppers in parsley sauce to chopped bacon,
melted cheese and tomato. Otherwise
there are good home-made soups flavoured
with fresh herbs from the garden, and
home-cooked specials such as braised
lamb cutlets or chicken Kiev. Tolly
Cobbold beers. No children.

WOODBRIDGE Suffolk   map 5

NEW ENTRY | Captain's Table [6/10]

3 Quay Street
TEL Woodbridge (039 43) 3145

Open noon to 2, 6.30 to 9.30 (10 Sat) &
Closed Mon; Sun autumn to spring; last week
Jan, first week Feb

In Tudor times this was a dairy farmhouse.
Later it became a pub, and it is now a
seafood restaurant, just up from the quay.
Bar snacks offer a chance to sample oysters
from Butley Creek and Pinney's smoked
salmon from Orford (see entry). there is
also good home-made taramosalata,
avocado and crispy bacon salad, plus
specialities such as kipper fillets cooked in
cream with shallots and red peppers.
Portions can sometimes seem rather
meagre. More expensive restaurant. To
drink there's Aspall cider, herb teas and a
choice of English wines.

NEW ENTRY | Royal Bengal [7/10]

4–6 Quay Street
TEL Woodbridge (039 43) 7983

Open noon to 3, 6 to 11
Closed Christmas Day

From the outside, this white-painted
building doesn't look much like an Indian
restaurant, but inside it has all the classic
curry-house trappings: flock wallpaper,
tassled curtains, wall-hangings of tigers
and waiters in cavalry-style tunics. The
menu is old-fashioned North Indian, with
tandooris, curries such as chicken dhansak
and lamb tikka masala, and more than a
nod to English and continental extras. Set
menus from £5.95. Drink lager. Useful in
the area.

Wine Bar [9/10]

17 Thoroughfare
TEL Woodbridge (039 43) 2557

Open noon to 2, 7 to 10
Closed Sun and Mon

Sally O'Gorman works minor miracles in
the tiny kitchen of this colourful wine bar
above an excellent provisions shop. She
changes her menu every week, cooks to
order, and offers great value for money.
The blackboard is full of surprises and
interesting ideas: walnut roulade filled
with mustard hollandaise, pork and mint
timbale with greengage compote, chicken
breast stuffed with apple and leek, turbot
with horseradish and crème fraîche sauce.
To finish there are fruit tarts and unusual
ice-creams made pretty with sweet herbs
and flowers from the garden. The
handwritten wine list has some decent
drinking for around £6 a bottle. No
children.

WRENTHAM Suffolk   map 5

Quiggins [7/10]

2 High Street
TEL Wrentham (050 275) 397

Open 10.30 to 2, 7 to 10 & (also WC)
Closed Sun, Mon; first 2 weeks Jan

A highly popular village restaurant with pastel colour schemes, long drapes and floor-length tablecloths. Light lunches feature one of the house specialities, Chicken Jane (a recipe well known to regulars). Dinners include the bestselling beef and oyster pie with fresh vegetables, as well as the renowned home-made chocolate fudge ice-cream. Other good dishes have included smoked mackerel mousse and spicy chicken tartlet. Useful wine list.

YOXFORD Suffolk   map 5

Eliza Acton [7/10]

Old High Road
TEL Yoxford (072 877) 637

Open 10 to 9.30 &
Closed 2 weeks Jan; few days Nov

Elizabeth Acton's restaurant feels like home, with its hand-embroidered tablecloths and vases of wild and garden flowers. Her honest, home-cooked food is exceptional value: three courses can be had for around a fiver. The style is cold cream of cucumber and mint soup, chicken with onions and cinnamon, Moroccan pork tajine. There are always fish and vegetarian dishes, plus plenty of fresh vegetables, such as parsnip purée or cabbage with almonds. The sweet trolley oozes whipped cream, but the lemon mousse is good. Coffee and tea are served during the day. The small wine list includes a local representative from Bruisyard St Peter.

North West

ALDERLEY EDGE Cheshire   map 7

Alderley Rose [6/10]

London Road
TEL Alderley Edge (0625) 585557

Open noon to 2, 5.30 to midnight (noon to midnight Sat and Sun) &
Closed Mon (exc bank hols); Tue L

The emphasis is on set meals at this Chinese restaurant in a small Cheshire village. The cheapest deal is £14.80 for two, which pays for chicken and sweet-corn soup, spring rolls, three main dishes, such as chicken with green peppers and black-bean sauce, plus fried rice, dessert and coffee. The full menu veers between sweet-and-sour chicken and fashionable teppenyaki sizzling steak.

ALTRINCHAM
Greater Manchester   map 7

 French [7/10]

25 The Downs
TEL 061-941 3355

Open noon to 2.30, 6 to 11.30
Closed Sat L

A converted shop in a terrace, transformed into a fashionable bistro with reproduction Regency furniture, a lot of plastic greenery and windows made from mirrored glass. There are good-value set lunches and pre-theatre meals (before 7pm) for £5.50, taking in duck pâté, venison sausages, coq au vin and tarte normande. Vegetables are skilfully cooked, salads are interesting and bread is good. Other meals are more expensive. The mainly French wine list has plenty of decent drinking for under £10 a bottle.

 Hanni's [7/10]

20 Church Street
TEL 061-941 2551

Open noon to 2, 6 (6.30 Fri and Sat) to 10.30
Closed last 2 weeks Aug

Mohamed Taraboulsi's Middle Eastern restaurant is marked by a brown canopy and smoked-glass windows. The décor is brown with gold-patterned panels; the menu is broadly based with the emphasis on kebabs and couscous, backed up by salads. The quality of the meat shows in the doner kebabs and the grilled marinated fillet of lamb. Meze starters (£3) are precisely arranged on the plate with pickled turnips and cucumbers. Carefully chosen wine, plus unusual liqueurs and brandies. Business lunch is £3.95; other meals will take the bill towards £10 a head without drinks.

Nutcracker [7/10]

43 Oxford Road
TEL 061-928 4399

Open 9am to 4.45pm (2pm Wed)
Closed Sun; bank hols

Altrincham is the headquarters of the Vegetarian Society, and this excellent café attached to a healthfood shop is decorated in muesli-coloured tones. A touch of imagination lifts the cooking above the vegetarian average. There are daily-baked stews and casseroles such as Indian vegetable pasanda, and traditional Dutch zyldyk; soups might include carrot and coriander or apple and cashew-nut; and there are also salads and quiches. Good biscuits, apricot slice and flapjacks. Unlicensed.

AMBLESIDE Cumbria   map 9

Drunken Duck Inn [6/10]

Barngates
TEL Hawkshead (096 66) 347

Open for food noon to 2 (1.30 Sun), 6.30 (7 Sun) to 9 & (also WC)
Closed Christmas Day

Named after a curious legend about a dead duck revived by beer from a broken barrel. These days the views over the fells and the good bar food are the main points of interest. Home-made pies are a feature, along with vegetarian chilli con carne, home-made pâté and hummus. Coronation chicken is a colourful assortment of meat and vegetables in curry mayonnaise spilling out of an envelope of pitta bread. Basket meals, appropriately, include duckling. Roly-poly or Cumberland rum nicky for pudding. Real ale and a good choice of malt whiskies.

Harvest Vegetarian [7/10]

Compston Road
TEL Ambleside (0966) 33151

Open 10.30 to 2.30, 5 to 8 &
Closed second week Nov to 27 Dec; Mon to
Thur New Year to Easter; Thur Easter to end
June; Thur Oct

Unpackaged, fresh home cooking succeeds
even in the plainest surroundings. The
façade may be gloomy, but the welcome is
warm and the food is well prepared.
Gillian Kelly's vegetarian restaurant takes
no short cuts, so the menu is concise and
changes each day. Look for the hot
specials, such as pasta, vegetable and
cheese bake, or sweet-and-sour aduki bean
and celery casserole. There's a hot pudding
each day (perhaps greengage crumble with
crunchy oat topping) and cold revani
(Turkish honey and almond cake) with
cream. Children may be offered cheese,
onion and millet burgers. Unlicensed, but
there are 'whisked drinks' such as orange
and pineapple with honey and egg or
rosewater and lemon with yoghurt and
honey.

Rothay Manor [8/10]

Rothay Bridge
TEL Ambleside (0966) 33605

Open 12.30 to 2, 3.30 to 5.30 & (also wc)
Closed Jan to mid-Feb

Apart from Sharrow Bay Hotel (see
Ullswater) this is the most elegant setting
for afternoon tea in the Lake District. The
Nixons' genteel Regency manor is posh
without putting on airs and graces. Tea is
laid out as a buffet: help yourself to all
manner of sandwiches, quiches, sausage
rolls, scones with home-made jam, tea-
breads, gateaux, and shortbread with
cream and fruit. There's no extra charge
for the beautiful surroundings, fine china
or courteous service. Cold buffet lunches
with soup and a sweet are around £6.
Dinners in the restaurant are a good deal
more expensive.

Sheila's Cottage [9/10]

The Slack
TEL Ambleside (0966) 33079

Open noon to 2.30, 2.30 to 5.30 &
Closed Jan

The best cottage café in this highly sought-
after tourist spot. Stewart Greaves combines local ingredients with ideas from
Switzerland, and there's no compromising
to suit the visitors. Cumberland sugar-
baked ham and home-potted Solway
shrimps rub shoulders with Gruyère
vegetable tart or a Swiss special of ham in
mushroom and sour cream sauce topped
with melted Raclette. Otherwise there
might be smoked salmon and avocado
roulade or Loch Fyne smoked trout pâté.
Sweets are the stars of the show: Viennese
Sachertorte with rum and black cherries,
raspberry and hazelnut roulade, banana
toffee tart. Excellent coffee.

Zeffirellis [7/10]

Compston Road
TEL Ambleside (0966) 33845

Open 10am to 9.45pm &

Not only a wholefood pizzeria, but a
stereophonic cinema, lounge bar, shopping
arcade and café as well. The chic, almost
Japanese décor is a weird contrast of huge
lanterns and fans with posters and photos
of film stars. The crisp pizzas come in
three sizes with a choice of six toppings,
and the menu is bulked out with garlic
mushrooms, full-flavoured lasagne packed
with aubergines and courgettes, omelettes,
and heavily laden creamy sweets. A
combined package of a cinema ticket and a
three-course dinner is £8.95. The Garden
Room Café downstairs serves coffee, light
lunches and teas.

APPLEBY Cumbria   map 9

| NEW ENTRY | ## Victorian Pantry [6/10] |

9 Bridge Street
TEL Appleby (076 83) 52593

Open 10 to 5.30 (9 Fri to Sun in summer; Fri and
Sat in winter) &
Closed Thur Oct to Mar; last 2 weeks Jan; 2nd
week June

This former grocer's shop has been transformed into a Victorian-style eating place
with high ceilings and a pine kitchen.
Through the day the range takes in home-

made soup, raised pies and quiches, plus salads, jacket potatoes and omelettes. Home-baked scones, croissants and waffles go with tea or coffee. Full evening meals feature creamy garlic mushrooms, steaks and lasagne. Wines by the glass.

ASHTON-UNDER-LYNE
Greater Manchester   map 7

Adam's Tandoori [6/10]

215 Old Street
TEL 061-330 7183

Open noon to 2.30, 6 to midnight (1am Fri and Sat, 1pm to midnight Sun) & (also wc)

Good North Indian food on the north-eastern outskirts of Manchester. The décor is functional, but the cooking is up to the mark. Tandooris are first rate – and the full mixed grill with nan or rice is more than enough for one person. Onion bhajias, moghlai lamb and chicken biriani have also been well reported.

BALLAUGH Isle of Man   map 9

Ravensdale Castle [6/10]

Ballaugh Glen
TEL Sulby (062 489) 7330

Open noon to 1.45 (12.30 and 1.30 for Sun L), 7 to 8.30 (9.30 Fri and Sat) & (also wc)
Closed Mon D; Sun D

The setting is an impressive castle built by one of Lord Nelson's captains with bounty money from the Battle of Trafalgar. The views are of the beautiful glen at the foot of Snaefell. Bar food takes in dishes such as beef Stroganoff, home-made steakburgers, and liver and bacon. Sunday lunches include a choice of roasts, grilled Dover sole, or chicken Mexican.

BASSENTHWAITE LAKE
Cumbria   map 9

Pheasant Inn [6/10]

TEL Bassenthwaite Lake (059 681) 234
5m E of Cockermouth on W bank of lake

Open for food 11am to 1.45pm (noon to 1.30 Sun) & (also wc)
Closed Christmas Day

The gardens slope down to beech woods and the interior is all warmth, comfort and antique furnishings. Bar lunches are soup and cold dishes with the emphasis on smoked fish and meats – from eel and trout to chicken. There are also potted Silloth shrimps, Cumberland pork, ham and egg pie, and crab salad. More expensive restaurant meals in the evening. Bass and Theakstons beers on handpump.

BIRKENHEAD Merseyside   map 7

Mersey Clipper Inn [6/10]

17 Prenton Road West
TEL 051-608 3446

Open for food noon to 2 (1.45 Sun), 7 to 9 & (also wc)
Closed Sun D

A chatty, comfortable pub decked out like a ship. Look for the daily specials, such as liver and onions or ham and cheese pasta. The standard menu has good steak and mushroom pie, and there's home-made strawberry gateau to finish. Sandwiches come open or closed on brown bread. Three-course Sunday roast is £4.25.

BLACKBURN Lancashire   map 7

Lovin' Spoonful [6/10]

76 King William Street
TEL Blackburn (0254) 675505

Open 9am to 4.30pm
Closed Sun; Mon (exc for take-aways)

Upstairs vegetarian restaurant offering a good choice of home-cooked dishes at low prices. Soups, quiches, and baked potatoes are backed up by dishes such as stuffed peppers. Organic produce is used where possible. All dishes served in the restaurant are available as freezer-packs and take-aways in the ground-floor shop.

Muffins [6/10]

5B Town Hall Street
TEL Blackburn (0254) 581707

Open 8.45am to 4.45pm & (also wc)
Closed Sun; bank hols

A no-frills café in a row of Victorian shops. Muffins and toasted tea-cakes appear alongside rarebits, salads, and gingerbread. There are also cheap lunches of hot-pot with red cabbage and mushy peas, liver and onions, hot buttered shrimps with salad, cheese and onion pie, and roast lamb. Finish with custard pie, or sherry trifle. Unlicensed. Take-aways.

Pizza Margherita [7/10]

New Park House, Preston New Road
TEL Blackburn (0254) 665333

Open 10.30am to 11pm (11.30pm Fri and Sat)
Closed Christmas Day, Boxing Day and 1 Jan

One of a trio of better-than-average pizza places in the north of England. For details see Lancaster.

BLACKO Lancashire   map 7

Moorcock Inn [6/10]

TEL Nelson (0282) 64186

Open for food noon to 2.30, 7 to midnight
&(also WC)

The Holts have given the food in this high moorland pub a strongly European flavour, with Austrian and Italian specialities to the fore. New additions to the menu are Viennese baton (Bratwurst in French bread with onions), ham shank with mustard sauce and sauerkraut, and cannelloni. Regular features are steak and kidney pie, savoury pancakes, and goulash with buttered noodles. Sunday roast is a joint of beef or lamb with all the trimmings for £3.25. Thwaites beers on handpump.

BLACKPOOL Lancashire   map 7

Bispham Kitchen [6/10]

14 Red Bank Road, Bispham
TEL Blackpool (0253) 592514

Open 6.30am to midnight (7.30am to 10.30pm Nov to May) &

This upmarket café/fish and chip restaurant stands out from the mediocre eating places in Blackpool. Steve Hoddy claims he can feed a family of four for under £10, from a menu of fish and chips, meat pies, quiches, burgers and salads. There are also fruit salads, gateaux and

scones. Dishes are freshly made from fresh ingredients. There is a branch at 7 Victoria Road West, Cleveleys. (TEL Blackpool (0253) 854185).

Bistro Number Sixteen [8/10]

16 Red Bank Road, Bispham
TEL Blackpool (0253) 53088

Open noon to 2, 7 to 11
Closed first 2 weeks Jan; second and third weeks Aug

This is a real find: a genuine bistro serving fresh food in a suburb of Blackpool. Originally a café, it has been stripped bare, revamped and painted green. There's a brunch and lunch menu of soup, pâté, ploughman's and omelettes, plus cakes, pastries and first-rate freshly ground coffee. The full menu centres on char-grilling – steak with frites, lamb cutlets with Cumberland sauce, and an excellent Fleetwood fish platter of poached haddock fillet, boned trout, and a wing of skate. Start with minestrone or avocado stuffed with prawns, cream cheese and walnuts, and finish with superb French apple tart. House wine by the glass.

Cottage [6/10]

31 Newhouse Road
TEL Blackpool (0253) 64081

Open 11.45 to 2, 5 to midnight &(also WC)
Closed Sun L

New owners are maintaining high standards at this long-established fish and chip shop, and are hoping to expand the business. Portions are huge and fish is priced according to size. Around £3 pays for a decent meal, and there are special deals, such as the massive mixed seafood platter with chips and mushy peas for under £5. A glass of wine is 80p.

Danish Kitchen [8/10]

95 Church Street
TEL Blackpool (0253) 24291

Open 9.15am to 5.30pm &
Closed Sun; Christmas Day and Boxing Day

One of the few cheap eating places in Blackpool to shun convenience foods and put its faith in fresh ingredients. All the baking is done on the premises, and the result is an impressive array of scones, Danish pastries, flans, fruit pies, choux buns and gateaux. Danish open sandwiches are still a feature of the place, although the choice of savoury dishes extends to salads, quiches, croque monsieur and chicken pie. The restaurant caters for children's parties, and provides buffets for people in their own homes.

Jasmine Cottage [6/10]

52 Coronation Street
TEL Blackpool (0253) 25303

Open noon to 2, 5 to midnight (all day in summer)
Closed Sat L and Sun L; L Nov to Feb

As Chinese restaurants go, this is an anachronism, although it has become part of Blackpool life. Holiday-makers, TV people and party workers all descend on the place at conference time. Steak and chips is as popular as Peking duck, and the menu ranges from chop sueys to large one-plate rice and noodle dishes. Set lunches are under £3.

Robert's Oyster Bar [5/10]

92 Promenade
TEL Blackpool (0253) 21226

Open 9am to 10.30pm (5.30pm in winter) &

Robert's is an unchanging Blackpool institution that comes to life during the holiday season. Native and Anglesey oysters and clams are priced by the half dozen; there are plates of cockles, mussels, and whelks as well as jellied eels, and dressed crab, and shrimps. Salads, cheese and biscuits, hard-boiled eggs, and cups of tea are part of the show. Established in 1876. Unlicensed.

BOLTON Greater Manchester   map 7

Tiggis [6/10]

63 Bradshawgate
TEL Bolton (0204) 397320

Open noon to 2, 6 to 11.30 (11 Sun) &
Closed Mon; Sun L; bank hols; Christmas Day

One of a trio of locally rated pizza/pasta places; for details see Preston.

BOWNESS-ON-WINDERMERE
Cumbria   map 9

Hedgerow Vegetarian Restaurant [7/10]

Lake Road
TEL Windermere (096 62) 5002

Open 11 to 2.30, 6 to 10
Closed Mon and Tue in winter

New owners are maintaining standards at this first-floor vegetarian restaurant above a bakery. The décor is folksy and informal, with dried flowers, simple wooden furniture, and watercolours on the walls. Soups, such as cucumber and courgette or apple and lentil, are well made, and the daily hot dishes could be lentil bake, stuffed marrow, or cheese and mushroom barley bake. Sweets and puddings are highlights: gooseberry crumble with yoghurt; plum and almond flan; butterscotch and hazelnut meringues. Home-baked scones and cakes are available during the afternoon. Wines by the glass.

Jackson's Bistro [7/10]

West End, St Martin's Place
TEL Windermere (096 62) 6264

Open 6.30pm to 11pm &
Closed Sun and Mon in winter; Christmas Day, Boxing Day and 3 weeks Jan

A consistent, informal bistro with a short menu that changes every few weeks. Regular deliveries of Scotch salmon in season widen the choice, which might also include pork fillet with home-made apricot relish, and lemon sole stuffed with prawn mousse in Muscadet sauce. Sweets range from ginger and lemon cheesecake to home-made blackberry pie. Three courses plus drinks will take the bill into double figures.

Rastelli [6/10]

Lake Road
TEL Windermere (096 62) 4277

Open 12.30 to 2.30, 6 to 10.30 & (also WC)
Closed Wed; Thur L; 12 Jan to 26 Feb

The friendly family atmosphere is a big plus in this cramped, bustling pizzeria. There are nine toppings for the pizzas (around £3 each); proper cannelloni is light with a fresh spinach stuffing and good bolognese sauce, pasta dishes are above average and there's good Italian trifle to finish. House wine by the glass.

BROUGHTON-IN-FURNESS
Cumbria   map 9

Square Café [6/10]

The Square
TEL Broughton-in-Furness (065 76) 388

Open 10am to 7pm &
Closed Mon to Fri Nov to Mar

A good café, noted for its home baking and home-cooked food. The range of cakes includes currant pasties and caramel shortbread; savoury dishes range from Cumberland sausage and chips to chicken chasseur. Omelettes and toasted sandwiches, too. Wine, beer and cider with meals.

BURY
Greater Manchester   map 7

Chadwicks Black Pudding Stall [5/10]

Bury Open Air Market
TEL Rossendale (0706) 226221

Open 9am to 4pm (4.30pm Sat) &
Closed Mon, Tue, Thur and Sun

A venerable institution, established in 1865 and one of the best-known purveyors of Bury black puddings. There is a lean and a fatty version: the latter is much the best. They are sold raw or cooked to order in copper vats, slit open and eaten with mustard or ketchup. The stall also sells tripe and elder. Long queues mid-morning and at lunch-time. Unlicensed.

BUTTERMERE Cumbria   map 9

Bridge Hotel [6/10]

TEL Buttermere (059 685) 252

Open for food noon to 2.30 (2 Sun), 6 to 9.30 & (also WC)
Closed 4 Jan to 1 Feb

There's a taste of the Lake District about some of the bar food served in this hotel. Spicy Cumberland sausages are made to a special recipe, Cumbrian hot-pot with black pudding, beef and lamb is served with red cabbage, and there's 'tattie ash' – a North Country stew. Otherwise the menu has massive omelettes, ploughman's, salads, and grills. Less choice in the evening. A note on the menu says that 'Vinegar is not served as the fumes affect real ale' which, incidentally, comes from Theakstons.

CALDBECK Cumbria   map 9

Parkend Restaurant [8/10]

TEL Caldbeck (069 98) 494

Open 12.30 to 5; 7.30 to 9
Closed Mon; Sun D; Tue L; Dec to Mar

Judith and Michael Pulger moved from Dulnain Park, Inverness, to take over this seventeenth-century Lakeland farmhouse. Menus follow the market; many ingredients are local; bread, jams and pickles are made on the premises. Lunches are good value: in September there might be cabbage and apple soup, broccoli, courgette and cheese flan, and a platter of Cumberland air-dried ham and smoked mutton, plus a hot dish such as ox-tail braised in port. The cheeseboard has home-made cream cheese, local goats' and Swaledale. More expensive dinners. Thirty-five wines with a good number of half-bottles. Children welcome at lunch-time.

CARLISLE Cumbria   map 10

Highland Chinese [6/10]

14–22 Lonsdale Street
TEL Carlisle (0228) 47602

Open noon to 2, 5.30 to 11.30 &
Closed Sun L

One of the few creditable Chinese restaurants in the far north-west of England. The cooking is fashionable: deep-fried wun-tun; sizzling fillet steak with satay sauce; birds' nests filled with scallops and vegetables; diced pork with cashews. Fried rice is the staple accompaniment.

CARTMEL Cumbria map 9

St Mary's Lodge [5/10]

TEL Cartmel (044 854) 379

Open 2.30pm to 5pm &
Closed mid-Nov to third weekend Mar

Afternoon tea is the main attraction in this unassuming guest house bedecked with hanging baskets. Sandwiches are daintily cut; scones are some of the best in the area and arrive with home-made jam and thick cream. All the cakes are baked on the premises, and hot buttered toast is also available. Set dinners for residents only.

CARTMEL FELL Cumbria map 9

Hodge Hill [6/10]

TEL Newby Bridge (0448) 31480

Open 12.30 to 2 & (also wc)

Traditional Sunday lunches are served with gusto in Beryl Blade's oak-beamed farmhouse dining-room with its log fire, grandfather clock and brasses. The fixed price of £7 pays for a big tureen of home-made chicken and vegetable soup before a roast (duckling, pork, or chicken) with all the trimmings. Sweets might include fresh apricot tart or brandy snaps, and there's a decent cheeseboard, too. Well worth a trip into the country. More expensive evening menu.

Masons Arms [6/10]

Strawberry Bank
TEL Crosthwaite (044 88) 486

Open for food 10.30 to 3 (noon to 2 Sun), 6 to 11 (7 to 10.30 Sun) &

A drinker's paradise, with an extraordinary collection of bottles from around the world, many British ales, plus ciders and perries on handpump. Outside there are views over Winster Valley, inside it is all flagstone floors and blazing fires. The food almost keeps pace, with an enterprising vegetarian selection, such as fennel casserole, mushroom and tofu salad, leek and butter bean pie, supplementing fish pie, lasagne, and sausage casserole. Very popular.

CASTERTON Lancashire map 7

Pheasant Inn [7/10]

TEL Kirkby Lonsdale (0468) 71230

Open for food noon to 1.45, 6.30 to 9 (9.30 in summer) & (also wc)

There are fine views of the Lune Valley from this attractive whitewashed inn. Go at lunch-time, when food is served in the bar and the dining-room. A standard menu of pâté, lamb chops with rosemary, and venison casserole is supplemented by blackboard specials: good mussels in white wine sauce; grilled Manx kippers; French onion soup; steak and kidney pie. The aspirations of the kitchen show in the calves' kidneys with cassis and blackcurrant sauce, and the crescent-shaped dishes of seasonal vegetables. Finish with gooseberry pie, old-fashioned trifle or brown-bread ice-cream. Dinners are more expensive.

CHESTER Cheshire map 7

Abbey Green [9/10]

2 Abbey Green, Northgate Street
TEL Chester (0244) 313251

Open 10 to 3 (4.30 Sat), 6.30 to 10.15 &
Closed Sun and Mon

Julia Lochhead was one of the first to place vegetarian food in an elegant rather than austere setting. Her restaurant is as civilised as a drawing-room, with blazing log fires and classical music. The lunchtime menu stays with simple, cheap dishes, such as falafels, chilli and tofu burgers, and carrot, cheese and onion pie backed up by salads and jacket potatoes. Evenings are more ambitious, taking in almond crêpes with Dubonnet and orange sauce, hot green banana curry, and stuffed pineapple with madeira sauce. Drink herb teas, freshly squeezed orange juice or wine.

Crypt [5/10]

34 Eastgate Row
TEL Chester (0244) 350001

Open 9.15am to 5pm
Closed Sun; Christmas Day and Boxing Day

The café is in a thirteenth-century crypt underneath Browns of Chester department store. Cheshire cheese comes with brown bread or fresh fruit, salads are transatlantic in flavour, and there are soups and savoury flans too. Simple wines as well as lager.

| NEW |
| ENTRY | **Fourgate's** [7/10]

126 Foregate Street
TEL Chester (0244) 315046

Open 11am to 10.30pm (noon to 2, 7 to 10 Sun) &
Closed Mon; Christmas Day D, Boxing Day and 1 Jan

The restaurant is a converted shop in a three-storey Georgian building not far from the city centre. The style is informal: it stays open all day and menus are chalked on a blackboard. Good dishes have included home-made tomato and lemon thyme soup, devilled mushrooms, and smoked Welsh poussin with cranberry sauce. Plaice comes with paprika and mushroom sauce; chicken suprême is stuffed and coated with spinach sauce. Vegetables are generous, and sweets might feature steamed carrot sponge cake. Plenty of choice for vegetarians. Around forty wines, with specials each month.

Mama Mia [6/10]

St Werburgh Street
TEL Chester (0244) 314663

Open 11.45 to 2.30, 6 (5.30 Sat) to 11 &
Closed Sun

Pizzas and pasta dishes are the best bets for cheap eating in this friendly trattoria by the back entrance of Woolworths. The former includes a range of eleven toppings; the latter has spaghetti, rigatoni, farfalle

and tagliatelle with various sauces. Main courses and steaks can take the bill into double figures. House wines by the glass or litre.

CHIPPING Lancashire   map 7

Dog and Partridge [6/10]

Hesketh Lane
TEL Chipping (099 56) 201

Open for food 11.30 to 3, 6 to 11 & (also WC)
Closed Christmas Day D and Boxing Day D

Extensively modernised country pub between Longridge Fell and Wolf Fell. The restaurant dominates, with a good-value (£6.75) set lunch taking in traditional roasts and dishes such as wild duck with honey and orange sauce. Basic bar snacks – soup, ploughman's, steak and kidney pie – are also available (though not on Saturday evening or at Sunday lunch-time). Tetleys beers.

CLEATOR Cumbria   map 9

Shepherd's Arms [6/10]

Ennerdale Bridge
TEL Lamplugh (0946) 861249

Open noon to 1.45 (1.30 Sun), 7 to 8.30
Closed Mon to non-residents; Jan

Small country hotel and pub with a dining-room in a separate barn for non-residents. Three-course set menus are £8 for the likes of crudités with avocado dip, roast quail, and rabbit casserole with mustard sauce. There are ploughman's and snacks in the bar. Real ale.

COCKERMOUTH Cumbria   map 9

Cheers [6/10]

22 Main Street
TEL Cockermouth (0900) 822109

Open 6.30 (7 Sun) to 10 (10.30 Fri and Sat) &
Closed Mon; Sun L; Christmas Day, Boxing Day and 1 Jan

The best way to eat cheaply in this bistro/wine bar is to stay with the pizzas and pasta dishes. Pizzas are made on the premises and there's now a choice of fifteen toppings, all costing around £3.

253

Eight pastas include tagliatelle romana. More expensive international dishes, such as spiced Persian lamb, will take the bill towards £10. Desserts include a sweet fondue – fresh fruit dipped into hot chocolate sauce. Wine by the glass. Take-aways.

Quince & Medlar [7/10]

13 Castlegate
TEL Cockermouth (0900) 823579

Open 7pm to 9.30pm
Closed Mon; Sun and bank hols in winter

The Whitehead-Whitings' attractive Victorian corner house is close to the castle. Inside it's pretty and pink, with floral décor, dark wood chairs and an original black-leaded grate. It serves excellent-value vegetarian meals in the evening; fresh tasting soups such as celery or Armenian apricot with rice and lemon, hummus, khitchari (mung beans and spiced rice with poppadums), baked avocado, vegetables and dried fruit cooked with allspice and coconut milk. Fresh raspberry ice-cream has been a good sweet. Decent house wine at £4.25 a bottle, and freshly brewed coffee.

Wythop Mill [8/10]

Embleton
TEL Bassenthwaite Lake (059 681) 394

Open 10.30 to 4, plus 6.30 to 8.30 Fri and Sat
Closed Mon

The restored mill is situated in a tiny hamlet that bears its name. It now has a dual function as woodworking museum and café. The Sealby family serve light meals during the day and take care with ingredients and presentation. Thick home-made tomato soup gets a twirl of cream and croûtons; salads are decorative and delicately dressed; vegetable lasagne is packed with chopped mangetout, broccoli, cauliflower and courgettes. Fruit pies are excellent. Evening meals on Friday and Saturday might produce courgette and prawn soup, fillet steak in puff pastry, or stuffed aubergines. Italian wine by the glass.

CONGLETON Cheshire   map 7

Oddfellows Wine Bar [8/10]

20 Rood Hill
TEL Congleton (0260) 270243

Open noon to 2, 6.45 to 10 (6.30 to 10.30 Fri and Sat)
Closed bank hols; Christmas Eve to 30 Dec

On the ground floor is the wine bar with self-service food; on the first-floor is the plush dining-room, and above that a toy museum. The menu has bistro staples such as moussaka, turkey and ham pie, and chilli, as well as more unusual garlic lamb kebabs flavoured with lime water, chicken breast in Jura wine sauce, and beef with garlic, cream and Marsala. The vegetarian choice is strong: Greek dips with salads, mushroom and Old Ale pâté, aubergine and potato bake, Stilton and potato casserole. An additional fish section is planned. One hundred wines and beers from around the world. Children welcome upstairs.

CONISTON Cumbria   map 9

Wheelgate [6/10]

Little Arrow, Torver
TEL Coniston (0966) 41418

Open noon to 6
Closed Nov to 1 Mar

It doesn't look much from the outside, but this well-run guest-house is an ideal base for local hill-walking. Afternoon teas are served amid the gleaming brass and copper. Brown bread sandwiches, fresh scones with raspberry jam and four kinds of cake go well with a pot of tea. The £8 set dinner (for residents only) runs along the lines of leek and oatmeal soup, poussin in beer sauce with vegetables, and sticky toffee pudding plus coffee to finish.

DENT Cumbria   map 10

Stone Close [9/10]

Main Street
TEL Dent (058 75) 231

Open 10.30am to 6pm (5.30pm in winter) &
Closed 24 Dec to 2nd week Feb

Chris and Louise Bonsall have elevated their simple, beamed, cottage dining-room into an exceptional eating place. Their aims are modest, but the freshness of the ingredients, the quality of the cooking and the value are outstanding. Through the day the menu is classic tea-shop: home-made soup with wholemeal bread, roasted ham salad, ploughman's with Wensleydale cheese, plus home-baked cakes, Yorkshire Dales ice-creams and a dish of the day, such as lamb kebabs with wild rice. Set meals in the evening (£6.50 for three courses, bookings only) might be potted cheese or three-bean salad before Exeter beef stew with Yorkshire pudding, pork in cider, or chicken in white wine and orange juice, followed by apple pie or gooseberry fool. Restricted opening October to May; telephone first.

DOUGLAS Isle of Man   map 9

Signorio's, Mannin Hotel [6/10]

12 Broadway
TEL Douglas (0624) 75335

Open 11am to 11pm
Closed Christmas Day, Boxing Day and 1 Jan

David Signorio has made changes in his restaurants in recent months. The comfortable basement wine bar/bistro serves meals in the evening to the accompaniment of live music. Pasta dishes, grills and pizzas are backed up with seafood crêpes and burgers. Upstairs is a carvery, offering breakfast, lunch and a good-value set dinner at £6.90 for three courses. The chef prides himself on his sweets trolley.

ESKDALE GREEN Cumbria   map 9

Brook House [6/10]

Boot
TEL Eskdale (094 03) 288

Open 10am to 8.30pm &
Closed Nov to Mar

This large Victorian corner house is open for food right through the day. The owners are vegetarian and this shows in the bias of the menu, which favours spicy lentil cakes, savoury nut loaf, and cheese and

onion quiche. Meat eaters are offered steak and mushroom pie, Cumberland sausage, and roast chicken. Home-made sweets come with Jersey cream.

FAR SAWREY Cumbria   map 9

Sawrey Hotel [6/10]

TEL Windermere (096 62) 3425

Open for food 11 to 2.30 (noon to 1.45 Sun), 7 to 8.45 & (also wc)
Closed Christmas

Just down the road from Beatrix Potter's village. This unpretentious hotel serves straightforward bar food, including cream of mushroom soup made with dark field mushrooms, locally smoked trout, grilled gammon with two fried eggs, and well flavoured quiche. A plateful of Cumberland sausage goes well with a pint of Theakstons or Jennings beer. The set dinners are £8.95.

GRANGE-OVER-SANDS
Cumbria   map 7

At Home [7/10]

Danum House, Main Street
TEL Grange-over-Sands (044 84) 4400

Open 10 to 2, 7 to 9
Closed Sun, Mon; Christmas Eve to 2 Jan; Feb; Nov

This converted kitchenware shop has a ground-floor restaurant, a cosy cellar bar and a tiny terrace for al fresco lunches. During the day the emphasis is on snacks – salads, omelettes, and sandwiches. In the evening (minimum charge £6) the kitchen turns out good bistro-style dishes, such as cauliflower and cheese soup, pork in orange, spicy prawns with rice, and game casserole. Crisp vegetables are given a few nice touches – green beans with almonds, honeyed beetroot. Good sweets. The house wine is Italian.

GRASMERE Cumbria   map 9

Rowan Tree [6/10]

TEL Grasmere (096 65) 528

Open 10.30am to 7.30pm &
Closed Mon to Fri Dec to Mar

This wholefood/vegetarian restaurant has been brightened up by new young owners. Good home-made cakes, pastries, and tea-breads are served through the day; there are also soups with farmhouse bread, ploughman's, and quiche with jacket potatoes. Look for the daily blackboard specials, such as beef cobbler, vegetable casserole, and cauliflower cheese. Apple and plum crumble is an excellent pudding. Tea by the pot, as well as wines and beers.

HAWKSHEAD Cumbria   map 9

Grandy Nook Tea Room [6/10]

Vicarage Lane
TEL Hawkshead (096 66) 404

Open 10.30am to 5.30pm &

Picturesque, tiny cottage, once Wordsworth's lodgings but now a modest unpretentious tea-room. Cakes and pastries are the highlights: try the sticky orange and almond gingerbread, huge slices of lemon meringue pie, and shortbread. The impressively risen scones are some of the largest in the North West. Lunchtime savouries include chicken breast in pastry, pork in cider, and cottage pie. Good cafetière coffee. Unlicensed.

Queen's Head Hotel [7/10]

TEL Hawkshead (096 66) 271

Open for food noon to 2 (1.45 Sun), 6.30 (7 Nov to Mar) to 9
Closed Christmas Day

Rated as one of the best pubs in the Lake District, this seventeenth-century beamed inn caters for hearty outdoor appetites. Bar meals take in bowls of ox-tail and red wine soup, Cumberland sausages, potted Morecambe Bay shrimps, and specialities such as venison casserole and mussels with white wine and herbs. Salads are crisp and attractive. More expensive restaurant menu. Hartley's beer on draught. Children's room.

HEADS NOOK Cumbria   map 10

String of Horses Inn [6/10]

Faugh
TEL Hayton (022 870) 297/509

Open for food 11.30 to 3 (12 to 2 Sun), 5.30 (7 Sun) to 11 & (also WC)

Ten minutes' drive from the M6 in an area of outstanding natural beauty. The inn was built at the end of the seventeenth century and still has its share of oak beams, open fires and antiques. Bar lunches include a cold table for £3.95 on Sunday (children under 10 with their parents eat free). During the week there are fish and chips with mushy peas, salads, and specials such as beef Madras, sweet-and-sour pork, and goulash. More expensive restaurant.

HESWALL Merseyside   map 7

Marco's [6/10]

168 Telegraph Road
TEL 051-342 1412

Open noon to 2.30, 5 to 11 (midnight Fri and Sat); Sun 1pm to 11pm &
Closed Christmas Day

This used to be Riley's, but the owners changed the name, and now put the emphasis firmly on Italian trattoria food. Fresh pasta dishes and pizzas are the best choices for cheap eating; there are also veal specialities and steaks. The espresso and cappuccino are as good as ever. Children's menu.

What's Cooking [6/10]

154 Telegraph Road
TEL 051-342 1966

Open noon (1pm Sun) to 11.30pm
Closed Christmas Day and Boxing Day

Almost every popular fast food in the business is represented at this lively, noisy restaurant: pizzas, burgers, home-made pastas, Mexican specialities, kebabs, ribs and so on. There are also vegetarian dishes, ice-creams and sundaes, and cut-price meals for the kids. Cocktails and milk shakes to drink. There's more space and more décor at the other branches: 34 Barks Road, West Kirby, Wirral, Merseyside (TEL 051-625 7579) and Units 3–4, Edward Pavilion, Albert Dock Village, Liverpool (TEL 051-709 4302).

HOLMROOK Cumbria   map 9

Bower House Inn [6/10]

Eskdale
TEL Eskdale (094 03) 244

Open for food noon to 2, 6.30 to 9
Closed Christmas Day D

The liveliest pub in the area, with the bonus of a pretty garden and fine views over the fells. The bar is a prosperous, convivial setting for spicy pâté, Cumberland sausage, light salads and hefty T-bone steaks. Sweets are home made, as is the bread. More expensive restaurant menu. Hartleys and Youngers Scotch Ale on handpump.

HYDE Greater Manchester   map 7

 Phoenix City [7/10]

10 The Square
TEL 061-368 4677/7694

Open noon to 2; 6 to midnight
Closed Christmas Day and Boxing Day

This Phoenix rose from the ashes of La Piazza, and serves some of the most creditable Cantonese food away from the centre of Manchester. Best value is the short list of dim-sum, taking in sui mai dumplings, paper-wrapped prawns, and spring rolls. Combine these with a one-plate dish of noodles or rice: special chow mein is £3.70. Set lunches are rather westernised but there are decent set dinners from £7.50 a head.

KENDAL Cumbria   map 10

Corner Spot [6/10]

2 Stramongate
TEL Kendal (0539) 20115

Open 8.30am to 4.45pm
Closed Thur, Sun

Founded as a baker's and confectioner's in 1850, this is now a homely licensed café, open through the day. Hot bacon butties make a good breakfast; quiches, jacket potatoes, and salads are the mainstays at lunch-time. There's also an array of flapjacks, deep custard pies, scones, toasted tea-cakes, and Eccles cakes. Wine by the glass.

Lord Ted [7/10]

21A Stramongate
TEL Kendal (0539) 33826

Open noon to 2, 7 to 9.15 & (also WC)
Closed Sun D

Ted Newell, self-appointed lord of this converted snack bar, still puts his faith in fresh ingredients. Lunches are popular and good value for excellent soups, spicy prawns in garlic, and baked avocado with Stilton cheese. There are substantial main dishes, such as beef in red wine, fresh sea bream, or chicken in white wine sauce. Vegetables are steamed and crisp. Ted's wife makes most of the sweets. Evening meals will take the bill beyond single figures.

Moon [9/10]

129 Highgate
TEL Kendal (0539) 29254

Open 7pm to 10pm (11pm Fri and Sat)
Closed Christmas Eve to Boxing Day, 31 Dec and 1 Jan

Val Macconnell has knocked down a wall to make more space and installed two enormous fans to relieve the atmosphere in her friendly restaurant opposite the Brewery Arts Centre. Nothing else has changed. The décor is bold, the menu imaginative and the cooking very good indeed. The style is still wholefood with a vegetarian bias and a loyalty to local ingredients. Fennel and courgette soup or asparagus mousse might precede vegetable, bean sprout and hazelnut bake, lamb and aubergine curry, or chicken with apricots and brandy. Sticky-toffee pudding keeps its place at the top of the popularity stakes, closely followed by fruit crumble and home-made ice-creams. Wine by the glass.

Dog and Gun [6/10]

TEL Keswick (0596) 73463

Open for food 11.30 to 2 (noon to 1.30 Sun),
6 (7 Sun) to 9.30 &
Closed Christmas Day

A lively town pub with slate floors, plenty of atmosphere, and a blazing log fire in winter. The menu tips its hat to vegetarianism with ratatouille on brown rice, otherwise it is a meaty assortment of stuffed poussin, roasted ham with baked onions and Cumberland sauce, beef curry with yoghurt, and Cumberland sausage in a hot brown loaf. Theakstons beers on draught. Children welcome at lunch-times and in the early evening.

King's Head [6/10]

Thirlspot
TEL Keswick (0596) 72393

Open for food noon to 2 (1.30 winter),
6.30 to 9 & (also wc)
Closed D in winter; Christmas and New Year

A long low pub out of Keswick on the road from Windermere. It serves big helpings of hearty, familiar food, and the quality is higher than average: excellent Cumberland sausages, meaty pork chops, good chips and an interesting array of salads. Baps are generously filled, too. Drink Jennings bitter.

Maysons [7/10]

33 Lake Road
TEL Keswick (0596) 74104

Open 9.30 to 5, 6 to 10.30 & (also wc)
Closed Sun; Wed Nov to Mar

The surroundings in this restaurant attached to a department store are light and airy, with tiled floors and lots of vegetation. 'Wholesome food' is the order of the day and the kitchen tries hard to deliver the goods. At lunch-time there's a self-service selection of quiches, pizzas and imaginative salads. In the evening the menu is global, roaming from guacamole with pitta bread and Algerian meatballs with apricot sauce to tandoori chicken and pork vindaloo. Sweets follow the same path: bread-and-butter pudding or Atholl brose alongside Lebanese fruit salad. House wine £4.50 a bottle.

Orchard House [7/10]

Borrowdale Road
TEL Keswick (0596) 72830

Open 6.30pm to 8.30pm

Paul and Wendy Steele are still going strong in their guest-house, offering 'international vegetarian cuisine and home baking'. The set menu is £7.50 and dishes are left on the table for guests to serve themselves. Typically there might be carrot and orange soup with wholemeal bread before Chinese vegetables in ginger sauce, with spiced chickpeas and noodles. Finish with apple pie or fresh fruit, cheese and biscuits and pickled vegetables. Tea and coffee include herbal and decaffeinated. Wine by the glass or carafe.

Mews Coffee House [6/10]

Main Street
TEL Kirkby Lonsdale (0468) 71007

Open 10am (1pm Sun) to 5pm & (also wc)
Closed Wed; Christmas Day and Boxing Day

The seaside décor and the adjoining delicatessen have gone, the kitchen has been enlarged and the coffee-shop has been given a facelift. Food still centres on good home baking: brown scones, deep fruit and lemon meringue pies, thick slices of chocolate cake. There are more savoury dishes now, not only good soups, quiches, and jacket potatoes, but also lasagne, chicken and leek pie, and steak and kidney pie. Unlicensed.

Sartfield Farmhouse [6/10]

TEL Kirk Michael (062 487) 280

Open 11am to 10pm (noon to 6pm Sun)
& (also wc)

A modernised farmhouse on mountain slopes overlooking the sea – a pleasant spot for Sunday lunch. Three courses are £5, including roast Manx lamb or beef with plenty of vegetables. Start with home-made vegetable soup and finish with trifle or apple pie.

LANCASTER Lancashire   map 7

Duke's, Dukes Playhouse [7/10]

Moor Lane
TEL Lancaster (0524) 76461

Open 10 to 2.30, 5.30 to 8.30 & (also WC)
Closed Sun; Mon D; bank hols

John Owen provides a valuable service to theatre-workers and the public by serving good-value snacks and light meals in this bustling restaurant. The menus cater for all tastes, with celery and tomato soup, Lancashire hot-pot, stir-fried vegetables, and paella among the attractions. Roast beef and Yorkshire pudding is excellent value at £1.95. There are also baked potatoes, ploughman's and wholefood sweets. Wine by the glass.

Libra [7/10]

19 Brock Street
TEL Lancaster (0524) 61551

Open 9am to 6pm, plus 7pm to 10pm Thur to Sat &
Closed Sun; bank hols

The café has been refurbished and now looks smart, with green tables and chairs. It is still relentlessly vegetarian, and reflects the alternative face of the city. Fur coats are out but leather jackets are *de rigueur*. Wholesome daytime staples, such as quiches, pizzas, and samosas, have been bolstered by aloo kofta (spicy potato balls) and harvest pie. From 7 to 10 Thursday, Friday and Saturday there are excellent-value dinners with a strong vegan bias. Cucumber and strawberry salad with lemon and wine might be followed by noodles with peanut and orange dressing, Indonesian rice or stuffed courgettes, with gooseberry pie or green fruit salad to finish. Herb teas; wine by the glass.

Orient Express [6/10]

38–42 Parliament Street
TEL Lancaster (0524) 33333/33332

Open noon to 2, 6.50 to 11

This popular restaurant attracts a good mixed crowd at lunch-time. The atmosphere is still predominantly Italian, though the menu travels across Europe like the eponymous train. From Italy come pizzas and pasta dishes, there are veal dishes from Switzerland, and a number of Middle Eastern specialities such as kebabs, pilaff and felfel (stuffed peppers with prawns and herbs). Regulars still rate the Italian dishes as the best. House wine; decent coffee.

Pizza Margherita [7/10]

2 Moor Lane
TEL Lancaster (0524) 36333

Open 10.30am to 11pm (11.30pm Fri and Sat) &
Closed Christmas Day, Boxing Day and 1 Jan

Perhaps the nearest northern equivalent of the London-based Pizza Express chain (see London). The Lancaster branch is a green and pleasant jungle of pot-plants, opposite the Dukes Playhouse. It is open right through the day for freshly-baked pizzas with interesting toppings: Clementine is a vegetarian version with artichoke hearts, sweetcorn, courgettes, and the like; pescatore has smoked mackerel, sardines and anchovies. Tuna and beans to start, home-baked chocolate fudge cake to finish. There are branches in Bradford and Blackburn (see entries).

Upper Crust [5/10]

2 James Street
TEL Lancaster (0524) 66985

Open 9.15am to 5pm (2pm Wed) &
Closed Sun; bank hols

Busy snack bar behind Marks and Spencer, very popular with weekday shoppers for lunch. Savoury dishes, such as cottage pie, are filling; salads are crisp. Highlights are the home-baked cakes, gateaux, tray bakes and Pavlovas. Freshly ground coffee and pots of tea. Take-aways. Unlicensed.

LIVERPOOL Merseyside   map 7

Armadillo [8/10]

20–22 Matthew Street
TEL 051-236 4123

Open 11 to 3, 5 to 10.30
Closed Mon D and Sun D; 1 week at Christmas

Martin Cooper's converted warehouse is
on the tourist's Beatles trail, being close to
the old Cavern. At lunch-time the food is
excellent value, with a strong vegetarian
bias: home-baked wholemeal bread,
excellent salads and quiches, and sticky
cakes appear alongside meaty hot dishes,
such as pork and gooseberry hot-pot.
House wine is £6.40 a bottle. Children's
helpings at lunch-times.

Café Tabac [6/10]

126 Bold Street
TEL 051-709 3739

Open 9.30am to 7.30pm
Closed Sun; bank hols

Oilcloths on the tables, fringe-activity
posters on the walls and thumping music
are the trappings in this archetypal student
bistro. The food is cheap and dishes are
split between meat, vegetarian and vegan.
Typically there might be a banger special,
beef Stroganoff with saffron rice, aduki
bean pie, and walnut and cheeseburgers.
Salads are fresh. Take-aways and outside
catering.

Casa Italia [6/10]

9–13 Temple Court, 40 Stanley Street
TEL 051-227 5774

Open noon to 10pm ♿ (also WC)
Closed Sun; bank hols

Temple Court is an eating complex,
housing three restaurants. Casa Italia is
the cheapest, serving a good range of pizzas
and pasta dishes for around £3. These are
flanked by a few starters and sweets.
Service is speedy; the atmosphere buzzes.
The house wine is Lambrusco at £6.30 a
litre. It's possible to eat in the nearby Villa
Italia trattoria for under £10 a head.

Everyman Bistro [7/10]

9–11 Hope Street
TEL 051-708 9545

Open noon to 11.30
Closed Sun; bank hols

For more than seventeen years this has
been one of the most popular bistros in
Liverpool. It is beneath the Everyman
Theatre, with metal signs and old posters
on the painted brick walls. The menu
balances meat and vegetarian specialities:
on one side there might be navarin of
lamb, pork afelia or home-made pasta with
ham and mushrooms; on the other, ricotta
lasagne, chickpea and fennel casserole, and
courgette and hazelnut bake. Soups, pizzas
and quiches complete the picture, along
with fruity sweets. Fresh orange juice,
house wine by the glass and beers from
around the world. Children welcome until
9pm.

Far East [9/10]

27–35 Berry Street
TEL 051-709 3141

Open noon to 11.30pm ♿ (also WC)
Closed Christmas Day and Boxing Day

A big-league Cantonese restaurant that
can run with the best in Manchester and
Soho. It is above the number-one Chinese
supermarket in Liverpool and scores with
the authenticity and power of its cooking.
The real bargains are not in the
westernised set meals but in the excellent
dim-sum snacks: steamed dumplings,
fried crabmeat balls, Chinese mushrooms
with meatballs, roast pork buns and yam
croquettes. There's also a dazzling choice
of around fifty one-plate rice, noodles and
soup dishes for a fine cheap meal; three
kinds of roasted meat on rice for £3.40
shows the quality. The restaurant has
introduced a vegetarian mini-menu and
offers a Thursday evening buffet for £9.50.

La Grande Bouffe [8/10]

48A Castle Street
TEL 051-236 3375

Open noon to 2.30, 6 to 10 (10.30 Sat)
Closed Sun; Sat L; Mon D

A neon sign in the window marks out this cellar restaurant from the other businesses in Castle Street. At lunch-time the long, narrow room functions as a brasserie, with an eclectic menu spanning smoked haddock mousse with spinach, devilled kidneys, navarin of lamb, and chicken wrapped in vine leaves. There are also salads, quiches, and cheese. Three-course set lunches are £6.95 for dishes such as grilled sardines and beef fillet in filo pastry with bordelaise sauce. More expensive evening meals. Excellent sandwiches to take away.

Greenhouse, Playhouse Theatre [6/10]

Williamson Square
TEL 051-709 7730

Open noon to 3, 5 to 10.30
Closed Sun; bank hols

The modern restaurant attached to the Victorian Playhouse Theatre maintains a better-than-average standard of catering. Pizzas and pasta dishes are backed up by coq au vin, Cumberland mixed grill, omelettes, and steak chasseur, with ice-creams and cheesecake to finish. A three-course lunch is £3.70; set evening meals are £5.80. After the show, any pizza or lasagne plus a glass of wine and coffee is £3.50.

Mandarin [6/10]

40 Victoria Street
TEL 051-236 8899

Open noon (5.30pm Sun) to 11.30pm
Closed bank hols

A useful choice for Chinese food away from Liverpool Chinatown. The lunchtime bargain is £3.20 for soup and a main course; otherwise the best value is in the set meals, from £7.80 a head. The menu straddles Pekingese and Cantonese, with the emphasis on the former: seaweed, crispy fragrant duck, sizzling lamb with ginger and spring onion, spare ribs in capital sauce.

| NEW ENTRY | **Mayflower** [8/10] |

48 Duke Street
TEL 051-709 6339

Open noon (6pm Sat and Sun) to 4am
& (1 step; also WC)

This pretty restaurant is rated second only to the Far East (see entry) for Cantonese food in Liverpool, although the menu ventures into Pekingese territory for some specialities. Cheap set lunches (£3 for the basic version, £5.50 for the more wide-ranging banquet) are good value. The latter includes Westlake beef broth, spare ribs in capital sauce, fried chicken with cashew-nuts, beef in satay sauce, plus fried rice and fresh fruit to finish. Set dinners begin at £7 a head for similar dishes.

| NEW ENTRY | **Orient** [7/10] |

54–54A Berry Street
TEL 051-709 2555

Open noon to midnight &
Closed Mon

For more than fourteen years Mr Liu's well-known restaurant has been serving Chinese regional dishes, specialising in the cooking of Peking and Shanghai. For cheap eaters, the news is that a dim-sum chef has been appointed to offer a range of good-value Cantonese snacks. Like the Far East (see entry) it offers a range of vegetarian dishes and a vegetarian banquet at £8.50, which is the cheapest of the set meals.

LYTHAM ST ANNES
Lancashire   map 7

Bennett's Bistro [7/10]

15 Park Street
TEL Lytham (0253) 739265

Open noon to 2.30, 7 to 10.30 &
Closed Sun and Mon

A converted late-Victorian semi with two downstairs dining-rooms. The wallpaper is yellow and so are the waiters' T-shirts. The place caters for large numbers, keeps its prices low and tries hard to offer attractive food. Dishes are given odd names: Tahiti tickler is avocado soup, Grewsome

Twosome is two fillets of steak, one with
madeira sauce, the other with béarnaise.
Bananas are wrapped in pancakes with
syrup and almonds; the cheesecake is
called Blueberry Hill, although it is
garnished with black cherries. House wine
is £4.95 a bottle.

Buttery Bar, Dalmeny Hotel [6/10]

19–33 South Promenade
TEL Lytham (0253) 725871

Open 8am to 11pm & (also wc)
Closed Christmas Eve to Boxing Day

The Buttery Bar is the cheap option in this
family-run hotel with four different
restaurants. Meals are served through the
day in an informal setting overlooking the
swimming-pool and sunbathing patios.
There are continental breakfasts,
afternoon teas and light suppers from a
menu that takes in home-made mushroom
and mustard soup, meat pie with mushy
peas and chips, Stilton and celery quiche
with salad, and sandwiches. Sweets are
prepared on the premises. To drink there's
a choice of teas, freshly squeezed orange
juice and wine at £5 a bottle.

KFOG [7/10]

54 Wood Street
TEL Lytham (0253) 725161

Open noon to 2.30, 7 to 10.30 & (also wc)
Closed Mon

This is a 'California-style restaurant'
according to chef/owner Su Bloomberg,
who trained at the Californian Academy of
Culinary Art. The name comes from the
famous FM radio station, the colours are
primary, and the casual style has vivid
American overtones. Lunch is the best
value for cheap eating, when the menu has
flashy salads, savoury croissants, deep-
fried potato skins, and teriyaki chicken in
a sesame bun. Sunday brunch is Santa
Monica steak sandwiches or smoked
salmon with toasted bagels to the sound of
smooth West Coast jazz. Dinner can take
the bill into double figures. Take-aways.

Lindum Hotel [6/10]

63–67 South Promenade
TEL Lytham (0253) 721534/722516

Open for food noon (12.45 Sun) to 2, 6 to 7

Still rated as offering the best Sunday
lunch for miles around. For £5.25 there is
roast beef and Yorkshire pudding, roast
Fylde chicken, or poached lemon sole,
preceded by soup or Mexican crab Creole,
and followed by sweets, ices or cheese,
plus coffee. Bar lunches are served from
Monday to Saturday with the emphasis on
fried dishes, ploughman's, and salads. A
giant chip butty with tomato sauce is 80p.
More expensive early evening meals.

NEW ENTRY Pleasant Street [7/10]

2 Pleasant Street
TEL Lytham (0253) 738786

Open 10.30 to 2.30, 6.30 onwards
Closed Christmas

Bare-boarded French bistro in a converted
auctioneer's warehouse. Philip Johnson
offers an interesting seasonal menu, with
the emphasis on char-grilling and local
seafood. Salad stuffs and vegetables are
grown in the neighbourhood, and marsh
samphire is an occasional wild harvest.
Start with grilled sardines or tagliatelle
verdi before barbecued lamb, moussaka, or
cassoulet. Finish with cabinet pudding or
apple pie laced with calvados. The owners
also run a wine shop, so there is some
interesting drinking from a wide ranging
list. Dinners may take the bill into double
figures.

Tiggis [6/10]

21–23 Rear Wood Street
TEL Lytham (0253) 711481

Open noon to 2, 6 to 11 (11.30 Fri and Sat)

One of a trio of locally-rated pizza/pasta
places (see Preston for details).

MACCLESFIELD Cheshire   map 7

Harlequin's [6/10]

68A Chestergate
TEL Macclesfield (0625) 32657

Open noon to 2.15, 5.30 (7 Sat) to 10.30 & (also
WC)
Closed Sun L; bank hols

Wine is the main business in this cheerful
converted barn with a new conservatory
restaurant. The list runs to about 150
labels and most are available at off-sales
prices. At lunch-time there's a decent
choice of cheap food. Jacket potatoes,
French bread sandwiches and pizzas are
supplemented by hot dishes, such as
Lancashire hot-pot, pork chop in cider
sauce, and liver and bacon. There are also
grills, plus a more expensive restaurant
menu.

MANCHESTER
Greater Manchester   map 7

Assam Gourmet [8/10]

17A Bloom Street
TEL 061-236 6836

Open noon to 2.30, 6 to 11.30 (midnight Fri and
Sat, 10.30 Sun)
Closed Christmas Day; Good Friday

Probably the only restaurant in the
country specialising in the cooking of
Assam, close to the Chinese border. Many
dishes are a revelation and far removed
from the standard fare of most Indian
restaurants. Crab is cooked with mustard
and spring onion sauce, duck is braised in a
pot with cardamom and cinnamon, grilled
venison comes with lemon sauce. Meeta
kayla pustholes is crispy deep-fried banana
with scampi. Set lunches from £2.95 stay
in more familiar territory of tikkas, keema
peas and mutton pilau. Full set meals from
around £8 a head. Drink Kingfisher beer or
exotic fruit juice.

NEW ENTRY | Basta Pasta [8/10]

Unit One, Piccadilly Plaza, Mosley Street
TEL 061-228 1203

Open noon to 11 &
Closed Sun; bank hols; 1 week Christmas

A greasy burger joint transformed into a
cool modish pasta and espresso bar done
out in snazzy steel and chrome with
terrazza floors, pastel colour schemes and
sinuous grey and white curves. It is run as
a co-operative and is the leading supplier
of fresh pasta in the city. Tagliatelle and
tagliarini are cut from sheets rolled in the
traditional way, and the menu also has
conchigle with garlic. Sauces are fresh and
herby: tomato and basil, peppers with
thyme and ham, sage and garlic butter.
There are also specials, such as courgette
soup and stuffed peppers. Genuine Italian
sweets; excellent coffee. Art-school
waiters in black and white logo T-shirts
reinforce the feeling of Milan in
Manchester. Unlicensed, but bring your
own.

NEW ENTRY | Billies [7/10]

115 Manchester Road, Chorlton
TEL 061-881 9338

Open noon to 2.30, 6 to 11
Closed Christmas

This vegetarian women's co-operative
wears its ideology on its sleeve with a
vengeance. 'Billie' refers to Billie Holliday
and a jazz theme runs through the décor
with apricot and grey marbled walls, black
vinyl-topped tables and a big mural of a
female jazz band. The menu spells out its
loyalties with an eclectic list of dishes
prepared from carefully chosen
ingredients: watercress soup, stuffed
choux buns, deep-fried potatoes on a bed of
herby risotto, Korean pancake with peanut
sauce, and vegetable galette. Drinks are
equally committed: organic wines; Hugh
Rock's elderflower wine; additive-free
beers, including Dark Star Brown Ale and
Czech Pilsner Urquelle. The ideology
extends to the nappy-changing facilities in
the men's as well as the ladies' toilets.

NEW ENTRY | Brasserie St Pierre [7/10]

57–63 Princess Street
TEL 061-228 0231

Open noon to 2, 6 to 11 &
Closed Sun; Sat L

Authentic-looking French brasserie with large plate-glass windows opposite Manchester Town Hall. The bargain here is the French provincial lunch: £5.75 pays for glazed onion soup, breast of chicken stuffed with Brie and tarragon butter plus vegetables or salad; coffee and a glass of wine are included in the price. Full meals from the main menu will take the bill into double figures. Good-value wines and Continental beers.

| NEW ENTRY | **Burns** [6/10] |

12 Warburton Street, Didsbury
TEL 061-434 0538

Open noon to 2, 5.30 to 10
Closed Sat L; bank hols (exc Good Friday)

Manchester's answer to the Seashell in London or Bryan's in Leeds is this converted warehouse in the suburb of Didsbury. The shed-like exterior with a car-park out front, and the open-plan dining-room with the kitchen at the end give it the feel of an American diner. Excellent fish and chips are cooked in groundnut oil, and portions are massive. Fish can be grilled or fried, on or off the bone, there's a fresh vegetable if you don't want peas, and a range of specials, such as grilled sardines or poached halibut with cucumber yoghurt. The front of the menu is a lesson in fish identification. House wine by the glass or carafe. Children welcome until 7pm.

Café Istanbul [7/10]

79 Bridge Street
TEL 061-833 9942

Open noon to 3, 6 to 11.30 & (also wc)
Closed Sun

One of Manchester's more conspicuous ethnic success stories, and well known as a meeting place for expatriate Turks. It gets crowded at lunch-time, when there's a good set menu for £4: spinach soup, hummus or tabbouleh salad before turlu (lamb casserole), stuffed green peppers or char-grilled minced lamb. The price also includes good Turkish coffee. The full

menu has an interesting range of meze, and it's possible to order just starters. Main courses centre on kebabs, steaks, and salads. Turkish wines for £6.65 a bottle, or house wine by the glass.

Christian World Centre [6/10]

123 Deansgate
TEL 061-834 6060

Open 10am to 6pm
Closed Sun; bank hols

Above-average café in the basement of the Christian bookshop. It convinces because the food is honest, freshly made and cheap. In the dim eating area with its pine tables and rush chairs you can sample good dishes, such as tomato and lentil soup, and apple and blackberry pie, along with quiches, scones, and roast ham. Coffee, teas and fruit juices to drink. Supplies can run out quickly, so it's best to go early. Unlicensed.

| NEW ENTRY | **Dragon Gate** [7/10] |

57 Faulkner Street
TEL 061-236 8307

Open noon to midnight

A narrow doorway leads to a small basement in the heart of Chinatown. The best deal in this new Cantonese restaurant is the choice of one-plate meals. The quality of the roast belly-pork, char siu and duck is better than average, portions are adequate and prices are lower than at most of the neighbouring restaurants. There's also a choice of workaday dim-sum.

Felicini's [6/10]

751 Wilmslow Road, Didsbury
TEL 061-445 2055

Open noon to 2, 6 (6.30 Sun) to 11.15 (11 Sun, 11.30 Wed and Thur, 11.45 Fri and Sat)
Closed Sun L; Christmas Day, Boxing Day and 1 Jan

Freshly cooked pizzas and pasta dishes are the highlights in this cheerful trattoria. Its success shows in the fact that it is proving a match for a recently opened pizza chain across the road. There's no booking, so be prepared to queue in the evening. There are two branches: 398 Barlow Moor Road, Chorlton, Manchester (TEL 061-881 6902) and 183 Ashley Road, Hale (TEL 061-928 1811).

 Gallery Bistro, Whitworth Art Gallery [6/10]

Oxford Road
TEL 061-273 1249

Open 10.30am to 4.15pm (8pm Thur) & (also WC)
Closed Sun; 10 days Christmas

The bistro is in a converted vestibule to the right of the main entrance to the Whitworth Art Gallery. Inside there are round tables and bentwood chairs; outside there are seats on the grass. The food is simple, fresh and home cooked: carrot and orange soup with excellent French bread, herb cheese pâté and salad, home-made ravioli with tomato sauce, omelettes, and jacket potatoes. There are also more substantial dishes of the day, such as lamb cutlets with orange and ginger. Good choice of teas, and wine by the glass. One of Manchester's best-kept secrets.

Gaylord [7/10]

Amethyst House, Spring Gardens
TEL 061-832 6037/4866

Open noon to 3, 6 to 11.30 (11 Sun)
Closed Christmas Day; 1 Jan

A famous name in international Indian restaurants with branches as far apart as Frankfurt and Hong Kong. The Manchester version offers some of the most subtle North Indian cooking in the city, service is smoothly efficient and the setting is a smart mix of beaded curtains and brassware. Tandoori dishes are the backbone of the menu, and there are also good reports of the korma badami, mixed bhajis, kulcha bread and pilau rice. Set lunches from £4.95.

Greenhouse [7/10]

331 Great Western Street, Rusholme
TEL 061-224 0730

Open noon to 2.45, 6 to 10.30 & (also WC)
Closed Thur L, Fri L and Sun L; Christmas to New Year

Interesting vegetarian food is served in this converted corner house with overgrown conifers outside and a splendid conservatory mural on one wall. The décor is all trailing plants, net curtains and square boarding-house tables. The menu takes in samosas, papaya stuffed with mango, baked avocado, and cashew and vegetable roast with satay sauce. Finish with Apfelstrudel or hazelnut ice-cream. The loyalty to organic produce extends to some of the wines.

Hong Kong [7/10]

47 Faulkner Street
TEL 061-236 0565

Open noon to midnight
Closed Christmas Eve and Christmas Day

The décor may be tidy and rather sterile, but the food in this first-floor Cantonese restaurant ranks highly in the city. Dim-sum are excellent, especially prawns in rice paper, bite-sized spare ribs, and fried crabmeat balls. There are good-value one-plate rice and noodle dishes, too. The best plan is to ignore the printed menu and simply ask for what you want. Many items from the main menu, such as grilled eel, are less pricey than at some competitors.

Hopewell City [8/10]

45–47 Faulkner Street
TEL 061-236 0091/0581

Open noon to midnight

This smart basement restaurant dominated by a fish tank is starting to challenge the front-runners in Manchester's Chinatown. For cheap eating, by-pass the set lunch and go for the competent selection of dim-sum and one-plate meals. Roast meats are a speciality here, with some items, such as ribs and smoked meat, not found elsewhere. The full, three-hundred strong menu is distinguished by careful cooking of good ingredients.

Indian Cottage [8/10]

501 Claremont Road, Rusholme
TEL 061-224 0376

Open noon to 2.30, 6 to 11.30

The plushest Indian restaurant near this stretch of the Wilmslow Road, which is dominated by cafés and sweet centres. It ranks as one of the best of its kind in the city, by virtue of the subtle spicing, fresh herbs and dishes cooked to order. The menu is an extensive range of North Indian curries and tandoori dishes, including haseen kebab, karahi dishes and marinated quail, as well as the usual offerings. Set dinners from £6.95; four-course lunch £4.50. Drink Kingfisher beer or masala tea flavoured with cardamoms.

Kathmandu Tandoori [7/10]

42–44 Sackville Street
TEL 061-236 4684

Open noon to 2.30, 6 to midnight
Closed bank hol Mon L; Christmas

Despite the name, this restaurant is more North Indian than Nepalese, with good reliable cooking. Tikkas, lamb dopiaza, kidney kebabs, and barbecued mackerel are among the attractions on the menu. Set lunches from about £3. The restaurant has been running for six years and has spawned several imitators with similar names.

Kosmos Taverna [8/10]

248 Wilmslow Road
TEL 061-225 9106

Open 6.30pm to 11.30pm (12.30am Fri and Sat) &
Closed Christmas Day, Boxing Day and 1 Jan

Serves some of the best Greek food in the north-west of England. Meals can easily creep into double figures, but the value for money is excellent. The mammoth meze at £8 a head comes in three great waves with up to fifteen dishes: dips, Feta cheese, dolmades, squid, braised dishes, kebabs and rice. Spicy lukanika sausages, grilled halloumi cheese, beef stifado, and lamb kebabs marinated in yoghurt and olive oil

have all been first rate. Also look for the seafood meze for the same price. Greek wines and Keo beer from Cyprus.

Leo's [6/10]

251 Monton Road, Eccles
TEL 061-789 2675

Open 12.30 to 2.30, 6 to 11
Closed Sat L and Sun L

Very cheap basement trattoria offering large portions of no-nonsense Italian food. Set lunch for £3.95 is a bargain for full-bodied minestrone, sizzling lasagne, and grilled trout. Service is speedy and the house wine is drinkable. Full meals from the main menu can still keep the bill in single figures.

NEW ENTRY Lime Tree Café [7/10]

9–11 Wilmslow Road, Rusholme
TEL 061-225 7108

Open noon to 2.30, 5.30 to 10.30
Closed Sun D; Mon

The cheaper offshoot of the Lime Tree Restaurant in Didsbury is in a converted transport café just beyond Manchester Royal Infirmary. The menu has taken some of the starters from the restaurant, plus casseroles, sandwiches, and special fish and chips. French provincial dishes dominate, although the black puddings are more Bury than boudin noir. Typically there might be leek and courgette soup, burgundy beef, navarin of lamb, or rabbit with rosemary and garlic sauce. There is a lot of chocolate in the puddings. Lunch prices are likely to find favour with the local student population.

NEW ENTRY Little Yang Sing [9/10]

17 George Street
TEL 061-228 7722

Open 5.30pm to 11.30pm (11.45pm Fri and Sat, noon to 10.30pm Sun)
Closed Mon

Warren Yeung has re-opened the original Yang Sing premises and the cooking has quickly moved into the first division of Manchester Chinatown restaurants. Dim-sum for cheap eaters rival those at the parent restaurant in Princess Street (see entry), with superb spring rolls, spicy meat and nut dumplings, fried crabmeat balls and sui mai. Dry-fried rice sticks with beef shows the quality of the one-plate meals. The full menu has excellent baked prawns with chilli and salt, and chicken with lemon and honey for a larger outlay.

Mulberry's [7/10]

400 Wilmslow Road, Withington
TEL 061-434 4624/4621

Open 7pm to 2am
Closed Sun; bank hols

The kitchen and the basement restaurant have been spruced up, but the fashionable crowd has moved on. Glass partitions divide the main dining-room from the Piano Bar where there are excellent-value light meals. There are home-made bouchées with savoury fillings, pizzas, and salads, plus restaurant starters such as pea and mint soup, fishcakes with curry sauce, minced lamb and mint croquettes and devilled chicken livers. Another bargain is the three-course set dinner in the restaurant, which is only £4.75 during the happy hour (7pm to 8pm). Live music most nights. Wines by the glass, and cocktails.

On The Eighth Day [9/10]

109 Oxford Road, All Saints
TEL 061-273 1850

Open 10am to 7pm (4.30pm Sat) ♿ (also WC)
Closed Sun

Excellent wholefood/vegetarian café run by a workers' co-operative. It is notable for its very low prices and high quality, although the choice is limited. Dishes are cooked fresh each day by different cooks. The pattern is one soup (such as split pea and mint), one stew (such as pinto bean and vegetable with rice), and one bake (pasta and fagioli or spaghetti bolognese). There are also vegetarian pâtés and a range of salads, plus a good choice of sweets including vegan cheesecakes and hot sponge puddings. Unlicensed but there are 19 teas, as well as juices.

Paradise [6/10]

123 Wilmslow Road, Rusholme
TEL 061-224 6443

Open noon to 2am ♿

This straightforward Indian café scores over most of the local competition with its fresh ingredients and good-quality cooking. The menu has the standard North Indian assortment of dhansaks, birianis and kormas, backed up by a section devoted to karahi dishes (including brains and quails). Rasmalai to finish, lassi to drink. Take-aways.

NEW ENTRY Pearl City [9/10]

33 George Street
TEL 061-228 7683

Open noon to 4am (midnight Sun)

The best set lunch in Manchester Chinatown, for as little as £2.50. This Cantonese giant of a restaurant up a flight of stairs also serves outstanding dim-sum: mixed meatballs with Chinese mushroom, beef dumplings with ginger and spring onion, and fried crabmeat balls are all first rate. The restaurant's reputation also rests with its roast meats and one-plate rice and noodle dishes, which are staunchly in the Cantonese tradition: cold roast duck is sumptuous, well lacquered and authentically fatty. If you are having lunch with the children order some Cokes and prawn crackers as diversions.

Pizzeria Bella Napoli [7/10]

6A Booth Street
TEL 061-236 1537

Open 12.15pm (6pm Sun) to 11.30pm
Closed Sun L; bank hols

An off-shoot of the more expensive Isola Bella restaurant serving some of the best pizzas in Manchester. A steep staircase leads down to the crowded cream and red dining-room and there are often queues for a table, although turnover is fast. Pizzas are generously topped, pasta dishes are reliable, and the cappuccino is frothy.

Three courses plus a drink should leave change from £6.

Romans [6/10]

36 John Dalton Street
TEL 061-835 1707

Open noon to 2.30 (3 Fri), 5.30 (6.30 Sun) to 11.30 (midnight Fri); noon to 11.30pm Sat ᏺ
Closed Sun L

Crowded city-centre trattoria and pizza place. Choose the excellent fresh pizzas rather than the run-of-the-mill pasta or more expensive steaks and veal dishes. Decent house wine by the glass or carafe.

Royal Oak Hotel [8/10]

729 Wilmslow Road, Didsbury
TEL 061-445 3152

Open for food 11 to 3, 5.30 to 11 (noon to 2, 7 to 10.30 Sun) ᏺ (also WC)

This red-brick corner pub lives in the past. Its atmosphere is heroically traditional, shunning muzak and fruit machines in favour of theatrical posters, Victorian tables with anti-spill rims, and lots of old china. In this setting it serves some of the biggest and best ploughman's in the land. Huge slabs of well-kept English and foreign cheeses come with equally large hunks of excellent French or locally-baked bread, plus pickles. To go with the food there's superb Marstons beer. Doggy bags are provided for the inevitable left-overs. The place is always crowded with local supporters. No children.

Sanam [8/10]

145–151 Wilmslow Road, Rusholme
TEL 061-224 1008

Open 10.30am to midnight (1am Fri to Sun) ᏺ (also WC)

The pick of the Indian cafés along the Wilmslow Road (see feature). The décor is a garish mix of red patterned wallpaper and arches, but the place is spotless, service is good, and the place is authentic. Quail and brains supplement the usual range of kebabs, pakoras, chicken pilau and tandooris. There's also a selection of

Indian sweetmeats. Take-aways. Unlicensed.

Siam Orchid [7/10]

54 Portland Street
TEL 061-236 1388

Open 11.30 to 2.30, 6.30 to 11
Closed Sat L and Sun L

The set lunch at £3.50 is a good introduction to the menu in Manchester's first Thai restaurant, marked by a large purple sign opposite the bus station. Dishes change weekly: beef satay, squid with garlic and peppers, and chicken soup with coconut milk, lemon grass and laos have all been good. The setting is embellished with fresh orchids, pictures of Thai boxers and waitresses in costume. Singha Thai beer is £1.90 a bottle.

Sinclairs [6/10]

Shambles Square
TEL 061-834 0430

Open for food noon to 2pm ᏺ
Closed Sun; Christmas Day and Boxing Day

An atmospheric eighteenth-century pub, restored when the surrounding shopping complex was built. The setting is incongruous, but inside there is a feel of the past, with lots of low beams, panelling, small alcoves and a tall, marble-topped serving counter. At lunch-time there are sandwiches upstairs and downstairs: the hot gammon is recommended. Live oysters are also a speciality in the downstairs bar, along with beef and oyster pie, pork pie with onions, barm cakes, and salads, as well as specials, such as beef and sweetcorn stew. Sam Smiths beer on handpump. No children.

Wild Oats [6/10]

88 Oldham Street
TEL 061-236 6662

Open 10 to 2 Mon to Fri, plus 5.45pm to 9.30pm Wed to Sat
Closed Sun to Tue; Christmas

On weekday mornings until 2pm this is a take-away sandwich bar. In the evenings

(Wednesday to Saturday) it becomes a modest wholefood restaurant offering dishes such as Gorgonzola pâté, stuffed fresh dates, Cuban chicken fricassee, and fennel florentine. Sweets include home-made ice-creams and lemon and pistachio cheesecake. Drink Theakstons bitter, country fruit wines or juices.

Wong Chu [7/10]

63–63A Faulkner Street
TEL 061-236 2346

Open noon to midnight

Simple Cantonese café with menus displayed under the glass table-tops and Chinese pictures on the walls. The range of dishes is extensive, although dim-sum are missing. Best bets here are bowls of roast meats and rice (which are smaller and cheaper than the full 'plate' versions). All the roast meats and take-aways are served from a special counter. Bowls of soup with noodles are also good value, and the long menu is strong on old-style authentic specialities, such as steamed minced pork with salted fish.

Woo Sang [8/10]

19–21 George Street
TEL 061-236 3697

Open noon to 11.45pm
Closed Christmas Day and Boxing Day

One of the great Cantonese stalwarts in Manchester's Chinatown. The restaurant is on two floors above its own supermarket. Dim-sum are highly rated, with some interesting items, such as Chinese sausage roll (wind-dried sausage in white bread dough), steamed chicken's web in soya bean, and vanilla sponge. Also good value are the massive one-plate rice and noodles dishes – a huge choice, from the Woo Sang special (number 169) to plain noodles in supreme soup (number 242). The cold roast duck is probably the best in Manchester. This is a good place to combine dim-sum and one-plate dishes. Set meals average £8 a head.

NEW ENTRY Yang Sing [9/10]

34 Princess Street
TEL 061-236 2200

Open noon to 11pm & (also WC)
Closed Christmas Day

Eating in the best Chinese restaurant in the country doesn't have to be expensive. Lunch can cost as little as £5 if you stay with the brilliant dim-sum snacks. Two frying trolleys are wheeled out into the middle of the room, serving spring rolls, crabmeat balls and superb Chinese fish-cakes. Steamed items are cooked to order in the kitchen: woo kok, char siu buns and cheung-fun are all filling and first rate. There are also spicy nut dumplings, steamed cockles and winkles, as well as superb egg tarts. The full menu is hard to resist, but will take the bill beyond single figures.

MARPLE Greater Manchester   map 7

Little Mill Inn [6/10]

Rowarth, Marple Bridge
TEL New Mills (0663) 43178

Open for food 11.30 to 2.30, 6 to 10.30 & (also WC)

The virtues of this pub in a converted mill are the attractive setting and the fact that it is a good venue for families with children. The food is Bury black puddings, roasts, casseroles and unusual items, such as smoked halibut. Sunday lunch is £5.75 (children eat for half price).

MELMERBY Cumbria   map 10

Shepherds Inn [6/10]

TEL Langwathby (076 881) 217

Open for food 11 to 2.30 (noon to 2 Sun), 6 (7 Sun) to 11 (10.30 Sun) &
Closed Christmas Day

Very different to the Village Bakery (see below) across the road, but worth a visit for its bar food and well-kept Marstons Pedigree real ale. Char-grills, ploughman's with home-baked bread, and Cumberland ham salad are supplemented by specials such as pork fillet in cream sauce,

Cumberland sausage hot-pot, and spiced lamb with prunes and raisins. In summer there are extra lunch-time dishes, ranging from ham and mushroom pie to cheese, onion and broccoli quiche. Sunday roast lunch is £3.20.

Village Bakery [9/10]

TEL Langwathby (076 881) 515

Open 8.30am to 5pm &
Closed Mon; Christmas to Easter

Liz and Andrew Whitley's remarkable village bakery is a working blueprint for the country restaurant of the future – an ecologically-minded enterprise in full swing. The use of energy and resources is brilliant: stoneground flour comes from the local watermill at Little Salkeld; organically grown vegetables, fruit, milk and wheat are from the smallholding behind the bakery. The wood-fired brick oven cooks the breads and pies in the first fierce heat of the day, cakes and biscuits as the fire subsides, pizzas on the brick sole, and meats and fish on the embers. The emphasis is on natural, wholesome food. You can have breakfast of Loch Fyne kippers, porridge or a bacon sandwich. Lunch might be three-bean salad, or cottage pie, or even Cumberland sausages with apple sauce. The cream is Jersey; butter is preferred to vegetable margarine. To drink there's not only organic apple juice but Jennings bitter as well.

MIDDLEWICH Cheshire   map 7

Tempters Wine Bar [7/10]

11 Wheelock Street
TEL Middlewich (060 684) 5175

Open 7pm to 10.30pm (11pm Fri and Sat)
Closed Sun and Mon; 1 week May; 2 weeks mid-Oct; Christmas Day to 6 Jan

Pam and Allen Diamond take care with shopping and supplies, which explains the quality of the food in their popular wine bar-cum-bistro. The menu is eclectic and changes regularly to take in caldo verde soup, spiced chickens' livers, beef provençale, and shoulder of lamb in honey and orange juice. Vegetables are fresh and handled with imagination; sweets might

include fresh fruit frangipane. Interesting wines with plenty of decent drinking in the £6 to £7 price range.

MORECAMBE Lancashire   map 7

Coffee Shoppe [6/10]

35 Princes Crescent
TEL Morecambe (0524) 414867

Open 9.30am to 6pm (5pm in winter; 10.30am to 5.30pm Sun) & (also WC)
Closed Christmas Day to 27 Dec, 1 and 2 Jan

This coffee-shop at the end of a parade leading down to the sea offers some of the best value in Morecambe. Sunday lunch is the star attraction, when a three-course roast can be had for under £4. Otherwise there is a typical snack menu of sandwiches, burgers, Cumberland sausage with baked potatoes, and vegetarian dishes such as cheese and nut bake. Unlicensed.

NANTWICH Cheshire   map 7

 A. T. Welch [6/10]

45 Hospital Street
TEL Nantwich (0270) 625491

Open 10am to 3.30pm (noon Wed) & (also WC)
Closed Sun and Mon; Wed pm

The Austin family, who have been in the provisions and cheese trade for three generations, have turned this pork butcher's into something of a centre for local produce. The coffee-shop at the back of the delicatessen serves an excellent hot lunch of home-made, additive-free pork sausages with plum tomatoes, brown sauce and brown bread for £1.75. Also there are ploughman's with blue and white farm-house Cheshire, jacket potatoes with minced meat, cottage pie with beetroot, quiches, and salad. Home-made fruit pies to finish. Excellent freshly ground coffee. 'The Yesteryear Shoppe' – a replica of an old-fashioned grocer's – is also worth a look. Unlicensed.

NORTHWICH Cheshire   map 7

Moorings [5/10]

Anderton Marina
TEL Northwich (0606) 79789

Open 10am to 10pm (6pm Sun) &
Closed Mon; Boxing Day

Functional café overlooking the marina
and the boats on the Trent and Mersey
Canal. Home-made soup, sandwiches,
pizzas, and jacket potatoes, plus chilli con
carne, and cottage pie. Scones, toasted tea-
cakes, and pastries for tea. Handy for
passing motorists and boat crews.

ORMSKIRK Lancashire   map 7

Old Dray [6/10]

47–49 Derby Street
TEL Ormskirk (0695) 78486

Open noon to 2.30, 7 to 9.30 &
Closed Mon; Sun D and Tue D

Once a brewery, but transformed into a
restaurant providing a great local service
for lunchtime meals, with a more
expensive menu in the evenings. The
daytime trade does well with hot savoury
croissants filled with seafood, jacket
potatoes with spicy chicken, double-
decker sandwiches and more substantial
dishes such as grilled gammon with peach
and cranberry sauce, or spaghetti and
crispy bacon in tomato sauce. The three-
course businessmen's lunch (£4.95)
centres on a roast or steak, kidney and
mushroom cobbler. House wine by
the glass.

PENRITH Cumbria   map 10

In Clover [7/10]

Poets Walk
TEL Penrith (0768) 67474

Open 9am to 5pm &
Closed Sun; Wed Nov to May; Christmas Eve
to 3 Jan

Dishes are cooked on the premises in this
wholefood restaurant with a strong
vegetarian bias. The short menu is in the
style of tomato, apple and celery soup,
broccoli and tarragon roulade, chicken and
chestnut pie with wholemeal pastry, and
bramble and apple roly-poly with Jersey
cream. Chilled meals are available to take
away. Wine by the glass, tea and juices.

NEW ENTRY Village Bakery Wholefood Café [7/10]

3 St Andrew's Churchyard
TEL Penrith (0768) 65256

Open 10am to 4.30pm
Closed Wed and Sun

An off-shoot of the Village Bakery,
Melmerby (see entry), above the Eden
Valley Craft Gallery. The simply furnished
café sells the whole range of produce from
the bakery, plus excellent salads and
sandwiches. Unlicensed. The Village
Bakery Foodshop in Angel Lane, Penrith, is
the related wholefood delicatessen.

PLUMLEY Cheshire   map 7

NEW ENTRY Smoker [7/10]

Plumley
TEL Lower Peover (056 581) 2338

Open for food noon to 3, 6 to 10
Closed Mon; Sun D

A sign outside reads, 'This inn was
privileged to serve the subjects of Queen
Elizabeth I and is still open. Long live Her
Majesty Queen Elizabeth II'. Situated in
the heart of Manchester stockbroker
country, this thatched pub/restaurant
serves excellent-value lunches for £6.50.
Roasts are the centrepiece, backed up by
sauté lambs' liver, braised ox-tail, and
goujons of plaice with plenty of vegetables.
Start with soup or seafood pancake; finish
with crème brûlée or fresh fruit salad.
Three-course dinners (£10.50) include half
a bottle of wine per couple. Bar snacks are
also available (sandwiches only at Sunday
lunch-time).

PORT ST MARY Isle of Man   map 9

Shore Hotel [6/10]

TEL Port St Mary (0624) 832269

Open for food noon to 2, 8 to 10 & (also wc)
Closed Sun D

Free-and-easy seaside pub by a watersports
centre. The landlord says that none of the
food is frozen and that he doesn't serve
chips. Instead, the menu relies on home-

made soup, chicken and mushroom pie, hot-pot, and pork with mushroom and cream sauce, with lemon torte or apple pie to finish. Garden, terrace and barbecue area.

POULTON-LE-FYLDE
Lancashire   map 7

Anna's Bistro [7/10]

15 Breck Road
TEL Poulton-le-Fylde (0253) 882336

Open 8.30 to 3.30, 7 to 10.30 (10.30 to 3.30 Sun) &
Closed bank hols

The setting is a small converted shop with pink cloths on the pine tables, and ladder-back chairs. Evening menus put it above the average café, with bistro-style dishes such as pork steak in ginger and orange sauce, roast duck with plum and brandy sauce, and broccoli and walnut bake. During the day there are pizzas, omelettes, and sandwiches. Sunday lunch is excellent value at £2.25 for the main course (add £1.25 for soup and sweet). Unlicensed, but bring your own wine.

Stocks [7/10]

2 Queens Square
TEL Blackpool (0253) 882294

Open 11.30am to 2pm, 7pm to 10pm
Closed L Sat to Wed; 2 weeks Aug

Aptly named, because it overlooks the ancient stocks in the centre of the town. The German mottoes on the painted black beams give a clue to the cooking, which is international with a Teutonic slant. Steaks are the main business but the menu roams around Europe. Two days a week there is a homely, old-world lunch menu of good-value dishes, from fish soup, Wurstsalat, and savoury mince with noodles to Russian eggs, Italian omelette and German goulash.

PRESTON Lancashire   map 7

 Auctioneer [8/10]

BCA Centre, Walton Summit, Bamber Bridge
TEL Preston (0772) 324870

Open noon to 2, 7 to 9.30
Closed Tue; Mon D and Sat L

In the bizarre setting of a second-hand car lot – actually the British Car Auction Centre – this restaurant is rated as giving the best value in the area by a long stretch. Dishes have 'lot numbers' and a 'reserve price' and menus are changed every two weeks. Lunch is the real bargain at £5 for three courses, and it's traditional: home-made soup, Yorkshire pudding, or egg mayonnaise before roast beef, roast pork, lamb cutlets or 'smooth kidneys' – cooked with prawns, lemon and cream sauce. Sweets are from the trolley. House wine by the glass. Easily reached from Junction 29 of the M6, behind the Novotel.

NEW ENTRY **Cayso** [7/10]

50 St Johns Square
TEL Preston (0772) 202214

Open 11.30am to midnight (4.30pm Mon, 2.30am Fri and Sat)
Closed Sun; Mon D

Something a little different in Preston – an all-day Caribbean restaurant offering all kinds of spicy possibilities. Lunch is served until 5pm; dishes such as chicken legs in spicy sauce with salad and well-flavoured rice can be had for around £2. The evening menu offers equally good value for ackee and saltfish, Caribbean curry, and peanut stew. Coo coo is corn-meal and okra cooked with coconut milk and fish; also look for the Dance Hall specials – 'dance and eat at the same time' – for £2.80.

Sanchos [6/10]

64 Friargate
TEL Preston (0772) 22993

Open 5pm (noon Sat and Sun) to 11.30pm
Closed L Mon to Fri

There are plenty of bargains in this warm, cosy Mexican restaurant. Have just a taco or a tostadita as a snack, or invest a little more in chimichangas, enchiladas or specialities such as asado à la tampiquena. 'Combination dinners' are excellent value: Yucatan (£4.75) has enchilada with cheese and chorizo sausage, plus Spanish rice, refried beans and chicken tostadita, with salad. Wines, beers and cocktails to drink.

Tiggis [6/10]

38–42 Guildhall Street
TEL Preston (0772) 58527

Open noon to 2, 6.30 to 11.30 (midnight Fri and Sat) &
Closed Sun

Busy, fast-food trattoria, rated locally as the best of the bunch in Lancashire. The uncluttered room is useful for parties. The focus is on pizzas and pasta dishes, but there are also more expensive options, such as punchy pollo di diavolo spiked with chillies. House wines by the glass or carafe. There are branches in Lytham St Annes and Bolton (see entries).

RAMSEY Isle of Man   map 9

Gophers [6/10]

2 West Quay
TEL Douglas (0624) 815562

Open 10am to 8pm (5pm Sun and in winter; 6pm Fri and Sat in winter)
Closed Sun Oct to end Feb; Christmas Day and Boxing Day

Useful quayside coffee-shop with beamed ceilings and good views of the harbour. French bread rolls are baked each day and filled with anything from corned beef and onion to cream cheese and chives. There are also baked potatoes, chicken curry, soup and a daily special, such as quiche with salad.

RAVENSTONEDALE
Cumbria   map 10

Black Swan [7/10]

TEL Newbiggin-on-Lune (058 73) 204

Open for food noon to 1.30, 7 to 8.45
& (1 step; also wc)
Closed Jan and Feb; Mon Oct to Dec, and Mar

A lakeland hotel less than ten minutes' drive from the M6. It is well worth a detour for its no-frills bar food, which takes in bowls of home-made vegetable soup, ploughman's with Wensleydale and other local cheeses, grilled Cumberland

sausage with spiced apple sauce, and home-baked ham. There are also potted shrimps and steaks. Puddings, such as walnut meringue pie and chocolate rum pot, are made each day. Youngers beers. More expensive restaurant meals.

ROCHDALE
Greater Manchester   map 7

Tony's [5/10]

417 Oldham Road
TEL Rochdale (0706) 42975

Open 11 to 2, 8.30 to midnight
Closed Sun; Christmas Day and Boxing Day; last week June and first week July; first week Sept

The queues are a good sign at this popular local chippie. The choice is limited, but fish is freshly cooked in crisp batter and chips are not greasy. Low prices, massive portions.

SALFORD
Greater Manchester   map 7

Mark Addy [6/10]

Stanley Street
TEL 061-832 4080

Open for food 11.30 to 3 (noon to 2 Sun), 5.30 to 11 (7 to 10.30 Sun)
Closed Christmas Day and Boxing Day

A modern conversion of an old riverboat waiting-room on the banks of the River Irwell, with lots of smoked glass, exposed brickwork and a waterside terrace. The pub is named after a Victorian hero who was famous for rescuing over fifty people from the murky waters. The food takes its cue from the Royal Oak, Didsbury (see entry): a vast range of cheeses (although none from the farmhouse) are matched with great hunks of excellent bread, pickled onions and dill cucumbers. Boddingtons beers, a good choice of generic wines, plus doggy bags.

NEW ENTRY Salford College of Technology [7/10]

Frederick Road
TEL 061-736 6541

Open noon to 2 Mon, Wed and Fri, plus 6 to 9.30
Tue and Thur
Closed 3 weeks at Christmas; 2 weeks at Easter;
Whitsun to Oct

The Hotel and Catering Department has
its own restaurant where students can put
theory into practice. Lunch is as little as
£2.50, dinner around £10 with drinks.
Typically, a starter of mixed sausage salad
might be followed by pot-roast chicken
and carefully cooked vegetables, with
orange soufflé to finish. Sixty wines, plus
cocktails and herb teas to drink.

SEATOLLER Cumbria   map 9

Yew Tree Country Restaurant [6/10]

TEL Borrowdale (059 684) 634

Open noon to 9pm (9.30pm Sat, 8pm Sun) &
(also wc)
Closed Mon; Fri L; Dec to mid-Mar

This whitewashed country restaurant in
two seventeenth-century lakeland
cottages at the foot of Coniston Pass has
long been a favourite of walkers, climbers
and ramblers. Inside the ceiling is beamed,
the floor stone-flagged and the log fire
burns on windy days. Lunch is a wholesome selection of home-made soup, toasted
sandwiches, ratatouille with melted
cheese, smoked meat and fish with salad,
plus omelettes, jacket potatoes, and
wholemeal rolls packed with hot beef and
garlic. Afternoon tea (from 2.30 to 4.30pm)
includes scones and hot gingerbread with
rum butter. More expensive dinners.

SLAIDBURN Lancashire   map 7

Hark to Bounty [6/10]

TEL Slaidburn (020 06) 246

Open for food 7.30am to 11pm & (also wc)

One virtue of this oak-beamed moorland
pub is its opening hours. Food is served
throughout the day. The backbone is an
extensive cold buffet, available from noon
to 9pm. Around that there is breakfast
(even for non-residents), mid-morning
scones and coffee, afternoon tea, and high
teas of haddock and chips or Cumberland
sausage with stuffing and apple sauce. Bar

snacks are also served during licensing
hours, with dishes such as soup from the
stock-pot, seafood gratin, steak and kidney
plate pie, and minced beef curry. More
expensive restaurant dinners. Thwaites
beer on draught.

SOUTHPORT Merseyside   map 7

Swan [6/10]

52–54 Stanley Street
TEL Southport (0704) 30720

Open 11.30 to 2, 4.30 to 11; carvery 6.30 (6 Fri,
Sat and Sun) to 9.30 (10.30 Fri and Sat) plus noon
to 4 Sun &

Downstairs is the best-value fish and chip
restaurant in Southport, with haddock and
chips, roast of the day and chips, or beefsteak pudding, gravy and chips for well
under £2. Business lunches are £2.50;
three-course high teas (4.30 to 7.30
Monday to Friday) are £2.75. Upstairs is a
carvery and restaurant, where the best deal
is the three-course special for £5.75.
Reduced prices for children upstairs
and down.

STANDISH
Greater Manchester   map 7

Beeches [7/10]

TEL Standish (0257) 426432

Open noon to 2, 7 to 10 & (also wc)

Best known for relatively expensive meals
in the corniced dining-room, this
converted Victorian mansion also serves
snacks in the lounge bar. Soups are based
on good stocks from the kitchen, salads
include some nouvelle ideas, and the
menu is biased towards fresh fish – sea
bass, queen scallops, Scotch cod. Meat
dishes might include sirloin strips in Dijon
mustard sauce or roast turkey. Home-
made ice-creams to finish. Reasonably
priced wines, Tetleys beers.

STOCKPORT
Greater Manchester   map 7

Coconut Willy's [7/10]

37 St Petersgate
TEL 061-480 7013

Open 10am to 10pm &
Closed Sun and Mon

PVC cloths deck the tables in this converted shop on the fringe of the town centre, and there are still one or two survivors from the plethora of toy parrots that lurked among the greenery. During the day it's self-service for crisp onion bhajias, stuffed aubergines, and harvest pie with wholemeal pastry. Sweets range from chocolate mousse to Caribbean coconut ice. Waitress service and a slightly more expensive menu in the evening. Interesting drinks, including organic wines, herb teas and naturally brewed Chimay beer from Belgium.

ULLSWATER Cumbria   map 9

Sharrow Bay [8/10]

Howtown Road
TEL Pooley Bridge (085 36) 301/483

Open 4pm to 4.45pm
Closed early Dec to early Mar

Afternoon tea at Sharrow Bay is a memorable way of spending £5. It is an occasion to sit, relax and be lavishly waited upon in one of the greatest and most English of country-house hotels. The setting is two ornamental rooms with deep sofas, heavy drapes and walls covered with paintings. The teapot and cups are brought in on a silver tray; heavily buttered scones are served with a big bowl of jam and whipped cream. There are rounds of hot buttered toast, savoury sandwiches and a great assortment of cakes cut into pieces. Meals in the restaurant are well outside the scope of this book. No children.

WARRINGTON Cheshire   map 7

Hilal [6/10]

Victoria Buildings, Stockton Heath
TEL Warrington (0925) 68199/64992

Open noon to 2.30, 5.30 to midnight
Closed Christmas Day and Boxing Day

More like an ornate pavilion than a standard curry house, although the menu holds few surprises. The usual range of dhansaks, bhunas and vindaloos are supplemented by tandooris and

specialities such as lamb pasanda. The price of curries includes rice and pickles. Set dinners from £9 a head; weekday lunches £4.50.

WATERMILLOCK Cumbria   map 9

Rampsbeck Hotel [7/10]

TEL Pooley Bridge (085 36) 442

Open noon to 2.30, 7 to 9

A fine old country house set in fourteen acres of grounds on the shores of Ullswater. It offers excellent-value lunches in an area densely populated with classy hotels. Have just one course or a full meal from a menu that takes in wild mushroom soup with smoked salmon ravioli, pork loin in pear and Stilton glaze, or breast of chicken stuffed with crab mousse in lemon sauce. There are also salads and a choice of sweets. More expensive dinners.

WHALLEY Lancashire   map 7

Tudor Rose [6/10]

73 King Street
TEL Whalley (025 482) 2462

Open noon to 2 (2.15 Sat, noon and 1.45 Sun), 4.15 to 6.15 (6.30 Sun) & (also WC)
Closed Mon (exc bank hols)

This restaurant aims to serve 'good-value' lunches (three courses for £4). Start with Lancashire rarebit made with Thwaites ale and Lancashire cheese or egg mayonnaise, before beef casserole with herb dumplings, grilled lamb cutlets or poached fillets of plaice with hot lemon butter, and finish with damson pie and custard, or peach and brandy syllabub. Afternoon teas are served Tuesday to Saturday. The restaurant is extremely proud of its fresh floral displays.

WHITEHAVEN Cumbria   map 9

Bruno's [6/10]

9–10 Church Street
TEL Whitehaven (0946) 65270

Open noon to 2.30, 6 to 10.30
Closed Sun L

Excellent-value lunches are served in this popular trattoria-cum-wine bar. Home-made pizza and pasta dishes are a good bet, otherwise there are daily specials, such as veal in white wine and mushroom sauce or fresh prawn tails in garlic, wine and herbs, for less than £2. Bread and sweets are made on the premises. Wine is 90p a glass. Take-aways.

WHITEWELL Lancashire   map 7

Inn at Whitewell [6/10]

Forest of Bowland, nr Clitheroe
TEL Dunsop Bridge (020 08) 222

Open for food noon to 2, 3 to 5.30, 7 to 9.15 &

The pub stands on its own by a church in the Forest of Bowland, and the River Hodder flows past the bottom of the garden. Bar lunches feature good North Country food with some fancy touches: spicy Cumberland sausages casseroled in red wine; local trout cured and smoked like salmon; chicken liver pâté laced with malt whisky. There's Lancashire cheese in the ploughman's and home-made ice-cream to finish. More expensive dinners. Moorhouses beers on draught. The pub has a wine merchant's and art gallery attached, plus eight miles of fishing rights.

WIGAN Greater Manchester   map 7

Roberto's [6/10]

Rowbottom Square
TEL Wigan (0942) 42385

Open noon to 2, 7 to 10 (10.30 Fri and Sat)
Closed Sun; bank hols

There's a cheap lunch menu in this trattoria-cum-pizza bar. Pizzas are freshly made; there's also a good choice of pasta, such as fettuccine alfredo, plus steak and mushroom pie, chilli con carne, and vegetable and nut pancake. Salads and omelettes complete the picture. Choose carefully from the main menu to keep the bill in single figures. Barbecues and take-aways.

WILMSLOW Cheshire   map 7

NEW ENTRY | Yang Sing Bistro [9/10]

70 Grove Street
TEL Wilmslow (0625) 528799

Open 5.30pm to 11pm, plus noon to 2.30 Sun
Closed Mon; Christmas Day

This branch of the brilliant Yang Sing in Manchester (see entry) is over a shop in the centre of town. The décor is all mirrors and colourful Chinese prints. Fourteen dim-sum show the same adventurous style as the city-centre giant: not only steamed prawn dumplings, spring rolls, and sesame prawn toasts, but also coconut-cream balls, deep-fried yam roll with almonds and glazed walnuts. A selection of these at £1 an item would make a fine lunch. For a bigger outlay, the full menu offers a similar blend of the classic and the original – from lemon chicken and Szechuan fish to beef with macadamia nuts, and venison with shredded Chinese mushrooms. Drink jasmine tea or Grolsch lager.

WINDERMERE Cumbria   map 10

NEW ENTRY | Miller Howe Kaff [9/10]

Lakeland Plastics, Station Precinct

Open 10am to 4pm &
Closed Sun

Like the Ram Jam Inn (see Stretton, Leicestershire, East Midlands) this high-class café is a down-market off-shoot of a prestigious restaurant. Robert Lyons from Miller Howe is the guiding light behind this unlikely set-up in a corner of the Lakeland Plastics factory behind the old Windermere railway station. Snacks are glimpses of the Miller Howe menu but at a fraction of the price. There are marvellous pâtés and terrines, such as cream cheese and herb or savoury duck and pistachio, salads with superb home-made mayonnaise or oily dressings, quiches, and dishes ranging from Cumberland sausage with apple sauce, date and onion chutney to bobotie (minced lamb with apricots and almonds topped with brandied egg custard). Sweets are classics from the John Tovey repertoire. New Zealand wines by the glass.

Poplars [7/10]

Lake Road
TEL Windermere (096 62) 2325

Open 6pm
Closed Dec and Jan

This homely guest-house serves good food with no short cuts. Fixed-price dinners (four courses plus coffee, at 6pm only) are not that cheap, but still excellent value at £7. Typically there might be sweet-and-sour stuffed pancakes before cream of leek and celery soup. Main courses, such as sugar-baked ham with cider sauce or stuffed poached plaice, come with excellent fresh vegetables. Sweets feature good Derbyshire tart with bananas and rum, frangipane filling and an apricot glaze. Bookings only.

Manchester's Chinatown

The restaurants and cafés in Chinatown have a reputation for quality and authenticity which attracts customers from all parts of the country. On Saturdays and Sundays, owners of chop suey houses and take-aways shop in the supermarkets and eat in the nearby restaurants. During the week, Manchester's Chinese community and European enthusiasts keep most of the dining-rooms pretty busy. Cheap eaters should go for dim-sum snacks which usually cost about £1 each, and one-plate meals – large dishes of rice or noodles with meat or seafood, which average about £3. It is a good idea to combine dim-sum with a one-plate meal for more variety. Set lunches vary a great deal from restaurant to restaurant. While most avoid the packet soups and bottled sauces found in chop suey houses away from Chinatown, they do tend to feature dishes that are popular with westerners. Pearl City is a notable exception. It is also worth remembering that roast meats can be bought ready cooked for eating at home; most restaurants will also provide cakes and buns if they have them.

1a Hopewell City
45–47 Faulkner Street (basement).
Now established as one of the smartest and best places for roast meats and dim-sum. Set lunches are less interesting. (See entry.)

1b Wing Yip Supermarket
45A Faulkner Street (first floor).
A major supplier of authentic Chinese foods and ingredients.

1c Hong Kong
47 Faulkner Street (first floor).
Still very popular and successful. One-plate meals and many of the dim-sum do not appear on the English-language menu. (See entry.)

2 Modern Cultural Services
18 Nicholas Street.
Importers of non-culinary Chinese goods.

3 Kai's
16 Nicholas Street.
This basement restaurant has lost some ground to the newer places. It is still cheap, open late and now has a Buddhist vegetarian menu.

4a Tak Sing Hong Supermarket
57 Faulkner Street (ground floor).
Useful source of authentic Chinese produce.

4b Dragon Gate
57 Faulkner Street.
Newish, smart-looking Cantonese restaurant in the basement below the supermarket. A good choice for roast meats and one-plate meals. (See entry.)

5 Wong Chu
63 Faulkner Street.
Bowls of rice and meat are the cheap bargain here, and are a better bet than the set lunches. (See entry.)

6 The Emperor's Garden Restaurant & Night Club
36 Princess Street.
Exactly what the name suggests.

7 Wing Hai Dong Supermarket
56 Faulkner Street.
Another of the good local supermarkets.

8 Ho's Bakery
34 Princess Street.
Two superb char siu buns will provide a filling lunch for less than £1.

9 Yang Sing
34 Princess Street.
Now rated as the finest Chinese restaurant in Britain. The basement restaurant serves incomparable dim-sum, but one-plate meals are not a strong point. (See entry.)

10 Kwok Man
28 Princess Street.
Popular basement restaurant, although less

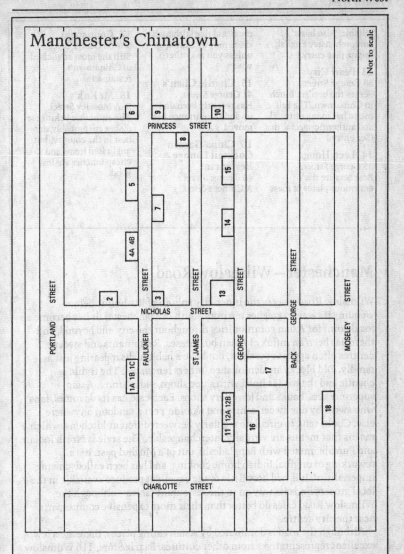

Manchester's Chinatown

Not to scale

PRINCESS STREET

NICHOLAS STREET

CHARLOTTE STREET

PORTLAND STREET

FAULKNER STREET

ST JAMES STREET

GEORGE STREET

BACK GEORGE STREET

MOSELEY STREET

6 · 9 · 10 · 8 · 5 · 7 · 15 · 14 · 4A 4B · 2 · 3 · 13 · 17 · 1A 1B 1C · 11 12A 12B · 16 · 18

impressive than some of
its neighbours.

11 Little Yang Sing
17 George Street.
The original Yang Sing
premises (see No. 9),
recently re-opened.

Superb dim-sum.
(See entry.)

**12a Woo Sang
Supermarket**
19–21 George Street.
The ground-floor super-
market is the most popular

with western shoppers.

12b Woo Sang
19–21 George Street.
The first-floor restaurant
has held its own against
the competition. Very

reliable. Also has a comprehensive English menu. (See entry.)

13 Pearl City
33 George Street.
Serves the best set lunch in Chinatown. The full menu has many unusual and authentic specialities. (See entry.)

14 Leen Hong
35 George Street.
Best bets are the enormous plates of roast meat and rice (although these may be heated up unless you ask otherwise

15 Charlie Chan's
41 George Street.
Has recently been done up and the entrance has moved.

16 China Garden Cocktail Lounge & Restaurant
46 George Street.
A Chinese disco.

17 Connaught
56–60 George Street.
Still the most anglicised of Chinatown's restaurants.

18 Mr Kuk's
55A Moseley Street.
The authentic Pekingese dishes are probably the best in the country, but anglicised items and cheap lunches are less good.

Manchester – Wilmslow Road

Wilmslow Road bisects the inner-city suburb of Rusholme before wending its way to greener territory south of Manchester. It has become a focal point for Asian communities throughout the city and beyond, and there has been an influx of Asian businesses. Restaurants and sweet-centres often appear overnight, but have a habit of disappearing just as rapidly. Old blocks are demolished, others renovated. The traffic is chaotic and the road is lined with saree shops, video stores, Asian supermarkets, banks and jewellery shops. Each café has its devotees, fans who swear by one sweet-centre and wouldn't eat a tandoori anywhere else. Cooks tend to circulate regularly between different kitchens, which means that menus are virtually interchangeable. The style is North Indian and Punjabi, mixed with Bangladeshi, out of a Moghul past. It's a reworking of original Indian home cooking, and has been called 'cuisine imperialism'. It is odd how little of the excellent produce available in the local grocers finds its way on to the restaurant tables – although the Wilmslow Road cafés do better than their more expensive counterparts near the city centre.

Although the road is dominated by Asian eating places, there are a few excellent representatives from other cultures. Lazziz Store, 116 Wilmslow Road, is a new Middle Eastern shop with enormous trays of sticky sweets as well as pickles, nuts, seeds and spices. Go there for preserved lemons, sumak powder, labneh in olive oil, pomegranate syrup and freshly made pistachio halva. Minar, on the corner of Park Crescent, specialises in East African dishes. Look for the 'spicy mince snake covered with mesh potatoes'. A few blocks away is Cowlishaws, one of the best English fish and game shops in the city.

Manchester – Wilmslow Road

1 Prime Grocers
Wilmslow Road.
New grocery store in a
purpose-built block.

2 Shere Khan
Wilmslow Road.
Large, new corner-
restaurant done out in
some style with an
open kitchen range along
one side. Specialises in
karahi dishes, dhansaks,
dopiazas and tandooris.

3 Shezan
64 Wilmslow Road.
The original, still with its
red and gold flock
wallpaper, though it is
beginning to show its age.
Famous for sabzi dishes
(meat and vegetables) and
pillow rice (sic).

4 I Singh & Sons
Wilmslow Road.
Indian grocers.

5 Sheraz
76 Wilmslow Road.
Standard restaurant. Only
open in the evening.

6 Punjab
Wilmslow Road.
Decorated in lurid shades
of pink and plum. Specials
include tandoori masala,
tikkas and kebabs. Offers
ten per cent discount to
students.

7 M/C Grocers
Wilmslow Road.
Halal meat and vegetable
store with a good
selection of fresh spinach,
coriander, methi and
mustard greens. Small
and modernised.

8 Indian Cottage
Wilmslow Road.
The smartest restaurant
on Wilmslow Road. Note
that the entrance is round
the corner at 501
Claremont Road.
(See entry.)

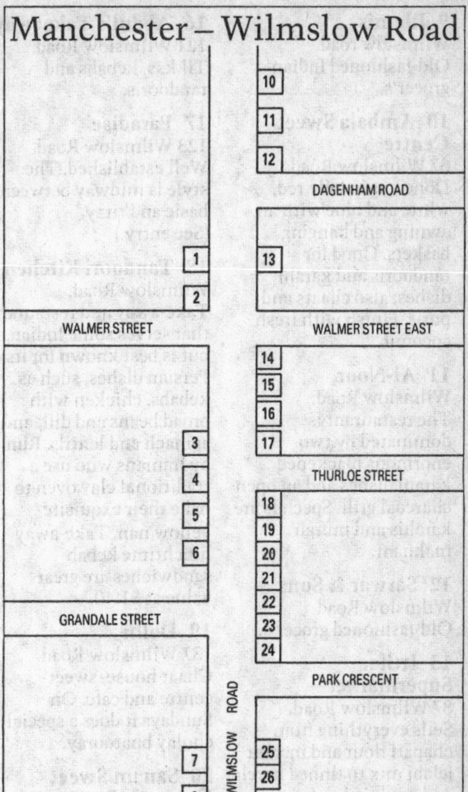

Map with the following street labels and numbered locations:

10, 11, 12

DAGENHAM ROAD

13

1, 2

WALMER STREET

WALMER STREET EAST

14, 15, 16, 17

THURLOE STREET

3, 4, 5, 6

18, 19, 20, 21, 22, 23, 24

GRANDALE STREET

PARK CRESCENT

WILMSLOW ROAD

25, 26

7, 8

CLAREMONT ROAD

27, 28, 29

9

RUSHOLME GROVE

30

DICKENSON ROAD

PLATT LANE

Not to scale

9 Jilamis
Wilmslow road.
Old-fashioned Indian
grocer's.

**10 Ambala Sweet
Centre**
67 Wilmslow Road.
Done out in jolly red,
white and blue with an
awning and hanging
baskets. Good for
tandooris and karahi
dishes, also chaats and
puris. Finish with fresh
coconut.

11 Al-Noor
Wilmslow Road.
The restaurant is
dominated by two
enormous blackened
karahi dishes and an open
charcoal grill. Specials are
karahis and murgh
makhani.

12 Sarwar & Sons
Wilmslow Road.
Old-fashioned grocer's.

**13 Ittifaq
Supermarket**
87 Wilmslow Road.
Sells everything from
chapati flour and instant
jelabi mix to tinned karela
and mega-tubs of ghee.

14 Jewel in the Crown
109 Wilmslow Road.
Has an eye-catching,
flashy green and white
sign, tinted windows and
waiters in full costume.
Specialities include
murgh massalam and
murgh tandoori. A good
vegetable thali for
two is £10.

15 Shezan
119 Wilmslow Road.
Large ornate restaurant
and take-away, with
rococo ceilings and
brown check cloths.
Usual menu range.
Related to No. 3.

16 Abdul's Takeaway
121 Wilmslow Road.
Tikkas, kebabs and
tandooris.

17 Paradise
123 Wilmslow Road.
Well established. The
style is midway between
basic and ritzy.
(See entry.)

18 Tandoori Kitchen
Wilmslow Road.
Take-away and restaurant
that serves some Indian,
but is best known for its
Persian dishes, such as
kebabs, chicken with
broad beans and dill, and
spinach and lentils. Run
by Iranians who use a
traditional clay oven to
bake their exquisite
yellow nan. Take-away
lunchtime kebab
sandwiches are great
value at £1.40.

19 Delhi
137 Wilmslow Road.
Chaat house, sweet-
centre and café. On
Sundays it does a special
cholay bhatooray.

**20 Sanam Sweet
Centre & Restaurant**
141 Wilmslow Road.
Large, plush and busy.
Outside there are gold
pillars and red canopies,
inside there are marble-
topped tables, fancy
chairs and an upper
gallery in pine.
Specialities include
brains, mackerel tandoori,
shahi kebab and heart and
kidneys karahi.

21 Halal Kebab House
Wilmslow Road.
Popular take-away.

**22 Mancunian Halal
Takeaway**
Wilmslow Road.
Take-away tikkas,
kebabs, pakoras and
bhajias.

23 Sanam
145–151 Wilmslow Road.
Well established, with a
window full of good
things. Specials include
jeera chicken cooked with
vinegar and black pepper.
On Sundays there are puri
chana and katlamma. (See
entry.)

24 Asia
Wilmslow Road.
Sweet centre and
restaurant. The décor is
showing its age, but the
place is as popular as ever.

25 Chuni's Food Store
Wilmslow Road.
Has recently taken over
the Indian Cottage across
the road (see No. 8).
Superb range of exotic
fruit and vegetables.

26 Amee Supermarket
Wilmslow Road.
Fruit, vegetables, utensils,
groceries and gifts. Also
an excellent choice of
rices, plus eight-feet high
sticks of sugar cane.

27 Ravi Food Store
213 Wilmslow Road.
Fruit, vegetables, nuts and
paneer.

**28 Sanam Sweet
House & Restaurant**
Wilmslow Road.
The original branch of
No. 20, with a smaller
menu.

**29 Probashi Food
Store** Wilmslow Road.
Halal meat and chicken,
plus fish and vegetables.

30 Wazi Foodstore
239 Wilmslow Road.
Sells spices, fruit,
vegetables, chicken, meat
and fish.

North East

APPLETREEWICK
North Yorkshire   map 7

Craven Arms [6/10]

TEL Burnsall (075 672) 270

Open for food noon to 2, 7 to 9.30 &

Gordon and Linda Elsworth put the
emphasis on meaty local produce in their
classic Dales pub. Sausages are made
locally, hams are home roasted and steaks
are from a nearby butcher. There's also
home-made soup, Cumberland sausage
with onion sauce, and a hefty mixed grill.
Tetleys, Youngers and Theakstons beers
on handpump.

ARNCLIFFE North Yorkshire   map 7

Raikes Cottage [6/10]

Malham Road
TEL Arncliffe (075 677) 240

Open 10am to 6.30pm &
Closed Mon; Nov to end Feb

Arncliffe is the kind of village that attracts
tourists: it is exceedingly pretty, it was a
source of inspiration to Charles Kingsley
when he was writing *The Water Babies*
and was the original setting for the TV
series *Emmerdale Farm*. The cottage tea-
room provides homely sustenance for the
crowds of visitors. Buttered scones,
toasted tea-cakes, Yorkshire rarebit with
chutney, and grilled gammon with farm
eggs and chips, are supplemented by
home-baked cakes. Wine by the glass.

BAINBRIDGE
North Yorkshire   map 10

Rose and Crown Hotel [6/10]

TEL Wensleydale (0969) 50225

Open for food 11.30 to 2.15, 7 to 9 & (also wc)

An ancient stone inn grouped with other
solid houses around a green. Outside there
are views of the moors; inside it is all
beams and comfortable settles. The bar
food is ample, although the quality has
been variable. Look for the excellent thick
vegetable soup with fresh wholemeal rolls,
the home-made pies, and the ploughman's
with Wensleydale cheese. McEwans 80/–

and Youngers Scotch on handpump. Take-
away snacks.

BARNARD CASTLE
Durham   map 10

Market Place Teashop [9/10]

29 Market Place
TEL Teesdale (0833) 690110

Open 10am (3pm Sun) to 5.30pm
Closed Sun Dec to Mar; 1 week at Christmas

The word 'tea-shop' hardly does justice to
the extraordinary range of food available in
this café. The success is in serving honest
home-cooked food without frills or
showiness. Snacks and full meals are
available all day, when the menu ranges
from cottage pie, Welsh rarebit and pizzas
to specials such as braised lamb's liver,
pot-roast brisket with Yorkshire pudding,
and breast of chicken stuffed with home-
made mushroom pâté. Vegetarian dishes
are now a feature: home-made samosas
and chilladas with fresh tomato sauce and
bean salad; baked spinach with cheese and
brown rice. To finish there are ice-creams
and to drink there's Hugh Rock's elderflower wine or Northumbrian spring water.

Secret Garden [7/10]

27 Haymarket
TEL Teesdale (0833) 38848

Open 9.30am to 5pm &
Closed Sun; Christmas Day

Mrs Straker has turned this huge, peak-
roofed barn into a beamed self-service
restaurant with a children's party room
upstairs. There's sawdust on the floors and
rustic murals on the walls. The range of
food takes in smoked chicken salad, and
liver casserole, as well as bean crumble
and home-made persimmon ice-cream.
Table licence at lunch-time.

BARTON-ON-HUMBER
Humberside   map 8

Elio's [6/10]

11 Market Place
TEL Barton-on-Humber (0652) 635147

Open noon to 2.30, 7 to 11 & (also wc)
Closed Sun; Mon L; bank hols L; Boxing Day

A useful choice for decent Italian food during an outing to the Humber Bridge. The décor is cheerful and bright, and the long menu has good-value pizzas and pasta dishes as alternatives to steak, veal, and fish. Fixed-price three-course lunches.

BAWTRY South Yorkshire map 7

 China Rose [7/10]

27 Market Place
TEL Doncaster (0302) 710461

Open 5.30pm to 11pm & (also WC)

By no means the cheapest Cantonese restaurant in the north of England, but nonetheless useful in the area, unpretentious and good value. Set meals from £8 a head show the mix of old-style and fashionable dishes: barbecued spare ribs and sweet-and-sour pork alongside sizzling chicken with black-bean sauce, fried beef with broccoli and fried rice. Go in a crowd to keep the bill within limits.

BERWICK-UPON-TWEED
Northumberland map 10

Scotsgate Wine Bar [7/10]

1 Sidey Court
TEL Berwick-upon-Tweed (0289) 302621

Open 10 to 3, 6.30 to 10.30 &
Closed Sun; Mon D; Christmas Day, Boxing Day and 1 Jan

Renamed the Scotsgate, this big panelled room with pine tables buzzes with activity. There's a good choice of classic wine-bar food taking in leek and potato soup, goulash with rice, and beef and vegetable curry. Vegetarians do well with assortments of potatoes, celery and carrots in a savoury sauce, or groundnuts, haricot beans, pasta shells and peppers on brown rice. Banoffi pie or walnut and caramel pie to finish. Decent house wine by the glass.

 Tweedview Hotel [7/10]

Tweed Street
TEL Berwick-upon-Tweed (0289) 307274/302789

Open noon to 2; 6 (7 Sun) to 10.30 & (also WC)

There are magnificent views of Stephenson's railway bridge and the mouth of the River Tweed from this small hotel near the station. Set lunches are good value at £5.95 for dishes such as coarse rabbit pâté, roast pork, or Eyemouth haddock in batter with decent vegetables, then apple pie or fruit mille-feuille. There are also bar snacks along similar lines. More expensive dinners in the restaurant.

BINGLEY West Yorkshire map 7

Beckside Fisheries [5/10]

1A Main Street, Cottingley
TEL Bingley (0274) 566354

Open 11.45 to 1.15, 8.30 to 11.30 (11.15 Mon), Wed, Fri and Sat &
Closed Sun; Tue; Thur; Mon L

This little wooden hut is the hub of the village. There's room for half a dozen people standing and the menu is pared down to the bone: fish, chips, fish and chips, fishcakes, peas, tea-cakes. Nothing else. Unlicensed.

BISHOP AUCKLAND
Durham map 10

Gabriele's [6/10]

15 Flintoff Street
TEL Bishop Auckland (0388) 604942

Open noon to 2, 6 to 11.30 &
Closed Sun; bank hols

Good-value trattoria serving some of the cheapest pastas and pizzas in the area. There are good reports of the minestrone, spaghetti bolognese, and garlic bread. Three-course set lunch is £2.95. Drinkable house red.

BOLTON ABBEY
North Yorkshire map 7

Bolton Abbey Tea Cottage [6/10]

The Green
TEL Bolton Abbey (075 671) 495

Open 10am to 6pm & (also WC)
Closed Dec to Feb; weekdays Oct to Dec, Feb to Easter

Everyone's idea of a country cottage tea-room, with beams, flagstoned floors and an enchanting garden, plus superb views overlooking Bolton Abbey. The food is home made, and afternoon tea is the star attraction. Sandwiches, scones and jam, cake, tea-bread and a pot of tea costs around £2. There are also savoury dishes, plus a good-value Sunday lunch.

BRADFORD West Yorkshire map 7

Baxendall's [5/10]

Kirkgate Market, Arndale Centre
TEL Bradford (0274) 726979

Open 8am to 4pm (2pm Wed)
Closed Sun; bank hols

A café in the row of cafés on the first floor of the modern market precinct. All-day cooked breakfasts are rated as some of the best in Bradford. Lunches begin at 10.30 in the morning with roasts, steak and onion pie, or three sausages with vegetables. There are pies and pasties with mushy peas and mint sauce, as well as freshly baked bread and currant cakes. Unlicensed.

Cocina [6/10]

64 Manningham Lane
TEL Bradford (0274) 727625

Open noon to 2, 6 to 11.30 &
Closed Sat L to Mon L

A good spicy alternative to Bradford's core of Indian cafés. This is a relaxed Mexican cantina with an authentic menu of tacos, burritos, chimichangas, enchiladas, and tostadas, with some vegetarian versions for good measure. Start with guacamole or seafood chowder, and finish with capirotada (Mexican bread-pudding) or pecan pie. Margaritas, Mexican beers and wine by the glass.

Kashmir [9/10]

27 Morley Street
TEL Bradford (0274) 726513

Open 11am to 3am

Regulars remember the days when curries in this odd little Asian café were 35p a

bowl, with as many chapatis as you could eat. Times have changed, but less than £2 still pays for a bowl of curry, three chapatis and yoghurt salad. The attraction is not the décor or the ambience, but the freshly spiced and deeply flavoured food. Chicken masala special with pungent gravy, and keema dhal laced with cumin have been outstanding. Chapatis are unbeatable: you can see them being made through a glass door. Three pairs of hands work all day and all night flattening the dough. They claim to make a thousand a day. Brilliant quality, brilliant value. Unlicensed.

Kebabeesh [6/10]

234 Whetley Lane
TEL Bradford (0274) 499985

Open noon to 3, 5 to 1am (noon to midnight Sun)

The glossy menu looks more like that of a burger joint, but the emphasis is on a mixture of Asian and westernised family food. On the one hand there are tikkas, pakoras, fish masala, and balti gosht with chapatis; on the other, garlic mushrooms, Southern fried chicken, and banana splits. Drink mango juice or a bottle of Grolsch. Take-aways.

Old Road Fish Shop [6/10]

138 Old Road, Great Horton

Open Open 11.30 to 1, 4.30 to 6, 8 (8.30 Sat) to 11.30
Closed Sun; Thur; Mon L and D; Tue tea; Wed D; Sat tea

There's no name on the front, just a 'fish shop' sign, but this take-away chippie rates as one of the best in Bradford. Fish comes fresh from Aberdeen – only two days out of port – and sells for 55p. Chips are rough cut and cost 30p. Seventeen-pence worth of mushy peas is ladled out of a silver churn. Unlicensed. Hard to beat.

Pie Tom [5/10]

Rawson Market
TEL Bradford (0274) 734112

Open 8am to 5pm
Closed Sun and Wed; bank hols; Christmas Day

This tiny pie and pea stall on the famous Rawson Market has an impressive turnover: three thousand pies are sold each week, plus six gallons of mint sauce and three hundred pounds of mushy peas. There are red pews and tables barely big enough to fit your plate on, but for cheap, honest food the place is exceptional. Nothing on the menu is more than £1; it's possible to eat for less. Take-aways. Unlicensed.

NEW ENTRY Pizza Margherita [7/10]

Argus Chambers, Hall-lngs
TEL Bradford (0274) 724333

Open 10.30am to 11pm
Closed Christmas Day, Boxing Day and 1 Jan

One of a trio of better-than-average pizza places in the North of England. (For details see Lancaster.)

Salty's [6/10]

159 St Helena Road, Wibsey
TEL Bradford (0274) 677734

Open 11.30 to 1.30, 4.30 to 6.30, 8 to 11.30
Closed Sun L, Mon L and Thur L

Barry and Mavis Waterworth continue to buy fresh haddock and plaice each day for their spotless chippie three miles from the centre of Bradford. He does the frying with beef dripping; she looks after the redecorated dining-room. Children's menu and reduced prices for senior citizens. Unlicensed.

Shah Kebab House [5/10]

107 Carlisle Road
TEL Bradford (0274) 496711

Open 2pm to 2am (3am Fri and Sat)

Smart, clean, Indian café with brass tubs of plants in the window and black varnished tables. The special lunch is a real bargain: chat salad with chickpeas, apple, potato, cucumber and tomato in a yoghurt dressing, chicken karahi, three chapatis and a plate of salad garnish, all for about £2. Dishes from the menu, such as meat korma or keema madras, are on a par with other cafés in the area. Drink lassi or lager.

Shiraz Sweet House [6/10]

Oak Lane
TEL Bradford (0247) 490176

Open noon to 2am (4am Fri and Sat) &

Like most of its neighbours, this popular Muslim café has a colourful display of excellent sweetmeats in the window. In a gaudy setting of black vinyl and textured Fablon it also serves authentic savoury dishes, which the staff will explain. There are good samosas, kebabs and tikkas to start, followed by classic keema (mince) dishes, kormas and birianis. The Shiraz specials are excellent value at £2.20. Dishes are served with three freshly griddled chapatis, or you can pay an extra 20p for rice. Drink creamy lassi. Unlicensed.

Sweet Centre [5/10]

110–112 Lumb Lane
TEL Bradford (0274) 731735

Open 7.30am to 11pm

Corner Indian café opposite the high side wall of a mill. Inside, it is spartan, functional and there's precious little décor. Breakfast is a couple of puris and a fiery chickpea broth. For the rest of the day, and in the evenings, the menu is similar to that of the other Indian and Pakistani cafés in Bradford. There's a useful restaurant next door, open 9pm to 2am, serving balti dishes, tikkas and masalas.

BRIDLINGTON Humberside   map 8

Marina [6/10]

16–18 South Marine Drive
TEL Bridlington (0262) 674076

Open 6am to 6pm &
Closed weekdays Oct to Feb; Christmas and New Year

A classic North Country seaside café, run with great friendliness by the James family. Breakfasts are big fry-ups and sausage sandwiches; three-course lunches of roasts, fried fish, and steak pie leave plenty of change from £5; high teas are mixed grills, steak, egg and chips, or York ham and eggs. There are also sandwiches, toasted tea-cakes, baked jam roll and gooseberry pie. Unlicensed.

CASTLE BOLTON
North Yorkshire   map 10

Bolton Castle [7/10]

TEL Wensleydale (0969) 23408

Open 12.30 to 2, 7.30 to 9.30
Closed Mon; Sun D

The Great Chamber of Bolton Castle is now the dining-room. The old stove is still there and big wooden pillars dominate the scene. Lunches are interesting and reasonably priced for 'natural' tomato soup, sherried lambs' liver with noodles, Barnsley chop with crab-apple jelly and vegetarian mixed grain risotto. Sweets are surprising: parsnip flan, cranberry ice-cream with rosehip syrup. Three-course Sunday lunches are £5.95 (children under twelve eat half-price) and there are four-course dinners for around £10 a head.

CLECKHEATON
West Yorkshire   map 7

Park Fisheries [6/10]

19–27 Dewsbury Road
TEL Bradford (0274) 872675

Open 11 to 1.30, 4 to 6, 8 to 11 (4 to 11.30 Sun) & (also WC)
Closed Sun L; Christmas Day and Boxing Day

An old-established chippie right in the middle of Cleckheaton. Fish is fresh and fried in crisp batter, chips are excellent and the peas are genuinely mushy. Frying is done with Yorkshire dripping. The shopper's lunch is a bargain at £1.85 for fish and chips plus bread and a cup of tea. Sit down or take-away. Unlicensed.

CLEETHORPES Humberside   map 8

Russell's Wine Bar [7/10]

34 High Street
TEL Cleethorpes (0472) 690050

Open noon to 2, 7.30 to 10
Closed Sun D, Mon D and Tue D; Boxing Day; 1 Jan

The best sticky-toffee pudding in Humberside is served here, in a setting of rickety chairs and oil-cloth covered tables. The food is fresh and mostly home made: cannelloni; turkey, ham and mushroom pie; navarin of lamb. Soups are good and vegetables first rate. Basic list of around thirty wines. Downstairs is the wine bar; upstairs is the bistro. No children.

Steel's Corner House [6/10]

Market Place
TEL Cleethorpes (0472) 692644

Open 10.30am to 10pm (11pm Sat)
Closed Christmas and New Year

Popular neighbourhood café famous for its fried fish. Big helpings of skate, haddock, and plaice are served all day with bread, butter and a pot of tea; grills, omelettes, and salads appear after 3pm. The three-course business lunch (£3.75) centres on roast beef, chicken or steak pie, with soup to start and fruit pie to finish. Unlicensed.

Willy's [6/10]

17 Highcliffe
TEL Cleethorpes (0472) 602145

Open 11 to 3 (noon to 2 Sun), 7 to 10.30 &
Closed Christmas Day

More of a pub than a wine bar. The menu has some decent home-made dishes: beef pies are laced with Guinness or Ruddles beer; pork comes in chilli sauce; and there's chicken Mexican for those who like their food spicy. The views from the mock-Tudor building are across the estuary to Spurn Head.

DARLINGTON Durham   map 10

| NEW ENTRY | # Boobi's [7/10] |

16–18 Coniscliffe Road
TEL Darlington (0325) 482529

Open noon to 2; 7.30 to 11
Closed Sun; Sat L

The setting may seem spartan, but the cooking in this bistro provides some of the best value in the area. At lunch there are simple dishes such as chicken liver pâté, lasagne, and chilli con carne with pitta bread, backed up by some interesting blackboard specials. Fresh fruit is an alternative to the calorific choice of toffee banana pie or chocolate marquise. More expensive dinners. House wine (£6.95) is bottled exclusively for the restaurant. No children.

DONCASTER
South Yorkshire map 7

 Three Cranes Coffee Shop [6/10]

248 Great North Road, Woodlands

Open 8.30am to 5pm (3.30pm Wed and Sat) &
Closed Sun; 2 weeks Christmas and New Year; bank hols

Stacey Rodgers runs this little place with her grandmother. It's a café-cum-bakery, although as a sideline they sell free-range eggs and silk flower arrangements. This is fresh, honest, café food: fry-ups cooked to order, bacon and egg sandwiches, chip butties, toasted tea-cakes, plus all kinds of home-baked pasties, sausage rolls, cakes and buns. On Thursday and Friday there's a roast with home-grown vegetables for £1.35, and pans of stew are always available in cold weather (85p a portion). Unlicensed.

DURHAM Durham map 10

 Almshouses [7/10]

Palace Green
TEL 091-386 1054

Open 9am to 8pm (5pm Oct to Easter) &

Self-service café in the converted seventeenth-century almshouses on Palace Green. The food has a healthy bias, but it's not exclusively vegetarian. An imaginative array of salads is backed up by an eclectic, colourful menu of cauliflower and cardamom soup, Javanese-style beef with nutty rice, herb pancakes stuffed with fennel and mushrooms. Kipper fillets in sour cream, aubergine and tahini purée, and pork pâté are served with real French bread. Cakes and pastries through the day. Freshly squeezed juices; freshly ground coffee and wine by the glass.

Giovanni and Fabio Pizzeria [6/10]

70 Claypath
TEL Durham (0385) 61643

Open 11.30 to 2, 6.30 to 11.30
Closed Mon; Sat L and Sun L

The best-value Italian food in Durham. A pizza, plus a sweet and coffee with half a carafe of wine can leave change from £5. There are also cheap midweek lunches for around £2. The menu runs through the familiar choice of trattoria staples, featuring some decent pasta dishes. There is a branch for take-aways at 2 Maynards Row, Gilesgate.

Ristorante de Medici [6/10]

21 Elvet Bridge
TEL 091-386 1310

Open noon to 2.30, 6.30 to 11
Closed Sun

Up a flight of stairs above a shop is this tiny, old-style bistro. The décor is minimal, the service is breathtakingly fast and the atmosphere exuberant. The menu has a decent choice of pasta (some freshly made) and you can make a meal of it for £5.75. Otherwise there are old-fashioned continental stalwarts, such as beef Stroganoff and tournedos Rossini. Italian house wine is 90p a glass.

Undercroft Restaurant [7/10]

The College, Durham Cathedral
TEL Durham (0385) 63721

Open 9.30am (11am Sun) to 5pm & (also WC)
Closed Christmas Day, Boxing Day and 1 Jan; Good Friday

Still the best place in the city for a daytime snack. This little pine restaurant through the cathedral cloister is another of Milburns' successful catering ventures in historic buildings. Coffee and teatime cakes and pastries are supplemented by lunchtime salads, savoury tarts, cold meats, and cheese, with some hot dishes added in winter. Wine by the glass.

ELLAND West Yorkshire   map 7

Berties Bistro [9/10]

7–10 Town Hall Buildings
TEL Elland (0422) 71724

Open 7pm to 11pm (5pm to 9.30pm Sun) &
Closed Mon; Christmas Day, Boxing Day
and 1 Jan

Standards continue to improve at this
Victorian-style bistro. The menu develops
as it changes, and it's possible to have
one course or a full meal. Dishes are
enterprising: warm salad of smoked
chicken and mango with coriander
dressing; carrot and chervil gateau with
spinach and mushroom sauce; poached
monkfish with white wine and herbs; beef,
Guinness and orange casserole. Stilton and
Guinness cake is a strange-sounding
sweet, otherwise look for steamed ginger
and apple sponge pudding. House wine by
the glass or litre.

Cafe McFly's [7/10]

The Cross
TEL Elland (0422) 79917

Open noon to 2.30, 7 to 11
Closed Sun D; Christmas Day

Related to Berties Bistro (see above). The
décor is smart 1920s/1930s and the food is
good-value bistro. Typically there might
be Jerusalem artichoke soup, avocado and
Mozzarella salad, and tortellini bake. More
substantial hot dishes range from beef and
Guinness pie to apricot glazed rack of
lamb. Sandwiches are also available, plus
sweets such as fruit and oat crumble.
Barbecues and fondues are a new feature.
Cocktails and strong coffee.

ELSLACK North Yorkshire   map 7

Tempest Arms [6/10]

TEL Earby (0282) 842450

Open for food noon to 2.15 (2 Sun), 6.30 (7 Sun)
to 10 &
Closed Christmas Day D

Fresh fish is a speciality in this eighteenth-
century village inn just off the A56. Fish
soup and fish pie are supplemented by
oysters, fresh salmon mayonnaise, and

grilled halibut, depending on the market.
There are also good soups, attractive
salads, and ploughman's with Wensleydale
cheese. More expensive charcoal-grills are
a new feature in the restaurant. Well-kept
Thwaites beers.

EPWORTH Humberside   map 7

Epworth Tap [8/10]

9–11 Market Place
TEL Epworth (0427) 873333

Open 7.30pm to 10.30pm &
Closed Sun and Mon; Christmas Eve to 2nd
week Jan

A paradise for wine buffs. The huge list has
an immense choice of high quality
drinking at extraordinarily low prices. The
food to match this is simple and bistro
style, but well prepared. Chicken liver
pâté really is home made, provençale fish
soup is delicate, and spare ribs are served
generously. Otherwise there are robust
casseroles, such as beef in red wine or pork
with sweetcorn. Sticky toffee pudding is a
favourite sweet. Three-course, fixed-price
menu (£9.50) on Saturdays.

FARNLEY TYAS
West Yorkshire   map 7

Golden Cock [7/10]

TEL Huddersfield (0484) 661979/663563

Open for food 12.15 to 2, 7.15 to 9.45 & (also WC)

The bar is set out rather like a bistro in
this pub on the edge of the Pennines, and
the emphasis is on food. There's a choice
of Whitby cod and chips, char-grilled
gammon sandwich, and pork steak with
sage, thyme and rosemary butter, plus
soup and home-made ice-creams. Upstairs
is the Charcuterie Restaurant (no
bookings) which specialises in carvery
meats and casseroles: three courses for
£6.50. More expensive meals are served in
the main dining-room.

GARGRAVE North Yorkshire   map 7

Edmondson's [6/10]

3 High Street
TEL Gargrave (075 678) 498

Open 11.30 to 1.30, 5 (4.30 Sat, 3 Sun) to 10
(9 in winter)
Closed Mon; Tue in winter; Tue L in summer;
Christmas week

The owner's family has been in the fish
and chip trade for more than sixty years.
Frying skills and batter recipes have been
handed on from father to son. King-size
portions of fresh fish are cooked in
dripping and served with good chips and
mushy peas. Pies are home made. The
place has a dining-room and is registered
as a 'hot food take-away' so that it can stay
open on Sunday for high teas and suppers.
Unlicensed.

GOATHLAND
North Yorkshire   map 10

Mallyan Spout Hotel [6/10]

TEL Whitby (0947) 86206

Open noon to 2, 6.30 to 9.30 &. (also WC)

The setting is a big plus at this Victorian
hotel named after a nearby waterfall, and
situated a mile up from the station on the
privately run North York Moors Railway.
By-pass the standard snack menu of
burgers and things with chips, and look for
the specials: home-made pea and ham
soup, Yorkshire puddings with mince,
onions and asparagus, okra and vegetable
curry, cassoulet of lamb. There are also
sandwiches, including Whitby crab in
season. Tetleys and Drybrough ales on
draught.

GOLCAR West Yorkshire   map 7

Weavers Shed [8/10]

Knowl Road
TEL Huddersfield (0484) 654284

Open noon to 2 (1.30 Sun) &.
Closed Mon; Sat L; first 2 weeks Jan; last 2
weeks July

Buffet-style Sunday lunches (£5.95,
including soup) are a big draw for cheap
eaters and families. In a setting of weaving
implements and prints of local churches
there are dishes such as roast ham with
parsley sauce, chicken and herb cheese
terrine, and smoked turkey salad. During
the week there are also good-value lunches
of Yorkshire pudding with onion gravy,

home-made game pie, and fillet of fresh
halibut, served with vegetables or salads.
Evening meals are more expensive.

GRANGE MOOR
West Yorkshire   map 7

Kaye Arms [6/10]

TEL Wakefield (0924) 848385

Open for food noon to 2, 7.30 to 10 &. (also WC)
Closed Mon L; Christmas Day and Boxing Day

A rare collection of whiskies lines the
walls of this old coaching-inn run by a
hard-working family. Lunchtime bar
snacks are interesting, ranging from good
rare beef sandwiches or ploughman's with
home-made chutney, to warm salad of
calf's liver and bacon on a bed of French
leaves. In between there's carrot and
orange soup, chicken and mushroom vol-
au-vent, barbecued beef on skewers and
smoked mackerel hot-pot. Daily specials
are chalked on the blackboard. More
expensive evening meals. No children.

GRIMSBY Humberside   map 8

Granary [7/10]

Haven Mill, Garth Lane
TEL Grimsby (0472) 46338

Open noon to 2.30, 7.30 to 10
Closed Sun; Mon D; bank hols; 2 weeks
early summer

This first-floor riverside restaurant still
feels like a granary. The décor is a bit
sparse, but Ron Houghton's cooking
makes up for the setting. The emphasis is
on fresh local ingredients, with fish dishes
now dominating the daily changing menu.
Norfolk oysters, bouillabaisse, grilled John
Dory, and Withernsea crab salad have all
featured, along with Stilton and chive
soup, braised rabbit with prunes, and
cassoulet. Finish with treacle tart or
strawberry meringues.

GUISBOROUGH Cleveland   map 10

NEW
ENTRY   # King's Head [6/10]

Newton under Roseberry
TEL Great Ayton (0642) 722318
3m SW of Guisborough

Open for food 11.30 to 2.45 (noon to 2 Sun),
7 to 10.30
Closed Christmas Day and 1 Jan

Brilliant steak and chicken double-decker
sandwiches are the star attraction in this
eighteenth-century pub at the foot of
famous Roseberry Topping. A big hunk of
meat is laid between two slices of buttered toast, topped with salad, egg and
mayonnaise, then another slice of toast.
The steak version is served with onion
rings; chicken with French fries. Excellent
value at £3.15 a go. Alternatively there are
dishes such as fillet of pork marsala and
steak au poivre, as well as grills and salads.
Sunday lunch is £6.45. The cocktail list
suits the slightly upmarket mood of
the place.

GUISELEY West Yorkshire   map 7

Harry Ramsden's [7/10]

White Cross
TEL Guiseley (0943) 74641

Open 11.30am to 11.30pm & (also WC)
Closed Christmas Day and Boxing Day

The most famous fish and chip shop in the
land has been trading for sixty years. It
now serves one and a half million
customers each year. The setting is a
huge institutional dining-room with
chandeliers, flock wallpaper and
waitresses in tight-fitting brown tunics;
outside there's parking space for four
hundred cars. Prodigious quantities of fish,
potatoes, dripping, bread, and tea are
needed to feed the ever-present queues.
Unlicensed.

HALIFAX West Yorkshire   map 7

Granary [7/10]

11 Northgate
TEL Halifax (0422) 58339

Open 10am to 10.30pm (11am to 3pm Mon, 9am
to 11pm Sat)
Closed Sun

Above a 'food therapy' shop selling
wholefoods and natural medical products.
The café has green-painted tables, pine
chairs, white net curtains and hanging
plants, and there's no standing on

ceremony. Interesting wholefood and
vegetarian dishes, such as nut and red
wine pâté, leek croustade, and stuffed
peppers, are backed up by meat and fish in
the form of game pie, beef Stroganoff and
zarzuela – a soup bowl packed with
prawns, swordfish, mussels and squid in a
tomato and wine sauce. House wine by the
glass or litre.

HAROME North Yorkshire   map 10

Pheasant Hotel [6/10]

TEL Helmsley (0439) 71241

Open for food noon to 2 & (also WC)
Closed Jan and Feb

Once the village blacksmith's, with two
cottages and a shop; now a popular family-
run hotel. Decent snacks are served at
lunch-time in the beamed bar. There are
good reports of the home-made cream of
vegetable soup, pâté, steak and kidney pie,
and roast beef. The menu also has cold-
smoked local trout, fisherman's pie, plus
apple pie or Wensleydale cheese to finish.
Sunday lunch is good, too. More expensive
dinners. No children under twelve.

HARROGATE
North Yorkshire   map 7

Bettys [8/10]

1 Parliament Street
TEL Harrogate (0423) 64659

Open 9 to 5.30 (10 to 6 Sun) &
Closed Christmas Day and Boxing Day

Classic North Country tea-rooms,
established in 1919, and now with
branches in York, Ilkley and Northallerton
(see entries). The atmosphere is old-
fashioned, with waitresses in white caps
and aprons rushing up and down among
the potted palms. Bettys is renowned for
its huge selection of traditional cakes and
Continental pâtisserie as well as huge
Yorkshire rarebits, fish and chips, and
omelettes. A new feature is a choice of
salad bowls such as avocado, mushroom
and tomato with olives and sunflower
seeds, or poached salmon and prawns with
cream and cucumber dressing. To go with
this there is an impressive range of teas

and coffees, as well as some interesting Alsace wines. Excellent facilities for young children – from nappies to additive-free baby foods.

Frank's Bar, Russell Hotel [6/10]

29 Valley Drive
TEL Harrogate (0423) 509866

Open noon to 2, 6 (7 Sun) to 9
Closed Christmas Day to 31 Dec

Best known for its classy restaurant, Hodgson's, this family-run hotel also has a good pub-style bar, serving light meals. The menu is short and to the point: garlic mushrooms; steak and game pie with French fries; steak sandwiches; smoked mackerel salad. There are also open and closed sandwiches. Sunday lunch is roast beef for £2.95. Tetleys and Theakstons beers on draught.

Shabab [6/10]

1 John Street
TEL Harrogate (0423) 500250

Open 11.30 to 2.30, 6 to 11.45
Closed Sun L; Christmas Day

This Indian restaurant impresses with its flamboyant, luxurious décor, attentive service and the presentation of carnations to ladies at the end of the meal. The food can be less memorable and some find the curries lack punch. But there are interesting dishes, including curried kidneys and crisp okra, among the stalwarts. Thalis are £8.50, and there are good-value set lunches.

William & Victoria Wine Bar [6/10]

6 Cold Bath Road
TEL Harrogate (0423) 506883

Open noon to 3, 6.30 to 11
Closed Sun; Sat L

The most promising wine bar in Harrogate. In the basement there's a blackboard menu of hearty dishes such as devilled kidneys, roast lamb on the bone with fresh mint, and chicken casserole with tomatoes and mushrooms. Treacle

tart is a favourite sweet, or there is a banana and caramel pie. A similar menu is available during the evening in the upstairs restaurant. House wines by the glass and some good-value bin ends.

HARTLEPOOL Cleveland   map 10

Krimo's [7/10]

8 The Front, Seaton Carew
TEL Hartlepool (0429) 266120

Open noon to 1.30, 7.30 to 9.30 &
Closed Sun; Mon; 2 weeks Aug

Krimo's has succeeded in putting Hartlepool on the food map. This bright, airy restaurant catches the eye at the end of terrace in a suburb of the town. The lunch menu is good value, and it's possible to have two courses for around £5. Starters of minestrone or prawns might be followed by home-made sausages, baked cod, chicken milanese, or roast beef with wine sauce. Sweets are mainly ice-creams. More expensive meals from the full menu. House wine by the glass or carafe.

HAWORTH West Yorkshire   map 7

Villette Coffee House [6/10]

113–115 Main Street
TEL Haworth (0535) 44967

Open 9am to 6.30pm (8.30am to 7pm Sat and Sun) &
Closed Oct to Mar (but open if weather's good)

This friendly self-service coffee-shop serves wholesome Yorkshire food for the Brontë-loving tourists. The menu of ox-tail soup, pork pie with peas, and lemon curd tart is supplemented by sandwiches and cream cakes. Bread is freshly baked; tea is well brewed. Unlicensed.

Weavers [7/10]

15 West Lane
TEL Haworth (0535) 43822

Open 7pm to 9.30pm (12.30 to 1.30 Sun)
Closed Mon; Sun D; 3 weeks June/July; 1 week at Christmas and New Year

Colin and Jane Rushworth's converted weavers' cottages have lots of North

Country trappings, but the style is more that of a bistro. For cheap eating there are light meals of pasta bake, samosas with home-made chutney, chicken fries with tartare sauce, and spinach and egg galette. It's also possible to have just starters and sweets from the full menu, which takes in Yorkshire pudding with onion gravy, seafood tartlets, and sticky toffee pudding. The set menu is £8.95 (not Saturdays).

HAYDON BRIDGE
Northumberland   map 10

General Havelock Inn [7/10]

Radcliffe Road
TEL Haydon Bridge (043 484) 376

Open for food noon to 1.30, 7.30 to 9 ᕱ (also WC)
Closed Mon (exc bank hols); Tue; 1 week Jan; last week Aug, first week Sept

Angela Clyde does the cooking, and even helps to serve in this unpretentious inn by the South Tyne. The emphasis is firmly on home-made soups, local fish and game, fresh vegetables, roasts, and pies. Lunches are excellent value for cream of tomato soup, dressed crab, home-made steak and kidney pie, and roast sirloin salad. Set Sunday lunch is £7; dinners are more expensive. Tetleys beers, house wine £2.95 a carafe.

HEBDEN BRIDGE
West Yorkshire   map 7

Watergate [6/10]

9–11 Bridge Gate
TEL Hebden Bridge (0422) 842978/842097

Open 9.30 (10.30 Sun) to 5 (5.30 Sat) ᕱ (also WC)
Closed Fri

Handy tea-shop-cum-café serving honest home-made snacks in a rather elegant setting of crystal chandeliers and antique dressers. Pizzas have been added to a menu that includes soup, quiches, and salads plus hot-pot, spaghetti bolognese, and cottage pie. Cakes, scones and fruit pies, plus exotic ice-cream specialities. Unlicensed.

HEDDON-ON-THE-WALL
Northumberland   map 10

Swan Inn [6/10]

TEL 091-984 3161

Open for food 11 to 3 (noon to 2 Sun), 7.15 to 9.45 ᕱ (also WC)
Closed Sun D

There are good views of the Tyne Valley from this stone pub close to Hadrian's Wall. Bar snacks centre on the salad bar, backed up by hot dishes such as chicken chasseur. Three-course set lunches in the restaurant are £5.95. More expensive à la carte menu.

HELMSLEY   North Yorkshire   map 10

Crown Hotel [6/10]

TEL Helmsley (0439) 70297

Open noon to 1.45 for L ᕱ (also WC)

Good-value lunches are served in the dining-room. The style is old-fashioned hotel cooking: beef consommé or egg mayonnaise before roast chicken with bread sauce and chipolatas, cold duck with salad, baked sole with parsley and shrimp sauce. Sweets are home-made fruit tarts and crumbles. Two courses can be had for £8. More expensive dinners.

HETTON   North Yorkshire   map 7

Angel Inn [9/10]

TEL Cracoe (075 673) 263

Open for food noon to 2, 7 to 10 ᕱ (also WC)
Closed Christmas Day

The latest 'real food' venture in this re-vamped Dales pub is the 'fish on Friday' menu. Supplies are obtained direct from Manchester's wholesale market for a list that might include provençale fish soup, poached baby halibut with mousseline of salmon, fresh crab salad, and grilled Arbroath smokies. Otherwise the choice of food can take in chicken liver terrine, a plate of prize-winning pork sausages on a bed of red cabbage with onions, apples and blackcurrants, brochette of pork with savoury rice, and aviyal – a mixed vegetable curry with coconut milk.

Theakstons and Timothy Taylors beers on handpump; decent wines by the glass.

HUDDERSFIELD
West Yorkshire   map 7

Byrams [7/10]

3 Byram Street
TEL Huddersfield (0484) 530243

Open 11.30 to 2.30, 6.30 to 11 &
Closed Sun

Very reliable, very popular bistro on two levels. Three courses plus drinks should cost around £10, but it's possible to eat for much less. Stay with the burgers, crêpes, and omelettes for a cheap meal. Otherwise the menu ranges from seafood salad to grilled chicken with oregano. House wine is £4.90 a litre.

NEW ENTRY Pisces [7/10]

84 Fitzwilliam Street
TEL Huddersfield (0484) 516773

Open noon to 2; 7 to 9.30 &
Closed Sun; Christmas Day; bank hols Mon

This seafood restaurant is good news for Huddersfield. The cellar of a converted warehouse has been given a facelift and transformed into an impressive dining-room with varnished pine floors and stained glass windows. Have just a bowl of soup or a sandwich at lunch-time. Otherwise settle for one of the fixed-price menus, which might include seafood salad with poached egg or sauté avocado with prawns before salmon in sorrel sauce or lamb cutlets with red and green peppers. Home-made sweets and coffee are included in the price. More expensive dinners.

Shabab [6/10]

37–39 New Street
TEL Huddersfield (0484) 49514

Open 11.30 to 2.30, 6 to 11.45
Closed Sun L; Christmas Day

This branch of a mini-chain of restaurants continues to offer good North Indian cooking; vegetables are particularly well handled. (For details see Harrogate.)

Sole Mio [6/10]

Imperial Arcade, Market Street
TEL Huddersfield (0484) 542828

Open noon to 2.30, 5.30 to 11.30
Closed Sun L; Christmas; bank hols

Still one of the most popular eating places in Huddersfield and excellent value if you stay with the pizzas and the good pastas (freshly made at the proprietors' own factory). Spaghetti and tagliatelle are served with classic sauces such as napoli or amatriciana; there's also penne, tortellini and ravioli. Look for the blackboard specials, such as crab salad. Basic house wine.

HULL Humberside   map 8

Medio [6/10]

Anlaby Common
TEL Hull (0482) 507070

Open noon to 2.30, 6 to 11.30
Closed Christmas Day, Boxing Day and 1 Jan

Although it is now owned by one of the chains, this pizza place has a lively atmosphere and ingredients are fresh. It is still the best place in Hull for a family meal of Italian-style food. Spare ribs with tomato sauce and stuffed cabbage leaves supplement the pizzas and pasta dishes.

ILKLEY West Yorkshire   map 7

Bettys [8/10]

32–34 The Grove
TEL Ilkley (0943) 608029

Open 9.15 to 5.30 (9.30 to 6.30 Sun) & (also ladies WC)
Closed Christmas Day and Boxing Day

A branch of the classic North Country tea-rooms, established in Harrogate in 1919; the best of its kind in the area. (See Harrogate for details.)

Olive Tree [8/10]

31 Church Street
TEL Ilkley (0943) 601481

Open 6.30pm to midnight &
Closed Christmas Day

Three kinds of meze (special, seafood and a cheaper vegetarian version) are the best value in this convivial Greek taverna. Otherwise the menu winds its way through fish soup, excellent dips, stuffed vegetables, and pastries, to good kebabs and slow-cooked dishes such as pork afelia and kleftiko. Greek coffee comes with Turkish delights; there are inexpensive wines. There's a new branch at Oaklands, Rodley Lane, Leeds (TEL 0532 569283).

Sabera [7/10]

9 Wells Road
TEL Ilkley (0943) 607104

Open noon to 2.30, 6 to midnight & (also WC)
Closed Christmas Day

This former Swiss restaurant on a hillside overlooking Ilkley Moor still has pine tables and benches, but the cooking now centres on Bangladesh. The menu states that no animal fats are used in the cooking, and there is plenty of choice for vegetarians – from cauliflower bhajias, samosas and puris to vegetable biriani and palak aloo. Meat eaters can try the special of liver, kidney and heart cooked with garlic and ginger and served with breads or rice. To drink there's Kingfisher beer, lassi or burhani (spiced yoghurt with mint).

KEIGHLEY West Yorkshire   map 7

Bella Napoli [6/10]

59 Main Street, Crosshills
TEL Crosshills (0535) 32224

Open noon to 2, 7 (6 Sun) to 10.30 (11 Fri and Sat) &
Closed Mon

It's worth the drive out of Keighley (follow the A629, then turn left on to the A6068) for the pizzas served in this popular restaurant. They are freshly baked in a stainless steel oven in full view of the customers. Pasta dishes are home made; other items may be disappointing. House wine by the glass. A good place to linger.

KNARESBOROUGH
North Yorkshire   map 7

Bond End Wine Bar [7/10]

6–8 Bond End
TEL Harrogate (0423) 863899

Open noon to 2, 7 to 10.30
Closed Mon; Tue L, Wed L and Thur L

Monochromatic wine bar operating separately from the more expensive Schwallers restaurant. Lunch has a Swiss flavour, with fondues, cheese fritters, and veal sausages with rösti potatoes. Evening meals can take in anything from tomato and oregano soup to passion-fruit sorbet. Thirty personally chosen wines.

LEEDS West Yorkshire   map 7

Brett's Fish Restaurant [6/10]

12–14 North Lane, Headingley
TEL Leeds (0532) 755228

Open 10 to 2.15, 4 to 7.30 & (also WC)
Closed Sun; Mon L; D Tue, Wed, Fri and Sat

The local rivalry between Brett's and its close neighbour Bryan's (see entry) may help to keep standards high. Both continue to serve fine fish and chips in the classic Yorkshire fashion. Brett's has been a family business since 1919 and is also renowned for its sweet treacle pudding. Unlicensed.

Bryan's [7/10]

9 Weetwood Lane, Headingley
TEL Leeds (0532) 785679

Open 11.30am to 11.30pm &
Closed Sun

Bryan's has maintained its reputation for more than fifty years, and there's now a perpetual queue – whatever the time of day. Fish is delivered fresh daily and the range includes baby and jumbo haddock as well as plaice, hake, and halibut. Frying is done by a team of four or five, using beef dripping. The décor may seem a bit clinical, but the head waitress ensures that the red-pinafored ladies perform their serving duties with speed and efficiency. Unlicensed.

NEW ENTRY **Carageen Vegetarian Café** [8/10]

17–19 Wharf Street
TEL Leeds (0532) 449588

Open noon to 2.30, 6.30 to 9.30
Closed Sun; D Mon to Wed; bank hols

Formerly the Wharf Street Vegetarian Restaurant, this hundred-year-old building is in an up-and-coming part of the city near the canal. The two rooms are divided by an archway, and there's a courtyard at the back for fine days. Lunch is self service for dishes such as cream of spinach and coconut soup, courgette and green pepper quiche, or Creole flan with red lentils and nuts. Salads might come with yoghurt dressing and there are wholefood sweets ranging from fruit crumble topped with spiced tofu to carob and walnut sponge. Dinners are in a similar vein and three courses should cost around £6. Vegetables are organic, and so are the wines and ciders; there's also naturally brewed Flag Porter and Sam Smiths lager.

Clinchers, Leeds Playhouse [6/10]

Calverley Street
TEL Leeds (0532) 442141

Open 10am to 7pm (7.30pm Mon and Tue)
Closed Sun; July; 2 weeks Aug

The restaurant attached to the Leeds Playhouse puts the emphasis on vegetarian dishes, with more appearing all the time. The cold buffet has spinach roulade, lentil roast, and nut and carrot loaf alongside vol-au-vent and galantine pie. There's a choice of ten salads, plus a hot dish of the day such as macaroni cheese, bean and pasta hot-pot, or tandoori chicken. Sweets are home made.

NEW ENTRY **Conservatory Café Bar** [7/10]

35A Albion Place
TEL Leeds (0532) 477320

Open for food 9am to 8pm & (also WC)
Closed Sun; bank hols

A 1930s-style café-bar in a basement once used by the Leeds YMCA. The décor has been lavishly revamped, with stained-glass windows, polished brass and a mahogany bar. The menu is short and familiar: pâté, quiches, smoked trout, and fresh salmon salads, plus hot dishes such as roast lamb, cottage pie, and chicken curry. The fruit salad is first rate. This is the acceptable face of mass-eating in the 1980s – lots of atmosphere, decent surroundings, all the trimmings. Teas and cocktails to drink. No children.

Da Marios [6/10]

105–107 The Headrow
TEL Leeds (0532) 460390

Open 10am to 11.30pm (5.30pm to 11pm Sun)
& (also WC)

A happy-go-lucky, open-all-hours pizza parlour with a standard menu of pasta, pizzas, and chicken Kiev. There are also one or two daily specials, seafood salad is good, and the puddings are home made. Wine by the glass. Take-aways.

Flying Pizza [7/10]

60 Street Lane, Roundhay
TEL Leeds (0532) 666501/661031

Open noon to 2.30 (12.30 to 3.30 Sun), 6 to 11.30 (6.30 to 11 Sun) &
Closed Christmas Day, Boxing Day and 1 Jan; Easter Sun

There's no booking, queues are long, and chauffeurs wait in parked Rollers outside this no-frills trattoria. Huge platefuls of spare ribs come in a rich honey and tomato sauce, tagliatelle verde is served with chopped ham and peas, and the pizzas are good, too. Most of the fashionable clientele come for the blackboard specials, which major in fish – anything from grilled brill to poached scallops.

Jumbo Chinese [8/10]

120 Vicar Lane
TEL Leeds (0532) 458324

Open noon to 11.45pm
Closed Christmas Day, Boxing Day and 27 Dec

The staff have become friendlier and the queues shorter in this well-established basement Cantonese restaurant. For cheap eating there is excellent dim-sum, and the copious chow mein dishes draw big crowds looking for a meal after closing time. Good dishes from the main menu have included fillet steak with OK sauce, and spare ribs with Peking sauce.

Mandalay [7/10]

8 Harrison Street
TEL Leeds (0532) 446453

Open noon to 2.30, 6 to 11.30 & (also WC)
Closed Sun; Sat L; Christmas Day, Boxing Day and 1 Jan

Sophistication and décor are the hallmarks of this chic Indian restaurant: the grand piano plays at weekends, and ceiling fans disperse the aromatic fumes from hot sizzling dishes. The cheapest way to appreciate all this is to go for lunch during the week, when there's a set menu for £4.95. Dishes from the more expensive main menu are distinguished by excellent-quality meats and carefully spiced sauces.

Pollards [6/10]

28 Lands Lane
TEL Leeds (0532) 433652

Open 10am (9.30am Sat) to 4.30pm
Closed Sun; bank hols

The café is above the proprietors' shop selling teas and coffees, so drinks are the main attraction. There are eighteen types of coffee, roasted on the premises, ground as ordered and served in cafetières. The choice of teas includes fine blends from Indian, Ceylon and China. To go with these there's a range of locally baked biscuits, crumpets and scones, plus a few lunch dishes, such as quiche and pizza. Unlicensed.

Salvo's [7/10]

115 Otley Road, Headingley
TEL Leeds (0532) 755017

Open noon to 2, 6 to 11.30 &
Closed Sun

Lively pizzeria noted for its queues and the quality of its food. Regulars adore the garlic bread, excellent minestrone, and garlic mushrooms. The list of good pizzas includes pizza Kiev (folded and stuffed with chicken, garlic butter and cheese). Also look for the blackboard specials, such as bouillabaisse, Chinese stir-fried pork, and aubergine parmigiana. Two starters will serve for a light meal. Families like to go between 6 and 7.30pm.

Sang Sang [8/10]

7 The Headrow
TEL Leeds (0532) 468664/435160

Open noon to 11.30pm &
Closed Christmas Day and Boxing Day

Currently the number one Cantonese restaurant in Leeds, still well patronised by local Chinese and Yorkshire business people. For cheap eating there's a good dim-sum menu, served from noon to 6pm. Otherwise look for the classic casseroles and one-plate meals – roast meats on rice, fried noodles or big bowls of noodles and seafood in soup. Set meals from £5.90 take in the likes of baked spare ribs, fried beef in oyster sauce, and king prawns with cashew nuts.

Shabab [6/10]

2 Eastgate
TEL Leeds (0532) 468988

Open 11.30 to 2.30, 6 to 11.45
Closed Christmas Day

The lights are low and the music soft in this branch of a mini-chain of popular Indian restaurants. Cheap lunches for around £3. (For details see Harrogate.)

Whan Hai [7/10]

20 New Briggate
TEL Leeds (0532) 435019

Open 11.30 to 2, 5 (3 Sun) to 11.30 (11.30 to midnight Sat)
Closed Mon

The first choice for authentic Pekingese food in Leeds. This no-frills restaurant above a casino and next to the Odeon cinema offers good-value set meals for about £8 to £9 a head. The range includes fried seaweed with grated fish, boiled dumplings, crispy duck with pancakes, and twice-cooked pork, as well as a few Szechuan specialities.

Whitelocks [6/10]

Turks Head Yard, Briggate
TEL Leeds (0532) 453950

Open for food 11 to 2.30, 5.30 to 8 & (also WC)
Closed Sun D

This famous old city tavern hasn't changed much in the last hundred years, although a few modern trappings have appeared alongside the mirrors, brass and tiles. The food is staunchly traditional: Yorkshire pudding, sausage and mash, bubble and squeak, jam roly-poly. There's Wensleydale cheese and apple pie too. McEwans 80/– and Youngers on draught.

LEPTON West Yorkshire   map 7

Dartmouth Arms [6/10]

Paul Lane, Flockton Moor
TEL Wakefield (0924) 848265

Open for food noon to 1.45, 7 to 9.15 & (also WC)
Closed Christmas Day D and Boxing Day D

Refurbished roadside pub handy for a quick meal. The waitresses move fast and turnover is rapid. The food is a wholesome mix of good pies cut from a big dish, proper wedge-shaped chips, grilled gammon and eggs, home-made soups and salads. Wednesday night is curry night.

LEYBURN North Yorkshire   map 10

Golden Lion Hotel [6/10]

Market Place
TEL Wensleydale (0969) 22161

Open 11.45 to 2, 7 to 9 & (also WC)
Closed Christmas Day

Anne Wood cooks the food and Richard Wood brews his own beer in this small hotel overlooking the market place. Lunch is a hearty assortment of home-made steak and kidney pie, roast beef, Yorkshire gammon, and omelettes backed up by sandwiches and ploughman's. Evening

meals in Mr Fothergill's Chop Shop are mainly grills, along with jugged Leyburn steak, baked trout, and casseroles. Start with Yorkshire pudding and onion gravy and finish with Wensleydale cheese.

LITTON North Yorkshire   map 7

Park Bottom [7/10]

TEL Arncliffe (075 677) 235

Open 7.30 for D

New owners Jan and Peter Singer are continuing the formula of four-course fixed-price dinners at this purpose-built guest-house. Minestrone soup or smoked haddock pancakes might be followed by gammon with tarragon sauce or lamb chops with rosemary. Sweets range from chocolate mint cheesecake to baked apples. The price (£7) includes cheese and coffee with mints. Short wine list. Children over five welcome.

MALTON North Yorkshire   map 7

Blue Ball Inn [6/10]

Newbiggin
TEL Malton (0653) 692236

Open for food noon to 2, 7 to 9.30
Closed Sun

The oldest pub in Malton, marked by the ancient sign of a medieval fortune teller, has been deliberately swept into the 1980s by Brian and Elaine Ray. The menu makes no bones about what is home made and what is bought in. Supporters of the former camp should look for dishes such as jugged hare, tripe and onions, shepherds pie and Mexican pepper pot. Tetleys and Whitbread beers on handpump; wine by the glass.

Florios [6/10]

11 Yorkersgate
TEL Malton (0653) 692008

Open 6 to 11, plus noon to 2 Fri to Sun
& (also WC)
Closed L Mon to Thur

Cheerful Italian restaurant serving good-value pasta dishes, pizzas and burgers in a pizza bread bun. Pizza vulcano is laced with garlic, Tabasco and pepperoni sausage; scozzese includes salmon. Other dishes can take the bill into double figures. House wine by the glass or carafe. The owner plans to open a cocktail bar in the cellar.

MARSDEN West Yorkshire   map 7

 Bellas Town Restaurant [7/10]

16 Peel Street
TEL Huddersfield (0484) 845542

Open 10.30 to 2.30 (noon to 5 Sun) &
Closed 27 Dec to 7 Jan

Originally this was a pork butcher's, then a wholefood shop and tea-shop, before the Wyers turned it into a cosy restaurant. Lunches (served from 11.30am) offer simple home-cooked dishes such as pasta shells with bolognese sauce, braised steak, and Cumberland sausage with mustard sauce. Vegetables are crisp; salads are fresh. Sweets are homely – apple pie and custard, baked jam roll, bread-and-butter pudding. On Sundays the proprietors draw the curtains and put pink cloths on the tables. Evening meals by arrangement. Wine by the glass.

MASHAM North Yorkshire   map 7

White Bear [6/10]

TEL Ripon (0765) 89319

Open for food noon to 2.30 (1.30 Sun)

Theakston's own pub in the yard of the original brewery headquarters. Drinking is the main business, but there's some no-frills lunchtime food to go with your pint: hot steak sandwiches, ploughman's with Wensleydale cheese, cottage pie, beef curry. Pub games new and old.

MIDDLESBROUGH
Cleveland   map 10

Rooney's [6/10]

23 Newport Road
TEL Middlesbrough (0642) 223923

Open 11am to 11.30pm
Closed Sun; bank hols (exc Good Fri)

Cod, haddock, plaice and skate are skilfully fried in this fish and chip restaurant above a bar; the catch comes fresh each day from Whitby. At lunch-time there's a good-value shoppers' special of cod and chips plus tea and bread and butter. Evening meals now include char-grilled steaks.

MORPETH Northumberland   map 10

 La Brasserie [7/10]

59 Bridge Street
TEL Morpeth (0670) 516200

Open noon to 2.30pm, 6.30 to 11
Closed Mon; Sun D

There are plenty of cheap options in Robert Wilkinson's local restaurant overlooking the Telford Bridge. Best value is the bistro lunch menu, which offers pasta dishes, noodles in cream sauce with smoked salmon, pizzas, and international dishes such as curried Turkish meat balls. There's a full vegetarian menu; a good-value pasta and pizza menu (operating Tuesday to Friday), plus a three-course grill menu from £5.95. The à la carte is more expensive. Around one hundred wines, with plenty of half-bottles.

MOULTON North Yorkshire   map 10

Black Bull [7/10]

TEL Barton (032 577) 289

Open for food noon to 2, 7 to 10.15
Closed Sun

The Black Bull is famous for its restaurants – especially the dining-room in the Brighton Belle Pullman carriage – but at heart it is also a village pub, with settles and whitewashed tables in the old beamed bar, log fires and a good menu of pub food. Black Bull terrine and smoked salmon pâté are perennial favourites, otherwise the choice ranges from steak sandwiches and jumbo sausages with mustard to moules marinière and gnocchi provençale. There's also a fixed price lunch for £7. Other meals are more expensive. No children.

NEWCASTLE-UPON-TYNE
Tyne & Wear   map 10

Amigo's [6/10]

21 Mosley Street
TEL 091–2321111

Open noon to 2 (2.30 Sat and Sun), 5.30 to 11.30
Closed bank hols L; Boxing Day and 1 Jan

This razzle-dazzle pizza/pasta place in an
old banking hall has kept its sense of fun
and its innovative, regularly changing
menu. Steaks, chicken dishes and
Mediterranean-style seafood specialities
supplement the basics. Pizzas and pastas
are half price from 5.30 to 7.30pm.

Jade Garden [8/10]

53 Stowell Street
TEL 091–261 5889

Open noon to midnight
Closed Christmas Day and Boxing Day

This old-style Cantonese restaurant has
resisted the temptation to move upmarket, and maintains its reputation with
the best selection of roast and barbecued
meats in Newcastle. The long menu has a
fine range of good-value one-plate meals of
soup, noodles and rice. Roast duck and
pork with noodles in soup is a huge
bowlful for about £3.20. Weekday set
lunches are £3; set evening meals start at
£4.20.

Madeleine's [9/10]

134 Heaton Road
TEL 091–276 5277

Open noon to 2, 7 to 10 &
Closed L Sat and Sun

An honest, unpretentious vegetarian
restaurant with a cosmopolitan menu of
imaginative dishes. The range shows in
peanut roast with Indonesian gado-gado
sauce; Mexican enchiladas; spinach and
almond korma with dry potato curry, and
Sicilian bake in a case of thinly sliced
aubergine. Start with broad beans in garlic
butter, and finish with apricot soya ice,
cassata or baked bananas with rum. Fruit
juices or house wines by the glass.

Mama Mia [7/10]

46 Pudding Chare
TEL 091–232 7193

Open noon to 2.30, 5 to 10.30 &
Closed Sun; Mon L; Christmas Day and 1 Jan

This place still serves the best pizzas on
Tyneside, although the rest of the menu is
not memorable. The pizzas themselves are
huge and rectangular, with a light base and
generous toppings: Mamma Mia special
comes with hard-boiled egg, ham, mushrooms and onions, plus a high dosage of
garlic. Much better value than its pizza-
chain neighbours. Full bodied house red.

NEW ENTRY Naked Lunch [7/10]

57–59 Melbourne Street
TEL 091–261 1663

Open noon to midnight
Closed Sun; bank hols

The first floor of a former warehouse is
now a vegetarian restaurant run by a
workers' co-operative. The exposed
brickwork and varnished wood are the
result of hard labour, which helps to keep
the prices low. Good-value specials, such
as parsnip and ginger soup, or vine leaves
stuffed with nuts and bulgur wheat,
supplement a simple menu of mushroom
goulash, stir-fried vegetables and peanut
pilau. Finish with carob and orange trifle
or brown-bread ice-cream. Short, enterprising wine list. A magician performs on
Thursday evenings.

NEW ENTRY New Emperor [7/10]

Berwick Street
TEL 091–232 8856

Open noon to 3.30am (2am Mon) &

Still one of the most genuine Chinese
restaurants in Newcastle, though the
décor has been given a facelift and the
menu is aimed at westerners. For cheap
eating there's a good range of dim-sum
snacks, as well as excellent noodle dishes
and roast meats. The Cantonese influence
also shows in crispy suckling pig, hot-pots
and steamed seafood. Set lunch from
£2.70.

Roulade Crêperie [6/10]

Queens Square
TEL 091-261 4811

Open 10am to 10pm (6.30pm Mon)
Closed Sun; Mon D; Easter Mon; Christmas
Day, Boxing Day and 1 Jan

A modern crêperie in a modern shopping
arcade, particularly useful for a light
lunch. There are several vegetarian,
savoury and sweet crêpes, plus pâté and
salads to start, and sweets such as home-
made blackberry mousse to finish. In the
evening the emphasis is on 'theme nights'.
Fresh fruit juice; decent house wine.

Rupali [7/10]

6 Bigg Market
TEL 091-232 8629

Open noon to 2.30, 6 (7 Sun) to 11.30 & (also WC)
Closed Sun L

Newcastle's favourite Indian restaurant,
and still the best-value curry house in
town. There are bargains at lunch-time
and for early-evening eaters (between 6
and 7pm Monday to Wednesday, 7 to 8pm
Sunday) when chicken curry is £1.30 and
lager 70p a pint. Also look for the
Thursday Happy Night, when a four-
course meal with liqueur and a glass of
wine is £5.95. As well as a good range of
North Indian curries, the menu features
better-than-average regional vegetarian
specialities.

NEW ENTRY Veggie's [7/10]

St Mary's Place
TEL 091–261 6330

Open 10am to 10pm
Closed Sun; bank hols

Nick Bell opened his vegetarian restaurant
in a converted Georgian terraced house,
and gets his chefs from the forward-
looking Plymouth Catering College (see
entry under South West). The cooking
shows some enterprising touches and
there are good dishes, such as mushroom
soup, cabbage and hazelnut bake, and
vegan broccoli flan. Salads are inventive:
pasta and hazelnut, courgettes provençale,

apple and celery. A plate of these for £1.25
would make a good light lunch. Fresh fruit
salad is the best of the sweets. Theakston's
bitter; decent house wine.

Willow Teas [6/10]

35A St Georges Terrace, Jesmond
TEL 091-281 6874

Open 8am to 9pm (5pm Sat)
Closed Sun

This café is a triumph of organisation: the
place is tiny, so much of the preparation is
done in advance and microwaved to order.
Dishes are the kind that don't suffer in the
process: mince and dumplings; beef
Stroganoff; liver and bacon casserole;
savoury aubergine crumble – all costing
£2.50. A big bowl of lentil and bacon or
broccoli soup with grated cheese and
French bread is a filling meal for £1.25.
Breakfast is bacon stotties or poached eggs
on toast, and there are scones, gateaux and
cheesecake to go with tea or coffee.
Unlicensed.

NORTHALLERTON
North Yorkshire   map 10

Bettys [8/10]

188 High Street
TEL Northallerton (0609) 5154

Open 9 (10 Sun) to 5.30 &
Closed Christmas Day and Boxing Day

A branch of the small chain of classic
North Country tearooms, established in
Harrogate in 1919 (see entry).

Ramsdens Fish Restaurant [6/10]

227 High Street
TEL Northallerton (0609) 5121

Open 11.15am to 1.15pm
Closed Sun and Mon

The Ramsdens get their haddock fresh
from Aberdeen, and their cod and plaice
from Hull. Decent portions are well fried
and served with chips, peas and bread and
butter. Children are offered 70p-worth of
pattie and chips or sausage and chips. The
menu also features spit-roast chicken, and

in winter there are bowls of home-made chilli con carne for £1. A small friendly place, not related to Harry Ramsden's in Guiseley (see entry). Unlicensed.

OSWALDKIRK
North Yorkshire   map 10

Malt Shovel [6/10]

TEL Ampleforth (043 93) 461

Open for food 11 (noon Sun) to 2, 7 to 9.30 (10 Fri and Sat)
Closed Mon D (exc bank hols); Christmas Day

Ancient manor-house – complete with a knot garden at the back – now a thriving pub with plenty of atmosphere. Bar food takes in black pudding with Dijon mustard and cider, lamb chops with mint butter, and chicken suprême in orange sauce, as well as open sandwiches with home-cooked Yorkshire beef, steak and mushroom pie, and fresh fish dishes. The Shovel Bun is an individual cottage loaf filled with curried chicken and served with Indian pickles; the Vegetarian Roast is hazelnuts and fresh vegetables with onion sauce. Real ale or Taylor's Yorkshire tea.

OTLEY West Yorkshire   map 7

Curlew [6/10]

11–13 Crossgate
TEL Otley (0943) 464351

Open 10.30 to 4.30, 7.30 on, Fri and Sat; noon to 5 Sun & (also WC)
Closed Mon to Thur

An enterprising workers' co-operative in a pair of converted eighteenth-century cottages, serving the most interesting vegetarian food in the neighbourhood. During the day the emphasis is on home baking, plus dishes from around the world: potato Romanoff with sour cream; green haggerty (layers of potato, spinach, cream and cheese with nutmeg and garlic), red bean chilli and pitta bread. In the evening, three courses plus tea or coffee is £7.75 for specialities such as courgettes stuffed with Brazil nuts and herbs, Mexican rice with cheese, sour cream and peppers and Yorkshire lemon pudding. Unlicensed, but bring your own (no corkage).

Davids [5/10]

Westbourne Fisheries, 132 Bradford Road
TEL Otley (0943) 463203

Open 11.30 to 1.30 Fri and Sat (1.15 Wed), plus 4.30 to 6.30 Mon, Wed and Fri (4 Sun, 4.15 Thur)
Closed 2 weeks Feb to Mar; 2 weeks Sept to Oct

David and Rita Wade fry their fish the Yorkshire way, in beef dripping. Haddock is by far the best seller, with plaice well behind in the popularity stakes. Jumbo haddock with chips, bread and butter and a pot of tea is £3.40; there are small portions for children. Unlicensed.

PATELEY BRIDGE
North Yorkshire   map 7

Willow [7/10]

8 Park Road
TEL Harrogate (0423) 711689

Open noon to 2, 6.30 to 9.30 &
Closed Mon and Tue; Sun D; Feb

The Naylors' restaurant has a quiet, friendly, family atmosphere. Set lunches and dinners are good value at £7.25, otherwise there's a blackboard of home-cooked specialities taking in Dales sausage with caramelised apples, wild rabbit in pastry, and halibut with cheese and smoked oyster sauce. There's usually something for vegetarians.

PICKERING North Yorkshire   map 10

Mulberry's [6/10]

5 Bridge Street
TEL Pickering (0751) 72337

Open 10am to 5pm
Closed Jan; Sun mid-Nov to mid-Mar

Excellent little tea-shop/café serving good afternoon teas with scones and home-made cakes for £2.60. There are lunches of Yorkshire ploughman's, casserole laced with Theakston's Old Peculier Ale, cottage pie and chilli, plus home-made biscuits and sweets. Wine by the glass.

PUDSEY West Yorkshire   map 7

 Aagrah [7/10]

483 Bradford Road
TEL Bradford (0274) 668818

Open 6pm (noon Sun) to 11.30pm (midnight Fri
and Sat) & (also wc)

A new branch of the well-established
Indian restaurant on the fringes of
Bradford. For details see Shipley (also West
Yorkshire).

RAMSGILL North Yorkshire   map 7

Yorke Arms [6/10]

TEL Harrogate (0423) 75243

Open for food noon to 2, 7.30 to 8.30

An old grey-stone pub at the north-west
end of Crouthwaite Reservoir, serving big
helpings of hearty food. Spinach flan,
home-made game pie and roast beef
sandwiches make good snacks. More
substantial offerings include braised steak
and onions, hot home-cooked tongue with
parsley sauce and roast turkey. Fruit pies
and tarts to finish. Theakstons beers.

REETH North Yorkshire   map 10

NEW ENTRY **White House** [6/10]

Village Green

Open 10.30 to 5 (5.30 Apr to Nov)
Closed Fri Nov to Apr; 3 weeks Feb

The best place for a snack in this popular
moorland village. The repainted house on
the green is full of flowers and pretty things
to buy. The menu is short and prices are
low. There are crumpets, muffins and
toasted tea-cakes as well as poached eggs on
toast, a massive ploughman's platter, pâté
and jacket potatoes, plus a hot dish of the
day. A favourite sweet is a pancake filled
with strawberries, crushed meringue and
ice-cream. Unlicensed.

RICHMOND North Yorkshire   map 10

Mary's Tearoom [6/10]

5–6 Trinity Church Square
TEL Richmond (0748) 4052

Open 9 to 5.30 in summer, 5 in winter (10 to 5.30
Sun in summer, noon to 5 Sun in winter)

A modest tea-room overlooking the
cobbled market square. Locally baked
cakes, gateaux and Yorkshire parkin are
served amid a cottage décor of hunting
prints and decorative plates. Useful for
morning coffee or afternoon tea. There are
also savoury lunchtime snacks, such as
hot-pot or steak and kidney pie.
Unlicensed.

RIPON North Yorkshire   map 7

Blackfriars Café [6/10]

Kirkgate
TEL Ripon (0765) 3617

Open 10 to 7, noon to 5 Sun &
Closed Wed

Mr and Mrs Nichol run this cheerful
daytime restaurant, which serves snacks
and full meals. Home-made burgers and
steak and kidney pie are firm favourites,
locally cured ham is served with egg and
chips, and the menu also has omelettes,
plus a few vegetarian specialities such as
chickpea rissoles with salad and pitta
bread. Special pancakes filled with fruit
and ice-cream are a favourite sweet. No
snacks in the evening or at Sunday lunch-
time. Wines by the glass; Theakston's
bitter on draught.

Old Deanery [9/10]

Minster Road
TEL Ripon (0765) 3518

Open noon to 2, 7 to 10 &
Closed Sun; Sat L; Christmas Day and Boxing
Day

The magnificent old ecclesiastical
building stands in the shadow of the
cathedral. It is an unlikely setting for an
easy-going restaurant with no bookings or
minimum charge. Have anything from
kidneys on toast or fennel and lemon soup
to roast rack of lamb with redcurrant and
rosemary, pork fillet in prawn curry sauce,
or sirloin steak. The Swiss influence
shows in perennial favourites such as
délice Helvetia (deep-fried balls of
spaghetti with cream and onions) or veal

with spätzli. Generous salads and good sweets. House wine by the glass or litre.

Warehouse [6/10]

Upper Court Terrace, Kirkgate
TEL Ripon (0765) 4665

Open 9.30 to 5.30
Closed Sun

The ground floor of this excellent café was originally stables, with a tinsmith's upstairs. Robust, home-cooked food is the order of the day, with spicy lentil soup, quiches, beef casserole with beans, and Cheddar cheese crumble all featuring on the menu. Wine by the glass. Mrs Balfour says she is thinking of retiring some time in 1988.

ROSEDALE ABBEY
North Yorkshire   map 10

Coach House [6/10]

TEL Lastingham (075 15) 208

Open 10 to 6, 7 to 11.30 (10 to 6 Sun) &
Closed Jan and Feb

The Bradley family offer plenty of no-frills food in their converted coach-house. Bar snacks and light lunches hold few surprises, but the likes of roast chicken, curry, and cottage pie are sustaining and good value. Three-course Sunday lunches are £5.30. Morning coffee and afternoon tea come with home-baked biscuits and cakes; there are also high teas of gammon and egg, grilled trout and burgers. More expensive evening meals.

ROTHERHAM
South Yorkshire   map 7

| NEW ENTRY | **Khanie's** [6/10] |

124 College Road
TEL Rotherham (0709) 563144

Open 7pm to 1am (3am Fri and Sat)

Authentic, little-known Indian restaurant next door to an Asian grocer. The tables are painted green, ferns hang from the ceiling, and the walls are decked with family photos and Indian paintings. Thick dhal, excellent onion bhajias, fresh-tasting

prawn and mushroom curry and karahi gosht are typical of the menu. Banana fritters are cooked in a bright-red batter that makes them look more like polony.

RUNSWICK BAY
North Yorkshire   map 10

Sandside Café [6/10]

TEL Whitby (0947) 840224

Open 10am to 6pm & (also WC)
Closed Nov to Easter

For more than thirty years this seaside shop and snack bar has stuck to its principles, offering genuine home-cooked food. The owners make their own scones, cakes and ice-cream and sell fresh crab and salmon, as well as locally cured ham and decent pork pies. Sandwiches are freshly made. Unlicensed.

SCARBOROUGH
North Yorkshire   map 10

Dilts [6/10]

2 Princess Square
TEL Scarborough (0723) 372863

Open 11.30 to 2, 8 to 11.30 Easter to June and Sept; 11.30am to 11.30pm July and Aug; 11.30 to 1.45, 8 to 11.30 Wed to Sat Oct to Mar
Closed Sun, Mon and Tue Oct to Mar

The best fish and chip shop in Scarborough is in a small square between the castle and the seafront. There is pine panelling everywhere and nets on the ceiling. It is a good neighbourhood meeting place, where the attraction is superbly fresh fish, with a few unexpected items: cod cheeks, whole dab, wooff (cat-fish), and 'pieces of eight' (nuggets of monkfish) as well as cod, haddock and plaice. Better than average wines for a chippie. Take-aways available.

| NEW ENTRY | **Hanover Fisheries** [5/10] |

14 Hanover Street
TEL Scarborough (0723) 362062

Open 11.30 to 1.30, 8 (4.30 Thur and Fri) to 11.45
Closed Sun; Mon L

There has been a chippie on these premises opposite the railway station for more than fifty years. The present owners, John and Jeanette Bray, get their fish fresh from the local ports and keep prices low. Haddock with big real chips fried in dripping is £1.15. Take-aways only. Unlicensed.

Pic a Dish [6/10]

103 Falgrave Road
TEL Scarborough (0723) 360563

Open 8am to 5pm (2pm Wed) &
Closed Sun; bank hols; Christmas Eve to 1 Jan

Three courses for about £3 is the amazing lunchtime deal at this busy main-street café. Start with a bowl of soup, then choose from a roast with all the trimmings, or steak and kidney pie with vegetables, and finish with home-made fruit pie, sherry trifle or hot chocolate sponge with lashings of custard. There are decent fry-ups for breakfast, plus snacks and grills through the day. Unlicensed.

Sarah Brown's [8/10]

13 Victoria Road
TEL Scarborough (0723) 360054

Open 10.30 to 4, 7.30 to 10
Closed Sun; Mon D; Tue D in winter

Vegetarian/wholefood restaurant owned by the TV cook and author. She doesn't work in the kitchen, but her imaginative, enterprising style runs through the menu. The food is colourful, slightly exotic, but accessible. Pans of soup are on show; huge bowls of salad are laid out for all to see. Typical of the menu are tomatoes stuffed with walnuts and tarragon, vegetable and miso soup, hazelnut and courgette roast, aubergine pâté and lentil loaf with gado gado sauce. Breads are from Sarah Brown's shop and there are home-made ice-creams to finish. Half-price portions for children.

Small Fry [5/10]

52 North Street
TEL Scarborough (0723) 367448

Open 11.30 to 2, 4.15 to 7.15
Closed Sun; Mon; Sat pm

A tiny take-away chippie in a row of Victorian cottages at the bottom end of Westborough shopping precinct. Long queues build up, with a line of up to fifteen people snaking round the shop. The Holmes family buy from the local boats where possible, and fry in vegetable oil. Unlicensed.

SCUNTHORPE Humberside   map 8

 Excel Fisheries [5/10]

126 Rowland Road
TEL Scunthorpe (0724) 844231

Open 11.30 to 1.45; 7.30 to 11.30, plus 4.30 to 7.30 Wed to Sat &
Closed Sun; bank hols; 2 weeks at Christmas

Massive portions of excellent chips and low prices make this one of the best chippies in the area. Fish comes fresh each day from Grimsby; potatoes are local ones. The Indian proprietor makes his own curries at the weekend, and sells samosas and bhajias during the week. Unlicensed.

Italian Garden [6/10]

89 Frodingham Road
TEL Scunthorpe (0724) 854859

Open noon to 2, 6 to 11 (11.30 Fri and Sat) & (also WC)
Closed Christmas Day, Boxing Day and 1 Jan

This colourfully decorated trattoria is still good value, although it pays to choose carefully. Of late, the superb garlic bread and pizzas have overshadowed the spare ribs and moussaka. Chicken Kiev is excellent if ordered with some spaghetti and tomato sauce, rather than chips and salad. Regulars lament the disappearance of the Italian trifle.

Jubraj Tandoori [6/10]

19 Doncaster Road
TEL Scunthorpe (0724) 842607

Open noon to 2.30; 6 to midnight & (also WC)
Closed Christmas Day

The average curry-house surroundings are improved with some curtained cabinets for discreet, intimate dining. The menu in this useful Indian restaurant is strong on tandoori dishes, backed up by the usual range of North Indian curries, from rogan josh to chicken dupiaza. Look for the chef's specials, including lamb pasanda, murgh pilau with rice, and karahi chicken. Thalis from around £7 a head.

SELBY North Yorkshire   map 7

Maltings Pizzeria [6/10]

Flaxley Road
TEL Selby (0757) 708065

Open 6 to 11.30 (6.30 to 10.30 Sun)

Fifteen pizzas and eight pasta dishes give plenty of choice for a cheap meal at this useful pizzeria in the old Selby Brewery maltings. Most of the food is freshly prepared and the atmosphere is cosy, though service can be slow. Veal, steaks and fish dishes are likely to take the bill into double figures. House wines by the glass plus a basic French/German list with bottles under £6.

SHEFFIELD South Yorkshire   map 7

| NEW ENTRY | Bay Tree [7/10]

19 Devonshire Street
TEL Sheffield (0742) 759254

Open 10 to 4, plus 7 to 11 Thur
Closed Sun; bank hols

Usefully placed between the university and the city centre, this wholefood/vegetarian restaurant has plant designs on the window glass and lots of stripped pine. The small menu changes daily and also includes at least one fish dish, such as salmon with a colourful oriental salad. Otherwise there is good carrot soup, crispy mushroom layer topped with sesame seeds and breadcrumbs, and chocolate cream roulade. Salads are imaginative and brown bread is cut from a loaf. Unlicensed, but good coffee and freshly squeezed juices.

City Bar, City Hall [6/10]

Barker's Pool
TEL Sheffield (0742) 734550

Open 11.30am to 2pm &
Closed Sun; bank hols; Christmas to New Year

The basement bar and buffet below the City Hall gets very busy at lunch-time with crowds of shoppers and people from the council offices. There's a choice of ten sandwiches, plus hot dishes such as roasts, deep-dish pies, casseroles and a vegetarian special. Healthy eating is the keynote of the salads. It is very brisk, with quick service by ladies in beige brown dresses. Help yourself to cutlery and fight for a seat.

Fat Cat [6/10]

23 Alma Street
TEL Sheffield (0742) 28195

Open for food noon to 2, 5.30 to 7 & (also WC)
Closed Sun D; Christmas Day

A pub for the 1980s in an industrial part of Sheffield near Keltham Island Museum. There are reminders of the past in the tiled fireplaces and pictures of the old city, otherwise the mood is of modern wall lights and bar mirrors, community entertainment, real ales and interesting ciders. There's also a no-smoking room and some gutsy food with a healthy vegetarian bias. The bread is wholemeal, coleslaw is home made, and dishes range from stuffed marrow to chilli and shepherd's pie.

| NEW ENTRY | Islamabad [6/10]

61–63 Attercliffe Common
TEL Sheffield (0742) 445586

Open 4.30pm to 1am

A family-run Indian restaurant about a mile and half out of the city centre. The décor is red flock, white onion-dome archways and brown plastic seats. Cutlery is supplied if you need it, and the waiters are courteous and cheery. Onion bhajias are served on top of a pile of raw onion and cabbage, parathas are huge, and the Islamabad special is a good stew of beef, chicken, prawns and mince with chickpeas, fresh tomato and green chillies. Pilau rice is pale buttery yellow. Flavours are direct rather than subtle, but value for money is excellent. Unlicensed.

Just Cooking [7/10]

16–18 Carver Street
TEL Sheffield (0742) 27869

Open 11 (10 Sat) to 3.30, plus 6 to 11 Fri
Closed Sun and Mon; Christmas Day to 1 Jan

Brian Rosen and John Craig change their
menus each day to reflect what is fresh
from the market. This translates into a
serving counter loaded with all kinds of
salads to go with quiches, jacket potatoes
with interesting fillings, and specials such
as spinach roulade with lentil purée and
Parmesan topping or beef with celery and
walnuts. There's also a good choice of
sweets, ranging from Normandy apple
galette to fresh strawberry Danish
shortcake. Morning coffee and afternoon
tea are also available, and there are more
formal meals on Friday evenings. Special
gastronomic events are a regular
attraction.

Mr Kites [6/10]

150–154 Devonshire Street
TEL Sheffield (0742) 726910

Open 11.30am (noon Sun) to 11.30pm
Closed Christmas Day, Boxing Day and 1 Jan;
Easter Sun

Through the day there's a cold buffet of
pâté, stuffed aubergines, and roast joints
with salads in this neighbourhood wine
bar. For lunch and in the evening, the à la
carte menu takes in mulligatawny soup,
escalope of veal marsala and beef
Stroganoff. On Sunday and Monday nights
there's live jazz, but no à la carte menu.

Nirmal's Tandoori [8/10]

193 Glossop Road
TEL Sheffield (0742) 24054

Open noon to 2.30, 6 to midnight (1am Fri
and Sat) &
Closed Christmas Day and Boxing Day

This is not only the best Indian restaurant
in Sheffield, but one of few in the country
with a lady proprietor. Nirmal's cooking is
exemplary: skilful tandooris, subtly spiced
curries and daily specialities: look for the
sour almond-flavoured soup, potato
'chops' with lentil stuffing, and mixed
pakoras. There are also excellent cheap
lunch dishes that can keep the bill in the
region of £5. Some new vegetarian dishes,
such as baigan bhartha and curried beans
have been added to the menu. Full set
meals from £9 a head.

Theatre Restaurant, Crucible Theatre [6/10]

Norfolk Street
TEL Sheffield (0742) 750724

Open 10.30am to 7.45pm & (also wc)
Closed Sun; bank hols

The Crucible has gained international
fame, not as a fine provincial theatre, but
as the setting for the World Snooker
Championships. It also has a decent
restaurant geared to the needs of theatregoers and city shoppers. The shopper's
lunch (£3.25) has dishes such as liver and
bacon or fish and chips; there's also a daily
roast, plus light meals of open sandwiches,
omelettes, salads and grills. Vegetarians
are offered aubergine moussaka, or sweet-
and-sour nut roast. Wine by the glass, good
coffee and generous goblets of juice.

Toffs [7/10]

23 Matilda Street, The Moor
TEL Sheffield (0742) 20783

Open 10am to 4pm & (also wc)
Closed Sun; 3 days at Christmas

New owner Bashid Ahmed Janjua is
maintaining standards at this spick-and-
span coffee-house/restaurant smartly
decked out like a kitchen conservatory.
There are plant troughs and hanging
baskets everywhere. It is very useful for
morning coffee and afternoon tea, as well
as for good-value lunches prepared from
fresh ingredients. Typically there might be
hazelnut roulade; chicken, cheese and
herb terrine; vegetable risotto; roast loin of
pork with vegetables. Sweets range from
apple frangipane to peach cheesecake.
Arrive early for the best choice.

Zing Vaa [6/10]

55 The Moor
TEL Sheffield (0742) 722432/729213

Open noon to midnight & (also WC)

Sheffield's oldest Chinese restaurant is
popular for its three-course lunch and
high-tea menu (served noon to 6 Monday
to Saturday). A starter, sweet and main
course such as squid with chilli and black-
bean sauce or fried beef in black pepper
sauce will leave change from £4. Over the
years the cooking has moved on from
glutinous sweet-and-sour pork to crisp stir
frying, although you still have to ask for
chopsticks. The full menu is a mix of
Cantonese and Pekingese specialities.
Smart service, smart décor.

SHELLEY West Yorkshire   map 7

Three Acres Inn [6/10]

Roydhouse
TEL Huddersfield (0484) 602606

Open for food noon to 2.45, 7.15 to 9.30
Closed Sat L

An oak-beamed pub between Shelley and
Flockton off the B6116. The emphasis is
on food, with tables neatly laid in the bar,
and two more expensive bistro-style
restaurants. For cheap eating there is a
choice of bar meals, such as home-made
soups, mushrooms in port and wine sauce,
steaks and sandwiches. The steak and
kidney pie is reliably good. Bass on
draught.

SHEPLEY West Yorkshire   map 7

Sovereign Inn [6/10]

TEL Huddersfield (0484) 606305

Open for food 11.30 to 2, 7.30 to 10 & (also WC)
Closed Christmas Day

This is rated as one of the best places for
bar food in the area. It gets very busy, but
standards remain high: pork sovereigns
cooked with onions, tomatoes,
mushrooms and cream are as good as ever,
and the steak pie is also recommended.
Beef and ham sandwiches are packed with
thick slices of lean meat, and salads are

generous. The standard menu is now
supplemented with a blackboard of
specials.

SHIPLEY West Yorkshire   map 7

Aagrah [7/10]

27 Westgate
TEL Bradford (0274) 594660

Open 6pm to 12.45am (1.45am Thur to Sat) &
(also WC)
Closed Christmas Day

A good contrast to the Muslim cafés and
sweet centres in Bradford. The restaurant
is run by Mr Sabir and his family, the
colourful basement has more décor than
most of its neighbours, and the cooking
can be vivid. Look for the house
specialities, such as shah jahan (meat,
chicken and prawns with fresh ginger,
green chillies and fresh coriander) and balti
chicken. Drink lassi or Kingfisher beer.

Da Tonino [6/10]

26 Avondale Buildings, Bradford Road
TEL Bradford (0274) 581195

Open noon to 5, 7 to 11.30 & (also WC)
Closed Sun; Mon L

Typical of many North Italian trattorias,
with a long menu of authentic food served
in a setting of Chianti bottles and Italian
songs. For cheap eating there are fourteen
kinds of pizza as well as some home-made
pasta dishes, such as tortellini bolognese.
Steak, veal and fish specialities are more
expensive. Basic wine list.

SKIPTON North Yorkshire   map 7

Herbs [6/10]

10 High Street
TEL Skipton (0756) 60619

Open 9.30am to 5pm
Closed Sun and Tue; Christmas Day and
Boxing Day

Genuine, enthusiastically run vegetarian
restaurant serving admirable light meals
through the day. Excellent salads, home-
made cakes, soups and sandwiches, plus a
daily special such as butter-bean cake.
Queues at lunch-time. Unlicensed, but has

a good choice of teas, coffees and fruit juices.

Tom Jones Carvery [6/10]

5 Albert Street
TEL Skipton (0756) 68799

Open noon to 2, 5.30 to 10
Closed Tue

The stable door of a converted warehouse opens onto a stone-flagged dining-room, where you drink hot punch while studying the menu written on rolled parchment. The English Heritage trappings don't detract from some robust cooking: good soups, mighty roasts, and flamboyantly described dishes such as Nan Sloucher's Reviver (pear with cream and tarragon dressing). This is not Merrie England, but it's fun – and there are plenty of whacky drinks to help you on your way.

SOUTH DALTON
Humberside   map 8

Pipe and Glass Inn [6/10]

TEL Dalton Holme (069 64) 246

Open for food noon to 2 (1.30 Sun), 7.30 to 10
& (also wc)
Closed Christmas Day

William Jackson, the Hull grocer's, have owned this country pub for more than thirty-five years. Bar snacks in summer centre on the cold table; in winter there are Yorkshire puddings with onion gravy, braised beef in Guinness, and grilled chicken with fiery piri-piri sauce. Bistro-style dishes, such as roast pork with apple and cider sauce, grilled sardines provençale and tagliatelle milanese are served in the Stable Bar on Friday and Saturday evenings. Good-value Sunday lunches.

SOWERBY BRIDGE
West Yorkshire   map 7

NEW ENTRY | Ash Tree [8/10]

Wharf Street
TEL Halifax (0422) 831654

Open 11.30 to 2.30 (noon to 1.30 Sun), 7 to 10 (6.30 to 11 Fri and Sat) & (1 step)
Closed Sun D; Christmas Day and Boxing Day

310

The setting is a classic, stone-built Yorkshire pub but inside there is a collision of cultures. In the bar locals drink Timothy Taylor's beer surrounded by Javanese masks, batik prints and maps of Indonesia. Gamelan music plays in the dining-room. Bar snacks and lunches give a taste of the full menu: Indonesian soups, nasi ramas, gado gado, satay and ayam goreng are typical. Also look for martabak – a crispy pancake stuffed with spinach, sweetcorn, cheese and egg. Other meals can take the bill into double figures. Indonesian Bintang pils goes well with the food.

STAITHES North Yorkshire   map 10

NEW ENTRY | Lane End Fish and Chip Shop [5/10]

Staithes Lane
TEL Whitby (0947) 840093

Open 11.30 to 1.15pm; 7.30 to 11.15 &
Closed 1 week Oct, 1 week Feb

Excellent neighbourhood chippie in a row of houses at the top of a picturesque fishing village. It is run by a Yorkshire couple who also do the cooking. Fresh fish from Middlesbrough is cooked in beef dripping; first-rate chips are made from local potatoes; pies are from the local butcher and fishcakes are made on the premises. One curiosity on the menu is battered and fried haggis. Take-away only. Unlicensed.

SUMMERHOUSE
Co. Durham   map 10

Raby Hunt Inn [6/10]

TEL Piercebridge (032 574) 604

Open for food noon to 2pm &

The choice and quality of vegetables marks out this little country pub six miles from Darlington. There's always a choice of four, plus new potatoes in summer, and creamed or jacket in winter. They accompany home-made steak pie, Cumberland sausage, and specials such as chicken breast in wine and mushroom sauce, braised steak with beer, or vegetable marrow stuffed with savoury mince. Theakstons beer; wine by the glass.

STAVELEY North Yorkshire   map 7

Royal Oak [6/10]

Main Street
TEL Copgrove (090 14) 267

Open for food noon to 2.30 & (also WC)
Closed Christmas Day

This is a proper old-fashioned pub. At
lunch-time the Gallaghers serve food in
the bar: good game pie and pâté, soup,
salads of smoked trout, beef or ham, and
ploughman's. A fisherman's platter of
salmon, smoked trout, prawns and salad is
£3.60. More expensive evening meals in
the restaurant. Theakstons beers.

SUTTON HOWGRAVE
North Yorkshire   map 7

White Dog Inn [6/10]

TEL Melmerby (076 584) 404

Open for food noon to 2.30 (2 Sun)
Closed Mon

A little village pub with the emphasis on
food. Lunchtime snacks are served in the
bar. Choose from French onion soup,
chicken and mushroom casserole,
omelettes and salads of smoked salmon or
garlic sausage. Also look for mariner's hot-
pot – seafood cooked with herbs, tomatoes
and lemon juice. More expensive evening
meals. No children.

THORNTON West Yorkshire   map 7

Villa Roma [6/10]

1519 Thornton Road, School Green
TEL Bradford (0274) 882480

Open noon to 2, 7 to 11.30 &
Closed Mon; Sat L and Sun L; Christmas Day
and Boxing Day

Stay with the pasta dishes and cooked-
while-you-watch pizzas to eat cheaply in
this family-run trattoria. Otherwise the
menu has the usual mix of more expensive
meat and fish dishes. The atmosphere is
Bradford/Italian and the place is popular
with families. Book well ahead for
weekends. House wine is £2.70 per
half-carafe.

THRESHFIELD
North Yorkshire   map 10

| NEW ENTRY | Old Hall [7/10] |

TEL Grassington (0756) 752441

Open for food 11.30 to 2, 6.30 to 9.30 (7 to 9
Sun) & (also WC)

This fine Victorian house with a secluded
garden looks more like a country residence
than a pub. Inside there's an impressive
display of oak panelling, shiny brass and
copper. Ian Taylor does most of the
cooking and offers a mix of traditional
North Country dishes, plus more bistro-
style specialities. Dales sausages, huge
helpings of steak and kidney pie, and
Cumberland rum Nicky share the bill
with carrot and orange soup, spare ribs
with barbecue sauce, and whole spring
chicken with fresh thyme and garlic. Fish
is a feature: salmon comes poached or en
croûte, squid rings are stuffed with
oysters, scallops and prawns; there's also a
mixed grill of halibut, tuna, monkfish, sole
and salmon. Vegetables are fresh, puddings
are home made. Timothy Taylor beers.

WAKEFIELD West Yorkshire   map 7

| NEW ENTRY | Crown Inn [6/10] |

20 Horbury Road
TEL Wakefield (0924) 272495

Open for food noon to 2 & (also WC)
Closed Sun; Christmas Day and Boxing Day

Giant Yorkshire puddings filled with beef
stew, mashed potato and vegetables are
the stars in this old stone pub. They are
eight inches across, take twenty minutes
to arrive and cost £1.70. Other good dishes
include the landlord's home-made chilli,
liver and onions, and sirloin steaks. The
décor is an assortment of brass ornaments,
jugs, swords and historically dressed dolls.
Real ales.

| NEW ENTRY | Pulse [7/10] |

10 Cross Square
TEL Wakefield (0924) 361755

Open 9.30 to 5
Closed Sun; bank hols

Carol Day's restaurant is a useful find in Wakefield. The style is wholefood with a vegetarian bias: butter-bean dip, falafels, bean Wellington, hazelnut and mushroom roast, plus quiches and salads. There's also a token showing of meat and fish, such as sirloin steak in red wine sauce, chicken florentine or sole bonne femme. Sweets are home made: blueberry cheese pie, lemon and ginger syllabub, and carob, peach and mandarin gateau. Herb teas, hot milk with honey and nutmeg, and wine. Self-service downstairs; waitress service upstairs.

Val's Tea Shop [6/10]

61 Kirkgate
TEL Wakefield (0924) 378996

Open 8.30 to 5.30 & (also WC)
Closed Sun; bank hols

Homely, Victorian-style tea-shop where the cakes are home made and the waitresses have white frilly aprons. Jacket potatoes have been added to a menu that features fried haddock, rarebit made with Yorkshire ale, ham and eggs, plus snacks, salads and sandwiches. Fry-ups for breakfast, pies and Yorkshire puddings for lunch.

WALKINGTON Humberside   map 8

Fergusson-Fawsitt Arms [6/10]

Main Street
TEL Hull (0482) 882665

Open for food 11 to 3, 7 to 10.30 (11 Fri and Sat)
Closed Christmas Day

The cold table is good value in this popular mock-Tudor pub: £2.50 pays for roast meat or dressed crab with a choice of at least eight salads. There are also hot dishes, such as chicken chasseur, turkey pie, and braised liver with Yorkshire pudding. A carvery operates from Wednesday to Sunday. There are plans to serve fish suppers at £2.50 a head (after 9pm) starting late summer 1988.

WATH-IN-NIDDERDALE
North Yorkshire   map 7

Sportsman's Arms [8/10]

TEL Harrogate (0423) 711306

Open for food noon to 1.45 & (also WC)

This is a marvellous setting for a classy Sunday lunch. The seventeenth-century house is reached over a small narrow bridge; the River Nidd runs past the bottom of the garden and all around are views of Nidderdale. Inside there are open fires and silver lamps, with an antique dresser for wines and liqueurs. The all-in price of £6.80 pays for three courses: start with Yorkshire pudding and onion gravy or chicken liver pâté before roast rib of beef, roast local lamb with tomato and basil sauce, sauté trout from the Dale, or fresh fish from Whitby. Sweets include excellent lemon chiffon torte or sticky toffee pudding.

WHITBY North Yorkshire   map 10

Magpie Café [9/10]

14 Pier Road
TEL Whitby (0947) 602058

Open 11.30 to 6.30
Closed end Oct to week before Easter

This brilliant café is still synonymous with cheap eating in Whitby. Go early if you want a ringside seat overlooking the fish quay, the harbours and the parish church. Excellent local fish and chips top the bill (look for the skinned cod or lemon sole), along with superb crab, salmon and lobster at knock-down prices in season. To finish there's a remarkable choice of some thirty home-made sweets. Children not only get mini-meals, but high chairs and toy-boxes as well. Wine is available by the glass, although most people still prefer pots of strong tea.

Shepherd's Purse [7/10]

Sanders Yard, 95 Church Street
TEL Whitby (0947) 604725

Open 10am to 9.30pm
Closed end Sept to Easter

Away from the bustle of the main streets, this converted mill is now a vegetarian/wholefood restaurant bristling with leather bottles, wooden spoons, dried posies and puppets. Fresh ingredients are used for a range of dishes from Stilton and onion soup to sticky puddings, with curries, stuffed pancakes, nut loaf and salads in between. Interesting teas and organic wines to drink. An enterprising vegetarian alternative to the strong fish and chip contingent in the town.

 ## Silver Street Fish and Chip Shop [6/10]

22 Silver Street
TEL Whitby (0947) 603087

Open 11.45 to 1.30; 8 (5.30 Fri and Sat) to 11.30
Closed Sun, Mon

Whitby understandably boasts a number of first-rate chippies and this is one of the best. It has been in business for nearly half a century and still puts the emphasis on fresh fish and locally grown potatoes. All the cooking is done by Derek and Mary Webb. Take-aways only. Unlicensed.

 ## Trenchers [7/10]

New Quay Road
TEL Whitby (0947) 603212

Open 11am to 9pm &
Closed Jan and Feb

Terry Foster has transformed this quayside eating place into an upmarket fish and chip restaurant. He gets up early to buy fresh from the boats, and the quality shows in the exceptional plates of fish and chips with bread and butter and a pot of tea. Otherwise there is salmon salad, fish casserole in a pot, and home-made steak pie. Puddings and sweets are no match for the Magpie Café (see entry), but otherwise this place is its nearest rival.

WHITLEY BAY Tyne & Wear   map 10

Provençale [7/10]

183 Park View
TEL 091-251 3567

Open noon to 2pm
Closed Mon, Wed

The best French restaurant in Whitley Bay serves excellent-value lunches – three courses can leave change from £5. Start with a bowl of French onion soup or a pot of fresh noodles in cream sauce, before chicken and asparagus crêpe, grilled pork chop with provençale sauce, poached lemon sole or a choux bun filled with artichoke and ham served with excellent vegetables or salad. Sweets range from French apple tart to rum and raisin ice-cream with meringue. More expensive dinners. House wines £5.80 a litre.

WOOLER Northumberland   map 10

Ryecroft Hotel [7/10]

TEL Wooler (0668) 81459

Open for food Sun L
Closed first 2 weeks Nov, 1 week at Christmas

Excellent Sunday lunches are served in this family-run hotel at the foot of the Cheviot Hills. Three courses can be had for £6: start with leek and Stilton soup or melon and mango cocktail, before a mighty roast topside of beef with Yorkshire pudding or steak, kidney and mushroom pie with vegetables. Finish with rhubarb and ginger sponge pudding or lemon cheesecake with frosted grapes. More expensive dinners. Real ales from Clark's and Lorimer's.

YARM Cleveland   map 10

Coffee Shop [6/10]

44 High Street
TEL Eaglescliffe (0642) 790011

Open 9am to 5pm
Closed Sun; Mon L

Admirable daytime coffee-house, handy for shoppers and tourists. The usual range of sandwiches, quiches and jacket potatoes is boosted by Brazil-nut pâté, cheesy prawns, and mushrooms provençale. There are also toasted muffins, Bakewell tarts, Yorkshire curd cakes and home-made ice-creams. Tea, coffee, lager and wine to drink.

NEW ENTRY Santoro [7/10]

47 High Street
TEL Eaglescliffe (0642) 781305

Open noon to 2, 7 to 10
Closed Sun; Sat L

Good-value lunches are served at this
well-heeled Continental restaurant with a
strong Italian flavour. For less than £5
there are dishes such as risotto milanese,
spaghetti vongole, barbecued spare ribs
and chicken peperonata. Sweets come
from a trolley of creamy Italian
confections. Garlic bread and coffee are up
to the mark. More expensive evening
meals. House wine is £6.30 a bottle.

YORK North Yorkshire   map 7

Bees Knees [8/10]

Millers Yard, Gillygate
TEL York (0904) 24045

Open 10am to 4pm
Closed Sun; Christmas Day; Boxing Day
and 1 Jan

Café linked to the best wholefood bakery
in York. The setting is a range of converted
buildings near the City Art Gallery, and
the cooking is uncompromising. Typically
there might be wholesome pease pottage,
excellent tofu burgers, and apple and cider
cake. The ploughman's comes with good
spiced apple chutney. Breads and pastries
are from the bakery, salads are fresh and
much of the produce is organic. Herb teas
and juices to drink. Unlicensed.

Bettys [8/10]

6 St Helen's Square
TEL York (0904) 59142

Open 9am (9.30am Sun) to 9pm &
Closed Christmas Day and Boxing Day

A branch of the small chain of classic
North Country tea-rooms, established in
Harrogate in 1919. Opening hours are
longer here, and there is a special evening
menu taking in cheese and herb pâté or
smoked salmon muffins before omelettes,
salads, haddock and chips or rarebit with
bacon rashers. For other details see
Harrogate entry.

NEW ENTRY Giovanni's [7/10]

12 Goodramgate
TEL York (0904) 23539

Open noon to 2; 6.30 to 11 &
Closed Sun L; Christmas Day, 1 Jan

A family-run trattoria just inside Monk
Bar. Lunch is the bargain for cheap eaters –
light meals are served in the bar and at
tables in the downstairs dining-room.
There are bowls of minestrone, baked
aubergines and lasagne, as well as tomato
and garlic broth with chickpeas and pasta,
vitello tonnato (cold veal with tuna
sauce), and seafood salad. A pair of pizzas
complete the menu. More expensive full
meals upstairs. House wine is £5.50
a bottle.

NEW ENTRY Royal York Hotel [7/10]

Station Road
TEL York (0904) 653681

Open 10am to 9.30pm (restaurant 7pm to
9.45pm)

Victorian hotel restored with great care to
something of its former style. The bar/
coffee shop menu is available right
through the day, and can be served in the
dining-hall where the central staircase is
highlighted by two Venetian crystal
chandeliers. There's a good range of club
and toasted sandwiches: the Royal York
Executive is brown wholemeal bread filled
with prawns, caviare and watercress.
Other dishes range from smoked chicken
with coleslaw and crushed walnuts to
grilled lemon sole with lime and herb
butter, seafood curry with white wine and
coconut, and vegetarian pancakes. Good
Yorkshire-style afternoon teas. More
expensive restaurant menu.

St William's [7/10]

3 College Street
TEL York (0904) 34830

Open 10am (noon Sun) to 5pm
Closed Christmas Day, Boxing Day, Good Friday

One of the Milburn chain of restaurants in
historic buildings. This is a self-service
cafeteria in an oak-beamed medieval

building next to the Minster. Old-English dishes, such as raised pork and apricot pie and Yorkshire curd cheesecake, appear alongside modern veal and rabbit terrine and courgette quiche. Soup is recommended and there is good prune and apple pie to finish. Morning coffee and afternoon tea come with home-made biscuits and pastries. Theakstons bitter; Hugh Rock's elderflower wine. Medieval banquets are staged on Tuesday and Wednesday evenings in summer.

NEW ENTRY | Sultans [7/10]

76 Skeldergate
TEL York (0904) 642738

Open 6.30pm to 11.30pm
Closed Wed; Christmas Day and Boxing Day

Small Turkish restaurant off Micklegate, across from a cobbled river wharf. Downstairs is the take-away; upstairs is the dining-room, with posters of Turkey and coffee pots round the walls. Meze is good value at £8.50 for imam bayeldi, stuffed vine leaves, koftas, doners and kebabs. There are also vegetarian specials, plus sweets such as cinnamon roll and baklava. Turkish wines.

Taylors Tea Rooms [7/10]

46 Stonegate
TEL York (0904) 22865

Open 9am to 5.30pm
Closed Christmas Day, Boxing Day and 1 Jan

Taylors was founded in 1886 to import and blend oriental and Empire teas and tropical coffees. Downstairs is the tea and coffee shop with its Victorian fittings and collection of antique teapots. Above it is a suite of nineteenth-century rooms serving toast and teacakes, Yorkshire rarebit made with Theakstons ale, plus roast ham, soups, such as cauliflower or watercress, and Yorkshire curd tarts. Wensleydale cheese appears in the ploughman's, omelettes and as the traditional accompaniment to slices of fruit cake. Unlicensed.

Wholefood Trading Co. [6/10]

98 Micklegate
TEL York (0904) 56804

Open 10 to 3.30, plus 7 to 10 Fri and Sat
Closed Sun; bank hols

This used to be York Wholefoods. The setting is stripped pine benches and rush mats; the food is hearty vegetarian/wholefood dishes, such as cashew-nut pâté, tofu and vegetable goulash, aduki bean crumble and orange cheesecake. Best to book for evening meals (minimum charge £3.80). Bring your own wine.

Scotland

ABERDEEN Grampian — map 11

NEW ENTRY Henry J. Bean's [7/10]

Windmill Brae
TEL Aberdeen (0224) 574134

Open 11am to midnight (6.30 to 11 Sun) & (also WC)
Closed Sun L; Christmas Day, 1 Jan

A northerly outpost of the famous American neighbourhood bars based in London (see entries), opened on Thanksgiving Day in 1985. The cheap daytime menu (served until 5pm) keeps prices down with trans-atlantic favourites such as potato skins, nachos, chilli, smokehouse burgers and ribs. To finish there's hot fudge sundae with sauce imported from the States. During the happy hour (5.30pm to 6.30pm Monday to Friday, 7pm to 8pm at weekends), drinks and cocktails are half-price. Look for the unique Chicago Old Gold beer, specially brewed for HJB's. No children under 14.

Jaws Cafe [6/10]

St Katherine's Centre, 5 West North Street
TEL Aberdeen (0224) 6456767

Open noon to 3 (9.30 Thur and Fri) &
Closed Sun; Christmas, 2 days at New Year

Popular vegetarian/wholefood café run by a women's co-operative and serving an excellent choice of salads, vegetable pies, soups, pizzas and a hot dish of the day – couscous, casserole, vegetable curry. Delicious fresh fruit salad or pies to finish. Herbal tea or fruit juice to drink. Unlicensed.

Music Cellar [6/10]

365 Union Street
TEL Aberdeen (0224) 580092

Open 11 to 2.30, 5 to 11 (midnight Fri; 11am to 11.30pm Sat)
Closed Sun; bank hols

Small and intimate wine bar beneath a music shop. Prawns, oak-smoked chicken, roast meats, and dressed crab are served with salads. There are hot specials, such as chicken bonne femme or vegetarian harvest pie, plus oysters in season. More than seventy wines to choose from.

ANSTRUTHER Fife — map 11

Cellar [7/10]

24 East Green
TEL Anstruther (0333) 310378

Open 12.30 to 1.30, 7.30 to 9.30 & (also WC)
Closed Sun; Mon L; Christmas

This low-ceilinged, narrow restaurant in the old part of town is known for its fish. At lunch-time two courses can be had for £6–£7, and there are three-course suppers for £9.95 (served from October to Easter). Crab and smoked salmon quiches are both excellent and good use is made of the catch from the Pittenweem boats. Full meals in the dining-room are more expensive.

ARDEONAIG Central — map 11

Ardeonaig Hotel [7/10]

TEL Killin (0567) 2400

Open for food 12.30 to 2
Closed Nov to Easter

There is a warm family welcome in this remote drover's halt on the banks of Loch Tay. Excellent bar snacks offer local salmon and salad, lamb's tongue with dill and lemon, haggis, venison chops in rowan sauce, and, occasionally, bubble and squeak. More expensive dinners are served in the dining-room.

ARISAIG Highland — map 11

NEW ENTRY Arisaig Hotel [6/10]

TEL Arisaig (068 75) 210

Open for food 12.30 to 2, 5.30 to 9 &
Closed Nov, Feb

A carefully restored eighteenth-century coaching-inn a stone's throw from the sea, overlooking the Inner Isles of Eigg, Muck and Rhum. Local seafood is the speciality, and bar lunches offer a good choice of seasonal items, from Mallaig herring in oatmeal to deep-fried Arisaig king prawns with salad. There is also locally smoked salmon, fried lemon sole and a mixed seafood salad. Home-made venison pâté, gammon or steaks for meat eaters. More expensive dinners. The bar has a selection of over a hundred malt whiskies.

AVIEMORE Highland map 11

Winking Owl [6/10]

TEL Aviemore (0479) 810646

Open 11 to 11 Dec to May; 11.30 to 2.30, 5 to 11 May to mid-Nov
Closed Nov to mid-Dec

Get off the slippery slope and into this pine-girt lodge for real ale après ski and a varied menu. There is home-made cock-a-leekie soup and steak pie, fricassee of veal, moussaka, and fillet of haddock, all with chips or salad, followed by kiwi-fruit Pavlova, sherry trifle, or apple pie and fresh coffee. Ask to see the vegetarian menu. Bar suppers and restaurant meals are also available.

AYR Strathclyde map 9

 Stables [7/10]

Queen's Court, Sandgate
TEL Ayr (0292) 283704

Open 10 to 4.45 &
Closed Sun

In a large complex of restored Georgian and Victorian buildings beside the Tourist Board offices. The old stables are now a daytime coffee-house that becomes a more expensive restaurant in the evening. During the day the emphasis is on home-baked cakes and pastries to go with coffee or tea. The menu also has potted meats, fry-ups, macaroni cheese, haggis, and special pies such as steak and pickled walnut or ham and haddie. Ice-creams and sorbets are home made. English and Scottish wines by the glass.

BALLATER Grampian map 11

Tullich Lodge [7/10]

TEL Ballater (0338) 55406

Open from 1 for L & (also WC)
Closed Dec to Mar

A fine old granite mansion with good-value, three-course light lunches at £5.50, including home-made soup and bread, open sandwiches, and grilled lamb cutlets. You can eat in the handsome dining-room if you book in advance; more expensive

meals are served there in the evening. Wines by the glass.

BLAIRGOWRIE Tayside map 11

NEW ENTRY Penny Black [7/10]

1 High Street
TEL Blairgowrie (0250) 5294

Open 10 to 9 & (also WC)

The old post office is now a cheerful, pine-walled café with a children's playroom full of toys and cartoon videos. Wholemeal bread is brought to the table in a basket and the menu has a good showing of home-made dishes, including thick cream of carrot soup, cream cheese and garlic pâté, and steak pie. Mince and tatties is one of the Scottish specials, and sweets range from apple crumble to baked pears with chocolate sauce. Home-made scones and shortbread with tea. Real fruit milk shakes, San Miguel beer and wine by the glass – plus Glüwein in the skiing season.

BRIDGE OF CALLY Tayside map 11

Bridge of Cally Hotel [6/10]

TEL Bridge of Cally (025 086) 231

Open for food noon (12.30 Sun) to 1.45, 7 to 8.30 &

A nineteenth-century coaching-inn with excellent bar lunches, plus set dinners for £9. Soups include pea, lentil, and celery, and there is Ayrshire gammon with mustard seed sauce. The salad platter has various cheeses and egg mayonnaise with wholemeal bread and butter. Sweets include home-made fruit Pavlova, and nutty syrup tart.

CALLANDER Central map 11

Myrtle Inn [6/10]

Stirling Road
TEL Callander (0877) 30919

Open 10.30 to 2.30, 6 to 11 & (also WC)
Closed 23 Dec to 14 Feb

Anne Hill has taken over this simply decorated cottage just outside the town on the Stirling road. The food is home cooked, and the choice ranges from excellent lentil and vegetable soup to attractively presented salads. Very useful in a sparse area. Real ales.

CANNICH Highland   map 11

NEW ENTRY Cozac Lodge [6/10]

TEL Cannich (045 65) 263

Open for food 12.45 to 2, 7.30 for 8 & (also wc)
Closed mid-Oct to Easter, exc Christmas and New Year

The hotel was originally one of a pair of hunting-lodges built in 1912 by the Chisholm of Chisholm. The second is now underwater in Loch Mullardoch. Good-value set lunches are served in the panelled dining-room (two courses for £6.50, three for £7.50). Start with soup or pâté before chicken pie, beef casserole, or prawn and mushroom curry. Sweets are home-made ice-creams, chocolate mousse, or mincemeat and apple tart. Set dinners are £15. Booking is advisable as the hotel is at the end of an eight-mile, single-track, no-through road (from Cannich, follow signs to Glencannich/Loch Mullardoch). No children.

CANONBIE
Dumfries & Galloway   map 9

Riverside Inn [9/10]

TEL Canonbie (054 15) 295/512

Open noon to 2, 7.30 to 8.30 & (also wc)
Closed Sun; 2 weeks Feb

Robert and Susan Phillips' converted fishing-lodge is now ranked as one of the most pleasant places to stay in Scotland. It is best known for its rooms and restaurant, but there are highly popular light meals in the bar at lunch-time. Home-made soups are adventurous: turnip and dill with pine kernels; cream of parsnip and leek. Locally smoked trout pâté is excellent and fresh salmon trout appears regularly in season. Other dishes range from chicken curry with brown rice to the renowned steak, kidney and oyster pudding. Main dishes are often served with stir-fried vegetables, and salads are dressed with virgin olive oil. House wines by the glass or Theakstons beers. More expensive dinners.

COLBOST (Isle of Skye)
Highland   map 11

Three Chimneys [8/10]

TEL Glendale (047 081) 258

Open 12.30 to 2, 7 to 9
Closed Sun L; end Oct to Mar

Eddie and Shirley Spear's restaurant in a bare stone-walled crofter's cottage continues to serve the best-value lunches on the island. Soups, such as scallop chowder or potato and oatmeal, come with home-made wholemeal bread or cheese scones, and fine sweets range from hot marmalade pudding to cranachan or brown-sugar meringues. In between there are tarts filled with crab, or peat-smoked salmon, wholemeal pizzas, and salad platters (including Skye salmon poached in silver birch wine, jumbo prawns, or peppered beef), which can be eaten with oatcakes. More expensive evening menu. Wine by the glass.

COLONSAY (Isle of Colonsay)
Strathclyde   map 11

Isle of Colonsay Hotel [7/10]

TEL Colonsay (095 12) 316

Open 12.30 to 1.30, 7.30 & (also wc)
Closed 1 Jan

The only hotel on this lovely but remote island served by an unsociable ferry (cutbacks in service are threatened). Bar lunches offer home-made beef broth, sandwiches, filled rolls, steamed Colonsay mussels, smoked Tobermory trout, and cheese with oatcakes. Summer bar suppers (£5.50) for yachtsmen or visitors who missed the ferry include soup and main dishes such as coq au vin or sole bonne femme, plus coffee. High teas are also available. House wine £3.35 a bottle. More expensive dinners.

CULLIPOOL (Isle of Luing)
Strathclyde   map 11

Longhouse Buttery [9/10]

TEL Luing (085 24) 209

Open 11 to 5 & (also wc)
Closed Sun; Oct to mid-May

It is worth making the journey for the views alone. From every table in the dining-room of this remote restaurant you can see Scarba, the Garvellachs and Mull. There is no fixed lunch-hour – the whole menu is available all day; the last car ferry leaves at 6pm. Locally caught wild salmon, lobsters, and large prawns are the highlights, served simply with salads or as open sandwiches. There is also soup, home-boiled gammon, or venison pâté, with frozen chocolate pot or triple meringues to finish. Home-made lemonade is 50p or there is house wine by the glass.

DRYBRIDGE Grampian   map 11

Old Monastery   [7/10]

TEL Buckie (0542) 32660

Open noon to 1.45, 7 to 9 (9.30 Sat)
Closed Sun and Mon; 2 weeks Oct; 3 weeks Jan

There are superb views over the Moray Firth from this converted monastery up a mountain road. Local produce is used extensively for the bar and restaurant. The comfortable Cloister Bar has cane furniture and glimpses of the Sutherland hills. Beautifully presented bar food includes real vegetable soup, seafood salad, pork escalope, smoked bacon chops, and orange and caramel mousse. More expensive restaurant meals. Good, carefully chosen wine list.

DULNAIN BRIDGE
Highland   map 11

Muckrach Lodge Hotel   [6/10]

TEL Dulnain Bridge (047 985) 257

Open noon (12.30 Sun) to 2 for L   ሌ (also wc)
Closed 1 Jan

An old shooting-lodge in secluded countryside, with modest bar lunches of home-made soups, such as lentil and ham, or cream of onion, and generous sandwiches with such fillings as home-cooked gammon, poached Spey salmon, ox tongue and salad. Home-made sweets include chocolate and orange trifle, Ecclefechan butter tart, and Drambuie

parfait. Sensible wine list or Arrols draught beer. More expensive meals in the dining-room.

DUMFRIES
Dumfries & Galloway   map 9

| NEW ENTRY | Old Bank   [6/10] |

94 Irish Street
TEL Dumfries (0387) 53499

Open 10 to 5
Closed Sun; Mon; 24 Dec to 14 Jan

This used to be a bank, but the attractive Georgian building has been converted into a restaurant and coffee-shop. Through the day there's a good range of cakes and snacks; lunch-time specials such as Stilton pâté with home-made oatcakes, watercress soup or smoked chicken with avocado cream boost the standard range of quiches and baked potatoes. Up to a dozen salads are well dressed. Chocolate roulade or apple tart to finish. Wines by the glass.

DUNFERMLINE Fife   map 11

New Victoria   [7/10]

2 Bruce Street
TEL Dunfermline (0383) 724175

Open 9.30 to 6.30 (10pm Fri and Sat)
Closed Sun

A determinedly old-fashioned, good-value restaurant where lunch, high tea and evening meals are served in a large dining-room up two flights of stairs, with views of the 900-year-old abbey, the glen and the park. Lunch includes home-made soups, such as chicken broth, and pea and ham, followed by haddock or sole, steak and kidney pie, savoury meat loaf, and macaroni cheese, all served with chips or boiled potatoes. There are a few vegetarian dishes and salads. Puddings recall childhood fun: sultana pudding with custard, fruit and jelly, peach sponge, and rhubarb crumble. Children's portions and high chairs are available. Wine by the glass.

DUNOON Strathclyde map 11

Ardenslate Hotel [7/10]

James Street, Hunter's Quay
TEL Dunoon (0369) 2068

Open for food 12.15 to 1.45, 6.30 to 8.30 (9 Fri
and Sat) & (also WC)
Closed Sun D; Nov; Mon to Thur Dec to May

There are fine views of the Holy Loch from
the dining-room of Mary Hunter's old-
fashioned Victorian house. Weekday
lunches offer good-value dishes, such as
spinach crêpes, salmon pie with cucumber
sauce, Tuscany fried liver, and home-made
damson ice-cream. Sunday lunch is a
three-course bargain for £5, and centres on
roast cardamom chicken, lamb and lime
casserole, or baked ham and pineapple.
Some vegetables come from the hotel
garden. More expensive dinners.

DUNVEGAN (Isle of Skye)
Highland map 11

NEW ENTRY | Harlosh Hotel [7/10]

TEL Dunvegan (047 022) 367

Open for food 10 to 5, 6.30 to 9
Closed mid-Nov to Easter

Snacks are served right through the day in
this remote hotel on the shores of Loch
Bracadale, a few miles south of Dunvegan.
As well as sandwiches there might be
broccoli soup, home-made pâté with
oatcakes, or haggis with clapshot (a
mixture of mashed potatoes and turnips
with chives). Seafood appears in the form
of fresh crab served in the shell, grilled
king prawns, or smoked mackerel. More
expensive dinners. House wine by the
glass and a good selection of malt
whiskies, including the hotel's own label.

EAST KILBRIDE Strathclyde map 11

Lafites [7/10]

46–50 Kirkton Park
TEL East Kilbride (035 52) 20112/46588

Open noon to 2, 5 (noon Sat) to midnight
Closed Sun L

Huge helpings are served at this Chinese
restaurant in a landscaped area a few

minutes' walk from the city centre. One
page of the menu has standard dishes, such
as special roast pork with noodles and
crisply fried spring onions, but look for the
separate section of regional specialities,
like moo shoo pork with mandarin
pancakes, spring chicken in rice paper, and
beef tong mein. The décor is an eccentric
mixture of French cabaret prints and
Taiwanese statues, the atmosphere is
lively and there's an impressive list of
wines and imported beers. Take-aways and
delivery service.

EDDLESTON Borders map 9

Horseshoe Inn [6/10]

TEL (072 13) 225

Open for food 11.30 to 2, 5 to 10 (12.30 to 2.15,
6.30 to 10 Sun) & (also WC)
Closed Christmas Day and 1 Jan

Windows shaped like horseshoes offer an
unusual welcome to this fine Borders pub.
Richly flavoured steak and Guinness
casserole does a star turn in the Smiddy
Bar, and other dishes include smoked fish
pie, crêpe Bretonne, and walnut and
aubergine lasagne. Salads, sandwiches, and
toasties, plus sweets such as fresh fruit
salad, sorbets, and sherry trifle. More
expensive restaurant meals. Draught beers
from Belhaven, McEwans and Theakstons.

EDINBURGH Lothian map 11

L'Alliance [7/10]

7 Merchant Street
TEL 031-225 2002

Open noon to 2, 6.30 to 10.30
Closed Sun; Sat L; 2 weeks at Christmas;
2 weeks in July

An atmospheric back-street bistro under a
road-bridge, set in a large, vaulted
windowless room. The set lunch at £6.75
is good value and may include gazpacho,
tapénade, or fresh noodles with pistou,
before chicken à la basquaise, or fillet of
sole with cream and tarragon, followed by
cheese or chocolate mousse. More
expensive evening menu. Extensive wine
list; house wine £6.80 a litre.

Alp-Horn [8/10]

167 Rose Street
TEL 031-225 4787

Open noon to 2, 6.30 to 10
Closed Sun, Mon; 2 weeks at Christmas,
3 weeks July

One of the best Swiss restaurants in the
country, serving genuine food in a setting
of cow-bells and alp-horns. There are air-
dried meats, intensely flavoured soups,
and fondue (£5.20 for two). Best value is at
lunchtime, when there are dishes such as
venison in a piquant sauce with rösti
potatoes, veal stew, and beef Stroganoff,
for around £5. The cheeseboard is an EEC
hybrid, ranging from Fontina to Stilton
and the inevitable Gruyère. A good wine
list includes two Swiss offerings.

Baked Potato Shop [5/10]

56 Cockburn Street
TEL 031-225 7572

Open 11 to 11 (noon to 6 Sun)

A small vegetarian take-away with a
couple of stools up at the counter. It scores
because the potato fillings (also served in
pitta bread) are well above the usual spud-
chain average: avocado and cheese, curried
lentil and pineapple, and vegetarian chilli
are all good. Salads come with home-made
mayonnaise, and sweet offerings include
carrot cake and banana bread. Unlicensed,
but there are herb teas and fruity home-
made yoghurt drinks instead.

Bar Italia [6/10]

100 Lothian Road
TEL 031-229 0451

Open 5pm to 2.30am &
Closed Christmas Day, Boxing Day, 1 and 2 Jan

Open into the early hours for excellent
pizzas made from scratch, and good-value
pasta dishes, such as penne al funghi.
Great atmosphere, loud music. Bar Roma,
39A Queensferry Street (TEL 031-226 2977)
has an identical menu and opening times.

Brasserie St Jacques, King James Hotel [7/10]

Leith Street
TEL 031-556 0111

Open 12.30 to 2.30, 6.30 to 10.30 & (also WC)

The café menu is the best bet for cheap
eating in this brasserie attached to one of
Edinburgh's business hotels. Danish open
sandwiches are a favourite, otherwise the
menu has pizzas, tuna fish salad, and
brioche with leeks, apples and Mozzarella.
The vegetarian choice is boosted by ravioli
in ratatouille sauce, and vegetable cutlet
with apple, walnuts, sultanas and cinnamon. To finish there's cranachan or Welsh
rarebit. The full brasserie menu will take
the bill into double figures. Wines by the
glass, plus a good choice of teas and
coffees.

Circles [6/10]

324 Lawnmarket
TEL 031-225 9505

Open 10 to 6 (11pm in summer) &

One of the better coffee-houses on the
Royal Mile, with a genuine Scottish
atmosphere. There are home-made soups,
salads, quiches, lasagne, and pies, plus
home-made scones, shortbread, and
flapjacks. A handy eating place during the
festival, when it is open until 11pm.

Clarinda's [6/10]

69 Canongate
TEL 031-557 1888

Open 8.30 (10 Sun) to 4.45 & (also WC)
Closed Christmas Day and 1 Jan; bank hols

This small tea-room offers good value at
the bottom of the Royal Mile. Home
baking is a feature, and there are simple
lunch dishes, such as omelettes, salads,
and chicken pie, plus some straightforward vegetarian alternatives, such as
ratatouille and cauliflower cheese.
Unlicensed.

Country Kitchen [7/10]

4–8 South Charlotte Street
TEL 031-226 6160

Open 8 to 7.30 &
Closed Sun; Christmas Day and 1 Jan

Fast, self-service restaurant that balances
brilliantly the needs of Princes Street
shoppers with those of vegans and
vegetarians. The emphasis is on healthy
eating, and the menu lists ingredients and
calories per portion for every item.
Vegetables are organically grown, only
lean cuts of meat are used, and instead of
chips there are fried parsnips. Excellent,
freshly baked bread and cakes. Take-
aways. Unlicensed.

Edinburgh Wine Bar [7/10]

110 Hanover Street
TEL 031-220 1208

Open 11.30 (6.30 Sun) to midnight (1am Thur to
Sat, 11pm Sun)
Closed Christmas Day and 1 Jan

A busy city-centre wine bar with a range of
at least five specials every day, such as
mussel and onion stew, tuna casserole,
and garlic mushrooms. There are
imaginative soups, for example courgette
and tarragon, a wide range of salads, and
home-made spicy sausages. Good wines or
local draught beer.

NEW ENTRY Factory Café [6/10]

38 Buccleuch Street
TEL 031-667 5750

Open 9.30am to 10.30pm
Closed Sun; bank hols; 23 Dec to 4 Jan

The owner started by setting up a business
making vegetarian savouries, such as
falafel and dhal pie, plus sugar-free sweets.
Next he opened a take-away and has
expanded into this café with a black and
white tiled floor and a patio for sunny
days. As well as the full range of savouries
and sweets, there are filled rolls, salads,
plus a soup and hot dish each day.
Unlicensed.

Fifth, Jenners [5/10]

48 Princes Street
TEL 031-225 2442

Open 9.30 to 5 Mon to Sat &
Closed Sun; Christmas Day, Boxing Day and
1 Jan

A coffee-bar on the fifth floor of Jenners
department store, offering high-quality
scones, pastries, and cakes at tea and
coffee time, with above-average main
dishes, too. Unlicensed.

Gallery of Modern Art [7/10]

Belford Road
TEL 031–332 8600

Open 10.30 (2 Sun) to 4.30 & (also wc)
Closed Christmas Day, Boxing Day, 1 and 2 Jan;
May Day hol

A spotless, cheerful cafeteria with blue
and white décor. The range of snacks and
sweets features home-made cakes,
biscuits, and scones, plus samosas,
savoury tarts, quiches, and interesting
salads. More substantial dishes include
beef and orange casserole, fish lasagne, and
chicken korma. Becks beer and wine by
the glass, as well as juices, tea and coffee.

Handsel's Wine Bar [9/10]

22 Stafford Street
TEL 031-225 5521

Open 10am to 11pm
Closed Sun; first week Jan; bank hols

This sumptuously revamped restaurant
has boosted the quality of eating in the
city. The ground-floor wine bar features
inventively constructed modern dishes:
sea trout with monkfish, mange-tout and
broccoli; breast of chicken with mango
and dill, red and green pepper and walnut
and apple salad. Soups come with unusual
breads, and freshly baked croissants are
filled with smoked bacon, chicken, tomato
and mayonnaise. Sweets include orange
chocolate pot with pistachio shortbread or
poached pears with bitter chocolate
mousse and caramel sauce. Good range of
well-balanced wines, including many half-

bottles. House French is £5.50. The upstairs restaurant is more expensive.

Helios Fountain [8/10]

7 Grassmarket
TEL 031-229 7884

Open 10 to 6 (8, and 11 to 5 Sun, during festival)
Closed Sun (exc during festival)

Part of a Rudolf Steiner book and craft shop in a Victorian Gothic tenement at the foot of the Grassmarket. The kitchen is committed to vegetarian and vegan food, but without puritanical zeal. There are good soups, quiches, and hot dishes such as Boston bean pie topped with light wholemeal pastry, meatless lasagne, and curries. Salads are inventive and come with a choice of yoghurt dressing or vinaigrette made with virgin olive oil. Sweets are in the wholefood tradition: vegan carob cake; tofu, banana and apricot cheesecake. Unlicensed, but there is a good choice of fruit juices.

Hendersons [7/10]

94 Hanover Street
TEL 031-225 2131

Open 8am to 11pm (plus 9 to 9 Sun during festival)
Closed Sun (exc during festival); Christmas Day, New Year; bank hols

Long-running basement vegetarian restaurant with booths and gentle live music. Be prepared to queue at busy times. Choose from stuffed aubergines with cracked wheat and vegetables, leek and potato pie, excellent salads, home-made wheaty rolls and fine cheeses. To drink there's real apple juice, wine and beer.

Kalpna [9/10]

2–3 St Patrick Square
TEL 031-667 9890

Open noon to 2, 5.30 to 11.30 &
Closed Sun; Christmas Day and 1 Jan

Reckoned by many to be one of the finest South Indian vegetarian restaurants in Britain. It also claims to be the first completely no-smoking Indian restaurant in the country. Thalis are particularly good value: on Wednesdays the Gujerati special has pakora, khichree, kadhi, stuffed vegetables, puris, poppadum, raita and gulab jamun for £5.50. There are recommendations for the kachori (deep-fried lentil balls), mushrooms with coconut and fresh coriander, and the excellent carrot halva. Brown rice is offered as an alternative to Basmati. Inexpensive lunches. The elephant logo symbolises the fact that it is possible to grow big and strong without eating meat.

Kweilin [7/10]

19–21 Dundas Street
TEL 031-557 1875

Open noon (5 Sun) to 11.15 (12.15 Fri and Sat)
Closed Christmas Day; 1 Jan; 3 days at Chinese New Year (Feb)

Well-established, bright and airy Cantonese restaurant on the corner of Northumberland Street, with cheap, plentiful food. The choice of dim-sum is the best bet for a cheap meal, although prices may seem a little high by London or Manchester Chinatown standards. Look for the steamed dumplings, deep-fried crab claws, paper-wrapped prawns and spring rolls. The full menu ranges from lemon chicken and crispy duck to squid in black-bean sauce with chilli. Set meals from £9.50 a head. No children under five.

Lachana [6/10]

3 Bristo Place
TEL 031-225 4617

Open noon to 2.30, 4.30 to 7 &
Closed Sat, Sun; Christmas Day, Boxing Day, 1 and 2 Jan; bank hols

Astonishing value for money is to be had in this vegan and vegetarian restaurant run by Seventh Day Adventists. A substantial meal will cost £2.99 a head for, say, lentil or French onion soup, plus bean burgers, cashew rice or tofu loaf plus bread and a large selection of salads. Bottled water and cereal drinks. Unlicensed. Handy for the University.

Laigh Kitchen [6/10]

117A Hanover Street
TEL 031-225 1552

Open 8.30 to 4 (7.30 during festival)
Closed Sun; Christmas Day, Boxing Day, 1 and 2
Jan; bank hols

Relax in an old Orkney chair and enjoy
home-made scones and oatcakes, or arrive
at lunch-time for something savoury.
Popular favourites are tuna pâté, pasta
salad, and apple and orange salad. There's
also soup and a choice of baked potatoes.
Unlicensed.

Lazio's [6/10]

95 Lothian Road
TEL 031-229 7788

Open noon to 2 & (also wc)
Closed Christmas Day and 1 Jan

Busy, bright and airy Italian café with wide
range of above-average trattoria food. Less
than £5 pays for peppers stuffed with
seafood, or tripe with tomato sauce. There
are spot-on, generously topped pizzas,
good salads, and pasta dishes such as
spaghetti marinara with lots of mussels
and Parmesan. The innocently named
sweet meringue has ice-cream, double
cream and chocolate mousse. House wine
at 90p a glass.

Loon Fung [8/10]

32 Grindlay Street
TEL 031-229 5757

Open noon (2 Sat and Sun) to midnight &
Closed Christmas Day and Chinese New
Year (Feb)

Some of the most authentic Cantonese
food in Edinburgh is served in this big,
cheerful restaurant not far from the Usher
Hall and the Lyceum. Dim-sum are served
through the day, and the list of eighteen
snacks has roast pork and oyster sauce
dumplings, steamed spare ribs, prawn
toasts and stuffed glutinous rice. Also good
value is the big selection of thirty-five rice
and noodle dishes, ranging from rice sticks
with mixed meat to crabmeat boiled
noodles and wun-tun soup noodles. The

main menu has some new-fangled
embellishments, such as meat-balls
braised in fresh pineapple, and mango
chicken served in a mango shell. There is a
branch at 2 Warriston Place (TEL 031-556
1781/557 0940).

Le Marché Noir [7/10]

2–4 Eyre Place
TEL 031-558 1608

Open noon to 2.30, 7 to 10.30 & (also wc)
Closed Sun; 3 weeks after festival

French country cooking with a few exotic
flourishes is the style in this unfussy
restaurant. Set lunches (£6.50) are good
value for dishes such as red mullet with
fennel, lamb stuffed with apricots, or crab
salad with aïoli. Start with mango mousse,
or grilled merguez with couscous, and
finish with flambé bananas or crème
caramel. Coffee is included in the price.
Big, interesting wine list. More expensive
dinners.

Netherbow Arts Centre [6/10]

43 High Street
TEL 031-556 9579

Open 10 to 4.30
Closed Sun; Christmas, New Year; 2 weeks Sept

The centre is run by the Church of
Scotland and the self-service restaurant is
mainly vegetarian. In summer the menu
includes cold home-made pies, pâté,
quiches, and cold meats with salads. In
winter the emphasis is on savoury
vegetable pie and Forfar bridies. There are
also filled rolls, jacket potatoes, home-
made sweets, and cheese with oatcakes.
Barbecues are held in the evening during
the festival. Unlicensed, but bring your
own wine.

New Edinburgh
Rendezvous [7/10]

10A Queensferry Street
TEL 031-225 2023

Open noon to 2, 5.30 (1 Sun) to 11.30 &
Closed Christmas Day, Boxing Day and 1 Jan;
3 days at Chinese New Year (Feb)

Up a flight of stairs is this large, bustling Chinese restaurant specialising in Pekingese cooking. At the back of the menu are the good-value snacks and one-plate meals, such as grilled dumplings, steamed shredded roll, soft noodles with minced pork in yellow-bean sauce, and fried pancake with spring onion. The £8.30 set dinner (for four) has an interesting selection, including sliced beef in oyster sauce, quick-fried prawns with green pepper, and barbecued spare ribs. Set lunches are £3.20.

NEW ENTRY North China [6/10]

3 Tarvit Street
TEL 031-229 6789

Open 5 to 1.30 &
Closed Christmas Day; Chinese New Year (Feb)

Usefully placed opposite the Kings Theatre, and handy for a late-night meal. The cooking is mainly Pekingese, with good dishes such as fried spring onion cakes, chicken in yellow-bean sauce, and beef in ginger, as well as Peking duck. Décor is minimal and turnover fast.

Queen's Hall [6/10]

87 Clerk Street
TEL 031-668 3456

Open 10 to 5 & (also WC)
Closed Sun; Christmas to New Year

Light lunches are served here and the hall is also convenient for eating before evening concerts. There is a strong vegetarian emphasis, as in vegetable soup, mushroom and cheese risotto, spinach tartlets, and savoury bean slices with salads, as well as haddock pie and cold roast pork. Sweets include strawberry pancake, butterscotch mousse, and dried fruit in soured cream. Home-baked cakes go with tea and coffee.

Raffaelli [7/10]

10 Randolph Place
TEL 031-225 6060

Open 12.15 to 2.45, 5 to 10.45 &
Closed Sun

A wine bar with an adjoining restaurant in the financial West End of the city. Salamis, hams, cheeses, lasagne, stuffed aubergines, and roast joints are available for cheap eaters. The wide-ranging restaurant menu has a strong Italian flavour and includes escalope zingara and osso buco alla Romana. House wine is £5.20 a bottle.

Raj [7/10]

91 Henderson Street, Leith
TEL 031-553 3980

Open noon to 2, 5.30 to 11.30 & (also WC)

The most visually appealing Indian restaurant in Edinburgh brightens up the dockland overlooking the waterfront at Leith. Inside it almost looks Georgian, with graceful lines, a cream colour scheme, and eighteenth-century prints on the walls. The cooking is North Indian, and the Bombay thali shows the range: good sag bhaji, aloo jeera with cumin seeds, fragrant pilau rice and well-made roti bread. Karahi chicken, Kashmiri prawns and achar gosht are good too. Business lunch is £4.95.

Seeds [6/10]

53 West Nicholson Street
TEL 031-667 8673

Open 10 to 8 &
Closed Sun; 1 week at Christmas; 1 week Mar, 1 week early Sept

A wholefood co-operative café near the University, firmly dedicated to vegan and vegetarian cooking. Butter, yoghurt and milk are available but are not used in the cooking. The emphasis is on organic produce and cakes and desserts are almost completely sugar-free. The menu changes constantly to take in carrot and cashew nut soup with home-made bread, vegetable chop-suey and brown rice, salads, tofu cheesecake and a wide range of pastries. Unlicensed.

Shrimp's [6/10]

107 St Leonards Street
TEL 031-667 9160

Open 11 to 3 &. (also WC)
Closed Christmas Day and Boxing Day

Danish food in a Victorian parlour with a welcoming log fire in winter. The emphasis is on smørrebrød, with seafood, rare roast beef, and salads.

T.G.'s [7/10]

135A George Street
TEL 031-225 3003

Open 8 to 5
Closed Sun

An elegant Georgian food hall run by the Willis family, including a butchery and bakery, with crystal chandeliers in the self-service restaurant. It is an excellent lunchtime venue, with such local favourites as haggis with neeps, potted hough, fillet of haddock in beer batter, rib of Scotch beef braised in Belhaven beer, plus home-made hamburgers, and salads. Bread and meat are supplied from the other Willis shops. There is a breakfast take-away service from 8am to 10.30am.

NEW ENTRY | Verandah Tandoori [7/10]

17 Dalry Road
TEL 031-337 5828

Open noon to 2.30, 5.30 to 11 &.

The most interesting of a clutch of Indian restaurants close to Haymarket railway station. The décor is mellow, with wickerwork chairs and wall hangings, the waiters are young and the pace is leisurely. For cheap eating there are thalis: the vegetarian version (£7.55) has vegetable massallam, tarka dhal, palak bhaji, chapati, pilau rice and chutney. Otherwise the menu has good pakoras spiked with green chillies, vegetable karahi, and North Indian specialities, such as chicken korma badami. Good breads.

Viva Mexico [7/10]

10 Anchor Close, Cockburn Street
TEL 031-226 5145

Open noon to 2.30, 6.30 to 10.30
Closed Sun; Christmas Eve to Boxing Day;
31 Dec to 2 Jan

Some of the best Mexican food in Edinburgh is served at this fast and furious restaurant bedecked with flags, posters and pictures and pulsating with Latin American music. The wide range of Mexican beers is the perfect foil to fiery dishes such as sonoras (bean and spices), nachos (corn tortillas covered in cheese and grilled), throat-burning guacamole, enchiladas and chimichanga. Desserts include cream caramel, carrot cake soaked in rum, and excellent mango mousse. The management claim to make the best Margaritas in Scotland.

Waterfront Wine Bar [8/10]

1C Dock Place, Leith
TEL 031-554 7427

Open 11 to midnight &.
Closed Sun

A busy wine bar in a pleasant old dockside setting with tables outside in good weather. Barbecues are the main feature when the sun shines, otherwise the kitchen turns out splendid pies served in pudding basins and bistro-style dishes, such as chicken breast stuffed with ricotta and spinach, or gurnard with fennel and dill sauce. A plateful of oatcakes and cheese is enough for two. Watch for Loch Sween oysters, or seafood lasagne when available. More than forty wines including Australian Chardonnay. Children over five welcome.

Whigham's Wine Cellars [7/10]

13 Hope Street
TEL 031-225 8674

Open 11 to midnight (1 Fri)
Closed Sun; Christmas Day, Boxing Day;
1 and 2 Jan

Basement wine bar reminiscent of a war-time pill-box, with stone walls, stone ceilings and flagstoned floor. It is often crowded at lunch-time as hungry hordes descend for real soups, cold roast meats, mature cheeses, excellent smoked salmon, and beef and oyster pie. Evenings are quieter and the menu is more restricted. Wine by the glass and good house claret.

GAIRLOCH Highland   map 11

Steading Restaurant [6/10]

TEL Gairloch (0445) 2449

Open 9.30 to 9 (5 Easter to May)
Closed Oct to Easter

Part of a former farmstead strung round a cobbled courtyard behind the Heritage Museum. The kitchen uses local produce, including fish fresh from the loch. The menu is available all day with a choice of soups, salads, hot dishes – such as venison casserole, roast chicken or haggis – and home-made oatcakes. A seafood platter for two is £11. The short wine list includes Moniack Highland Birch, and there is excellent coffee. More expensive evening menu.

GALASHIELS Borders   map 9

Red Gauntlet [6/10]

36 Market Street
TEL Galashiels (0896) 2098

Open noon to 2, 7 to 9.30 &
Closed Sun; Mon Oct to Mar; 2 days at Christmas, 2 days at New Year

Wholesome, good-value food in a comfortable dining-room in the centre of a mill town. The sensible, short menu has freshly made chicken and mushroom pie, home-made minestrone soup, spaghetti and beans, lasagne, fillet steak garni, followed by fruit pie, brandy scrolls, and profiteroles. Good house red.

GLASGOW Strathclyde   map 11

Amritsar Tandoori [7/10]

9 Kirk Road, Bearsden Cross
TEL 041-942 7710

Open noon to 2, 5 to midnight & (also WC)
Closed Sun L

A very useful neighbourhood Indian restaurant with plenty of atmosphere and very helpful service. Staples such as excellent fish pakora, chicken chat and lamb korma can be more successful than some of the gimmicky ideas (venison tikka, veal nentara). Basmati rice and breads are well handled. There are thalis from £5.95, as well as cheap business lunches. Children have their own mini-menu of tandooris and curries. Lager comes by the jug.

NEW ENTRY Bar Luxembourg [7/10]

197 Pitt Street
TEL 041-332 1111

Open 11am to 1am
Closed Sun L

One of Glasgow's newest wine bars feels as if it could be in Marbella: it is huge and airy, with white sails billowing from the ceiling, grey and white marble-effect tables and cream leather sofas. The waiters wear neat uniforms. The menu is a mixture of fashionable warm salads, daily changing pasta dishes cooked al dente and served with freshly grated Parmesan, and a long list of American-style dishes, from burgers to open sandwiches on rye bread. Excellent coffee.

La Bavarde [7/10]

9 New Kirk Road, Bearsden
TEL 041-942 2202

Open noon to 1.30, 6.30 to 9.30 & (also WC)
Closed Sun and Mon; 2 weeks at Christmas; last 3 weeks July

Good-value set lunches are served in this crowded neighbourhood bistro. The menu is international, ranging from tripe trevisano and spinach pancake with bolognese sauce to grilled herrings. There are excellent soups to start and exotic fresh fruit or Stilton cut from a whole cheese to finish. More expensive evening meals.

Belfry [8/10]

652 Argyle Street
TEL 041-221 0630

Open noon to 2.30, 5 to 11
Closed Sun; Christmas, 1 Jan and bank hols

A good place for a stylish lunch in an old-fashioned setting of antiquarian books, mirrors and dark wood. The quality of the meat and fish is excellent and the skill shows in the hot dishes. Choose carefully to keep the bill below double figures. Starters and snacks are the likes of Oban mussels in white wine, or sauté chicken livers with orange and watercress salad. Main courses include special omelettes with smoked chicken, cheese and asparagus, char-grilled chopsteak topped with blue cheese and crispy bacon, and chicken and broccoli pie with braised rice. There are also vegetarian dishes such as feuilleté of courgette provençale with spinach. Good coffee and excellent house wine.

NEW ENTRY Bonham's Wine Bar [6/10]

194 Byres Road
TEL 041-357 3424

Open for food 11 to 3
Closed Christmas Day, 1 Jan

One of the most atmospheric wine bars in Glasgow, with wrought-iron and woodwork purloined from old houses, a modern stained-glass window and good live jazz at Sunday lunch-time. The food is a simple range of hot dishes, such as chilli and lasagne, backed up by good cold meats and salads: smoked pork loin goes well with pasta and carrot. Decent wines and beers.

Café Gandolfi [8/10]

64 Albion Street
TEL 041-552 6813

Open 9.30am to 11.30pm
Closed bank hols

One of the most genuine all-day eating places in Glasgow. The décor recreates Mackintosh in robust vein, the atmosphere is bright and lively and the menu is built round good raw materials. There is a 'Good Morning' choice of eggs en cocotte, or cheese and ham on Italian rolls, before an interesting choice of hot and cold dishes ranging from excellent pastrami on rye, warm chicken and bacon salad with honey vinaigrette, or pissaladière, to Finnan haddock with potatoes, and choux pastry stuffed with Stilton. Smoked venison with dauphinois potatoes is an intriguing idea. There are

also croissants and home-made ice-cream. To drink, coffee, tea, wine by the glass and wonderful Duvel beer from Belgium.

Le Café Noir [7/10]

151 Queen Street
TEL 041-248 3525

Open 8.30 (noon Sun) to midnight (11.45 Sat, 11 Sun) & (also wc)
Closed Christmas Day

A stylish Viennese-style brasserie with green tiles and *chansons* in the background. The downstairs bistro (where children are welcome) has a menu of vegetable pakoras, baked Brie with apple purée, steaks, burgers, and pasta dishes such as tagliatelle carbonara. There's also a two-course set lunch for £3.95. Upstairs is a salad bar, with cold food and French-style sandwiches. Teas, coffees and wine by the glass. There are branches in Waverley Market, Edinburgh and St John's Centre, Perth.

NEW ENTRY Café Sannino [6/10]

18A Gibson Street, Hillhead
TEL 041-339 5294

Open 9 to 6 (11 to 5 Sun) &

This lively coffee-shop-cum-delicatessen serves some of the best-value food close to the University. The décor is a mixture of bargain-basement furnishings and tubular frame tables and chairs. There are news-papers to read and old songs play in the background. The choice of sandwiches ranges from favourites such as egg and salad, to turkey breast with cranberry sauce or pastrami with Gruyère cheese. There are continental platters, hot croissants and bagels as well as home-baked pastries. Take-aways. Unlicensed.

NEW ENTRY De Quincey's [7/10]

71 Renfield Street
TEL 041-333 0633

Open 11 to midnight
Closed Sun, Christmas Day, 1 Jan

Famous for its unique décor. During renovation the extraordinary Victorian tiling was exposed; it covers the arcades, walls and ceilings. To match this there are brown club sofas and wicker tub seats in the comfortable bar. The food centres on salads with plenty of olives and peppers, to go with Glasgow-style French bread, excellent cinnamon-baked ham, apple-roast pork, and salmon en croûte. Inexpensive hot snacks and jugs of lager are served in the cellar bar. No children.

 ## Diva, Beacons Hotel [6/10]

7 Park Terrace
TEL 041-332 3520

Open 11 to 10.30 (11.30 Thur to Sat)

The revamped basement of the Beacon Hotel is now an upmarket bar in modish grey and white with op-art and polished aluminium tables. The food is American-style bistro with 'taste of health' salads including a low-fat section. Good range of wines and beers.

 ## Fazzi's [7/10]

65–67 Cambridge Street
TEL 041-332 0941

Open 8 to 6 (also wc)
Closed Sun

An authentic Italian coffee-bar attached to a delicatessen. The family proprietors make their own sausages and salamis, roast their own coffee beans and serve some of the cheapest pasta dishes in Glasgow. Huge sandwiches are made with crisp French bread and there's a range of continental pastries. A big platter of cold meats with olives and salad is £3.50. Excellent cappuccino. Unlicensed.

Fixx [6/10]

82–86 Miller Street
TEL 041-248 2859

Open for food 11 to 7
Closed Sun, Christmas Day, Boxing Day, 1 and 2 Jan

There is a speakeasy atmosphere in this lounge bar serving food until 7pm. Try the home-made soups and varied salads, such as shrimp and pasta, or one of the

traditional roasts. Coffee is cafetière. There are American film posters and photos on the walls, a rhino's head, a worldwide selection of beers, and fancy cocktails such as Bossanova and the non-alcoholic Mickey Mouse, so called because 'it dis'nae work'. Open late for drinks only.

Gallery Coffee Shop [6/10]

2 Creswell Lane
TEL 041-339 0968

Open 10 (noon Sun) to 6
Closed Christmas Day, Boxing Day, 1 and 2 Jan

In an underground basement with a craft shop selling paintings, sculptures, and designer sweaters. It is one of the cheapest and most cheerful eating places off the Byres Road shopping area. A daily changing menu of hot dishes ranges from chicken and mushroom pie and beef provençale to stuffed vegetables, quiches and lasagne. There are also home-baked apple pies, scones and cheesecake. Unlicensed.

Granary [7/10]

82 Howard Street
TEL 041-226 3770

Open 9 to 6 (also wc)
Closed Sun

Some of the best home baking in Glasgow is served at this country-style dining-room with white walls and old wooden furniture. Quiches are excellent, rolls are made with Italian wholemeal flour, and hot lunch dishes may include broccoli and tomato soup, leek and potato pie, haddock bake, and walnut cheeseburger. Good choice of salads and delicious sweets, including nutty meringues and seasonal fruit pies. Bring your own wine.

Granny Black's [6/10]

55–57 Candleriggs
TEL 041-552 2470

Open for food noon to 2.30, 3.15 to 4.30

As rumbustious and extrovert as ever, this classic city pub still exudes genuine Glaswegian atmosphere. The food is good and amazingly cheap: home-made soup 50p, mince and tatties £1, chicken curry (and tatties) also £1, a decent helping of roast chicken and potatoes £1.90. Big filled rolls and real ales. No children.

Grosvenor Café [6/10]

31 Ashton Lane
TEL 041-339 1848

Open noon to 3, 5 to 8 (noon to 8 Fri and Sat)
Closed Sun; Christmas Day; 1 Jan; last 2 weeks July

A very popular neighbourhood café that has been run by the same family for more than fifty years. In the cramped downstairs room there's espresso coffee, all kinds of filled rolls, and cakes from a local bakery. The upstairs restaurant serves home-made soups, pasta dishes, vegetarian specialities, and ice-creams. Unlicensed.

Loon Fung [8/10]

417 Sauchiehall Street
TEL 041-332 1240

Open noon to 11.30 &

New owners and a new head chef from Hong Kong have taken over this popular Cantonese restaurant, and standards are still high. It is one of the best choices for dim-sum in the city – with all kinds of steamed dumplings and interesting items such as stuffed duck web. The vast menu has classic dishes, such as Chinese sausages with vegetables, duck with spring onion, and pork with bean curd. Three-course vegetarian set dinners are a new feature.

NEW ENTRY Miller Street Catering Company [6/10]

61 Miller Street
TEL 041-226 5359

Open 8am (9am Sun) to 10pm
Closed Christmas Day

A bustling and animated café with excellent coffee and an interesting selection of cold meats and sandwiches. There is a range of cold fish dishes, good crudités with dips, and stuffed peppers

with savoury tomato and rice stuffing. Sweets include caramel shortbread and a range of Californian cookies. Two hundred wines in stock. A much better bet than the cafés in the local department stores.

Nile Bar [6/10]

58 West Nile Street
TEL 041-248 6830

Open for food 10.30 to midnight (6.30 to 11 Sun) &

There's a lot of décor in this cool bar, with its imitation marble, mirrored walls and modern colour schemes. The menu includes baked potatoes with above-average fillings, lasagne, spaghetti, and dishes such as ham and sweetcorn casserole. There's also a good range of cold meats. Decent coffee, excellent choice of beers. No children.

NEW ENTRY Pavarotti Trattoria [6/10]

91 Cambridge Street
TEL 041-332 9713

Open noon to 2.30, 5.30 to 11 &
Closed Sun; some bank hols

Probably the most useful place in Glasgow for a cheap Italian meal before a night at the opera. There are cheerful red gingham cloths on the tables and a poster of Placido (not Luciano) on the wall. Pasta tastes like the real thing, and sauces are cooked from scratch: look for the gutsy fettucine Pavarotti. Two-course lunches are £3.50. Even with wine the bill can be under double figures.

Peking Inn [7/10]

191 Hope Street
TEL 041-332 8971

Open noon to midnight (1am Fri and Sat) &
Closed Sun

A cramped basement restaurant with some of the best Pekingese and Cantonese cooking in the city. The menu has well-presented scallops and Chinese leaves with ginger and onion, shredded pork with Szechuan vegetables, and fried king prawns in chilli. Fish is delicately handled.

Best bets for a cheap meal are the excellent dim-sum – little dumplings, paper-wrapped prawns, bean curd dishes, and silver thread roll. Service is friendly and caring.

NEW ENTRY | P.J.'s [8/10]

Ruthven Lane, Byres Road
TEL 041-339 0932

Open noon to 2.30, 5 to 11.30 (12.30 Fri); noon to 1am Sat (11.30 Sun) & (also WC)
Closed 1 Jan

Formerly Poachers, this converted farmhouse is now a pastaria specialising in fresh pasta and pizzas. Tagliatelle, penne, fusilli and conchiglie are served with interesting sauces such as courgettes, garlic and yoghurt, or cider, apples and smoked salmon. There is minestrone to start and noodles with fruity sauce to finish. Otherwise the menu has good light pizzas, seafood risotto, and chicken with grapes and wholegrain mustard sauce. Special lunches for under £3. Drinkable house wine or two-pint jugs of lager.

Pollok House [6/10]

2060 Pollokshaws Road
TEL 041-649 7547

Open 10 (2 Sun; 1 Sun in summer) to 4.30 & (also WC)

Useful for a cheap, leisurely meal after a visit to the Burrell Collection. The setting is a fascinating kitchen complete with a superb cast-iron range and a nineteenth-century Napier coffee machine. To eat there is a decent haddock with good fresh chips, gammon, quiches and salads. Coffee, tea and fruit juices to drink. Unlicensed.

Preet Palace Tandoori [7/10]

Unit 1, Finefare Shopping Centre, Milngavie Road
TEL 041-942 9067

Open noon to 11.30 & (also WC)
Closed Sun L; 1 Jan

The business lunch at £3.45 offers a good choice of meat and vegetable curries, with pakoras to start and gulab jamun to finish. There are tandooris, karahi dishes and birianis on the main menu, along with a big assortment of curry house favourites, from chicken jalfrezi to methi keema. Look for the nargisi kebab – rather like an Oriental Scotch egg – and khir (an Indian version of rice pudding). Mini-menu for children.

Ristorante Genova [6/10]

Byres Road
TEL 041-357 0994

Open noon to 2, 6.30 (6 Sat) to 11 & (also WC)
Closed Sun; Christmas Day

Very popular and very cheap. The three-course set lunch at £2.90 is one of the great trattoria bargains in the neighbourhood. Otherwise this cosy Italian restaurant is rated for its good pasta dishes and its veal. Have two starters or a starter and a main course. Unlicensed.

Rogano [9/10]

11 Exchange Place
TEL 041-248 4055

Open noon to midnight
Closed Sun; Christmas Day and 1 Jan

Now run by Alloa Brewery, this elegant place is perhaps the best pub-restaurant in the U K. Light snacks are served amid the art deco in the Oyster Bar, with its mirrors, gold fans on paper and wood panels with mermaids and seagulls. There are sandwiches, soups, and salads, plus dishes such as seafood quiche, or turkey, ham and mushroom pie. The all-day bistro downstairs offers a slightly more expensive menu dominated by fish – crab bisque, moules marinière, seafood lasagne – plus meaty Americana such as burgers, chilli, Philadelphia cheese steak and BLTs. The main restaurant is more expensive.

Sannino [6/10]

61 Elmbank Street
TEL 041-332 3565

Open noon to 2.30, 5 to midnight
Closed Sun; Christmas Day and 1 Jan

Good-value business lunches are available in the basement pizzeria. The biggest pizza – meant for two – measures 16 inches in diameter. There are pasta dishes, too.

Shish Mahal [6/10]

45–47 Gibson Street
TEL 041-339 8256

Open 11.45 to 11.30 (11.45 Fri and Sat) &

The best value in this popular Indian restaurant is at lunch-time, when there's a 20 per cent discount on prices. Otherwise the extended menu has a full range of curry house specialities, from pakoras and mixed tandooris to chicken patia and prawn punjabi masala. The restaurant is now licensed.

Smiths [6/10]

47 West Nile Street
TEL 041-221 4677

Open 10 to 11 & (also WC)
Closed Sun; bank hols; 2 days at Christmas, 1 Jan

The atmosphere is hectic and the décor eccentric in this popular wine bar with its plaster of Paris heads and crazy hats along the top shelf. It is a useful bet for lunch, when there's a good choice of baked potatoes with fillings, all kinds of fresh salads, and hunks of chicken and ham pie. Decent range of wines and beers, as well as punch. No children.

Tolbooth [6/10]

11 Saltmarket
TEL 041-552 4149

Open for food 11 to 11 (12.30 to 2.30, 6.30 to 11 Sun) & (also WC)

Saved from dereliction by the tiny Strathalbyn brewery of Clydebank, this pub breathes more of the life of old Glasgow than its trendy merchant-city neighbours. The food – served all day – is cheap and simple: large bowls of vegetable soup, bridies, lamb and mushroom pie, jumbo sausage and chips for £1.20. Main courses come with vegetables, such as turnip and cabbage. It is difficult to spend more than £2 on a substantial two-course meal. Strathalbyn beers. No children.

Ubiquitous Chip [9/10]

12 Ashton Lane
TEL 041-334 5007

Open noon to 2.30
Closed Sun

There are ways of eating cheaply at the Chip, if you stay in the bar rather than the experimental, idiosyncratic restaurant. Bar food includes tomato and lentil soup, chicken, turmeric and ginger casserole, beef and ham terrine, Trossachs pike with orange mayonnaise, and roast pork with apple vinaigrette. There is a generous selection of vegetarian salads, plus fresh fruit Pavlova, or chocolate and Grand Marnier mousse to finish. Fresh coffee, wine, draught beer, German lager and malt whisky.

Willow Tea Rooms [8/10]

217 Sauchiehall Street
TEL 041-332 0521

Open 9.30 to 4.30
Closed Sun; bank hols

Not to be missed by visitors to Glasgow, this famous tea-room was originally designed by Charles Rennie Mackintosh and brought back to life in the early 1980s by Anne Halliday. There are exquisite art nouveau designs, perfectly preserved doors with brooding maidens, leaded glass mirrors and high-backed chairs. Afternoon tea rivals London's best, but you must be prepared to wait for freshly cut sandwiches, scones, lemon meringue pie, chocolate fudge cake, and apple and cherry pie. There are also savoury toasties and chilli and pitta bread, tea and good coffee. Unlicensed.

Winter Green Café [6/10]

People's Palace Museum, Glasgow Green
TEL 041-554 0195

Open 10 to 3.45 & (also WC)

As the address suggests, the café is a workers' co-operative, and has four full-timers. The setting is beautiful, with palms soaring up to the roof of the Victorian conservatory, stained glass panels of Biblical fruits and flowers, and elegant tables and chairs. Friendly waitresses serve lentil and tomato soup, broccoli and tomato quiche, wholemeal pizza, filled rolls, croissants, cakes, and scones. An oasis for parents with children. Unlicensed.

GLENDEVON Tayside   map 11
Tormaukin Hotel [6/10]
TEL Muckhart (025 981) 252

Open for food noon to 9.30 ♿ (also WC)
Closed Jan

Beams, an open fire and antiques feature in this cosy bar. Pâté and pies are home made, the soup is good and there are recommendations for the haddock and chips, ploughman's, and cheeseburgers. The bar has an all-day licence and there is a limited menu of soup and salads between 2pm and 5.30pm. Sunday lunch is a cold buffet. Children welcome until 7pm.

GRANTOWN-ON-SPEY Highland   map 11
 ### Ice-Cream Parlour and Coffee House [6/10]
31–35 High Street
TEL Grantown-on-Spey (0479) 2001

Open 9 to 7 ♿ (also WC)
Closed Sun; first 3 weeks Jan

This is the most attractive eating place on the main street, with its big windows and red-painted floorboards. The coffee-house part of the menu has a good showing of home-baked scones, pastries, and gateaux, plus baked potatoes, locally smoked salmon with scrambled eggs, pâté, and salads. True to its name, the café also serves all kinds of freshly made ice-creams and sundaes: peach suprême is apricot ice-cream with brandy-soaked peaches and fresh cream. Espresso and cappuccino come from a huge coffee machine. Unlicensed.

HELENSBURGH Strathclyde   map 11
Le Jardin, Ardencaple Garden Centre [6/10]
Rhu Road Higher
TEL Helensburgh (0436) 2245

Open 10 to 2.30 (midnight Fri and Sat) ♿
Closed Sun

The restaurant is on the edge of a garden centre not far from Glasgow. The lunch menu offers home-made soup with crusty bread, haddock and sweetcorn in cheese sauce, open sandwiches of tongue or ham, Indian salad, and hazelnut and courgette loaf. Finish with hot waffles and maple syrup or pears in red wine. Pots of tea, coffee, wine or beer. More expensive evening menu.

INVERNESS Highland   map 11
Brookes [8/10]
75 Castle Street
TEL Inverness (0463) 225662

Open 11.30 to 3, 5 to 11 (1am Thur and Fri, 11.45pm Sat) ♿
Closed Sun; bank hols; 2 weeks Jan

Good-value wine bar nestling at the foot of Inverness Castle with a range of enterprising dishes, including apple, tomato and celery soup, leek and lovage quiche, savoury beef italienne, pan-fried monkfish and scallops, and watercress and smoked trout roulade. There is a separate evening menu. All the ingredients are fresh and prepared on the premises. Long wine list includes some good vintages plus decent house wines by the glass.

 ### Loch Ness House Hotel [6/10]
Glenurquhart Road
TEL Inverness (0463) 231248

Open for food noon to 2, 6 to 9 ♿ (also WC)

An old, family-run hotel with lovely gardens looking out to the Caledonian Canal. Cheap lunches are served in the dimly lit bar: decent cauliflower soup, chicken liver pâté, lasagne, and specials such as lamb casserole served with good buttery mashed swede. Otherwise the menu is in the prawn cocktail/gateau mould. More expensive Taste of Scotland dinners in the restaurant. Children welcome until 7.30pm.

Nico's Bistro, Glen Mhor Hotel [6/10]

9–12 Ness Bank
TEL Inverness (0463) 234308

Open noon (12.30 Sun) to 2.15, 5 to 10.30 (9.30 Sun to Thur Oct to May)

Off-beat bistro in conventional hotel. Fleshy herring is highly recommended, or try more expensive local salmon, or roast lamb with fresh steamed vegetables. Scottish specialities include haggis with neeps and tatties, or mussel stew. There are also jacket potatoes with a choice of fillings, and barbecued beef or lamb. Fixed-price business lunches during the week cost £2.75. Short wine list.

KENTALLEN Highland   map 11

 Holly Tree [7/10]

TEL Duror (063 174) 292

Open 12.30 to 2.30, 6.30-9.30 May to Oct & (also WC)
Closed Fri to Mon Easter to May; Mon to Wed and Sun L Oct to Easter

The restaurant is in a converted Edwardian railway station on the shores of Loch Linnhe and there are magnificent views from the windows of the dining-room. Cheap lunches are a mixture of snacks and simple items from the evening menu: for light meals there is avocado with orange and cottage cheese, bacon and banana bake, or pear and Stilton salad. More substantial dishes are the likes of pigeon with port and orange, or sole with cucumber and dill sauce. Sweets range from crème caramel to brandy, sultana and walnut flan. More expensive dinners.

KILFINAN Strathclyde   map 11

Kilfinan Hotel [6/10]

TEL Kilfinan (070 082) 201

Open for food noon to 2, 3 to 5, 6.30 to 9.30

A remote old coaching-inn with locally caught fish, shellfish and game. Lunchtime bar meals include home-made soup, smoked trout salad, jumbo prawns, venison burger, and steak and kidney pie, followed by ice-cream with butterscotch or banana Pavlova. Afternoon tea is also served and the restaurant provides more expensive evening meals backed by a sound wine list. There is draught beer in the bar.

KILLIECRANKIE Tayside   map 11

Killiecrankie Hotel [7/10]

TEL Pitlochry (0796) 3220

Open for food 12.30 to 2, 7 to 10
Closed mid-Oct to late Mar

Local produce and Scottish recipes dominate the menus in this lively and welcoming hotel. Bar meals feature game soup with oatcakes, home-made game and redcurrant pie, smoked haddock flan, raspberry shortcake and Atholl brose, plus a good range of salads and sandwiches, including smoked Ayrshire ham and Angus beef. More expensive restaurant meals. The extensive wine list includes many half-bottles, plus house wine by the glass.

KILMUN Strathclyde   map 11

Coylet Inn [6/10]

Loch Eck
TEL Kilmun (036 984) 322/426

Open 11.30 (noon Sun) to 2, 5 (7 Sun) to 10
Closed Christmas Day and 1 Jan

Simple, straightforward cooking served in a small and often crowded restaurant with stunning views. The menu, plus daily specials chalked on a blackboard, includes reliable home-made soup, macaroni cheese with baked potato, fresh langoustines, and fillet and sirloin steaks. Sweets are from a trolley. Good carafe wines and real ale.

LERWICK Shetland   map 11

Royal National Mission to Deep Sea Fishermen [5/10]

Harbour Street
TEL Lerwick (0595) 2703

Open 8 to 6 (2 Sat)
Closed Sun

The utilitarian cafeteria on the ground floor of the mission specialises in excellent and cheap fish dishes. The men from the boats eat there, which testifies to the quality. Try fresh herrings fried in oatmeal with a large mug of tea. Unlicensed. Don't miss the exhibition devoted to the Shetland fishing industry.

LINLITHGOW Lothian   map 11

Champany Inn [9/10]

Champany Corner
TEL Philpstoun (050 683) 4532/4388

Open noon to 2.30, 6.30 to 10 &

Still the best steak-house in Britain. The public bar attached to the prestigious restaurant is a chop and ale house serving family meals at lower prices but with no drop in quality. Superb char-grilled Aberdeen Angus steaks are the mainstay, from T-bones to lesser-known cuts such as rib eye (from the heart of the rib). There are burgers, home-made all-meat sausages, lamb chops, and veal, backed up by seafood platters, pickled fish, and apple pie. The lunchtime buffet has cold joints and a choice of ten salads for £4.95. House wine by the glass, real ale.

MELROSE Borders   map 10

 NEW ENTRY **Marmion's Brasserie** [7/10]

Buccleuch Street
TEL Melrose (089 682) 2245

Open 10 to 11 (1 to 5 Sun) & (also WC)

Some of the best value in the Borders is to be found in this lofty, wood-panelled dining-room. It is brasserie by name and brasserie by nature, with a flexible menu of two dozen dishes. Croque monsieur and potato soup are good starters or light meals; more substantial offerings range from pork hongroise to scampi with cream and tomato sauce. Vegetables are fresh and sweets have included superb oven-fresh profiteroles. Lunches are a bit cheaper than evening meals. Coffee ad lib; house wine by the glass or half-bottle.

MEMUS Tayside   map 11

Drovers Inn [6/10]

TEL Foreside (030 786) 322

Open for food noon to 2, 7 to 9 (9.30 Fri to Sun) & (also WC)

This small country inn is surrounded by farmland and warmed by open fires in the old kitchen range. Food is a good mix of home cooking with some adventurous touches. There is always a soup, such as strongly flavoured cock-a-leekie or cream of carrot and turnip, before dishes such as stuffed trout with orange sauce, roast venison or pork chop in cider and raisin sauce. Sweets include locally-made ice-creams. The beer garden and salad bar are summer attractions.

MOFFAT
Dumfries & Galloway   map 9

Black Bull Hotel [6/10]

TEL Moffat (0683) 20206

Open for food noon to 2, 7 to 9 & (also WC)
Closed 1 Jan

Hearty pub fare in this sixteenth-century inn where Robbie Burns scrawled his *Epigram to a Scrimpit Nature* on a window pane (since transported to Moscow). Lunchtime bar food offers haggis, fish pie, cold roast beef, macaroni cheese, or pork and egg pie. More expensive evening meals include trout and steaks. Greenmantle Ale on draught.

NEWTON STEWART
Dumfries & Galloway   map 9

NEW ENTRY **Creebridge House Hotel** [7/10]

TEL Newton Stewart (0671) 2121

Open noon to 2.30, 7 to 9 & (also wc)

An eighteenth-century grey stone hunting-lodge set in over three acres of grounds. Fishermen congregate in the bar, where there is real ale and a good choice of snacks. The long menu has Cullen skink, scampi Mornay, chilli, and grilled lamb cutlets with rosemary, as well as salads (including Galloway beef, Ayrshire gammon, and Cree salmon), plus vegetarian dishes such as curried vegetables or stuffed peppers. More expensive dinners in the restaurant.

OBAN Strathclyde   map 11

| NEW ENTRY | **Manor House Hotel** [6/10] |

Gallanach Road
TEL Oban (0631) 62087

Open noon to 2 &
Closed Christmas Day, 1 and 2 Jan

This converted Georgian dower-house near the ferry terminal is the best bet for a cheap lunch in Oban. The emphasis is on home-made soups, such as cream of mushroom, seafood salads, and grills. Hamburgers are made on the premises. Hot dishes come with chips or baked potatoes. Dinners in the restaurant are more expensive.

ONICH Highland   map 11

Lodge on the Loch [6/10]

Creag Dhu
TEL Onich (085 53) 238

Open 12.30 to 2.30; 7 to 9.30 & (also wc)
Closed 31 Oct to mid-Mar

Good bar lunches are served in this quiet, comfortable hotel. Home-made Scotch broth with rolls, smoked fish pâté, and grilled salmon with decent helpings of fresh vegetables have been recommended. More expensive Taste of Scotland menu in the evening, although it is still possible to eat for under £10.

PEEBLES Borders   map 10

Kailzie Garden Centre [6/10]

Kailzie Estate
TEL Peebles (0721) 22807

Open 11 to 5.30 &
Closed mid-Oct to 1 Apr

The restaurant is in a converted stable-block adjacent to the gardens in the beautiful Tweed valley. Morning coffee comes with home-baked cakes and biscuits. Lunches centre on the salad bar, with quiches, open sandwiches, and omelettes, plus a hot dish of the day. Sweets include decent apple pie, and coffee and walnut gateau. Wine by the glass.

PERTH Tayside   map 11

Brown's [6/10]

67 George Street
TEL Perth (0738) 32693

Open 10 (noon Sun) to 10 May to Oct; 10 to 6 (noon to 5 Sun) Oct to May
Closed Christmas Day; 1 and 2 Jan

Coffee and ice-cream are the specialities in this handsome Victorian-style café. Cakes and scones are home baked and there are open sandwiches, salads, soups, and specials such as lasagne and moussaka. Ice-cream special and hot chocolate fudge cake are recommended and coffees range from cappuccino to Viennese. Unlicensed.

Timothy's [8/10]

24 St John Street
TEL Perth (0738) 26641

Open 10 to 11.30, noon to 2.30, 7 to 10.15 & (also wc)
Closed Sun, Mon; 3 weeks in summer

The Laings' town-centre restaurant excels at 'snitter' and 'smørrebørd'. The former are little Danish snacks such as crabmeat wrapped in smoked salmon, or salmon with potato salad and sweet pickle; the latter are more substantial open sandwiches topped with anything from ham with sweetcorn and home-made mustard relish to prawns with spaghetti and salad. There are also big cold platters of meat or seafood, plus soup and ice-cream sweets. Fondue with Scottish beef is a speciality. Ice-cold akvavit to drink.

PITCAPLE Grampian   map 11

Bank Inn [6/10]

Durno
TEL Pitcaple (046 76) 220

Open for food noon (12.30 Sun) to 2.30, 6.30 to 10 (1 Fri, midnight Sat) & (also WC)

This converted village shop and community centre was once used for barn dances; now it is a pub with a roaring trade in bar meals. The vegetarian owner will arrange special dishes, such as Brazil nut roast with tomato sauce, or fruit pudding with soya cream. There is also a restaurant.

ST ANDREWS Fife   map 11

Brambles [7/10]

College Street
TEL St Andrews (0334) 75380

Open 10 to 5
Closed Sun; Mon; 2 weeks over Christmas and New Year

Long queues appear at lunch-time in this tiny vegetarian café where you can have a main course, sweet, glass of wine and coffee for around £3. All the food is home made; it includes cream of lettuce soup, vegetable and haricot broth, nut roast, vegetable couscous, Greek spinach and pasta pie, whisky cake and oatcakes and cheese. Jean Hamilton, the proprietor, is a former domestic science teacher who cheerfully varies the size of portions to suit appetites.

Grange Inn [7/10]

Grange Road
TEL St Andrews (0334) 72670

Open for food 12.15 (12.30 Sun) to 2, 7 to 10 &
Closed 24 Dec to 4 Jan

Simple country cooking is the style in this old inn and everything is made on the premises, from the bread rolls to the ice-creams. Bar meals always include good soups, such as fennel and lettuce or celery and Stilton, before excellent freshly baked pies: beef and venison, mussel and onion, lamb with rosemary. There are fresh fish dishes, too, plus vegetarian options like broccoli and hazelnut crêpes with tomato and red pepper sauce. Lunch is a bit cheaper than supper, and there are more expensive restaurant meals. No children in the bar.

NEW ENTRY **New Balaka** [7/10]

3 Alexandra Place, Market Street
TEL St Andrews (0334) 74825

Open noon to 2.30, 5.30 to midnight; noon to 1am Fri and Sat (5.30 to 12.30 Sun) &
Closed Sun L

There are flats above this ground-floor Indian restaurant and a sign says, 'After 11pm please be as quiet as possible, so that we may remain friends with the lady who lives upstairs'. The menu stays with familiar curries, such as king prawn madras, and tandoori specialities (including chicken wings). Vegetable dishes are distinctively spiced, and there's a good-value vegetarian thali for £7.50. Drink lassi or lager, otherwise there is a Blue Nun of a wine list.

NEW ENTRY **West Park House** [6/10]

St Mary's Place
TEL St Andrews (0334) 75933

Open 10 to 2.30, 7 to 8.30 & (also WC)
Closed Sun; Mon; Christmas and New Year

The MacLennans run this Georgian building as a guest-house with a restaurant attached. Good-value lunches might begin with soup, such as vegetable and watercress or carrot and apple, before grilled kidneys with bacon, grilled lemon sole, or roast leg of Forfar lamb with mint sauce. There are also salads and seafood platters, plus fruit pies to finish. More expensive dinners. Children welcome at lunch-time.

ST MARY'S LOCH Borders   map 9

Tibbie Shiels Inn [6/10]

St Mary's Loch
TEL Selkirk (0750) 42231

Open for food noon to 9 Easter to end Oct, noon to 2, 6.30 to 8.30 rest of year & (also WC)
Closed Christmas Day

A remote lochside inn named after the wife of a nineteenth-century mole-catcher. Bar meals are served during opening times and there is always at least one vegetarian dish, such as bulgur wheat and walnut casserole, along with home-made soup, Yarrow trout, chilli con carne, and beefburgers, all served with chips and vegetables or salad. Evening meals include home-made venison ragout, and Tweed Kettle – local salmon, mushroom and prawns cooked in wine. Afternoon teas and high teas are also served. Usually a draught beer on handpump.

SCARISTA (Isle of Harris)
Highland   map 11

Scarista Studio [6/10]

TEL Scarista (085 985) 224

Open 10.30 to 9
Closed mid-Oct to Easter

A small café attached to a gallery specialising in contemporary art. All the baking is done on the premises and many of the vegetables, fruits and herbs are grown in the garden. Interesting soups include cream of cucumber and mint, or lentil and lovage, served with wholemeal bread, and main courses range from mushroom, green pepper and cheese roast to wholemeal pizza with salads. Good sweets and cakes. Unlicensed.

SELKIRK Borders   map 9

Philipburn House Hotel [7/10]

TEL Selkirk (0750) 20747

Open 12.15 to 3, 6.30 to 9.30 &. (also wc)

The 'Quick Bite' menu is the best value in this otherwise quite expensive country hotel. There are Loch Fyne herrings, gravlax made from local salmon with a dash of malt whisky, lasagne, croque monsieur and madame, and an Austrian meat, bacon and potato dish called Tiroler Grostel. Sweets include cream meringue, apple pie and Sachertorte with whipped cream. Vegetarian dishes such as crispy Gruyère fritters, mushrooms in garlic butter, or tagliatelle are also available. In summer there are tables by the swimming-pool and children can have fun on the trampoline.

STRATHCARRON
Highland   map 11

Carron [6/10]

Cam Allt
TEL Lochcarron (052 02) 488

Open 10 to 9 &.
Closed Sun; mid-Oct to 1 Apr

This is hardly the most accessible eating place in Britain, but the owners still manage to obtain good local produce. For around £6 a head, including wine, there is home-made soup with hot wholemeal rolls, followed by quiche, grilled sausages, and ham salad. More expensive char-grills include salmon, trout, and venison in season. Sweets range from almond cheesecake to pear flan with wholemeal pastry. Afternoon teas come with home-made pastries.

STROMNESS Orkney   map 11

Ferry Inn [6/10]

John Street
TEL Stromness (0856) 850280

Open for food 11.45 to 2, 6 to 10 &. (also wc)
Closed 1 to 3 Jan

There are fine views of the harbour from this split-level pub, with the mahogany lounge resembling the inside of a schooner. Food is served in generous portions seven days a week. Daily specials may include Orkney farmhouse pâté or beefsteak pie with green beans, potatoes and grilled tomatoes. The cheeseboard includes several local varieties and there's cloutie dumpling with cream for sweet.

TARBERT Strathclyde   map 11

West Loch Hotel [8/10]

TEL Tarbert (088 02) 283

Open for food noon to 2, 7 to 8.30 &. (also wc)
Closed Nov

This attractive stone building is on an old drovers' road overlooking West Loch pier and the Islay ferry. Inside it is calm, cosy and pleasingly old-fashioned. Lunchtime bar snacks are excellent value for home-made soup, pan-fried lambs' liver and bacon, venison chop with red wine and mushrooms, grilled fresh herrings with mustard butter, and pork en croûte. There are definitely 'no chips, no sandwiches, no toasties'. More expensive evening meals in the restaurant.

TOBERMORY (Isle of Mull)
Strathclyde map 11

Gannets [6/10]

25 Achaneil, Main Street
TEL Tobermory (0688) 2203

Open 9 to 10 Mar to end Oct; 10 to 3 Nov to Feb ♿ (also wc)
Closed Sun Nov to Feb

Long opening hours make this double-fronted restaurant an asset to the island. Seafood is the speciality and much of it is local, ranging from crab surprise and salmon with butter and dill to scallops collected by the scuba divers. Full three-course meals may take the bill into double figures, but the place also serves light snacks, sandwiches, and home-baked cakes through the day. Picnics are also available to take away and eat on the heights overlooking the bay and the harbour.

TURRIFF Grampian map 11

NEW ENTRY Towie Tavern [7/10]

Auchterless
TEL Auchterless (088 84) 201

Open for food noon to 2, 6.30 to 9 ♿ (also wc)
Closed Sun D and Mon D; Christmas Day, 1 Jan; 3 weeks Jan

Peter and Marilyn Rattray have turned a run-down roadside pub into a thriving tavern with a good line in food. Inside the décor is 'auld Scottish', with two dining-rooms, banqueting suite and a bar with ornately carved wooden seats. The food has a vegetarian bias, and lunches are good value. Soups, such as potato, leek and cauliflower, are recommended and main dishes range from vegetable and nut bake with tofu sauce to smoked chicken gratin, and steaks. Sweets are creamy and often alcoholic. Also look for the day's specials – called Towie Treats. More expensive dinners. Wine by the glass.

TYNDRUM Central map 11

Clifton Coffee House [7/10]

TEL Tyndrum (083 84) 271

Open 8.30 to 5.30 ♿ (also wc)
Closed Nov to Mar

Home cooking is the heart of this efficient self-service café on the A82 between Loch Lomond and Fort William. Soups include Fife broth and cock-a-leekie, backed by stovies with sausages, cold salmon, and tipsy laird cake. There are usually some vegetarian alternatives. Bulgarian house wine at 75p a glass. The coffee-house is part of a tourist complex that includes a food shop specialising in Scottish produce.

ULLAPOOL Highland map 11

NEW ENTRY Ceilidh Place [8/10]

14 West Argyle Street
TEL Ullapool (0854) 2103

Open 10 to 10 (8pm winter) ♿

An old boat-shed opposite the loch has been turned into a coffee-shop-cum-restaurant with pine tables and a big display of puddings and cheeses. The style is eccentric bistro, with the emphasis on vegetarian dishes such as spinach roulade or bean moussaka, backed up by excellent fresh fish – grilled haddock, Dover sole, salmon. Good soups, such as cream of onion or Stilton, and sweets ranging from fruit trifle to hazelnut and apple cake. Salads are crisp, bread is home baked. Events, entertainments and exhibitions are staged regularly.

NEW ENTRY Morefield Motel [7/10]

TEL Ullapool (0854) 2161

Open for food noon (12.30 Sun) to 2, 6 to 9.30 ♿ (also wc)

The hotel is a modern, low-slung building a mile out of the town on the road to Achiltibuie. Good-value snacks and meals are served in the lounge bar, with the emphasis on locally caught seafood, salads, and Aberdeen Angus steaks. Thick home-made broth is a meal in itself and the menu has good prawn curry, haggis on oatcakes, and fried scampi served with baked potato. Excellent coffee. House wine is £4.95 a bottle. The Steak Plaice restaurant is more expensive.

UNAPOOL Highland   map 11

Kylesku Hotel [6/10]

TEL Kylestrome (097 183) 231

Open 8.30 to 2.30, 5 to 8
Closed end Oct to April

The proprietor's own boat lands the catch for this comfortable lochside hotel with spectacular views of sea and mountains. Bar food offers a choice of seafood – scallops, prawns in garlic butter, or fish pie – as well as chicken Maryland, burgers, and pizzas. The set dinner menu (£9.80) is a Taste of Scotland.

WESTER HOWGATE
Lothian   map 11

Old Howgate Inn [8/10]

TEL Penicuik (0968) 74244

Open 11.30 (12.30 Sun) to 2.30, 5 (6.30 Sun) to 10
Closed Christmas Day and 1 Jan

An historic eighteenth-century coaching-inn with a blazing fire, specialising in a vast range of Danish open sandwiches such as herring, smoked eel with scrambled egg, lobster, ox tongue with spinach pâté, and fillet of beef with raw egg yolk. There are soups, cold meat platters, fondue and char-grilled steaks, all washed down with Danish lager, akvavit or wine.

WHITEBRIDGE Highland   map 11

NEW ENTRY # Knockie Lodge [7/10]

TEL Gorthleck (045 63) 276

Open for food 12.30 to 1.30, 7.45 for 8
Closed end Oct to end Apr

The Millwards serve very good bar lunches in their two-hundred-year-old shooting-lodge. Soups such as cream of cauliflower or courgette and fennel are well made, and there are simple main dishes including various quiches (Lorraine, or salmon and dill, or spinach and cream cheese) and decent ham salad with sauté potatoes. The cheeseboard looks healthy and there is superb ginger bombe with blackcurrant coulis for sweet. Strong coffee, wine by the glass. More expensive dinners, reservations only. Children over ten welcome.

Wales

ABERAERON Dyfed   map 6

Black Lion Hotel [6/10]

Alban Square
TEL Aberaeron (0545) 570576

Open for food 11 to 3, 5.30 to 11
Closed Sun

The atmosphere is of a basic Welsh seaside
town pub, and the food is home made.
Liver, bacon, onions and peas at £2.50 are
good value and there are also pies and
quiches, excellent cawl, beef cooked in
stout and a selection of salads. Tables
outside in the summer and an upstairs
room for parties.

Hive on the Quay [8/10]

TEL Aberaeron (0545) 570445

Open 10.30 to 5 (10 to 9.30 6 July to end Aug)
Closed Sept to spring bank hol

Excellent harbour-side café with a
conservatory restaurant overlooking the
water. It is owned by the Holgate family,
and their honey appears in jars for sale, on
the baked ham, and in the honey ice-
cream. The daytime menu is home-made
bread and cakes, plus soup, pâtés, pies and
local cheeses. During high season there are
good-value dinners, including cawl served
with bread and a hunk of cheese, Welsh
pancakes, and enterprising specials such as
lamb chops with laverbread sauce, roast
bacon with parsley sauce and butter beans,
and mackerel stuffed with cockles,
wrapped in bacon and served with potato
cakes. Children are, quite rightly, offered
small portions of the grown-ups' food.
Wine, beer and cider to drink.

ABERDOVEY Gwynedd   map 6

Old Coffee Shop [6/10]

13 New Street
TEL Aberdovey (065 472) 652

Open 10 to 5
Closed Mon; 2 weeks Nov, 3 weeks Jan

A tiny, folksy coffee-shop serving snacks
and light meals all day. Prepare to queue at
lunch-time for ham salad, ratatouille,
lasagne, and a wide range of serve-yourself

salads. Good home-baked cheesecake,
chocolate fudge cake, raspberry and
hazelnut meringue can be enjoyed with
afternoon tea. Out of season, the kitchen
turns its hand to beef in Guinness, and
chicken and leek pie. Unlicensed.

ABERGAVENNY Gwent   map 6

NEW ENTRY

Bagan Tandoori [7/10]

35 Frogmore Street
TEL Abergavenny (0873) 4790

Open noon to 2.30, 6 to 11.30 &
Closed Christmas Day

The popular choice for Indian food in
Gwent. 'Bagan' means 'garden' and the
restaurant is suitably decorated with
plants, a waterfall and a big mural
depicting Indian garden scenes. The menu
tries to offer something more than the
usual curry-house fare, with sizzling
karahi dishes, murgh massalam and lamb
badam pasanda, as well as birianis and
dhansaks. Also look for the thalis (£6.50
and £6.95) and varied set meals, which
begin at around £8 a head. Exotic fruits and
Indian sweetmeats on the trolley. To
drink, try Indian Taj Mahal lager.

Clam's Coffee House [6/10]

Lion House, King Street
TEL Abergavenny (0873) 4496

Open 9.30 to 5.30 &
Closed Sun in winter

Jane Phillips has moved down the road to a
renovated 1930s house, and the emphasis
is still on home cooking. Try the excellent
quiche and salad, home-made pizzas,
chicken and mushroom pie, and salmon
fish-cakes. There are sandwiches, filled
jacket potatoes and a good range of sweets
and cakes. Children's meals are available.

Malthouse [7/10]

Newmarket Close
TEL Abergavenny (0873) 77842

Open 11 to 3, 7 to 10 &

This fifteenth-century monastic malthouse is now a bustling wine bar serving

hearty but low-fat dishes. Light lunch-time snacks might include Welsh broth, prawns by the pint or lasagne with salad. There are also daily specials, such as roast leg of Welsh lamb with gooseberry sauce, plus jacket potatoes and char-grilled burgers. Sunday lunch is a buffet. Wine by the glass and bottled beers from all over the world.

ABERSOCH Gwynedd　　　　map 6

Porth Tocyn Hotel [6/10]

TEL Abersoch (075 881) 2966

Open for food 12.30 to 2
Closed Nov to Mar

There are magnificent views across Cardigan Bay to Snowdonia from this long-established, family-run hotel. Mrs Fletcher-Brewer puts on bar lunches for guests and occasional callers, to eat inside the hotel, out in the garden or by the pool. The simple menu is in the style of vegetable soup and smoked chicken in apricot and mustard sauce, backed up by salads, sandwiches and chocolate brandy cake. There's a cold buffet on Sunday evenings. Dinners in the restaurant are more expensive.

ABERYSTWYTH Dyfed　　　　map 6

Connexion [6/10]

19 Bridge Street
TEL Aberystwyth (0970) 615350

Open 10 to 4.45, 6.30 to 9.30
Closed Sun; Christmas Day and Boxing Day; first 2 weeks Sept

A low-wattage coffee bar-cum-restaurant with late-Georgian windows, six tables in alcoves and, occasionally, a live guitarist. It is popular with students. Ex-actress and comedienne Jane Fuerst offers anything from home-made soup and tagliatelle verdi to king prawns in garlic butter or paella, with hummus, chicken Kiev and steaks in between. There's also a good showing of home-made cakes, ice-creams and sundaes, plus a separate vegan menu. Wine by the glass. Children under five are not encouraged in the evening.

Corners [7/10]

21 Chalybeate Street
TEL Aberystwyth (0970) 611024

Open 10 to 2, 7 to 9.30 &
Closed Sun

Cardigan Bay salmon and crab, Welsh lamb and farmhouse cheeses all feature on the menu in the Reynolds' converted corner shop. She cooks and he runs the front of house. Lunches for under £5 are good stock-pot soups, salads, curries and lasagne. Suppers show off the raw materials: loin of pork with provençale sauce; beef Stroganoff; nut and vegetable roast. Sweets are served with local farm cream. Espresso coffee, short wine list.

NEW ENTRY　Gannets [8/10]

7 St James Square
TEL Aberystwyth (0970) 617164

Open noon to 2, 6 to 9.30 & (also WC)
Closed Sun

David Mildon and his wife share the duties in the admirable bistro tucked away in a back street near the old market. Lunches are excellent value for dishes such as Welsh lamb cutlets in mint gravy, poached salmon in lemon butter, and ratatouille niçoise. Sweets are in the style of pine-apple cheesecake, hot raspberries with home-made ice cream, and lemon meringue pie. Prices are slightly higher in the evening. Italian house wine is £5 a litre.

BANGOR Gwynedd　　　　map 6

Grape Expectations [7/10]

322 High Street
TEL Bangor (0248) 355015

Open noon to 2.30, 6.30 to 9 (9.30 Fri and Sat) &
Closed Sun; Mon in winter; Christmas Day and Boxing Day

More of a bistro than a wine bar, offering some of the best value in the area. Starters include seafood smokie or courgettes stuffed with tomato and celery, followed by main dishes such as lamb and apricot pie, Hungarian beef pasta, and kidney casserole with fresh vegetables. Finish with a pudding – fudge cake, steamed syrup pudding, or wholemeal cherry pie – or a large chunk of Brie. The carefully chosen wine list includes some half-bottles and bin-ends.

BARMOUTH Gwynedd   map 6

Angry Cheese [6/10]

TEL Barmouth (0341) 280038

Open 6 to 10 & (also wc)
Closed Sun to Wed Nov to Mar

Home cooking is the speciality of this oddly-named holiday-resort restaurant. The £7 set menu is good value for three courses plus coffee. Start with home-made soup or tuna fish salad before savoury chicken pancake, rainbow trout with sage or vegetable cutlets, and finish with profiteroles or fresh fruit salad. The more expensive *carte* includes local seafood when available, plus sweets such as the Angry Cheese special – black cherries in hot maraschino liqueur, vanilla ice-cream and whipped double cream. Wine by the glass.

BETWS-Y-COED Gwynedd   map 6

 ## Bubbling Kettle [6/10]

Holyhead Road
TEL Betws-y-Coed (069 02) 667

Open 11 to 5.30 &
Closed 2 weeks in Oct, Jan and Feb

A small, grey Victorian house on the outskirts of the village, where Mrs Davies and Mrs Hughes turn out some excellent home baking: scones with local Jersey cream, various fruit loaves, apple pie and all kinds of cakes. A three-course lunch is £2.95; an evening meal (by prior arrangement) £5, which includes a glass of wine.

Royal Oak [6/10]

TEL Betws-y-Coed (069 02) 219

Open 7.45am to 9pm & (also wc)
Closed Christmas Day and Boxing Day

Good-value lunches are served in the Grill Room attached to this converted pub overlooking the River Llugwy. Start with a

plate of mussels or home-made soup, before duck with sage and onion stuffing, chicken curry or whiting in a cheese sauce. There are Manx kippers, pizzas and good omelettes, plus bread-and-butter pudding to finish. Afternoon teas are served, too.

BONTDDU Gwynedd   map 6

 ## Farchynys Cottage Garden [5/10]

TEL Bontddu (034 149) 245

Open noon to 6, from 7
Closed Sat; 31 Oct to 1 Apr

The setting is everything: a converted gardener's cottage on the Mawddach estuary, surrounded by four acres of rambling landscaped gardens. It is perfect for a summer afternoon tea away from the crowds and the traffic. Scones, bara brith and cakes are home made and there are also fruit pies and salads. Homely dinners in the guest-house are £7.50 for three courses. Unlicensed.

BRECHFA Dyfed   map 6

Old Tailor's [5/10]

TEL Brechfa (029 789) 266

Open 10 to 5.30
Closed Christmas to Easter; weekdays Nov to Christmas

A small refreshment area in a craft centre converted from a tailor's shop and post office. Downstairs there are pots of tea and coffee, plus good flapjacks and gingerbread. Upstairs you can buy quality Welsh craft goods, cards and confectionery or visit the exhibition room. Unlicensed.

BROAD HAVEN Dyfed   map 6

Druidstone Hotel Bar [6/10]

TEL Broad Haven (043 783) 221

Open for food 12.30 to 2.30, 7 to 10.30
& (also wc)
Closed Nov

Sea views, good hospitality and decent bar food are the attractions in Rod and Jane Bell's hotel. Light lunches in the cellar bar might take in mushroom and fennel soup, avocado mousse or vegetable and lentil pie, as well as salami platter and spaghetti napolitana. To finish there are alcoholic ice-creams or French apple tart. Suppers are more filling dishes, such as lamb with herb stuffing. Worthington B B and malt whiskies galore.

BYLCHAU Clwyd   map 6

Sportsman's Arms [6/10]

Bryntrillyn
TEL Nantglyn (074 570) 214

Open for food noon to 2.30, 6 (7 in winter) to 10 & (2 steps)
Closed Christmas Day

The highest pub in Wales, up in the mountains with wild moorland all around. Despite this, it is highly popular for Welsh singing, good beer and robust food. Home-made pâté and pies share the bill with seasonal mussels, grilled herring fillets and big steaks. Three-course Sunday lunches are a major attraction, and there's a salad bar at weekends during the summer. Lees beers on handpump.

CAERNARFON Gwynedd   map 6

Bakestone [9/10]

26 Hole in the Wall Street
TEL Caernarfon (0286) 5846

Open 12.30 to 2.30, 6.30 on &
Closed Mon; Thur L; Sun D

This modest one-up, one-down bistro by the castle has been stripped back to its bare stonework and wooden beams. Yves Monin's cooking is genuine, unadorned bistro with a daily changing menu of fresh ingredients. It is good quality; it is also excellent value. Crêpes are the mainstay, cooked on an electric bakestone and filled with anything from cheese and mushrooms to the house special of fresh spinach, smoked bacon, cheese and egg. Lunch and dinner menus also include dishes such as baked sausage with apples and mustard sauce, potted trout with smoked prawns and dill, and braised spring lamb with prunes. Also look for seasonal fish and game: baked sea bass or salmon escalope with fresh thyme sauce.

Excellent fruit flans to finish. Afternoon teas are available at 24 hours' notice.

CARDIFF
South Glamorgan   map 6

Armless Dragon [9/10]

97 Wyvern Road, Cathays
TEL Cardiff (0222) 382357

Open 12.30 to 2.30, 7.30 to 10.30 &
Closed Sun; Sat L

Good English and Welsh cooking with occasional international influences in a setting of farmhouse tables and artificial flowers. The menu follows the local markets for crab soup, roast Welsh lamb with laver sauce, and salmon grilse with samphire. And it pays homage to the dragons of the east with stir-fried squid, Thai-style mushroom and almond toasts, and crispy winglets with Chinese five-spices. There is a vegan platter – laverburger, stuffed tomato, stuffed pepper, onion bhajia and gravy – for £5.80. Children tolerated.

La Brasserie [7/10]

60 St Mary Street
TEL Cardiff (0222) 372164

Open noon to 2.45, 7 to 12.15
Closed Sun

In the same mould as Champers, Cardiff (see entry). Steaks, kebabs and fish are charcoal grilled to order and there's a range of help-yourself salads to go with them. Cold dishes include French cheeses as well as dressed crab, pâté, and garlic bread. The waiters handle the wine behind the long oak bar.

Champers [7/10]

61 St Mary Street
TEL Cardiff (0222) 373363

Open noon to 3, 7 to 12.30 &
Closed Sun L; Christmas Day

Consistently reliable wine bar with echoes of a Spanish bodega in the flamboyance of the waiters and the list of over a hundred Rioja to drink. Charcoal grilling is the order of the day and the idea is to choose your own steak, kebab or chop to be cooked, order a jacket potato and put together a salad from the selection of raw chopped vegetables. Children over five welcome.

Crumbs [5/10]

33 David Morgan's Arcade
TEL Cardiff (0222) 395007

Open 11.15 to 3 &
Closed Sun; bank hols

It's difficult to spend more than £2 a head in Judy Ashley's tiny vegetarian café. The menu is short – there is only one hot dish each day – but the emphasis is on salads using coleslaw, red cabbage, brown rice, yoghurt, pine kernels, nuts and sultanas. Take-aways. Unlicensed.

Everest [7/10]

43–45 Salisbury Road, Cathays
TEL Cardiff (0222) 374881

Open noon to 2.30, 6 to midnight (to 1 Fri and Sat) & (also WC)
Closed Christmas Day

Not the cheapest Indian restaurant in Cardiff but the first choice for value and quality. Good curries and tandoori dishes are served in a setting of table lamps, varnished wood and velvet upholstery. Go for the thalis: meat eaters are offered shami kebab, tandoori chicken or lamb curry with nan, massala poppadum, rice and ice-cream for around £6. Vegetarians pay even less for bhajis, bread and the rest.

NEW ENTRY Happy Gathering [7/10]

233 Cowbridge Road East, Canton
TEL Cardiff (0222) 397531

Open noon to 11.45

This Cantonese restaurant hits a peak on Sundays, when the Chinese community descends in force for dim-sum lunches. In addition to these excellent cheap snacks, the menu takes in fashionable sizzling dishes and edible birds' nests as well as Peking duck. Drink Chinese tea or French wine.

Himalaya [6/10]

Millfield Road
TEL Cardiff (0222) 491722

Open noon to 3, 6 to 2 (3 Fri) & (also WC)
Closed Sun L

A long-established Indian restaurant serving well-cooked and spiced dishes. The menu is straightforward, but there are good reports of chicken biriani, beef and mushroom curry, and Bombay potato. Special set meals begin at £11.50 for two, for onion pakora, tandoori chicken, rogan josh, vegetable curry, rice and nan. Minimum charge £5.35.

NEW ENTRY The Kitchen, Chapter Arts Centre [6/10]

Market Road, Canton
TEL Cardiff (0222) 372756

Open 10 to 10 & (also WC)
Closed 10 days at Christmas

The Chapter Arts Centre is in an old school which now houses two cinemas, a theatre and art galleries as well as the Kitchen restaurant. The black-floored hall with its wooden tables and bench seating serves wholefood dishes with vegetarian leanings, plus highly calorific sweets. Vegetarian lasagne and moussaka are reliably good, and the menu takes in stuffed aubergines, bean burgers and vegetable curry, as well as fish pie and nut and fish rissoles. Imaginative salads, wholemeal pies and crumbles. Wine by the glass.

NEW ENTRY Luciano's [7/10]

9 Park Lane
TEL Cardiff (0222) 40397

Open noon to 2.30, 6 to 11
Closed Sun

An exuberant Italian restaurant on two floors behind the Park Hotel. Upstairs is the most popular, and there are views of the kitchen through a glass panel. The menu has a good range of pizzas, including calzone folded around ham, tomato, Mozzarella and anchovies, and main course pasta dishes for around £3. Thick minestrone or tuna and bean salad make good starters, and there are specialities, such as lamb steak with rosemary or chicken with green peppercorn sauce, if you want to spend more. Inexpensive, drinkable house wine.

Madhav [5/10]

59 Lower Cathedral Road, Riverside
TEL Cardiff (0222) 372947

Open 10 to 8 &

Asian grocer's in a row of shops around the back of Cardiff Arms Park selling good Indian snacks to take away only. Batata vadas, vegetable samosas and lentil katchoris can cost as little as 20p, with no extra charge for the cooking while you wait. Oriental sweetmeats, too.

Peppermint Lounge [6/10]

34 Woodville Road, Cathays
TEL Cardiff (0222) 374403

Open noon to 3 (5 Sun), 5.30 to midnight

A rough-and-ready café where the food is more important than the furniture. Dishes are freshly prepared and cater for all tastes: baked Brie with toasted almonds or vegan lentil curry on the one hand; burgers, chilli, or chicken and walnut salad on the other. Popular with students; opening hours may be less reliable outside term-time.

Riverside [8/10]

44 Tudor Street
TEL Cardiff (0222) 372163

Open noon to midnight (12.15 Fri and Sat; 11 Sun)
Closed Tue D; Christmas Eve and Christmas Day

The best choice for authentic Cantonese cooking in Cardiff. Dim-sum are served until 8pm, and the choice of over twenty snacks takes in sui mai, chicken and taro croquettes, spare ribs in black-bean sauce and stuffed glutinous rice in lotus leaves, with egg tarts and water-chestnut jelly for sweet. The full menu has dishes such as

crispy stuffed duckling and fried scallops with seasonal greens. Set meals begin at £7.50 a head.

NEW ENTRY | Sage Wholefood [6/10]

Wellfield Court, Wellfield Road, Roath
TEL Cardiff (0222) 481223

Open 9 to 5 &
Closed 1 week at Christmas

Joanna and Jan Bradford spotted a gap in Cardiff's eating scene and opened this informal vegetarian café in a smart new shopping arcade. All the cooking is done in full view, and dishes are prepared with flair. The blackboard changes regularly, but the emphasis is on soups (such as mulligatawny), nut bakes, hot bean casseroles, flans and pizzas, backed up by salads. Sweets might include a small ramekin with carob, hazelnuts, Greek yoghurt and sliced bananas. Herb teas, barley cup or Hugh Rock's elderflower wine to drink. Hot lunchtime dishes available between 11.45am and 3pm.

St David's Hall, Level 3 Buffet [6/10]

The Hayes
TEL Cardiff (0222) 42611

Open noon to 2.30 & (also WC)
Closed Sun

A buffet bar on level three of the brilliantly conceived hall, with live music some lunch-times and half-price beer on special occasions, courtesy of the local brewers. The menu has home-made soup and pies, fresh fish and a large range of salads – aubergine and tomato with yoghurt dressing; brown rice and aduki beans. Finish with health-food desserts.

Savastano's [6/10]

North Road, Gabalfa
TEL Cardiff (0222) 621018

Open noon to 2.30, 7 to midnight &
Closed Sun; bank hols; last week July; 2 weeks Aug

Giacomo Savastano hails from Naples and provides good cheap pasta, veal, chicken and steak dishes in his trattoria en route for the M4. Lunchtime service is fast and efficient and there are two sittings in the evening. Try spaghetti Sofia Loren with ham, tomatoes and nutmeg in a cream sauce. Three courses and a drink for around £10.

Spanghero's Bistro [9/10]

Westgate House, Westgate Street
TEL Cardiff (0222) 382423

*This restaurant was sold as
we went to press.*

Welsh National Opera Canteen [7/10]

John Street
TEL Cardiff (0222) 464666

Open 12.30 to 2.30
Closed Sat and Sun

WNO's reputation for excellence in all things extends to a canteen that is not a private affair but open to the public, on the first floor of the company's head office. The serve-yourself counter offers home-made soup, filled jacket potatoes, quiche and salad with two hot dishes of the day – one meat, one vegetarian. Chicken and leek pie, spiced lamb with apricots, or sausage and mash line up alongside courgette and tomato bake, laverbread rissoles or broccoli and almonds with

Stilton sauce. Home-made chocolate pond pudding or fruit crumble to finish.

CARDIGAN Dyfed   map 6

Granary [7/10]

Teifi Wharf
TEL Cardigan (0239) 614932

Open 9.30 to 10
Closed Oct to Easter

An enterprising seasonal café on the banks of the River Teifi, overlooking Cardigan Bridge and the castle. It is a good place for families with children, and the atmosphere is relaxed and accommodating. The emphasis is on local produce – fresh salmon, Welsh lamb, vegetables from growers in the neighbourhood. Curries are carefully spiced; succulent beef comes with excellent salads. Real ale from Brains. Occasionally, live folk and jazz in the evenings.

CARMARTHEN Dyfed   map 6

Eifiona's Restaurant and Coffee Rooms [6/10]

31 Lammas Street
TEL Carmarthen (0267) 230883

Open 7.30 (11.30 Sun) to 9

Go at lunch-time. Dishes of the day in this cheery upstairs room are amazing value. During the week, a choice of meat and three fresh veg. is £1.80; Sunday lunch (with a choice of six veg.) is £2.95. Alternatively there is thick cawl with home-baked bread, salads and sandwiches. Grills and steaks in the evening. Welsh afternoon teas are a new attraction. Wine by the glass.

*This restaurant was closed
as we went to press.*

Old Curiosity [6/10]

20A King Street
TEL Carmarthen (0267) 232384

Open 9.30 to 4.30 (5 Sat) & (also WC)
Closed Sun; bank hols

Popular café-cum-restaurant in the old
part of town. Tomato soup with basil or
Welsh cawl might be followed by beef
Stroganoff or chicken risotto. The menu
also has omelettes, jacket potatoes and
toasted sandwiches. The vegetarian
influence shows in the mushrooms in
coriander butter on toast, ratatouille, and
nut roast salad. Russian tea and wine by
the glass. Take-aways.

Waverley [6/10]

23 Lammas Street
TEL Carmarthen (0267) 236521

Open 9 to 5 (2 Thur) &
Closed Sun; bank hols

This popular vegetarian restaurant behind
a health-food shop is now self-service,
with a menu that changes each day.
Vegetable soup is a good starter; lasagne,
vegetable burger or chilli beans and rice
can be eaten with a choice of more than
ten salads, with extra garlic potatoes and
mushrooms for good measure. Cheesecake, fruit crumble and fresh fruit salad to
finish.

CHEPSTOW Gwent   map 6

| NEW ENTRY | ## Thang Long [7/10] |

17 St Mary Street
TEL Chepstow (029 12) 2959

Open noon to 2, 5.30 to 11.30
Closed L Sun to Tue, Christmas Day

The Welsh border country is an unlikely
setting for a Vietnamese restaurant, but
this functional café in a narrow street is
the real thing. Run by a young couple – he
cooks, she serves – it has an authentic
menu, though bowing to local tastes by
offering omelettes, steaks and chips as
well as a wide range of seafood, pork and
beef with curried specialities, rice and
noodles. Spicy Vietnamese pancakes are
freshly made and stir-fried beef with
vegetables is good, too. Set dinners are
excellent value, from £12.50 for two.
Drink tea or saké.

CILGERRAN Dyfed   map 6

Castle Kitchen [9/10]

High Street
TEL Cardigan (0239) 615055

Open 11 to 5.30 (noon to 5 Sun), 7.30 to 10.30 &
Closed daytime Nov to Easter

Barbara and Elizabeth Moore's cottage
restaurant is in the centre of the village
close to the dramatically sited castle.
Almost everything is made on the
premises, which stay open for lunches,
afternoon teas and dinners. The style is
English home cooking, with some
historical touches and a few exotic
flourishes. Lunch is a choice of snacks,
such as Cornish pasty, local cheese and
bread or hummus, as well as salads, home-
made pies, such as gammon and apricot,
and casseroles, from beef and walnut in
beer to spicy bean. Evening meals are still
excellent value for more intriguing dishes
such as Teifi salmon with Grenville sauce
or a version of 'hindle wakes' – a medieval
dish of chicken thighs cooked with lemons
and prunes. Upton Farm ice-creams to
finish. House wine is £4 a bottle.

COLWYN BAY Clwyd   map 6

Majestic Grill [6/10]

Seafront
TEL Colwyn Bay (0492) 31489

Open 10 to 9.30 (3 Tue and Wed, 5 Sun) &
Closed Mon

Cheery seafront café with fine views of the
beach and a welcoming family atmos-

phere. The first-floor coffee lounge has a rocking horse and toys for the children while parents enjoy lunch and a glass of wine. The 'six of the best' lunch menu of six home-made dishes of the day (£1.75 Tuesday to Saturday) might include Stilton and walnut quiche with jacket potato, fillet of cod Mornay with broccoli, or bacon chop, sausage and egg. Three-course Sunday lunch is £4.95 (£2.75 for children under twelve).

COWBRIDGE
South Glamorgan   map 6

Basil's Brasserie [9/10]

2 Eastgate
TEL Cowbridge (04463) 3738

Open noon to 2, 7 to 10 &
Closed Sun, Mon; 2 weeks Aug, 1 week at Christmas

Lunch for a fiver, dinner for around £10 in this pastel-painted building marked by a signpost of a horse acting as a waiter. Order from the counter and the food is brought to your table. The remarkable choice ranges from fish chowder or duck rillettes to tortellini with Mexican sauce, stir-fried monkfish with Chinese vegetables, and steak, kidney and claret pie. Steaks, Welsh lamb cutlets and loin of pork are grilled over charcoal. Wine by the glass.

CRICCIETH Gwynedd   map 6

 Blue China Tearooms [7/10]

Lon Felin
TEL Criccieth (076 671) 3239

Open 10 to 6 &
Closed Jan

Established in the 1930s, this tea-room is part of local life in Criccieth. It is in a perfect position, right by the lifeboat station with views across Cardigan Bay to the mountains of Snowdonia. Home baking is the speciality, with drop scones, toasted teacakes, Welsh cakes and bara brith alongside fruit and nut toffee pie. There are also savoury dishes, such as chicken and leek pie, cheese and

mushroom flan, vegetable risotto, toad in the hole and barbecued nut dumplings. Finish with treacle tart or real ice-cream from Thayers. Unlicensed.

CRICKHOWELL Powys   map 6

Nantyffin Cider Mill Inn [6/10]

Brecon Road
TEL Crickhowell (0873) 810775

Open for food 11.30 to 2.30 (1.30 Sun), 7 to 10 (9.30 Sun) & (also WC)
Closed Christmas Day

Pork and cider pie and cider syllabub are the only reminders of the past in this converted rough stone inn. Otherwise the menu takes in kedgeree, tagliatelle with walnuts and cream cheese, devilled prawns and rum and raisin cheesecake. The old cider barn has been turned into a function room, and these days the cider is from Bulmers.

DINAS MAWDDWY
Gwynedd   map 6

Coffee Shop [7/10]

TEL Dinas Mawddwy (065 04) 338

Open 9 to 5 & (also WC)
Closed Dec, Jan (exc 27 Dec to 5 Jan), Feb

Rated as one of the best coffee-houses in Wales, this delightful converted building is in an old mountain railway station on the outskirts of a small village. Good home-made Welsh fare includes bara brith, Welsh cakes, and lentil and vegetable soup. The flour is stone ground. There are several teas, including a herb variety, plus filter coffee and wines.

ERBISTOCK Clwyd   map 6

Boat Inn [6/10]

TEL Bangor-on-Dee (0978) 780143

Open noon to 2.15, plus 7 to 10.30 Fri, 7 to 11 Sat &
Closed Christmas Day; Boxing Day and 1 Jan

There are superb views from this cottage restaurant that opens up its riverside terrace on warm days. The menu offers soup, vegetable lasagne, stuffed aubergine and nut cutlets with wild rice, a cold table, and barbecued steaks at weekends. The River Room is open from April to September; for the rest of the year bar lunches are served in the main restaurant, which offers more expensive meals.

GLANWYDDEN Gwynedd   map 6

Queen's Head [7/10]

TEL Llandudno (0492) 46570

Open for food noon to 2.15, 7 to 9
Closed Sun D in winter

Local seafood appears on the menu in this comfortable beamed pub between Llandudno Junction and Colwyn Bay. Conway mussels are sauté and topped with smoked cheese, salmon comes with salad or parsley sauce, and plaice is cooked whole. There are scallops, too. Alternatives for meat-lovers might include steak and mushroom pie, lamb with tomato and ginger, or kidneys dijonnaise. An impressive list of home-made sweets ranges from treacle tart to chocolate fudge pie. Real ales. No children.

HARLECH Gwynedd   map 6

Plas Café [6/10]

High Street
TEL Harlech (0766) 780204

Open 9.30 to 8.30 &
Closed end Oct to mid-Mar

Once the summer retreat of the Earl of Winchelsea, this is now a family restaurant with a long, elegant dining-room and veranda overlooking the sands and sea of Tremadoc Bay. The food is an honest mix of steak and kidney pie, fish and chips, poached salmon salad and cheese and onion flan. Hot rolls for breakfast, toasted teacakes and bara brith for tea.

NEW ENTRY Yr Ogof [7/10]

TEL Harlech (0766) 780888

Open 6.30 to midnight (noon to 6.30 in winter, plus Fri and Sat D in winter)
Closed Christmas, Jan

Yr Ogof means 'the cavern', and this stone-walled bistro is set under some shops close to Harlech Castle. The standard menu of jacket potatoes, open sandwiches and grills is supplemented by more promising blackboard specials, such as French onion soup, fillet of trout with gooseberry sauce, beef in Guinness, and Barnsley chop with apricot sauce. Vegetarians have plenty of choice, from bean goulash to bulgur wheat and walnut casserole. There's also a salad bar. Children welcome until 8pm.

HAY-ON-WYE Powys   map 6

NEW ENTRY Granary [7/10]

Broad Street
TEL Hay-on-Wye (0497) 820790

Open 9 to 6 (10 Fri and Sat)
Closed Sun

On the lower slopes of the hill by the clock tower. This is a big converted barn with bare rafters and floorboards, rough stone walls and steep wooden stairs to the dining-room on an upper level. It is casual, relaxed and convivial. The menu runs through the day and is strong on curries and vegetarian dishes. Spicy royal beef comes with a creamy almond sauce, poppadum and pickles; the Indian choice also extends to beef korma and lamb with spinach. Vegetarians might be offered ratatouille with brown rice, nut roast or Stilton and mushroom quiche. Home-baked cakes look good. To drink there's wine by the glass and Dunkerton's cider, as well as ginger beer and barley cup.

Lion's Corner House [8/10]

6 Market Street
TEL Hay-on-Wye (0497) 820175

Open 11 to 2, 7 to 9.30 &
Closed Sun L; Sun D and Mon D in winter

Informality rules, with waiters dressed as they like and a menu that changes every few weeks. The restaurant has moved to the centre of town; the dining-room has been enlarged and there are seats outside in fine weather. Lunches are excellent value. Choose from stuffed peppers, braised chilli chicken or tagliatelle provençale, before sampling one of the excellent sweets. Up to a dozen are often available, from summer pudding and pashka to orange and coffee bombe. Lighter snacks include open sandwiches or vegetable terrine and salad. More expensive dinners.

LALESTON Mid Glamorgan   map 6

 NEW ENTRY ### Great House [6/10]

High Street
TEL Bridgend (0656) 57644

Open noon to 2, 6.30 to 9.30 & (also wc)
Closed Sun; Sat L

The house is a sixteenth-century yeomans' cottage, later enlarged and now thriving as a classical French restaurant. In addition there are excellent cheap lunchtime snacks in the Leicester Room. The menu is a straightforward mix of salads, chicken and mushroom curry with brown rice, beef and onion pie, spaghetti bolognese; most dishes are about £2. Afternoon teas are also available from 3pm to 5pm.

LLANARTHNEY Dyfed   map 6

NEW ENTRY ### Golden Grove Arms [7/10]

TEL Dryslwyn (055 84) 551

Open for food 12.15 to 2.30, 7.15 to 10.15
Closed Sun D

A solid stone coaching-inn on the back road between Carmarthen and Llandeilo, well placed for good fishing in the Tywi Valley. Fresh fish appears on the menu in the solid, local bar and the choice might include anything from crab and lobster to sewin, grey mullet and monkfish. Otherwise there are hearty pub staples, such as beef and beer casserole, gammon and eggs, and steak and kidney pie followed by pear frangipane or bread-and-butter pudding. At weekends, Bensons bistro/wine bar serves sizzling steaks and seafood backed up by Spanish wines. More expensive meals in the Georgian dining-room.

LLANBEDR Y CENNIN
Gwynedd   map 6

NEW ENTRY ### Olde Bull Inn [6/10]

TEL Dolgarrog (049 269) 508/359

Open for food 11.30 (noon in winter) to 3, 6.30 to 11 (noon to 2, 7 to 10.30 Sun)

Genuine 'olde' inn dating from the sixteenth-century, with heavy beams and views over the Conwy Valley. It is a cosy, comfortable pub in an area where decent hostelries are thin on the ground. Bar food is good and wholesome: home-made pies, ham and eggs, pork chop topped with toasted cheese. There are salads and sandwiches plus good home-made apple pie to finish. Lees beers on draught.

LLANDDERFEL Gwynedd   map 6

NEW ENTRY ### Bryntirion Inn [6/10]

TEL Llandderfel (067 83) 205

Open for food noon to 2, 7 to 9.30
Closed L all week and Mon D, Tue D, Oct to Easter

Friendly seventeenth-century inn with a good-looking cold table that includes slices of crisp roast belly-pork and thick pieces of cold sausage. Sweets seem equally appetising. Portions are ample.

LLANDDOWROR Dyfed   map 6

Old Mill [6/10]

TEL St Clears (0994) 230836

Open noon to 2.30, 7 to 10 & (also wc)
Closed Mon L, Sun D

This converted wool mill is two eating places. One part is a busy transport café catering for passing trade along the A477 and serving four kinds of breakfast, as well as lunches of fish and chips or roast beef with vegetables. Next door is a restaurant offering more expensive evening meals, but with an interesting vegetarian menu that should keep the bill in single figures. The restaurant is licensed; the transport café is not.

LLANDEILO Dyfed   map 6

Cawdor Arms [6/10]

TEL Llandeilo (0558) 823500

Open for food 12.30 to 2
Closed Sun; Christmas Day and Boxing Day

Good-value light lunches are served
Monday to Saturday in this refurbished
hotel, formerly known as the Bear Inn. The
special brunch for £3.60 is a brace of eggs,
mushrooms, bacon, sausage and tomato;
alternatively, choose from poached local
salmon with salad and potatoes, prawn
and tuna cocktail, grilled mussels with
garlic butter, or Welsh rarebit with bacon
and grilled tomato. There are salads and
sandwiches, too. Table d'hôte in the
evening is £14.50.

LLANDEWI SKIRRID
Gwent   map 6

Walnut Tree Inn [9/10]

TEL Abergavenny (0873) 2797

Open for food noon to 2.30, 7.15 to 10
Closed 4 days at Christmas; 2 weeks Feb

Not only is this the best cooking in Wales,
but Franco Taruschio has also proved that
it is possible to be serious about food
without being pompous. His attitude is
flexible, which means that this pub/
restaurant cannot be pigeon-holed. One
menu serves the bistro and the dining-
room, and it is possible to have just one
course. If the style is bistro, the quality is
nonetheless that of a first-division
restaurant. The menu is a succession of
brilliant, unshowy dishes: asparagus soup
with tarragon, Piedmontese peppers, roast
mallard and blackberries, fish casserole,
rabbit with Dijon mustard. Then there are
the sweets – summer pudding, Sicilian
cheesecake, rose-petal sorbet. House wine
by the glass or carafe.

LLANDUDNO Gwynedd   map 6

Casanova [6/10]

18 Chapel Street
TEL Llandudno (0492) 78426

Open 6 to 10.30
Closed Christmas Day

A no-nonsense restaurant/pizzeria with
chrome chairs and cheerful waiters in red
shirts. Veal and steak dishes set the tone of
the menu and there are generous portions
of lasagne. Puddings include daunting
portions of banana ice-cream. Take-aways.

St Tudno Hotel [6/10]

North Parade
TEL Llandudno (0492) 74411

Open 12.30 to 1.45, 6.45 to 9.30 &
Closed Christmas and New Year

This Victorian hotel scores heavily with
its setting: it stands on the promenade
opposite the pier, the ornamental gardens
and the beach. In the yellow-painted coffee
lounge there are light snacks with
morning coffee or afternoon tea, as well as
simple lunch-time dishes, such as
mushroom and celery soup and
sandwiches. The cheapest deal in the
restaurant is the fixed-price lunch at £7.95.

LLANDYBIE Dyfed   map 6

Cobblers [8/10]

3 Church Street
TEL Llandybie (0269) 850540

Open noon to 2, 7.30 to 9.30 & (also WC)
Closed Mon; Thur and Sun; Christmas Day

Ingredients are local and flavours are
patriotically Welsh in this excellent little
restaurant. The menu promotes regional
specialities and lunch-time bar meals are a
good way of sampling the range. Savoury
'cobblers' – meat or fish and vegetables
topped with a wholemeal herb scone – are
substantial enough for a full lunch. The
choice ranges from laverbread and white
fish in garlic sauce to cured Welsh ham
with parsley and carrots. The menu also
has cawl, Glamorgan sausages (made with
cheese), omelettes, grills and poached
salmon or sewin with herb butter.
Reduced prices for children. More
expensive evening meals.

LLANDYSUL Dyfed   map 6

 Bryn Cerdin Farm Tearooms [6/10]

Capel Cynon, Ffostrasol
TEL Rhydlewis (023 975) 371

Open 10.30 to 6.30 &
Closed Oct to Easter

This is a working farm north-west of
Llandysul on the A486, offering tours
round the animals, displays of milking and
a dairy exhibition. The whitewashed tea-
room tacked on to the farmhouse is
decorated with cattle-show rosettes and
serves first-rate cream teas with cream
from the Jersey herd. Liz and Ray Wynne
make their own ice-cream and use home-
reared meat for their pâtés, pies and cawl.
They also serve salads and farmhouse
cheeses. Unlicensed.

LLANELIDAN Clwyd   map 6

Leyland Arms   [6/10]

TEL Clawdd Newydd (082 45) 207

Open for food noon to 2.30, 7 to 10.30
& (also WC)
Closed Christmas Day

Village life seems to revolve round this
fourteenth-century inn next to the church.
Salmon, trout, grouse, pheasant and hare
are all bagged locally, and the menu also
features good salads, creamy soups and
dishes such as steak and mushroom and
Guinness pie. Sunday lunch is a roast.
Burtonwood beers on handpump.

LLANGOLLEN Clwyd   map 6

Gales   [7/10]

18 Bridge Street
TEL Llangollen (0978) 860089

Open noon to 2, 6 (7 Sun) to 10.15
Closed Sun and Mon Sept to May;
Christmas week

On the ground floor of a mid-eighteenth
century brick building is this oak-panelled
wine bar with old chapel pews and a
blackboard menu that blends wine bar
favourites with a few unexpected ideas.

Watercress and potato soup, courgette and
onion quiche and sugar-baked ham rub
shoulders with tuna and sour-cream
mousse or lamb cooked to a French
country-style recipe. Ginger and lemon
cheesecake is a good sweet. A hundred
good wines, including several by the glass.
No bookings.

LLANGRANOG Dyfed   map 6

Y Gegin Fach   [5/10]

TEL Llangranog (023 978) 642

Open 9 to 10 & (also WC)
Closed Nov to Mar

Sunshine, a fresh crab salad and a bottle of
Hock is the perfect combination at this
beach-side café. Otherwise it's Kenco
coffee and ice-cream. The attached
restaurant and take-away is less of an
attraction.

LLANYNYS Clwyd   map 6

Cerrigllwydion Arms   [6/10]

TEL Llanynys (074 578) 247

Open for food 11.30 to 3 (noon to 2 Sun), 7 to
9.30 (10 Fri and Sat) &
Closed Mon

An attractive family-run country pub with
superb views down the Vale of Clwyd
from the garden. There is bar food plus a
restaurant, both using local fresh produce.
Chicken breast comes sliced in a white
wine and cream sauce; locally smoked trout
is backed by an imaginative range of salads.
Children welcome in the dining area.

LLOWES Powys   map 6

NEW ENTRY **Radnor Arms** [6/10]

TEL Glasbury (049 74) 460

Open for food noon to 2.30, 7 to 10
Closed Sun D and Mon in winter

Old stone-built inn on a drovers' route,
with fine views across the valley to the
Black Mountains. Inside there are
scrubbed pine tables and a welcoming
open fire in winter. The vast menu is
chalked on a blackboard: carrot and orange
soup, prawns in pots, fresh pasta, hot pork

and apple pie, omelette filled with kidneys, Welsh rarebit. Huge brown rye rolls are scooped out and crammed with all kinds of fillings. Felinfoel Bitter and Everards Tiger on draught.

MACHYNLLETH Powys map 6

Felin Crewi [7/10]

Penegoes
TEL Machynlleth (0654) 3113

Open 10.30 to 6 & (also WC)
Closed Nov to Mar

Barry and Patti Partridge have brought this seventeenth-century water-mill back to life and turned it into an award-winning working enterprise. The café serves a simple home-cooked menu of soup, filled jacket potatoes, tomato and courgette gratin, plus scones, bara brith, flapjacks and cookies. During the weekends in summer there are evening meals, including lasagne with garlic bread, chicken in orange and coriander sauce, and lentil and chickpea curry. Pots of tea and wine by the glass.

Quarry Shop [6/10]

13 Maengwyn Street
TEL Machynlleth (0654) 2624

Open 9 to 5, plus 7 to 9 Wed to Sat, and 10 to 4 Sun July and Aug &
Closed Thur pm; Sun

Local organic vegetables are used whenever possible in this café linked to the Centre for Alternative Technology. The loyalty to natural ingredients shows in the home-made soup and rolls, wholemeal pizzas, stuffed jacket potatoes, samosas and excellent salads. Unlicensed, but there is hibiscus tea, barley cup or ground coffee to drink. There is a well-stocked wholefood shop attached.

MERTHYR TYDFIL
Mid Glamorgan map 6

Shunters [5/10]

Brecon Mountain Railway, Pant Station, Dowlais
TEL Merthyr Tydfil (0685) 4854

Open 10 to 5 (when trains run), 7.30 to 9.30 & (also WC)
Closed Sun; Mon; Tue D; L Oct to Mar; Christmas Day

Splendid café serving cheap home-made snacks for visitors to the Brecon Mountain Railway. Worth a visit even if you are not a steam-train enthusiast. Table licence.

MILTON Dyfed map 6

Milton Brewery [6/10]

TEL Carew (064 67) 202

Open for food noon to 2.15, 7 to 10.30 & (also WC)

Mike Griffin cooks 364 days a year in this roadside pub with plants outside and pine tables in the bar. The food is simple, generous and good value: big helpings of avocado and prawns, large salads, good steaks with chips or new potatoes. On Christmas Day there's a free cold buffet in the morning. Better-than-average pub wines.

NANNERCH Clwyd map 6

Cherry Pie [6/10]

Denbigh Road
TEL Hendre (035 283) 279

Open noon to 3, 7 to 10 & (also WC)

There are cherries in the décor and cherry pie for sweet in this stylish restaurant and wine bar with marble tables and modern brickwork. The bar menu includes local trout or plaice, cottage pie, beef curry, chilli, and aubergine and mushroom lasagne. Main courses come with chips or jacket potatoes and salad garnish. Set lunch in the restaurant is £4.95. All the cooking is done on an Aga.

NEWCASTLE EMLYN
Dyfed map 6

Pensarnau Arms [6/10]

Pentre-Cagal
TEL Velindre (0559) 370339

Open for food noon to 2.15 (1.15 Sun), 6.30 to 10 (7 to 9 Sun) &
Closed Sun D Nov to Easter

A former home-brew house for quarrymen, now offering real ales straight from the casks, as well as some genuine bar food. Highlights are the home-made soups, such as celery and cashew nut; one hundred per cent pork sausages made and seasoned in the pub and then put into skins by a local butcher, one hundred per cent lamburgers, sesame chicken and pork tenderloin in cider. The Jacksons eschew all the fashionable pub trappings: there's no jukebox, no pool table, no fruit machine.

NEWPORT Dyfed   map 6

Cnapan [8/10]

East Street
TEL Newport (0239) 820575

Open 10 to 5 (L 12.30 to 2.30)   ♿ (also WC)
Closed Tue; Nov to Easter

Samphire and laverbread emphasise the move towards more local produce in this pale-pink guest-house with a restaurant. Lunches are the best value for cheap eating, when the emphasis is on simple dishes with a wholefood bias: robust soups, savoury flans with oatmeal bases, salads with organic ingredients and puddings such as apricot and date slice. Dinners are more expensive, but still good value for Jamaican chicken casserole or Peking fish with noodles. House wine is £4.25 a bottle.

NEWPORT Gwent   map 6

Bolero's [7/10]

34 Cambrian Road
TEL Newport (0633) 58585

Open 12.30 to 3.30, 6.30 to 1
Closed Sun

There is dark panelling and dim lighting in this wine bar across the road from the station. Dishes are served generously with above-average garlic bread and help-yourself salads. Kebabs and char-grilled fresh fish are supplemented by burgers, spare ribs and jacket potatoes. House wine by the glass or bottle, from an extensive range.

NEW QUAY Dyfed   map 6

NEW ENTRY Hungry Trout [6/10]

TEL New Quay (0545) 560680

Open 10 to 3, 6.30 to 11.45   ♿ (also WC)
Closed Sun D; Nov to Mar

There are superb views across the harbour from the bay windows of this converted post office. The daytime menu has plenty of bargains, including good home-made soup, bacon butties and Welsh rarebit, as well as pies, a roast, pizzas and home-made lasagne. In the early evening there are quick single-dish meals, such as prawn curry or gammon with prawn sauce, for around £3. Full evening meals can take the bill into double figures. To drink, try locally produced Wern Deg wine.

PONTYPRIDD
Mid Glamorgan   map 6

John & Maria's [7/10]

1–3 Broadway
TEL Pontypridd (0443) 402977

Open 11.30 to 2.30, 5.30 to 10 Mon to Sat
Closed Sun, bank hols

The first Italian immigrants to South Wales were called Bracchi and neighbourhood trattoria are known as bracchi in the region. The Orsi family offer excellent value in a former transport café opposite the railway station, now decorated with Chianti bottles and pictures of the family's home village. Lunch is particularly good value, with lasagne or spaghetti bolognese, plus a glass of wine, costing around £3. Steak and kidney pie or cod and chips are even cheaper. Take-aways by prior arrangement.

RHAYADER Powys   map 6

 Carole's Cake Shop and Tea Room [6/10]

South Street
TEL Rhayader (0597) 811060

Open 9 (10.30 Sun) to 7 (6 in autumn, 5 in winter)

An old bakery close to the Elan Valley reservoirs transformed into a smart café offering teas and light meals. Honey is used in the cooking and is also on sale. In the afternoon there is a Welsh tea, with scones, toasted tea-cakes and bara brith. The menu includes soup, home-made steak and kidney pie, lasagne, wholemeal pizzas and chilli, with such snacks as scrambled eggs and Welsh rarebit. There are also salads, and picnic lunches can be arranged. Unlicensed.

RHYD-DDU Gwynedd   map 6

Cwellyn Arms [6/10]

TEL Beddgelert (076 686) 321

Open for food noon to 3, 7 to 10.30 (11 Fri and Sat)

This splendid Snowdonia pub feeds hillwalkers and families on a hefty diet of steaks, home-made pies (such as curried beef or chicken and prawn) and half-pound burgers. There are variations on the ploughman's theme: 'climber's' has roast beef stuffed with garlic, 'hiker's' is hazelnut, lentil and mushroom pâté. Mrs Bamber describes her chips as real. Children's menu, plus an adventure playground and barbecue area in the garden.

RHYL Clwyd   map 6

Coffee Gallery [5/10]

29 Wellington Road
TEL Rhyl (0745) 54381

Open 10 to 6 & (also WC)
Closed Sun in winter

Friendly service and traditional food at remarkable prices, with steak and kidney pudding, chips and peas costing under £2. There are freshly made pancakes, fruit pies and scones in the coffee-shop. Unlicensed.

ROSSETT Clwyd   map 6

Churtons [7/10]

Chester Road
TEL Rossett (0244) 570163

Open noon to 2.15, 7 to 10 &
Closed Sun; bank hols; Christmas to New Year

A converted barn with a first-floor dining area. The menu includes cream of cauliflower and onion soups, potted Flookburgh shrimps, cod florentine and Indonesian chicken. There are excellent home-made sweets and good cheeses, plus a fine wine list, with wines served in large long-stemmed glasses. Children welcome, except at Saturday lunch-time.

RUTHIN Clwyd   map 6

Bay Tree [6/10]

The Craft Centre
TEL Ruthin (082 42) 2121

Open 10.30 (noon Sun) to 5 & (also WC)
Closed sometimes Sun in winter

Beamed restaurant attached to the Ruthin Craft Centre. Hot lunches (noon to 2.30) include chilli with rice and wholemeal bread, beefburger and onions, roast chicken and chips, lasagne. Afternoon tea (from 3pm) comprises wholemeal cucumber or tomato sandwiches with a pot of tea, a scone with cream and jam, and bara brith. Coffee, lager and wine by the glass.

ST DAVID'S Dyfed   map 6

St Non's Hotel [6/10]

TEL St David's (0437) 720239

Open for food noon to 2, 7 to 9 &

A comfortable, well-run hotel near the cathedral, offering bar meals and a cold buffet. Fresh crab salad with a glass of Worthington has been excellent. Other dishes include soup, jacket potatoes, salad niçoise, pepper and potato salad, plus a range of cold meats. More expensive restaurant.

ST DOGMAELS Dyfed   map 6

Y Felin Tea Room [5/10]

TEL Cardigan (0239) 613999

Open 10.30 (2 Sun) to 5.30
Closed Sat late Oct to Easter

The working water-mill is the centre of attraction, but the tea-room provides sustenance for visitors. On fine days, meals are served at the millstone tables on the patio. The mill grinds the Welsh wheat, which is turned into scones, home-baked biscuits and cakes. Light lunches include salads and bowls of cawl. Unlicensed.

SAUNDERSFOOT Dyfed map 6

Jones'ys [6/10]

2 Brewery Terrace
TEL Saundersfoot (0834) 813615/811255

Open 7 to 11.30 (10.30 Sun) & (also WC)
Closed Mon Oct to Easter

An informal bistro atmosphere in a sawdust-and-murals restaurant constructed from two terraced houses. Steaks and kebabs come sizzling to the table on cast-iron platters, acccompanied by baked potatoes and salads. There is a vegetarian menu as well and a take-away service. More expensive three-course meals.

Royal Oak [6/10]

Wogan Terrace
TEL Saundersfoot (0834) 812546

Open for food noon to 2.30, 6 to 10 &

Friendly pub that puts the emphasis on fresh fish and local produce alongside bar-food staples. On the one hand there's crab, Dover sole and roast Welsh lamb, on the other, home-made burgers and steak sandwiches. Vegetables are usually fresh.

SIGINGSTONE
South Glamorgan map 6

Victoria [6/10]

TEL Cowbridge (044 63) 3943

Open for food 11.30 to 2.30 & (also WC)
Closed Sun

Renovated eighteenth-century country pub full of antiques and old china. The food is home cooked, with steak and kidney pie as the bestseller. Otherwise the regularly changing menu can include cod provençale, chicken in mushroom sauce, and liver and bacon casserole. Roast beef is served on Wednesdays. There are plans to

extend the eating area and serve food in the evenings and on Sundays.

SWANSEA
West Glamorgan map 6

Annie's [7/10]

56 St Helen's Road
TEL Swansea (0792) 55603

Open noon to 2, 7 to 10.30
Closed Sun; Sat L and Mon L

A café-bar has been opened in the basement of this roadside restaurant on the Mumbles road. Lunches and supper have a French regional flavour, with dishes such as pot au feu, rabbit cooked in red wine and galettes filled with Mediterranean vegetables and nuts. Crudités are on the house. The full restaurant menu is more expensive, though there's a set menu at £8.80 (Tuesday to Friday) featuring sewin with watercress sauce or grilled loin of pork with tomato sauce and fennel. Summer pudding or sorbets to finish.

Barrows [6/10]

42 Newton Road, Mumbles
TEL Swansea (0792) 361443

Open 11.30 to 3.30, 5.30 (7 Sun) to 10.30 (11 Fri and Sat)
Closed Sun L

Excellent-quality food and a modest but interesting wine list feature in this smartly redecorated wine bar where the menu changes weekly. Anchovy provençale with brown bread is a good starter, before quiche, casserole or curry. The repertoire might also include more ambitious ragout of sea bass with Pernod, salad of goose breast with raspberry vinaigrette, or beef steak, oyster and wild mushroom crumble. Wines come mainly from the Loire.

La Bussola [6/10]

217 Oxford Street
TEL Swansea (0792) 55780

Open 11.30 to 2.30, 6.30 to 11.30 &
Closed Sun

Popular Italian restaurant where a simple lunch can cost less than £5. Try lambs' liver with orange, beef pizzaiola, or fried plaice. Pasta is home made. Wine by the glass or carafe. Open late for dinner after the theatre.

NEW ENTRY P.A's [7/10]

95 Newton Road, Mumbles
TEL Swansea (0792) 367723

Open 12.30 to 2.30, 5.45 to 9.30
Closed Christmas Day

Paul Davies and Andrew Hetherington (P and A of the name) run this converted shop with views of Oystermouth Castle. The atmosphere is more like a coffee-shop-cum-bistro than a traditional wine bar. The menu has everyday dishes, such as lasagne, grilled lamb chops and tagliatelle with tomato and basil sauce, plus blackboard specials. Ham and lentil soup is the real thing; garlic mushrooms are served on a croûton with a mild cream sauce; excellent escalopes of veal come with a lemon and herb sauce. Useful list of French country wines, plus house wine by the glass. No children .

Schooner [8/10]

4 Prospect Place
TEL Swansea (0792) 49321

Open 11.30 to 3 (noon to 2.30 Sun), 6 to 11 ⅃ (also WC)
Closed Sun D

Christine and Raymond Parkman have turned this converted dockland building into one of the best-value eating places in Swansea. The emphasis is on local produce: most vegetables are from farms on the Gower Peninsula, fish is from the coast, and venison from nearby Margam Park. Lunches are the real bargain; for less than £3 there are dishes such as stuffed lambs' hearts, French onion tart, or chicken in wine and tarragon with a great assortment of fresh vegetables. Pies are made on the premises, as are the sweets. More expensive evening meals. No children.

Treasure [6/10]

Beau Nash House, 1–4 Caer Street
TEL Swansea (0792) 50742

Open 9 to 5.30
Closed Sun; bank hols

David Kendall, the inspiration behind this admirable self-service restaurant in a department store, has left, but the food is still up to standard. In summer the place stakes its reputation on a formidable array of salads, each marked with nutritional content. In winter there is more emphasis on hot dishes such as mushroom Stroganoff, pizza, or meat and two veg. Freshly squeezed juices; wine by the glass.

TENBY Dyfed   map 6

NEW ENTRY Mews Bistro [7/10]

The Mews, Upper Frog Street
TEL Tenby (0834) 4068

Open noon to 2, 7.30 to 10 ⅃ (also WC)
Closed Sat L

Oliver Wooles has spruced up this bistro set in a row of shops, and also does the cooking. Half the room has cane furniture, the other glass-topped tables. A huge fan whirls from the brick-red ceiling. The menu is flexible and it's possible to have just a cup of coffee or two starters. Lunchtime dishes such as ratatouille bake, Spanish omelette, or beefsteak and mushroom pie are boosted in the evening by warm chicken liver salad, pan-fried skate, or chicken breast with tarragon and lemon butter. Salmon is the wild kind from Cardigan. Crisp salads, good sweets and wine by the glass.

TREFRIW Gwynedd   map 6

NEW ENTRY Chandler's [8/10]

TEL Llanrwst (0492) 640991

Open noon to 2, 7 to 10
Closed Mon; 1 week Oct; 4 weeks Jan to Feb

A converted ship-chandler's in an old slate and wool trading village with a history of river trade along the Conway. New owners have transformed it into a good-value restaurant with a menu based on local produce. Conway and Anglesey fish supplement a small choice of dishes such as lamb cutlets in leek sauce or chicken breast with apple, walnut and Stilton sauce. There's also game in season. Interesting puddings, such as damson and apple tansy or rum and raisin cheesecake. Sunday lunch is a help-yourself carvery (three courses for £6.75). Tables in the garden on fine days.

TRELLECH Gwent   map 6

Lion Inn [7/10]

TEL Monmouth (0600) 860322

Open for food 11.30 to 2.30 (3 Sat), 6 (6.30 Sat) to 11 (noon to 2, 7 to 10.30 Sun) &

Linda and Dennis Churchill offer some surprisingly good cooking in this remote little pub that caters for locals and tourists on walking holidays. Late suppers for £2.75 – vegetable lasagne, cheesy fish bake or tandoori chicken – cater for stragglers. Vegetables are fresh and given some fancy touches: beetroot in red wine; carrots with butter and orange; courgettes with lemon. Good dishes have included fresh Wye salmon, beef and Guinness pie, and chicken with celery and lemon. Ice-creams and sorbets are made locally. Bass, Crown and Wadworth ales on draught.

WELSHPOOL Powys   map 6

Powis Castle [6/10]

TEL Welshpool (0938) 4336

Open noon (11 July and Aug) to 5 & (also wc) Closed Mon; Tue Easter to end June and Sept, Oct; Nov to Easter

The art of traditional afternoon tea survives in the converted stables attached to this beautifully preserved and decorated Welsh castle run by the National Trust. Scones, cream and home-baked cakes, including bara brith, are the main lines. There are also light lunches of soup, salads, ham and quiche. Unlicensed.

WOLF'S CASTLE Dyfed   map 6

Wolfscastle Country Hotel [7/10]

TEL Treffgarne (043 787) 225

Open for food noon to 2, 7 to 9.30

Bar meals prepared from fresh local ingredients are excellent value in this quiet and comfortable country house. Eat for under £5 from a menu that takes in soup, spinach and mushroom roulade, and sea trout salad with new potatoes. More expensive restaurant.

WREXHAM Clwyd   map 6

Bumble [6/10]

1–2 Charles Street
TEL Wrexham (0978) 355023

Open 9 to 4.45
Closed Sun; Good Fri; Christmas and New Year

A good place for a cheap lunch. The menu is based on home-made dishes, such as pork casserole with mashed potatoes and vegetables. A three-course meal with a drink can leave change from £3. No chips; no licence.

Coffee Shop, Arts Centre [6/10]

Central Library
TEL Wrexham (0978) 352334

Open 9.30 to 8.30 (6 Sat)
Closed Sun; bank hols

Busy and deservedly popular café behind the Guild Hall, with the cooking duties shared by four ladies. The dish of the day, such as chicken casserole, has both rice and creamed or jacket potato. There are quiches, savoury pies and salads, plus a large range of cakes, biscuits and pastries. Unlicensed. The owners have recently opened The Blue Bell Restaurant, 65 Northgate Street, Chester.

List of entries

Beckhampton Wiltshire (South)
Wagon & Horses
Bedford Bedfordshire (Central)
Park
Santaniello's Pizzeria
Benenden Kent (South East)
King William IV
Berkhamsted Hertfordshire (Central)
Cook's Delight
Berwick-upon-Tweed Northumberland (North East)
Browns Hotel
Scotsgate Wine Bar
Tweedview Hotel
Bewdley Hereford & Worcester (West Midlands)
Pack Horse Inn
Bexhill on Sea Sussex (South East)
Trawlers
Biddenden Kent (South East)
Claris's Tearoom
Ristorante Da Claudio
Three Chimneys
Billericay Essex (East Anglia)
Webber's Wine Bar
Bingley West Yorkshire (North East)
Beckside Fisheries
Birkenhead Merseyside (North West)
Mersey Clipper Inn
Birmingham West Midlands
Acropolis
Adil
Andes
Bobby Browns in Town
Cafe Papillon
Casa Paco
Chung Ying
College of Food and Domestic Arts
Days of the Raj
Forbidden City
George Smith
Hawkins
Horts Wine Bar
Ho Tung
Loon Fung
Milan
Pearce's Shellfish
Plaka
Plough and Harrow Hotel
Rajdoot
Royal Al-Faisal
Rustie's Caribbean Restaurant
Salamis Kebab House
La Sante
Satay House
Shah Bagh
Thai Paradise
Wild Oats
Wild Thyme

Bishop Auckland County Durham (North East)
Gabriele's
Bishops Lydeard Oxfordshire (Central)
Kingfishers Catch
Blackburn Lancashire (North West)
Lovin' Spoonful
Muffins Cafe
Pizza Margherita
Blacko Lancashire (North West)
Moorcock Inn
Blackpool Lancashire (North West)
Bispham Kitchen
Bistro Number Sixteen
Cottage
Danish Kitchen
Jasmine Cottage
Robert's Oyster Bar
Blakeney Norfolk (East Anglia)
Drifters
Bledington Gloucestershire (South West)
Kings Head
Blickling Norfolk (East Anglia)
Buckinghamshire Arms Hotel
Bodmin Cornwall (South West)
Lanhydrock House
Bolham Devon (South West)
Knightshayes Court
Bolton Greater Manchester (North West)
Tiggis
Bolton Abbey North Yorkshire (North East)
Bolton Abbey Tea Cottage
Boston Lincolnshire (East Anglia)
Eagles
Botley Oxfordshire (Central)
Tong San
Bournemouth Dorset (South)
Coriander
Crust
Henry's
Le Buffet
Bowness on Windermere Cumbria (North West)
Hedgerow Vegetarian Restaurant
Jackson's Bistro
Rastelli
Brackley Northamptonshire (East Midlands)
Brackley Tandoori
Bracknell Berkshire (Central)
Oscar's
Bradford West Yorkshire (North East)
Baxendall's

Cocina
Kashmir
Kebabeesh
Old Road Fish Shop
Pie Tom
Pizza Margherita
Salty's
Shah Kebab House
Shiraz Sweet House
Sweet Centre
Brancaster Staithe Norfolk (East Anglia)
Jolly Sailors
Brandon Suffolk (East Anglia)
Collins
Brandon Creek Norfolk (East Anglia)
Ship Inn
Branscombe Devon (South West)
Masons Arms
Brentwood Essex (East Anglia)
Pizza Express
Bridgnorth Shropshire (West Midlands)
Old Colonial
Bridlington Humberside (North East)
Marina
Brighton Sussex (South East)
Al Duomo
Al Forno
Allan Johns
Billabong
Chilka
Clarence Wine Bar
Food For Friends
Latin in the Lane
Market Cafe
Melrose
Mock Turtle
Pie in the Sky
Pizza Express
Brightwell Baldwin Oxfordshire (Central)
Lord Nelson Inn
Brimfield Hereford & Worcester (West Midlands)
Poppies
Bristol Avon (South West)
Bell's Diner
Berkeley Brasserie
Cafe De Daphne
Cherries Vegetarian Bistro
51 Park Street
Ganges
Guild
Half Baked Cafe
Henry J Bean
Malacca
Mandarin
Pizza Express
Racks Wine Bar
Rajdoot
Taj Mahal
Vintner Wine Bar

Coggeshall Essex (East Anglia)
White Hart
Colchester Essex (East Anglia)
Bistro Nine
Clowns
Tillys
Wings
Colyton Devon (South West)
White Cottage Hotel
Congleton Cheshire (North West)
Oddfellows Wine Bar
Congresbury Avon (South West)
White Hart & Inwood
Coniston Cumbria (North West
Wheelgate
Corscombe Dorset (South)
Fox
Corse Lawn Gloucestershire (South West)
Corse Lawn House
Corton Wiltshire (South)
Dove Inn
Coventry West Midlands
A-Roma Snack Bar
Cottage Teashop & Gallery
Friends Corner
Herbs
Ostlers
Cowley Gloucestershire (South West)
Green Dragon
Cranleigh Surrey (South East)
Bricks
La Scala
Crick Northamptonshire (East Midlands)
Edwards of Crick
Cropredy Oxfordshire (Central)
Brasenose Inn
Croydon
Hockneys
La Vida
Munbhave
Tung Kum
Cumnor Oxfordshire (Central)
Bear and Ragged Staff
Danehill Sussex (South East)
Coach & Horses
Darlington County Durham (North East)
Boobi's
Dartington Devon (South West)
Cranks
Dartmouth Devon (South West)
Cherub
Daventry Northamptonshire (East Midlands)
Huffadine's

Deal Kent (South East)
Going Dutch
Deddington Oxfordshire (Central)
Kings Arms
Dent Cumbria (North West)
Stone Close
Derby Derbyshire (East Midlands)
Ben Bowers
Bennetts Coffee Shop
Lettuce Leaf
Water Margin
Devizes Wiltshire (South)
Bear Hotel
Diss Norfolk (East Anglia)
Diss Coffee House
Doddiscombsleigh Devon (South West)
Nobody Inn
Doncaster South Yorkshire (North East)
Three Cranes Coffee Shop
Dorchester Dorset (South)
Bridge Between
Potter In
Dorrington Shropshire (West Midlands)
Country Friends
Douglas Isle of Man (North West)
Signorio's
Dover Kent (South East)
Moonflower
Down Thomas Devon (South West)
Langdon Court Hotel
Dunster Somerset (South West)
Olde Tea Shoppe
Dunwich Suffolk (East Anglia)
Flora Tea Rooms
Ship Inn
Durham County Durham (North East)
Almshouses
Giovanni & Fabio Pizzeria
Ristorante de Medici
Undercroft Restaurant
Earl Soham Suffolk (East Anglia)
Victoria Public House and Brewery
Earls Colne Essex (East Anglia)
Colne Valley Tandoori
East Haddon Northamptonshire (East Midlands)
Red Lion
East Ilsley Berkshire (Central)
Crown and Horns
East Meon Hampshire (South)
George

Eastbourne Sussex (South East)
Bosworth's Wine Bar
Qualisea
Eastleigh Hampshire (South)
Piccolo Mondo
Eastling Kent (South East)
Carpenters' Arms
Easton Suffolk (East Anglia)
White Horse
Eathorpe Warwickshire (West Midlands)
Auberge-Inn
Edenham Lincolnshire (East Anglia)
Five Bells
Egham Surrey (South East)
Jack's
Elland West Yorkshire (North East)
Berties Bistro
Cafe McFly's
Elslack North Yorkshire (North East)
Tempest Arms
Ely Cambridgeshire (East Anglia)
Peking Duck
Empingham Leicestershire (East Midlands)
White Horse
Epworth Humberside (North East)
Epworth Tap
Esher Surrey (South East)
Greek Vine
Eskdale Green Cumbria (North West)
Brook House
Eton Berkshire (Central)
Eton Wine Bar
Everleigh Wiltshire (South)
Crown
Evesham Hereford & Worcester (West Midlands)
Cedar Restaurant
Scottie's
Ewell Surrey (South East)
Taste of Bengal
Ewhurst Surrey (South East)
Windmill Inn
Exeter Devon (South West)
Bottlescreu Bill's
Coolings
Herbies Wholefood
Eyam Derbyshire (East Midlands)
Miners Arms
Eye Suffolk (East Anglia)
Dove House
Fakenham Norfolk (East Anglia)
Chadwicks Wine Bar
Falmouth Cornwall (South West)
De Wynn's Coffee House

List of entries

Louth Lincolnshire (East
Anglia)
Mr Chips
Lower Swell Gloucestershire
(South West)
Old Farmhouse Hotel
Luton Bedfordshire (Central)
Casa Bianca
Man Ho
Lutterworth Leicestershire
(East Midlands)
Paper Tiger
Lydford Devon (South West)
Castle Inn
Lympstone Devon (South
West)
Globe Inn
River House
Lytham St Anne's Lancashire
(North West)
Bennett's Bistro
C'est La Vie
KFOG
Lindum Hotel
Pleasant Street
Tiggis
Macclesfield Cheshire (North
West)
Harlequin's
Maidenhead Berkshire
(Central)
Jack of Both Sides
Maidensgrove Oxfordshire,
(Central)
Five Horseshoes
Maidstone Kent (South East)
Pizza Express
Pye Peppers
Russett
Maldon Essex (East Anglia)
Maldon Coffee Shop
Wheelers
Malmesbury Wiltshire
(South)
Vine Tree
Malton North Yorkshire
(North East)
Blue Ball Inn
Florios
Malvern Hereford &
Worcester (West Midlands)
Enigma
Manaccan Cornwall (South
West)
New Inn
Manchester Greater
Manchester (North West)
Assam Gourmet
Basta Pasta
Billies
Brasserie St Pierre
Burns
Cafe Istanbul
Christian world Centre
Felicini's
Gallery Bistro

Gaylord
Greenhouse
Hong Kong
Hopewell City
Indian Cottage
Kathmandu Tandoori
Kosmos Taverna
Leo's
Lime Tree
Little Yang Sing
Mulberry's
On the Eighth Day
Paradise
Pearl City
Pizzeria Bella Napoli
Romans
Royal Oak Hotel
Sanam
Siam Orchid
Sinclairs
Wild Oats
Wong Chu
Woo Sang
Yang Sing
Mansfield Nottinghamshire
(East Midlands)
Pizzeria La Bella Napoli
March Cambridgeshire (East
Anglia)
Acre
Marhamchurch Cornwall
(South West)
Bullers Arms
Market Harborough
Leicestershire (East Midlands)
Taylor's
Marlborough Wiltshire
(South)
Bentley's Wine Bar
Pollys Tea Rooms
Marple Greater Manchester
(North West)
Little Mill Inn
Marsden North Yorkshire
(North West)
Bellas Town Restaurant
Marshwood Vale Dorset
(South)
Shave Cross Inn
Masham North Yorkshire
(North East)
White Bear
Matlock Derbyshire (East
Midlands)
Riverside
Mawgan Cornwall (South
West)
Yard Bistro
Melmerby Cumbria (North
East)
Shepherds Inn
Village Bakery
Mevagissey Cornwall (South
West)
Mr Bistro

Middle Wallop Hampshire
(South)
Fifehead Manor
Middlesbrough Cleveland
(North East)
Rooney's
Middlewich Cheshire (North
West)
Tempters Wine Bar
Minstead (South Hampshire)
Honeypot
Monksilver Somerset (South
West)
Notley Arms
Morecambe Lancashire
(North West)
Coffee Shoppe
Moretonhampstead Devon
(South West)
White Hart Hotel
Morpeth Northumberland
(North East)
La Brasserie
Moulton North Yorkshire
(North East)
Black Bull
Much Birch Hereford and
Worcestershire (West
Midlands)
Old School House
Much Wenlock Shropshire
(West Midlands)
George and Dragon
Scott's
Mullion Cornwall (South
West)
Old Inn
Nantwich Cheshire (North
West)
A. T. Welch
Nassington Northampton-
shire (East Midlands)
Black Horse Inn
Newark Nottinghamshire
(East Midlands)
Gannets
Old Kings Arms
Newbury Berkshire (Central)
Bacon Arms
Newcastle upon Tyne Tyne
& Wear (North East)
Amigo's
Jade Garden
Madeleine's
Mama Mia
Naked Lunch
New Emperor
Roulade Creperie
Rupali
Veggie's
Willow Teas
Newmarket Suffolk (East
Anglia)
Jane's Wine Bar
Pablo's Cantina

371

Ripon North Yorkshire (North East)
Blackfriars Cafe
Old Deaners
Warehouse
Rochdale Greater Manchester (North West)
Tony's
Rochester Kent (South East)
Casa Lina
Romford Essex (East Anglia)
Moon House
Romsey Hampshire (South)
White Horse Hotel
Rosedale Abbey North Yorkshire (North East)
Coach House
Ross on Wye Hereford & Worcester (West Midlands)
Meader's Hungarian Restaurant
Wine Bar
Rotherham South Yorkshire (North East)
Khanie's
Rothley Leicestershire (East Midlands)
Red Lion
Rugby Warwickshire (West Midlands)
Dilruba
Pepper's Coffee House
Shaheen Pan and Sweet Centre
Runswick Bay North Yorkshire (North East)
Sandside Cafe
Ryton-on-Dunsmore Warwickshire (West Midlands)
Ryton Gardens
Saffron Walden Essex (East Anglia)
Eight Bells
Old Hoops
Staircase Cellar
Sue Eaton
Salford Greater Manchester (North West)
Mark Addy
Salford College
Salisbury Wiltshire (South)
Harper's
Haunch of Venison
Hob Nob Coffee Shop
Just Brahms
Mainly Salads
Michael Snell Tea Rooms
Mo's
Stoby's
Scarborough North Yorkshire (North East)
Dilts
Hanover Fisheries
Pic A Dish
Sarah Brown's
Small Fry

Scole Norfolk (East Anglia)
Scole Inn
Scotter Lincolnshire (East Anglia)
Gamekeeper Inn
Scunthorpe Humberside (North East)
Excel Fisheries
Italian Garden
Jubraj Tandoori
Seaford Sussex (South East)
Hole in the Wall
Seatoller Cumbria (North West)
Yew Tree Country Restaurant
Seaview Isle of Wight (South)
Seaview Hotel
Selby North Yorkshire (North East)
Maltings Pizzeria
Sellack Hereford and Worcestershire (West Midlands)
Lough Pool Inn
Selling Kent (South East)
White Lion
Shamley Green Surrey (South East)
Red Lion
Shanklin Isle of Wight (South)
Cottage
Shardlow Derbyshire (East Midlands)
La Marina Ristorante
Sheffield South Yorkshire (North East)
Bay Tree
City Bar
Fat Cat
Islamabad
Just Cooking
Mr Kites
Nirmal's Tandoori
Theatre Restaurant
Toffs
Zing Vaa
Shelley West Yorkshire (North East)
Three Acres Inn
Shepley West Yorkshire (North East)
Sovereign Inn
Shepton Mallet Somerset (South West)
Blostin's
King's Arms Inn
Shere Surrey (South East)
Asters Tea Shop
Shipley West Yorkshire (North East)
Aagrah
Da Tonino
Shipston on Stour Warwickshire (West Midlands)
White Bear

Shipton under Wychwood Oxfordshire (Central)
Lamb Inn
Shaven Crown
Shrewsbury Shropshire (West Midlands)
Delanys
Good Life
Old Police House
Raven Bar
The Pengwern Hotel
Sileby Leicestershire (East Midlands)
Bunter's
Skipton North Yorkshire (North East)
Herbs
Tom Jones Carvery
Slaidburn Lancashire (North West)
Hark to Bounty
Snape Suffolk (East Anglia)
Golden Key
Soham Cambridgeshire (East Anglia)
No 38
South Dalton Humberside (North East)
Pipe and Glass Inn
South Leigh Oxfordshire (Central)
Mason Arms
South Molton Devon (South West)
Stumbles
South Woodchester Gloucestershire (South West)
Ram Inn
Southampton Hampshire (South)
Alice's
La Brasserie
Kohinoor
Kuti's
Lunch Break
Maxwells
Pearl Harbour
Piccolo Mondo
Southend on Sea Essex (East Anglia)
Pearl Dragon
Pipe of Port
Tomassi's
Truffles
Southport Merseyside (North West)
Swan
Southsea Hampshire (South)
Barnaby's Bistro
Colombo's
Country Kitchen
Mayfair Chinese
Midnight Tandoori
Rosie's Vineyard
Southwold Suffolk (East Anglia)
Crown

Minivers
Squiers
Sowerby Bridge West Yorkshire (East)
Ash Tree
Speen Buckinghamshire (Central)
Atkin's
Spilsby Lincolnshire (East Anglia)
Buttercross
St Albans Hertfordshire (Central)
Alban Tandoori
Garibaldi
Garibaldi Pub
La Province
Marmaris
Pizza Express
St Columb Major Cornwall (South West)
Not Just Pizza
St Dominick Cornwall (South West)
Barn Restaurant
St Ives Cornwall (South West)
Woodcote Hotel
St Michael's Mount Cornwall (South West)
Sail Loft
Staithes North Yorkshire (North East)
Lane End Fish and Chip Shop
Stamford Lincolnshire (East Anglia)
George
Standish Greater Manchester (North West)
Beeches
Stanford Dingley Berkshire (Central)
Farmer's Table
Old Boot Inn
Stanton Harcourt Oxfordshire (Central)
Harcourt Arms
Staveley North Yorkshire (North East)
Royal Oak
Steep Hampshire (South)
Harrow Inn
Stewkley Buckinghamshire (Central)
Swan Inn
Stockport Greater Manchester (North West)
Coconut Willy's
Stoke Lacy Hereford and Worcester (West Midlands)
Plough Inn
Stone Staffordshire (West Midlands)
La Casserole
Stone Kent (South East)
Ferry Inn

Stony Stratford Buckinghamshire (Central)
Old George
Stourbridge West Midlands (West Midlands)
French Connection
High Street Tandoori
Mr Dave's
Stourport on Severn Hereford and Worcester (West Midlands)
Severn Tandoori
Stow Bardolph Norfolk (East Anglia)
Hare Arms
Stow on the Wold Gloucestershire (South West)
Prince of India
Stratford upon Avon Warwickshire (West Midlands)
Slug and Lettuce
South Warwickshire Catering College
Stretton Leicestershire (East Midlands)
Ram Jam Inn
Stroud Gloucestershire (South West)
Mother Nature
Studley Warwickshire (West Midlands)
Peppers
Summerhouse County Durham (North East)
Raby Hunt Inn
Sutton Coldfield West Midlands (West Midlands)
Wyndley Leisure Centre
Sutton Howgrave North Yorkshire (North East)
White Dog Inn
Swindon Wiltshire (South)
Mamma's Kitchen
Tarrant Monkton Dorset (South)
Langton Arms
Taunton Somerset (South West)
Porters Wine Bar
Tedburn St Mary Devon (South West)
Log Cabin
Tewkesbury Gloucestershire (South West)
Crown
Telfords
Thornton West Yorkshire (North East)
Villa Roma
Three Legged Cross Sussex (South East)
Bull

Threshfield North Yorkshire (North East)
Old Hall
Ticehurst Sussex (South East)
Plantation Tea Company
Tideswell Derbyshire (East Midlands)
Poppies
Tideswell Fish and Chip Shop
Tonbridge Kent (South East)
Office Wine Bar
Torcross Devon (South West)
Start Bay Inn
Torquay Devon (South West)
Mulberry Room
Torrington Devon (South West)
Rebecca's
Totnes Devon (South West)
Cafe KL
Lyssers
Willow
Towcester Northamptonshire (East Midlands)
New Bekash Tandoori
Trebarwith Cornwall (South West)
House on the Strand
Old Millfloor
Treen Cornwall (South West)
Logan Rock Inn
Tring Hertfordshire (Central)
Kings Arms
Truro Cornwall (South West)
Attic Feast
Bustopher Jones
Tunbridge Wells Kent (South East)
Downstairs at Thackeray's
La Galoche
Rag-A-Muffins
Royal Wells Inn
Turvey Bedfordshire (Central)
Ye Three Fyshes
Ufford Cambridgeshire (East Anglia)
Old White Hart
Ullswater Cumbria (North West)
Sharrow Bay
Uppingham Leicestershire (East Midlands)
Baines
Upton Grey Hampshire (South)
Hoddington Arms
Upton upon Severn Hereford and Worcester (West Midlands)
Old Bell House
Wakefield West Yorkshire (North East)
Crown Inn
Pulse
Val's Tea Shop

List of entries

York North Yorkshire (North East)
Bees Knees
Bettys
Giovanni's
Royal York Hotel
St William's
Sultans
Taylors Tea Rooms
Wholefood Trading Co.
Yoxford Suffolk (East Anglia)
Eliza Acton

SCOTLAND

Aberdeen Grampian
Henry J Bean
Jaws Cafe
Music Cellar
Anstruther Fife
Cellar
Ardeonaig Central
Ardeonaig Hotel
Arisaig Highland
Arisaig Hotel
Aviemore Highland
Winking Owl
Ayr Strathclyde
Stables
Ballater Grampian
Tullich Lodge
Blairgowrie Tayside
Penny Black
Bridge of Cally Tayside
Bridge of Cally Hotel
Brodick Strathclyde
Glencloy Farm Guest House
Callander Central
Myrtle Inn
Cannich Highland
Cozac Lodge
Canonbie Dumfries &
Galloway
Riverside Inn
Colbost Highland
Three Chimneys
Colonsay Strathclyde
Isle of Colonsay Hotel
Cullipool Strathclyde
Longhouse Buttery
Drybridge Grampian
Old Monastery
Dulnain Bridge Highland
Muckrach Lodge Hotel
Dumfries Dumfries &
Galloway
Old Bank
Dunfermline Fife
New Victoria
Dunoon Strathclyde
Ardenslate Hotel
Dunvegan Highland
Harlosh Hotel

East Kilbride Strathclyde
Lafites
Eddleston Borders
Horse Shoe Inn
Edinburgh Lothian
L'Alliance
Alp-Horn
Bake Potato Shop
Bar Italia
Brasserie St Jacques
Circles
Clarinda's
Country Kitchen
Edinburgh Wine Bar
Factory Cafe
Fifth
Gallery of Modern Art
Handsel's Wine Bar
Helios Fountain
Hendersons
Kalpna
Kweilin
Lachana
Laigh Kitchen
Lazio's
Loon Fung
Marche Noir
Netherbow Arts Centre
New Edinburgh Rendezvous
North China
Queen's Hall
Raffaelli
Raj
Seeds
Shrimp's
TG's
Verandah Tandoori
Viva Mexico
Waterfront Wine Bar
Whigham's Wine Cellars
Gairloch Highland
Steading Restaurant
Galashiels Borders
Red Gauntlet
Glasgow Strathclyde
Amritsar Tandoori
Bar Luxembourg
Belfry
Bonham's Wine Bar
Cafe Gandolfi
Cafe Sannino
De Quincey
Diva
Fazzi's
Fixx
Gallery Coffee Shop
Granary
Granny Black's
Grosvenor Cafe
La Bavarde
Le Cafe Noir
Loon Fung
Miller Street Catering
Company
Nile
Pavarotti Trattoria

Peking Inn
PJ's
Pollok House
Preet Palace Tandoori
Ristorante Genova
Rogano
Sannino
Shish Mahal
Smiths
Tolbooth
Ubiquitous Chip
Willow Tea Rooms
Winter Green Cafe
Glendevon Tayside
Tormaukin Hotel
Grantown on Spey Highland
Coffee House & Ice Cream
Parlour
Helensburgh Strathclyde
Le Jardin
Inverness Highland
Brookes
Loch Ness House Hotel
Nico's Bistro
Kentallen Highland
Holly Tree
Kilfinan Strathclyde
Kilfinan Hotel
Killiecrankie Tayside
Killiecrankie Hotel
Kilmun Strathclyde
Coylet Inn
Lerwick Orkney & Shetland
Royal National Mission
Linlithgow Lothian
Champany Inn
Melrose Borders
Marmion's Brasserie
Memus Tayside
Drovers Inn
Moffat Dumfries & Galloway
Black Bull Hotel
Newton Stewart Dumfries &
Galloway
Creebridge House Hotel
Oban Strathclyde
Manor House Hotel
Onich Highland
Lodge on the Loch
Peebles Borders
Kailzie Garden Centre
Perth Tayside
Brown's
Timothy's
Pitcaple Grampian
Bank Inn
Scarista Orkney & Shetland
Scarista Studio
Selkirk Borders
Philipburn House Hotel
St Andrews Fife
Brambles
Grange Inn
New Balaka
West Park House
St Mary's Loch Borders
Tibbie Shiels Inn

Strathcarron Highland
Carron
Stromness Orkney &
Shetland
Ferry Inn
Tarbert Strathclyde
West Loch Hotel
Tobermory Strathclyde
Gannets
Turriff Grampian
Towie Tavern
Tyndrum Central
Clifton Coffee House
Ullapool Highland
Ceilidh Place
Morefield Motel
Unapool Highland
Kylesku Hotel
Wester Howgate Lothian
Old Howgate Inn
Whitebridge Highland
Knickie Lodge

WALES

Aberaeron Dyfed
Black Lion Hotel
Hive on the Quay
Aberdovey Dyfed
Old Coffee Shop
Abegavenny Gwent
Bagan Tandoori
Clam's Coffee House
Malthouse
Abersoch Gwynedd
Porth Tocyn Hotel
Aberystwyth Dyfed
Connexion
Corners
Gannets
Bangor Gwynedd
Grape Expectations
Barmouth Gwynedd
Angry Cheese
Betws Y Coed Gwynedd
Bubbling Kettle
Royal Oak
Bontddu Gwynedd
Farchynys Cottage Garden
Brechfa Dyfed
Old Tailor's
Broad Haven Dyfed
Druidstone Hotel Bar
Bylchau Clwyd
Sportsman's Arms Inn
Caernarfon Gwynedd
Bakestone
Cardiff Glamorgan
Armless Dragon
Brasserie
Champers
Crumbs Salad Restaurant
Everest
Happy Gathering
Himalaya

Kitchen
Luciano's
Madhav
Peppermint Lounge
Riverside
Sage Wholefood
Savastano's
Spanghero's
St David's Hall
Welsh National Opera
  Canteen
Cardigan Dyfed
Granary
Carmarthen Dyfed
Eifiona's Restaurant and
  Coffee Rooms
Hoi San
Old Curiosity
Waverley
Chepstow Gwent
Thang Long
Cilgerran Dyfed
Castle Kitchen
Colwyn Bay Clwyd
Majestic Grill
Cowbridge Glamorgan
Basil's Brasserie
Criccieth Gwynedd
Blue China Tearooms
Crickhowell Powys
Nantyffin Cider Mill Inn
Dinas Mawddwy Gwynedd
Coffee Shop
Erbistock Clwyd
Boat Inn
Glanwydden Gwynedd
Queen's Head
Harlech Gwynedd
Plas Cafe
Yr Ogod
Hay on Wye Powys
Granary
Lion's Corner House
Laleston Glamorgan
Great House
Llanarthney Dyfed
Golden Grove Arms
Llanbedr Y Cennin Gwynedd
Olde Bull Inn
Llandderfel Gwynedd
Bryntirion Inn
Llanddowror Dyfed
Old Mill
Llandeilo Dyfed
Cawdor Arms
Llandewi Skirrid Gwent
Walnut Tree Inn
Llandudno Gwynedd
Casanova
St Tudno Hotel
Llandybie Dyfed
Cobblers
Llandysul Dyfed
Bryn Cerdin Farm Tearooms
Llanelidan Clwyd
Leyland Arms

Llangollen Clwyd
Gales
Llangranog Dyfed
Y Gegin Fach
Llanynys Clwyd
Cerrigllwydion Arms
Llowes Powys
Radnor Arms
Machynlleth Powys
Felin Crewi
Quarry Shop
Merthyr Tydfil Glamorgan
Shunters
Milton Dyfed
Milton Brewery
Nannerch Clwyd
Cherry Pie
New Quay Dyfed
Hungry Trout
Newcastle Emlyn Dyfed
Pensarnau Arms
Newport Dyfed
Cnapan
Newport Gwent
Bolero's
Pontypridd Glamorgan
John & Maria's
Rhayader Powys
Carole's Cake Shop and Tea
  Room
Rhyd-Ddu Gwynedd
Cwellyn Arms
Rhyl Clwyd
Coffee Gallery
Rossett Clwyd
Churtons
Ruthin Clwyd
Bay Tree
Saundersfoot Dyfed
Jones'ys
Royal Oak
Sigingstone South Glamorgan
Victoria
St Davids Dyfed
St Non's Hotel
St Dogmaels Dyfed
Y Felin Tea Room
Swansea West Glamorgan
Annie's
Barrows
La Bussola
P.A's
Schooner
Treasure
Tenby Dyfed
Mews Bistro
Trefriw Gwynedd
Chandler's
Trellech Gwent
Lion Inn
Welshpool Powys
Powis Castle
Wolfs Castle Dyfed
Wolfscastle Country Hotel
Wrexham Clwyd
Bumble
Coffee Shop

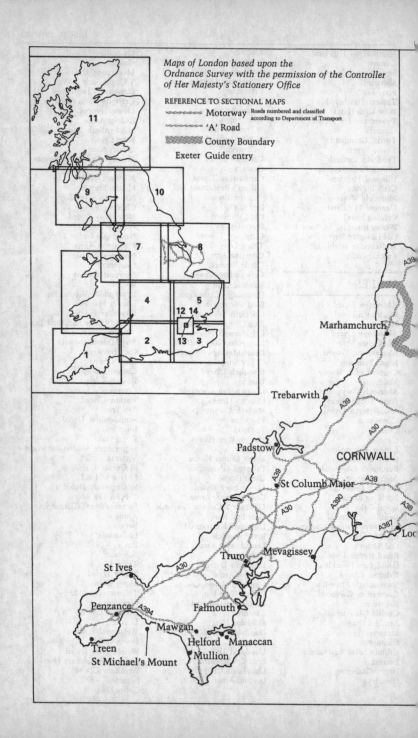

Maps of London based upon the
Ordnance Survey with the permission of the Controller
of Her Majesty's Stationery Office

REFERENCE TO SECTIONAL MAPS

Motorway   Roads numbered and classified
according to Department of Transport

'A' Road

County Boundary

Exeter   Guide entry

11

9   10

7   8

4   5

12 14

2   13 3

1

Marhamchurch

Trebarwith

Padstow

CORNWALL

St Columb Major

Loc

Truro   Mevagissey

St Ives

Penzance   Falmouth

Mawgan

Treen   Helford   Manaccan

St Michael's Mount   Mullion

MAP 1

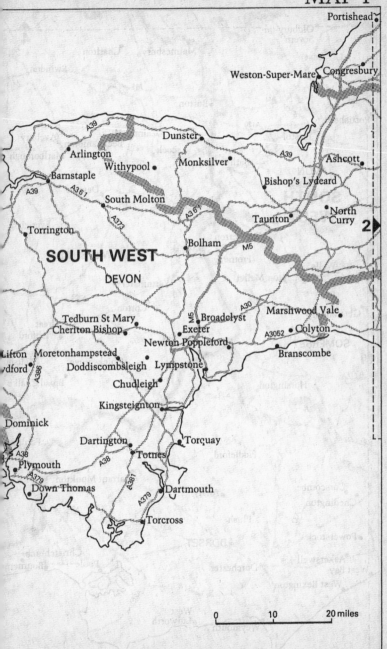

Portishead

Weston-Super-Mare • Congresbury

A39
Dunster
Arlington
Withypool • Monksilver • Ashcott
Barnstaple
A39 A361 Bishop's Lydeard
South Molton A361 North Curry
Torrington Taunton 2
Bolham M5

SOUTH WEST

DEVON

A30
Tedburn St Mary Broadclyst Marshwood Vale
Cheriton Bishop M5 Exeter Colyton
Newton Poppleford A3052
Lifton Moretonhampstead Lympstone Branscombe
ydford Doddiscombsleigh
A386 Chudleigh
Kingsteignton
Dominick
Dartington Torquay
A38 Totnes
A38 A361
Plymouth
A379 A379
Down Thomas Dartmouth

Torcross

0   10   20 miles

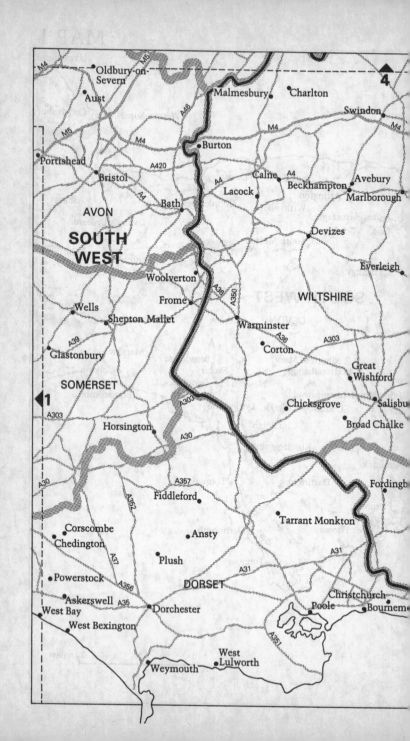

MAP 2

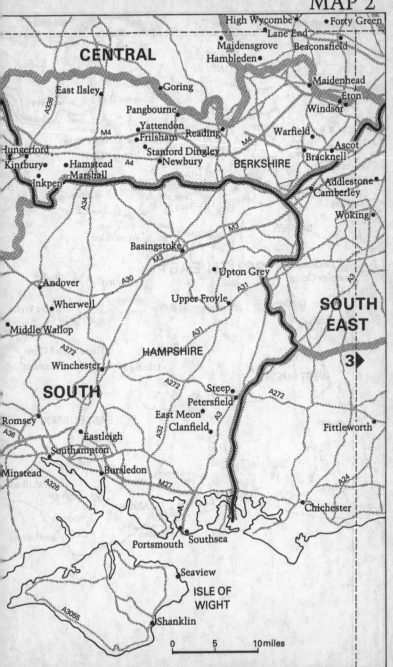

CENTRAL

High Wycombe•
•Lane End
•Forty Green

Maidensgrove•
Beaconsfield•
Hambleden•

Maidenhead•
Eton•
East Ilsley•
•Goring
Windsor•

Pangbourne•
Ascot•
Yattendon•
Warfield•
Bracknell•
Frilsham•
Reading•

Hungerford•
Stanford Dingley•
Addlestone•
Kintbury•
•Hamstead
A4
•Newbury
BERKSHIRE
Camberley•

Inkpen•
Marshall
Woking•

Basingstoke•

Andover•
A30
•Upton Grey

Wherwell•
Upper Froyle•
SOUTH
EAST

Middle Wallop•
3▶

HAMPSHIRE

Winchester•

SOUTH
•Steep
Petersfield•
East Meon•
Romsey•
Clanfield•

Eastleigh•
Fittleworth•
Southampton•

Minstead•
Bursledon•
M27

Chichester•

Portsmouth•
Southsea•

Seaview•

ISLE OF
WIGHT

Shanklin•

0   5   10 miles

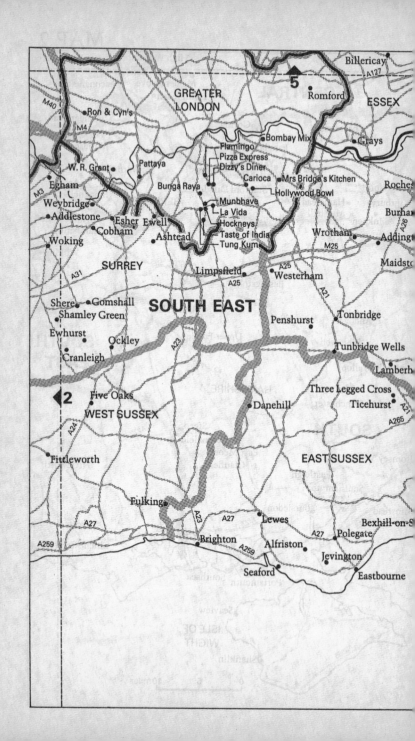

MAP 3

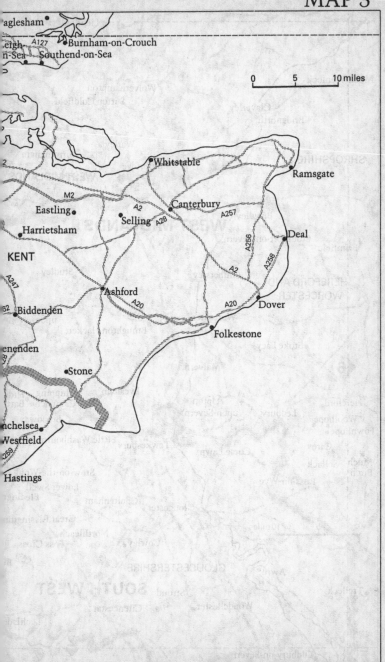

aglesham

A127 Burnham-on-Crouch
eigh·
n-Sea· Southend-on-Sea

0   5   10 miles

Whitstable

Ramsgate

M2
Eastling·   A2   Canterbury
         Selling·   A28   A257
Harrietsham·

KENT   A256   Deal

                                        A2   A258

A247   Ashford   A20   Dover
62 Biddenden·   A20
                              Folkestone
enenden

·Stone

nchelsea·
Westfield

Hastings

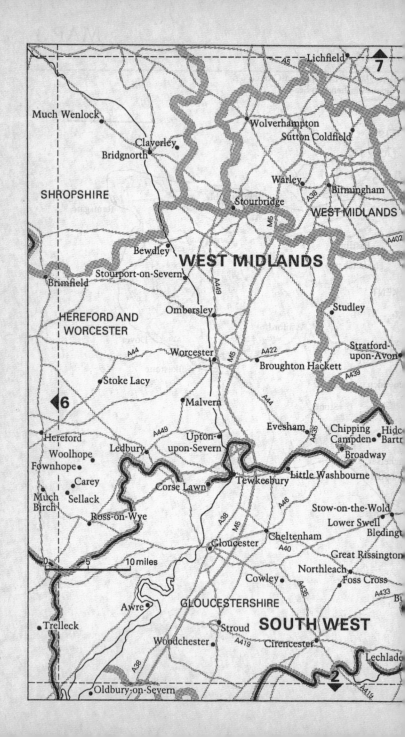

Much Wenlock

Claverley
Bridgnorth

SHROPSHIRE

Wolverhampton
Sutton Coldfield

Warley
Birmingham

Stourbridge

WEST MIDLANDS

M5

A402

Bewdley

WEST MIDLANDS

Stourport-on-Severn

Brimfield

Ombersley

A449

Studley

HEREFORD AND
WORCESTER

A44

Worcester

M5

A422

Broughton Hackett

Stratford-
upon-Avon

A439

Stoke Lacy

Malvern

A44

Evesham

A435

Chipping
Campden

Hidc
Bartr

A449

Upton-
upon-Severn

Broadway

Hereford
Woolhope
Fownhope

Ledbury

Little Washbourne

Carey

Corse Lawn

Tewkesbury

Much
Birch

Sellack

Stow-on-the-Wold

Ross-on-Wye

A38

M5

A46

Lower Swell
Bledingt

Gloucester

Cheltenham

A40

Great Rissington

0   5   10 miles

Northleach

Foss Cross

A433

Cowley

A435

B

Awre

GLOUCESTERSHIRE

Trelleck

Stroud

SOUTH WEST

Woodchester

A419

Cirencester

Lechlade

A38

Oldbury-on-Severn

A419

MAP 4

LEICESTERSHIRE

Whitwell
Empingham

Leicester

Uppingham

A47

A6

A5

EAST MIDLANDS

Market Harborough

A45

Walcote
Lutterworth

Harrington

A6

A43

Coventry

Ryton-on-
Dunsmore

Rugby

Crick

Lamport

Kenilworth

Leamington Spa

NORTHAMPTONSHIRE

East Haddon

Ashby St Ledgers

Wellingborough

Warwick

Eathorpe

WARWICKSHIRE

Daventry

M1

Weedon

Northampton

5▶

Badby

A5

Turvey

A361

Towcester

A43

Newport Pagnell

M1

Cropredy

M1

A422

Banbury

Shipston-on-Stour

Brackley

Stony Stratford

M1

A361

Adderbury

Deddington

Buckingham

A421

Woburn

Long Compton

A413

A5

Chipping Norton

Stewkley

Leighton
Buzzard

J61

OXFORDSHIRE

BUCKINGHAMSHIRE

Shipton-under-Wychwood

Aylesbury

South
Leigh

Woodstock

Tring

Aldbury

A40

CENTRAL

Berkhamsted

Witney

Stanton
Harcourt

Botley

Oxford

A40

Waterperry

Cumnor

A329

Clanfield

Ley Hill

Longworth

Abingdon

Speen

Amersham

Fyfield

Brightwell Baldwin

High Wycombe

Clifton Hampden

Lane End

Forty Green

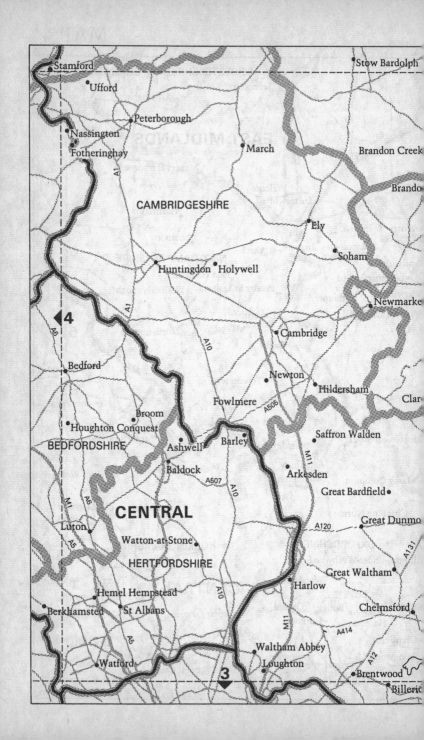

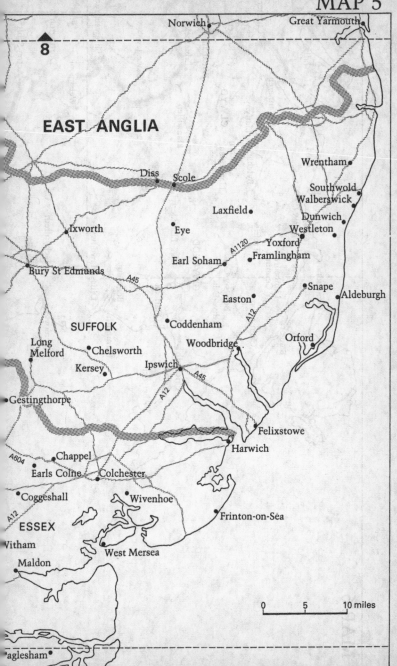

MAP 5

8

EAST ANGLIA

Norwich •   Great Yarmouth •

Wrentham •

Diss •   Scole •
Southwold
Walberswick •
Laxfield •   Dunwich •
Ixworth •   Eye •   Westleton •
Yoxford •
A1120   Framlingham •
Earl Soham •
Bury St Edmunds •   A45
Snape •
Easton •   Aldeburgh •
A12

SUFFOLK   Coddenham •
Woodbridge •   Orford •
Long
Melford •   Chelsworth •
Kersey •   Ipswich •   A45
A12
Gestingthorpe •

Felixstowe •
Chappel •   Harwich •
A604
Earls Colne •   Colchester •
Coggeshall •
A12   Wivenhoe •   Frinton-on-Sea •
ESSEX
Vitham •
Maldon •   West Mersea •

0   5   10 miles

aglesham •

MAP 6

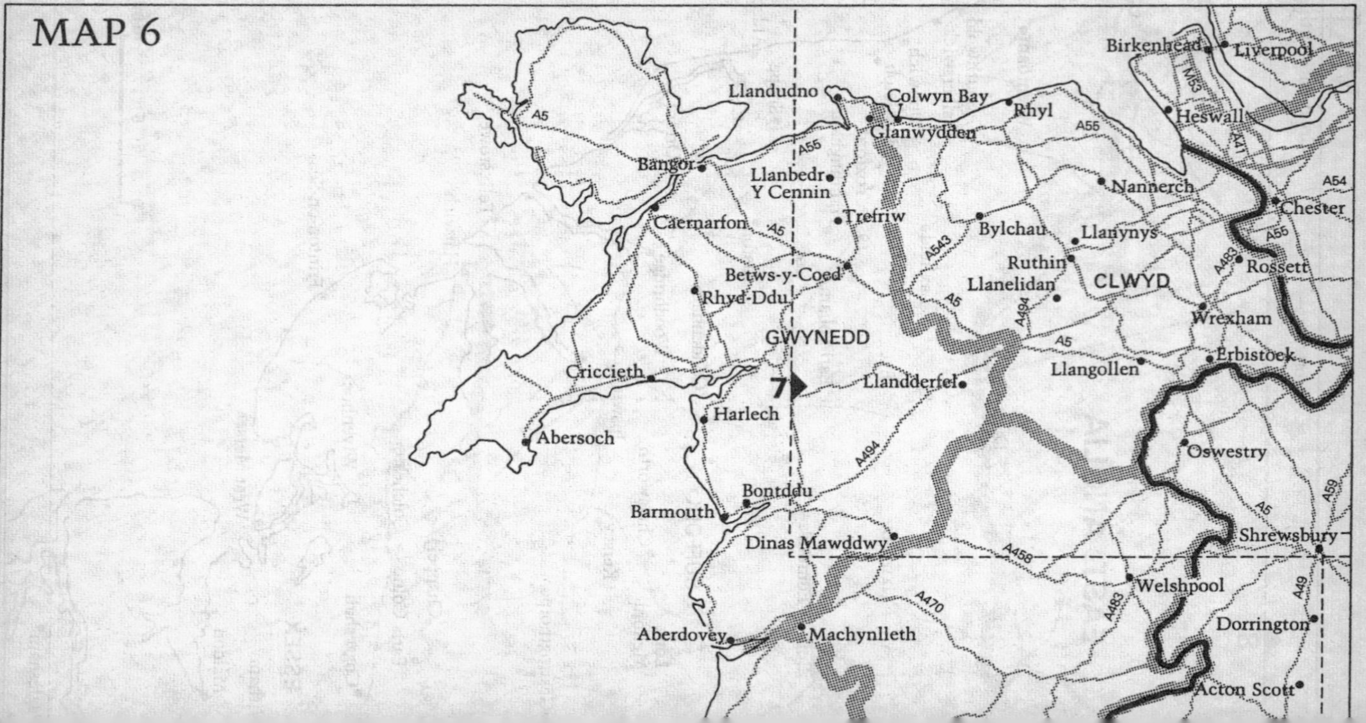

Liverpool
Birkenhead
Heswall
A550
M53
Chester
A54
A55
Rossett
A51
Nannerch
Llanynys
Wrexham
Erbistock
Rhyl
Bylchau
Ruthin
CLWYD
A494
Llanelidan
Llangollen
A5
Oswestry
A5
Shrewsbury
A49
A483
Welshpool
Dorrington
Acton Scott
Colwyn Bay
Glanwydden
A55
Trefriw
A543
A5
Llandderfel
A5
A456
Llandudno
Llanbedr
Y Cennin
A55
A5
Betws-y-Coed
A494
A470
Machynlleth
Bangor
Caernarfon
Rhyd-Ddu
GWYNEDD
7
Bontddu
Dinas Mawddwy
A5
Harlech
Barmouth
Aberdovey
Criccieth
Abersoch

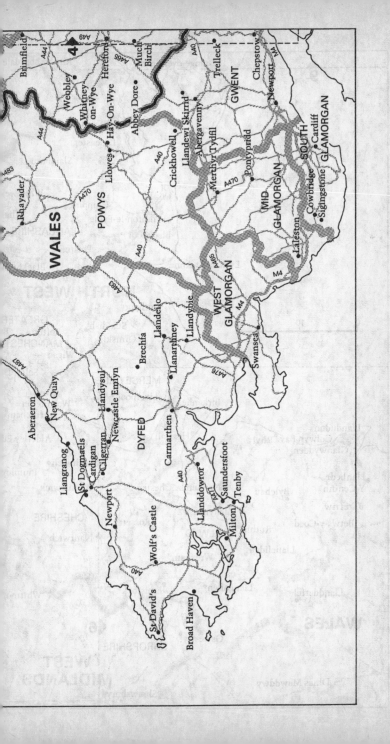

MAP 7

Masham
Sutton
Howgrave
10
Litton
Ramsgill
Ripon
Malton
Arncliffe
Wath-in-Nidderdale
NORTH YORKSHIRE
Treshfield
Pateley Bridge
Staveley
etton
ppletreewick
Knaresborough
A59
Gargrave
Bolton Abbey
Harrogate
A59
York
lack
Skipton
Ilkley
NORTH EAST
Keighley
Otley
A65
A1
Bingley
Guiseley
A64
Shipley
A163
M62
Haworth
Bradford
Leeds
Selby
Hebden
Thornton
Pudsey
A650
A19
Bridge
Halifax
Cleckheaton
M62
owerby Bridge
Elland
WEST YORKSHIRE
8
Rochdale
Colcar
Lepton
Wakefield
Grange Moor
Scunthorpe
A62
Huddersfield
M18
M180
Marsden
Farnley
Shelley
Tyas
Shepley
A1
Ashton under Lyne
A616
Doncaster
Epworth
Hyde
SOUTH YORKSHIRE
Scotter
chester
Glossop
M1
arple
Rotherham
Bawtry
A631
ckport
Hayfield
Sheffield
Gainsborough
nslow
A57
Macclesfield
Eyam
Tideswell
Litton
Chesterfield
A57
Little Longstone
Bakewell
A1
A46
ngleton
A6
Over Haddon
M1
A523
Matlock
Mansfield
Hartingdon
Lea
NOTTINGHAMSHIRE
slem
DERBYSHIRE
Newark
y
Hulland
EAST MIDLANDS
 nley
A52
Froghall
Ashbourne
A46
A50
A52
Nottingham
Stone
Derby
A51
A38
Long Eaton
Plumtree
Shardlow
STAFFORDSHIRE
Old Dalby
Wilson
Loughborough
A34
A60
M1
A6
Stretton
4
Ashby de
la Zouch
Rothley
Sileby
Langham
A696

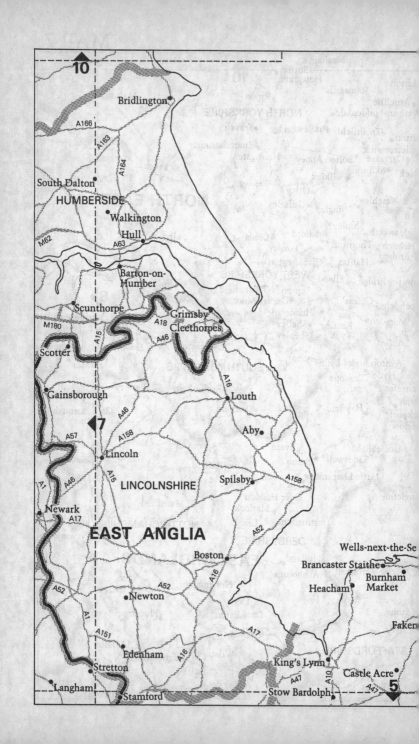

Bridlington

A166

A163

A164

South Dalton

HUMBERSIDE

Walkington

M62

Hull

A63

Barton-on-Humber

Scunthorpe

Grimsby

M180

A18

Cleethorpes

Scotter

A46

A15

Gainsborough

Louth

A16

A46

A57

A158

Aby

Lincoln

A15

LINCOLNSHIRE

Spilsby

A158

A1

A46

Newark

A17

EAST ANGLIA

A52

A52

Boston

Wells-next-the-Se

A16

Brancaster Staithe

A52

Newton

Burnham
Market

A1

Heacham

A151

A16

Faken

A17

Edenham

A16

King's Lynn

Castle Acre

Stretton

A10

Langham

Stamford

Stow Bardolph

A47

MAP 8

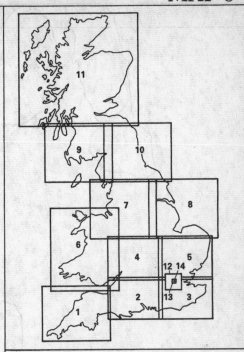

Maps of London based upon the
Ordnance Survey with the permission of the Controller
of Her Majesty's Stationery Office

REFERENCE TO SECTIONAL MAPS

〰〰〰 Motorway   Roads numbered and classified
according to Department of Transport

‒‒‒‒‒ 'A' Road

▓▓▓▓ County Boundary

Exeter   Guide entry

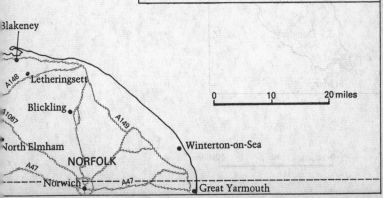

Blakeney

A148

Letheringsett

Blickling

A1067

A149

North Elmham

A47

NORFOLK

Winterton-on-Sea

Norwich — A47 —

Great Yarmouth

0   10   20 miles

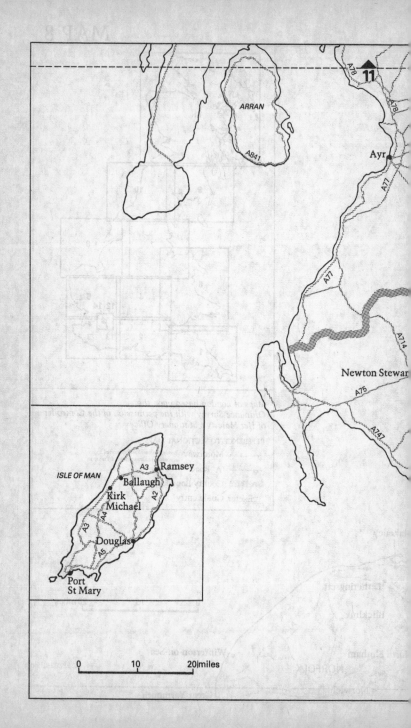

MAP B

11

ARRAN

A841

Ayr

A78

A77

A77

A714

Newton Stewar

A75

A747

ISLE OF MAN

A3 Ramsey
Ballaugh
Kirk
Michael   A2

A3   A4

Douglas

A5

Port
St Mary

0   10   20 miles

MAP 9

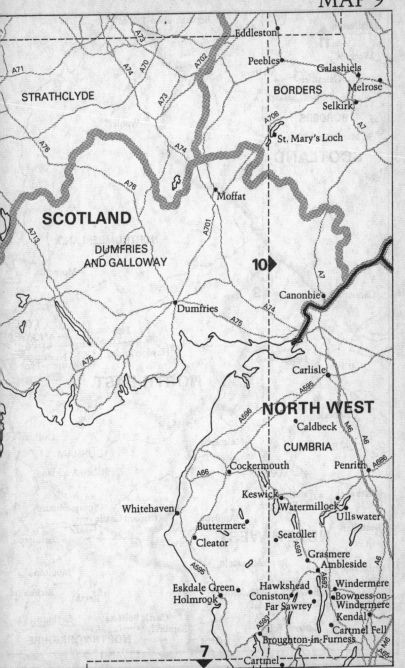

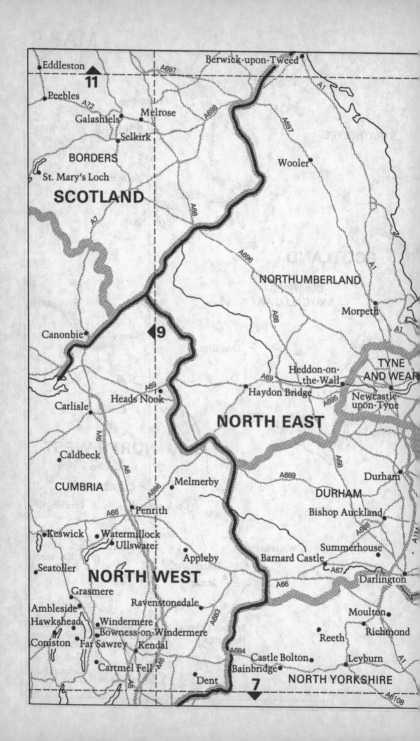

MAP 10

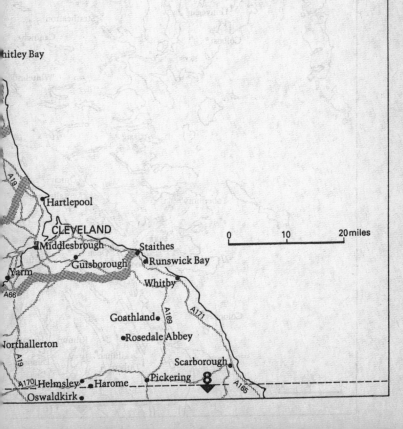

hitley Bay

Hartlepool

CLEVELAND

Middlesbrough

Staithes

Guisborough

Runswick Bay

Yarm

Whitby

Goathland

Rosedale Abbey

Northallerton

Scarborough

Helmsley

Harome

Pickering

Oswaldkirk

A19

A66

A169

A171

A170

A19

A165

0   10   20 miles

MAP 10

Unapool

A837
LEWIS
A858
WESTERN
ISLES

Scarista

Ullapool

HIGHLAND

Gairloch

A832

A835

A832

A855

Dunvegan

A890
Strathcarron

Colbost

Cannich

SKYE

A87
Whitebridge

A9

Arisaig

A86

A830

A861
Onich

A82

Kentallen

Tobermory

A828

MULL

Oban

A85
Tyndrum

Cullipool

A816

A83

Colonsay

A815

JURA

Kilmun
Helensbur

Kilfinan

Dunoon

Tarbert

A78

9 STRATHCLYDE

ISLAY

0   10   20miles

MAP 11

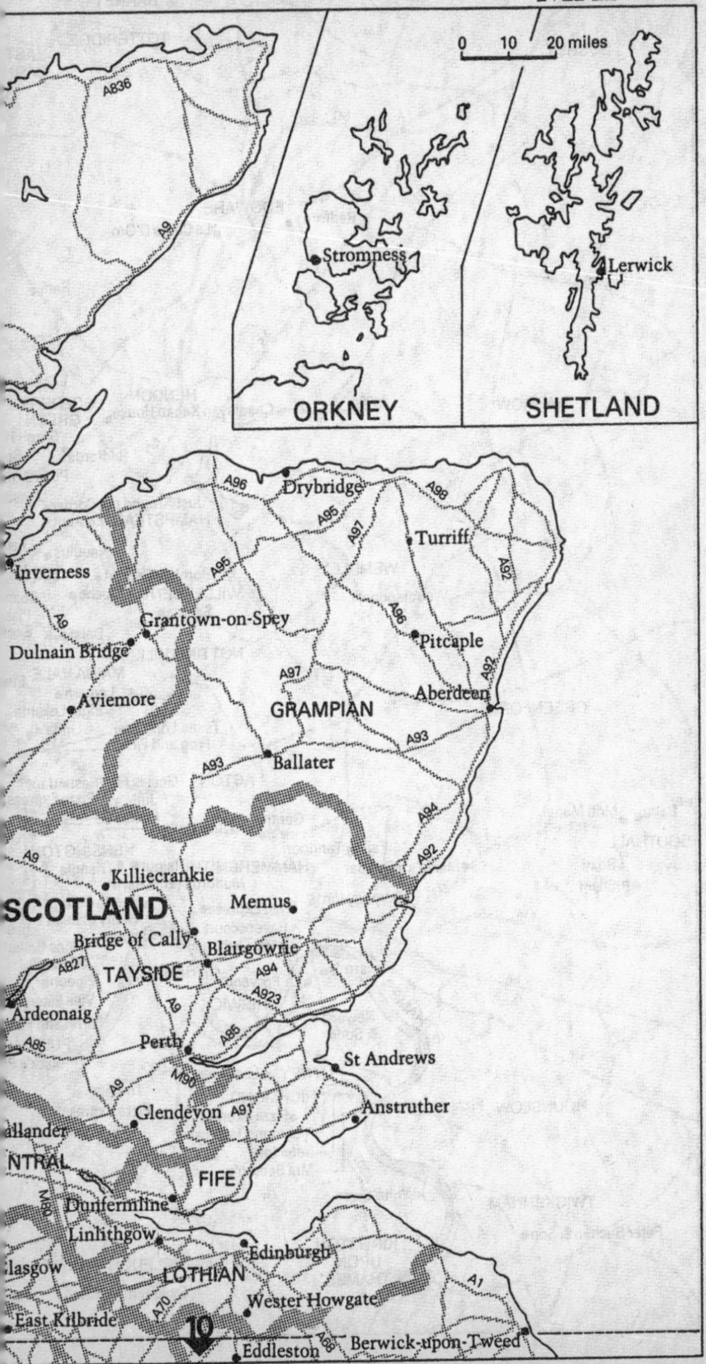

0   10   20 miles

Stromness

ORKNEY

Lerwick

SHETLAND

A836

A9

Inverness

A96   Drybridge

A95

A97

Turriff

A92

A95

Grantown-on-Spey

A96

Dulnain Bridge

A97

Pitcaple

Aviemore

GRAMPIAN

Aberdeen

A92

A93

Ballater

A93

A94

A9

A92

Killiecrankie

Memus

SCOTLAND

Bridge of Cally

Blairgowrie

A827

TAYSIDE

A94

A923

Ardeonaig

A9

A85

A85

Perth

St Andrews

A9

M90

Glendevon   A91

Anstruther

allander

CENTRAL

FIFE

Dunfermline

Linlithgow

Glasgow

Edinburgh

LOTHIAN

A1

East Kilbride

A70

Wester Howgate

10

Eddleston

Berwick-upon-Tweed

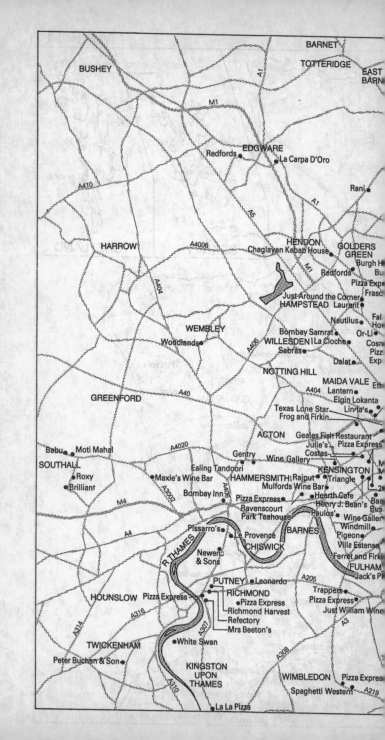

MAP 12

El Greco

A111
Southgate Technical
College

EDMONTON

A10

Pizzeria Bel-Sit

M11

HLEY

O6

TOTTENHAM

WALTHAMSTOW

A112

A12

Penang
Satay House

HORNSEY

GATE

A12

Earth
Exchange

Beewees

Jai Krishna

STOKE
NEWINGTON

Millwards

Valentino's

A503

Peppe's Pizza

Indian
Ocean

Paradise
Tandoori
oyski's

A1

A10

Hodja
Nesreddin

Samsun

Oasis

A11

Downs

A118

F. Cooke

Le Petit Prince

Yerakina

ISLINGTON

13

B.G.'s

Faulkner's

WEST HAM

Flounder and Firkin

Cherry Orchard

Falcon & Firkin

A124

A13

Dino's Grill

Bloom's

Whitechapel Cafe

Star Bhel-Poori House

CITY

Seoul

Chinatown

Lahore
Restaurant

R THAMES

tipasto
Pasta

A2

Goddard's
Eel and Pie House

GREENWICH

on's

Oval Tandoori

Rebato's

Maharani

TTERSEA

Tea Rooms
des Artistes

CAMBERWELL

Crowders,
Greenwich Theatre

Pizza
Express

Cosmos

Phoenix and Firkin

LEWISHAM

A2

Beehive

Leek's Fish Bar

Fox and Firkin

A20

Pizza
e Roma

Punters' Pie

Bon Ton Roulet

Dulwich Tandoori

Babur Brasserie

ebriated
ewt

CLAPHAM

Ormes

DULWICH

ults

Punjab House

A23

A205

nservatory

A21

A214

STREATHAM

Little Caesar's Pizza

ree Krishna

Pizza Express

A215

A23

Etawan

0   1   2   3 miles

Odette's
Mustoe Bistro
Le Bistroquet
Cheguers
Pasta Underground
CAMDEN
TOWN

PRIMROSE HILL

Queen's Grove

Cafe Delancey

ST JOHN'S
WOOD

Prince Albert Rd

Raj Bhel Poori
Daph

Harry Morgan's

Applejacks

Great
Nepale

REGENT'S PARK

Ravi Shankar
(Bhel Poori House)
Diwana Bhel Poori
Brizzi Snack Bar

MARYLEBONE

Sagarmatha
Anwars
Indian YMCA
Vasis
Bistro du Village
Habitat
Cafe
Greenh

Seashell

Ragam
Brunel
Cranks
Ikkyu

Raw Deal
Maison
Sagne
Efes Kebab
House
Sawasdee
Venus
Mande

Hungrys
Nanten Yakitori Bar
Woodlands

Reuben's
Langham Pl
Hare Krishna Curry Ho

Wigmore St
Grahame's
Govinda
Seafare

Knoodles
Chicago Pizza
Pie Factory
SOHO

BAYSWATER
Bayswater Rd
Oxford St
Justin de Blank
Gould
Shamper
Cranks
Wine Bar

Kitchen Yakitori
Pizzeria Condotti

KENSINGTON
GARDENS
HYDE PARK
Reeds
Japan
Country Life
Centre
Curri-Express
MAYFAIR
Granary
Dover Street Restaurant & Wine Bar
Fortnum
Mason

Piccadilly
Crowns
Pall Mall

Hard Rock Cafe
GREEN
PARK
WESTMINS

Kensington Rd
Knightsbridge
Pizza Express
ST JAME
PARK
Chicago Rib Shack
L'Express
BUCKINGHAM
PALACE
KNIGHTSBRIDGE
Metro Wine Bar
Petty Fr
Pizza Express
Way In
Restaurant
Methuselah

Victoria and
Albert Museum
Victoria St

Wine Gallery
Daquise
Spago
La Brasserie
Seafresh
Fish Restaurant
Texas Lone Star
General
Trading Company
Ebury Wine Bar
Bar Escoba
Roux!
Britannia
Charco's
Wine Bar
Le Casino
Lou Pescadou
CHELSEA
Como Lario
Orange Brewery
PIMLICO
Peters
Habitat Cafe
Henry J. Bean's
King's Rd
Ambrosiana
Crêperie
Veritable Crêperie

MAP 13

Mercury
Roxy Café Cantina
Suruchi
ISLINGTON
Upper Street Fish Shop
Solopasta
Pizza Express
Goan
Fallen Angel
Pentonville Rd
Ganpath
City Rd
FINSBURY
Pheasant
and Firkin
East West
North Sea
Old St
Rouxl Britannia
Clerkenwell Rd
October Gallery
Fox and Anchor
Bleeding Heart
Museum
of London
Pavilion
Nosherie
Pizza Express High Holborn
London Wall
CITY
HOLBORN
Ginnan
Le Poulbot
Birley's
14
Fleet St Ludgate Hill Cheapside Cornhill
Albion
Food for Health
Simpson's of
Cornhill
Covent
Garden
Mkt.
India Club
Queen Victoria St
Thames St
Victoria Embankment
Lower Thames St
Dining Room
Archduke
Cooke's Eel
and Pie Shop
SOUTHWARK
Westminster Bri
Long Lane
Footstool
Imperial Tandoori
Goose and Firkin
Lambeth
Bri
LAMBETH
New Kent Rd
Pizzeria Castello
WALWORTH
Windmill Fish Bar
Station Grill
Kennington La
0   ½ miles

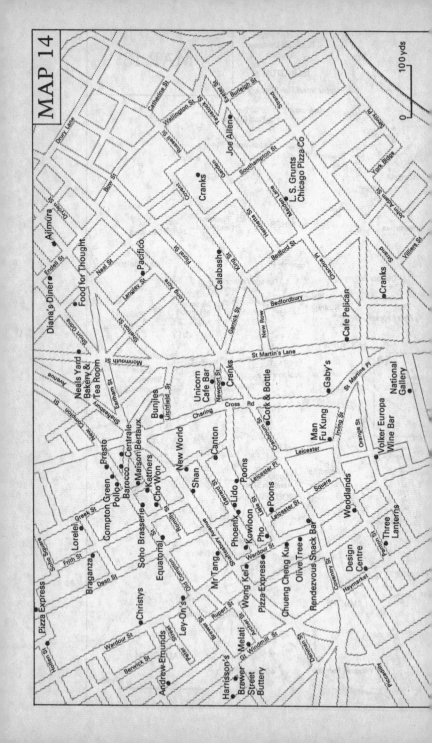

MAP 14

100 yds

0

Dunn Lane

Ajimura
Food for Thought
Diana's Diner
Endell St

Neals Yard
Bakery &
Tea Room

Pacifico
Neal St
Langley St

Earlham St

Short's Gdns
Monmouth St

Seven Dials
Shorts Gdns

Presto
Centrale
Barocco
Maison Bertaux
Kettners
Cho Won
Pollo
Compton Green

Soho Brasserie

Braganza
Lorelei
Greek St
Frith St

Pizza Express
Italian St

Wardour St
Berwick St

Andrew-Edmunds
Ley-On's
Christys

Harrisson's
Brewer
Street
Buttery

Melati
Wong Kei
Mr Tang
Equatorial
Dean St

Gt. Windmill St
Archer St

Rupert St

Wardour St
Pizza Express

Berwick St
Peter St

Brewer St

New World
Shan
Canton
Lichfield St

Bunjies

Unicorn
Cafe Bar
Newport St

Cranks

St Martin's Lane

Phoenix
Lido
Kowloon
Poons
Pho

Poons

Shaftesbury Avenue

Leicester St
Leicester Pl

Chueng Cheng Ku
Olive Tree
Rendezvous Snack Bar

Leicester St

Cranbourn St
Cork & Bottle

Man
Fu Kung

Charing Cross Rd

Leicester
Square

Woodlands

Design
Centre

Three
Lanterns

Panton St

Coventry St

Haymarket

Cranks

Joe Allen

Exeter St
Burleigh St

Wellington St
Catherine St

Tavistock St

Southampton St

L. S. Grunts
Chicago Pizza Co

Bow St
Floral St

Russell St

Maiden Lane

Bedford St

Bedfordbury

Calabash
Bear St

Chandos Pl

New Row

Garrick St

Cafe Pelican

Gaby's

St Martins Pl

Volker Europa
Wine Bar

National
Gallery

Cranks

York Bridge

Union Jack St
Villiers St

Craven St

Orange St

Irving St

Gabys

Report form

To **Cheap Eats**
FREEPOST, 2 Marylebone Road, London NW1 1YN
No stamp is needed.

I ate at:

Establishment name _____

Address _____

_____

_____

_____ Telephone _____

on the _____ of _____ 198 ___

From my experience it **should be**

should not be   in the next edition.

I would rate it _____ out of 10

What kind of eating place is it? (eg fish and chip shop, bistro etc)

_____

_____

Where is it? (eg in the town centre behind Tesco) _____

_____

_____

What is it like inside? (eg pine tables, blackboard menu, candles on tables)

_____

_____

_____

Please give details of the food overleaf

What did you eat? _____

_____

_____

_____

_____

_____

_____

What did you drink? _____

_____

_____

Are there any special features that you think should be mentioned
in the next edition? _____

_____

_____

_____

_____

My meal cost £ _____ for _____ people.
I am not connected with the management.

Name and address (Please use block capitals or we may not
be able to acknowledge your report) _____

_____

_____

_____

Report form

To **Cheap Eats**
FREEPOST, 2 Marylebone Road, London NW1 1YN
No stamp is needed.

I ate at:

Establishment name _____

Address _____

_____

_____

_____ Telephone _____

on the _____ of _____ 198 ___

From my experience it **should be**

      should not be in the next edition.

I would rate it _____ out of 10

What kind of eating place is it? (eg fish and chip shop, bistro etc)

_____

_____

Where is it? (eg in the town centre behind Tesco) _____

_____

_____

What is it like inside? (eg pine tables, blackboard menu, candles on tables)

_____

_____

_____

Please give details of the food overleaf

What did you eat? _____

_____

_____

_____

_____

_____

What did you drink? _____

_____

_____

Are there any special features that you think should be mentioned
in the next edition? _____

_____

_____

_____

_____

My meal cost £ _____ for _____ people.
I am not connected with the management.

Name and address (Please use block capitals or we may not
be able to acknowledge your report) _____

_____

_____

_____

Report form

_____

To **Cheap Eats**
FREEPOST, 2 Marylebone Road, London NW1 1YN
No stamp is needed.

_____

I ate at:

Establishment name _____

Address _____

_____

_____

_____ Telephone _____

on the _____ of _____ 198 _____

From my experience it **should be**

                     should not be   in the next edition.

I would rate it _____ out of 10

What kind of eating place is it? (eg fish and chip shop, bistro etc)

_____

_____

Where is it? (eg in the town centre behind Tesco) ___

_____

_____

What is it like inside? (eg pine tables, blackboard menu, candles on tables)

_____

_____

_____

Please give details of the food overleaf

What did you eat? _____

_____

_____

_____

_____

_____

What did you drink? _____

_____

_____

Are there any special features that you think should be mentioned
in the next edition? _____

_____

_____

_____

_____

My meal cost £ _____ for _____ people.
I am not connected with the management.

Name and address (Please use block capitals or we may not
be able to acknowledge your report) _____

_____

_____

_____

_____

Report form

To **Cheap Eats**
FREEPOST, 2 Marylebone Road, London NW1 1YN
No stamp is needed.

I ate at:

Establishment name _____

Address _____

_____

_____

_____ Telephone _____

on the _____ of _____ 198 ____

From my experience it **should be**

should not be   in the next edition.

I would rate it ____ out of 10

What kind of eating place is it? (eg fish and chip shop, bistro etc)

_____

_____

Where is it? (eg in the town centre behind Tesco) _____

_____

_____

What is it like inside? (eg pine tables, blackboard menu, candles on tables)

_____

_____

_____

Please give details of the food overleaf

What did you eat? _____

_____

_____

_____

_____

_____

_____

What did you drink? _____

_____

_____

Are there any special features that you think should be mentioned
in the next edition? _____

_____

_____

_____

_____

My meal cost £ _____ for _____ people.
I am not connected with the management.

Name and address (Please use block capitals or we may not
be able to acknowledge your report) _____

_____

_____

_____

_____

Report form

To **Cheap Eats**
FREEPOST, 2 Marylebone Road, London NW1 1YN
No stamp is needed.

I ate at:

Establishment name _____

Address _____

_____

_____

_____ Telephone _____

on the _____ of _____ 198 ___

From my experience it **should be**

                           should not be   in the next edition.

I would rate it _____ out of 10

What kind of eating place is it? (eg fish and chip shop, bistro etc)

_____

_____

Where is it? (eg in the town centre behind Tesco) _____

_____

_____

What is it like inside? (eg pine tables, blackboard menu, candles on tables)

_____

_____

_____

Please give details of the food overleaf

What did you eat? _____

_____

_____

_____

_____

What did you drink? _____

_____

_____

Are there any special features that you think should be mentioned
in the next edition? _____

_____

_____

_____

_____

My meal cost £ _____ for _____ people.
I am not connected with the management.

Name and address (Please use block capitals or we may not
be able to acknowledge your report) _____

_____

_____

_____

Report form

To **Cheap Eats**
FREEPOST, 2 Marylebone Road, London NW1 1YN
No stamp is needed.

I ate at:

Establishment name _____

Address _____

_____

_____

_____ Telephone _____

on the ____ of _____ 198 ___

From my experience it **should be**
                      should not be   in the next edition.

I would rate it ____ out of 10

What kind of eating place is it? (eg fish and chip shop, bistro etc)

_____

_____

Where is it? (eg in the town centre behind Tesco) _____

_____

_____

What is it like inside? (eg pine tables, blackboard menu, candles on tables)

_____

_____

_____

Please give details of the food overleaf

What did you eat? _____

_____

_____

_____

_____

_____

What did you drink? _____

_____

_____

Are there any special features that you think should be mentioned in the next edition? _____

_____

_____

_____

_____

My meal cost £ _____ for _____ people.
I am not connected with the management.

Name and address (Please use block capitals or we may not be able to acknowledge your report) _____

_____

_____

_____

_____

Report form

To **Cheap Eats**
FREEPOST, 2 Marylebone Road, London NW1 1YN
No stamp is needed.

I ate at:

Establishment name _____

Address _____

_____

_____

_____ Telephone _____

on the ____ of _____ 198 ____

From my experience it **should be**
                              should not be in the next edition.

I would rate it ____ out of 10

What kind of eating place is it? (eg fish and chip shop, bistro etc)

_____

_____

Where is it? (eg in the town centre behind Tesco) _____

_____

_____

What is it like inside? (eg pine tables, blackboard menu, candles on tables)

_____

_____

_____

Please give details of the food overleaf

What did you eat? _____

_____

_____

_____

_____

_____

What did you drink? _____

_____

_____

Are there any special features that you think should be mentioned
in the next edition? _____

_____

_____

_____

_____

My meal cost £ _____ for _____ people.
I am not connected with the management.

Name and address (Please use block capitals or we may not
be able to acknowledge your report) _____

_____

_____

_____

Report form

To **Cheap Eats**
FREEPOST, 2 Marylebone Road, London NW1 1YN
No stamp is needed.

I ate at:

Establishment name _____

Address _____

_____

_____

_____ Telephone _____

on the _____ of _____ 198 ____

From my experience it **should be**

                     should not be   in the next edition.

I would rate it ____ out of 10

What kind of eating place is it? (eg fish and chip shop, bistro etc)

_____

_____

Where is it? (eg in the town centre behind Tesco) _____

_____

_____

What is it like inside? (eg pine tables, blackboard menu, candles on tables)

_____

_____

_____

Please give details of the food overleaf

What did you eat? _____

_____

_____

_____

_____

_____

_____

What did you drink? _____

_____

_____

Are there any special features that you think should be mentioned in the next edition? _____

_____

_____

_____

_____

My meal cost £ _____ for _____ people.
I am not connected with the management.

Name and address (Please use block capitals or we may not be able to acknowledge your report) _____

_____

_____

_____

_____